PROPERTY OF WESTERN TECHNICAL-COMMERCIAL
SCHOOL MATHEMATICS DEPARTMENT

S0-ARY-962

Gage
Finite Mathematics
A SEARCH FOR MEANING

Gage
Finite Mathematics
A SEARCH FOR MEANING

Authors

John Egsgard
Department of Mathematics Head
Patrick Fogarty Secondary School
Orillia, Ontario

Gary Flewelling
Mathematics Consultant
Wellington County Board of Education
Guelph, Ontario

Craig Newell
Department of Mathematics Head
St. George's School
Vancouver, British Columbia

Wendy Warburton
Department of Mathematics Head
Havergal College
Toronto, Ontario

Editorial Adviser
Wendy Warburton

gage EDUCATIONAL PUBLISHING COMPANY
A DIVISION OF CANADA PUBLISHING CORPORATION
TORONTO ONTARIO CANADA

Copyright © 1988 Gage Educational Publishing Company
A Division of Canada Publishing Corporation

All rights reserved. No part of this book may be reproduced in any form without permission in writing from the publisher. Reproducing passages from this book by mimeographing or by photographic, electrostatic, or mechanical means without the written permission of the publisher is an infringement of copyright law.

Care has been taken to trace ownership of copyright material contained in this text. The publishers will gladly take any information that will enable them to rectify any reference or credit in subsequent editions.

Canadian Cataloguing in Publication Data

Main entry under title:

   Gage finite mathematics: a search for meaning.

For use in high schools.

Includes index.

ISBN 0-7715-3505-8

1. Mathematics—1961-   I. Egsgard, J.C., 1925-

                              II. Title: Finite mathematics

QA39.2.G34 1988   510   C87-094984-5

ISBN: 0-7715-**3505**-8

3 4 5 6 7 8 BP 99 98 97 96 95 94

Printed and bound in Canada.

Cover photograph
Ted Grant/Masterfile

Design
Newton Frank Arthur Inc.

Technical art
Pronk&Associates

Typesetting
Trigraph Inc.

Consultants
Arthur Abramovitch
Department of Mathematics Head
High School of Commerce
Ottawa, Ontario

Evelyn Bayefsky
Education Centre Library
Toronto Board of Education
Toronto, Ontario

George Duff
Department of Mathematics
University of Toronto
Toronto, Ontario

Alton Olson
Department of Secondary Education
University of Alberta
Edmonton, Alberta

Jeffrey A. Irvine
North Park Secondary School
[*contribution to Matrices chapter*]

Acknowledgments and Picture Credits
Courtesy of Air Canada, 46; Courtesy of Anchor Shoring & Caissons Ltd., 233; Courtesy of the Canadian National Institute for the Blind, 15; Courtesy of Canada Post Corporation, 40; CUSO, 151; Barry Dursley, 224, 225; Gary Fong, 127; Courtesy of Heidelberg Canada, 183; Jerry Hobbs/Squash Life, 127; Ken Jones, 2, 3, 194; Brian Kent/The Vancouver Sun, 242; Masterfile, 99; Courtesy of McDonald's Restaurants Canada, 343; Courtesy of Ontario Association of Archers Inc., 313; Courtesy of the Ontario Ministry of Agriculture and Food, 262; Courtesy of Petro-Canada Inc., 150; Courtesy of Philips Electronics Ltd., 139; Courtesy of the Royal Bank of Canada, 10; Courtesy of Sony of Canada Ltd., Walkman is a registered trademark of Sony Corporation, 73; Courtesy of Texas Instruments, 113; The Toronto Star, 83, 314; Carol Waldock, 14, 46, 127; Robert Waldock, 17, 32, 37, 47, 92, 93, 139, 187, 194, 199, 209, 277, 315; Miram and Ira Wallach Division of Art, Prints and Photographs, The New York Public Library, 218; Sean West, 47.

CONTENTS

Introduction
Text Organization

1 Combinatorics

1.0 Introduction *2*
1.1 Counting Objects in Sets *4*
1.2 The Fundamental Counting
Principle *10*
1.3 Arrangements *17*
1.4 Arrangements and Factorial
Notation *21*
Making Connections:
Information, Please *24*
In Search of
a Computer Program *26*
In Search of
One Hundred Natural
Numbers *26*
1.5 Arrangements with Like
Elements *27*
1.6 Counting Subsets *30*
In Search of
an Understanding of Poker *37*
1.7 Power of a Set *38*
Summary *41*
Inventory *42*
Review Exercises *43*

2 Probability

2.0 Introduction *46*
2.1 Experimental Probability *48*
2.2 Sample Spaces and Events *51*
2.3 Uniform Probability Models *57*
2.4 Probability and Combinatorics *65*
2.5 Independent Events *70*

In Search of Non-uniform
Probability Models *75*
2.6 Conditional Probability *78*
In Search of a Solution
to the Birthday Problem *84*
Making Connections:
Petals Around the Rose *86*
Summary *88*
Inventory *89*
Review Exercises *90*

3 Matrices

3.0 Introduction *92*
3.1 Introduction to Matrices *94*
Making Connections:
Game Theory *98*
3.2 Addition and Scalar Multiplication
of Matrices *100*
3.3 Multiplication of Matrices *105*
In Search of a Computer Program to
Multiply Matrices *112*
3.4 Matrices Used in Coding *114*
In Search of Inverse Matrices *118*
3.5 Matrices Used in Networks *120*
3.6 Simple Markov Chains *128*
Summary *133*
Inventory *134*
Review Exercises *135*

4 Solving Systems of Equations and Inequalities

4.0 Introduction *138*
4.1 Mathematical Modelling *140*

Making Connections:
Models for Inherited Human
Characteristics *144*

4.2 Solving Systems of Equations
By Elimination *146*
In Search of a Vector Method for
Solving Linear Systems *152*

4.3 Using Matrices to Solve
Systems of Equations *153*

4.4 Special Cases *157*

4.5 m Equations in n Variables, where
$m \neq n$ *166*

4.6 Systems of Linear Inequalities *169*

4.7 Formulation of Linear Programming
Problems *175*

4.8 Solving Linear Programming
Problems *178*

4.9 Solving Linear Programming
Problems by Simplex
Techniques *184*

Summary *188*
Inventory *189*
Review Exercises *191*

5 The Binomial Theorem

5.0 Introduction *194*

5.1 An Investigation of the Expansion
of $(a + x)^n$, $n \in W$ *196*

5.2 The Expansion of $(a + x)^n$ for
$n \in W$ *198*

5.3 A Proof of the
Binomial Theorem *200*
In Search of the Expansion of
$(a + x)^n$ for $n \in R$ *205*

Making Connections:
Food Needs and
World Resources *206*

5.4 The General Term of $(a + x)^n$ *208*

5.5 Pascal's Triangle *211*
In Search of
Patterns in Pascal's Triangle *214*

Summary *216*
Inventory *216*
Review Exercises *217*

6 Finite and Infinite Series

6.0 Introduction *218*

6.1 Series, Sequences and
Sigma Notation *220*
Making Connections:
Mathematics Contests *224*

6.2 Arithmetic and Geometric
Series *226*

6.3 The Sum of an Arithmetic
Series *231*

6.4 The Sum of a Geometric
Series *235*

6.5 The Infinite Geometric Series *238*
In Search of the Sum of Other
Infinite Series *244*

6.6 Other Series *245*
In Search of
Proof Without Words *251*

6.7 Mathematical Induction *252*
In Search of a Proof
of the Binomial Theorem *256*

Summary *257*
Inventory *258*
Review Exercises *259*

7 Applications of Probability

7.0 Introduction *262*
7.1 Random Variables *264*
7.2 Probability Distributions and
　　Expected Value *271*
7.3 Uniform Probability
　　Distributions *276*
7.4 Binomial Experiments *283*
　　Making Connections:
　　Probability in Insurance *288*
7.5 Binomial Distributions *290*
　　In Search of
　　the Poisson Distribution *298*
7.6 Hypergeometric Variables *299*
7.7 Hypergeometric Distributions *303*
Summary *309*
Inventory *310*
Review Exercises *311*

8 Statistics

8.0 Introduction *314*
8.1 Frequency Distributions *316*
8.2 Summary Statistics *321*
　　In Search of
　　the Tchebychev Inequality *328*
8.3 Probability and Statistics *329*
8.4 Normal Distributions *335*
　　Making Connections:
　　May I Have Your Opinion? *342*
8.5 Applications of
　　Normal Distributions *344*
　　In Search of the Mathematics of the
　　Normal Distribution Curve *351*

8.6 Normal Distribution Approximations
　　of Binomial Distributions *353*
Summary *358*
Inventory *360*
Review Exercises *361*

Problem Supplement *364*
Answer Key *372*
Glossary *416*
Index *420*

Finite Mathematics aims to increase students' enjoyment of mathematics. With enjoyment will come understanding of, interest in, and enthusiasm for the subject.

Finite Mathematics involves the study of various mathematical models applied to real-life applications. The text includes a wealth of examples and exercises from the fields of business, science, technology, sports, medicine and the arts.

Each chapter starts at a level suitable for students who have mastered grade 11 mathematics and proceeds until it challenges gifted pre-university students. The text contains explanations that are full and complete.

Finite Mathematics provides opportunities for students to develop further their problem-solving abilities and to extend their communication skills. Appropriate use is made of 'proof' throughout the text.

The calculator and computer are powerful tools which the students are encouraged to use whenever appropriate.

Text Organization

- The text is divided into 8 chapters.
- *In Search of* sections within each chapter encourage students to investigate and explore challenging topics individually or in small groups.
- *Making Connections* pages relate mathematics to other fields and disciplines, and encourage a greater understanding of the nature and purpose of mathematics.
- The *problem supplement* at the end of the text provides an opportunity for students to synthesize the skills and ideas acquired throughout the course.
- The *answer key* provides answers for all exercises, reviews, and inventories, as well as for the problem supplement.
- The *glossary* provides definitions of relevant mathematical terms.
- The *index* lists topics and main concepts for easy reference.

Chapter Organization

- Each chapter begins with a discussion of a problem which can be solved using the mathematics developed throughout the chapter.
- Teaching material is clearly separated from exercise material.
- Worked examples enhance the understanding of each topic.
- Color is used to highlight generalizations, rules, and formulas.
- Mathematical terms appear in **boldface** type when they are first introduced. All relevant terms are defined in the glossary.
- *Italic* type is used for emphasis.
- Exercise material is carefully sequenced from questions that utilize and apply knowledge to those that develop critical thinking skills.
- The main concepts covered in each chapter are listed concisely in the *Chapter Summary*.
- The *Chapter Review* provides additional opportunities for students to apply their problem solving skills.
- The *Chapter Inventory* provides students with an opportunity to test their skills and understanding of the mathematical concepts in the chapter.

Gage
Finite Mathematics
A SEARCH FOR MEANING

CHAPTER ONE

Combinatorics

It is 7 p.m. Saturday October 1st.
Barb and Gary are getting ready to go out on their first date together.

In preparation for the date, they are each busily trying out a variety of outfits, trying to pick the one outfit out of all possible outfits that will be just right for the occasion.

Gary has narrowed his wardrobe selection down to picking one item from each of three pairs of shoes, five shirts, four pairs of pants, six sweaters, three belts and two jackets.

Barb is trying to put together her 'one' outfit from four pairs of pants, four belts, four blouses, four sweaters, four jackets, four pairs of shoes, four necklaces and four pairs of earrings.

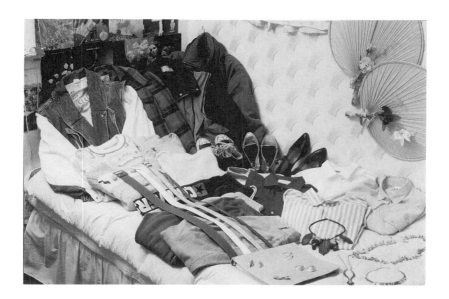

Assume they each spend an average of one minute putting on and evaluating one article of clothing or accessory.

Gary would be ready to make his selection by 7 a.m., Monday morning, assuming he does not eat or sleep in the interim.

Barb on the other hand would not have tried every outfit combination until approximately 7:15 a.m. Wednesday, November the 9th, forty days later!

This chapter is devoted to the theory of counting that allows us to arrive at such conclusions. The theory of counting is called **combinatorics**.

1.1 Counting Objects in Sets

This chapter focusses on counting collections of objects. To be able to answer a question of the form "How many are there?" is of fundamental importance. This chapter will review some important counting techniques. These sophisticated counting techniques will allow you to determine the number of objects in a set without actually counting them. You will need these techniques to help you carry out investigations in algebra and probability in later chapters.

The objects to be counted can be any variety of real things, actions or symbols, for example,

$A = \{1, 2, 3, 4, \ldots 20\}$, a set of numbers

$B = \{$ABCFI, ABEFI, ABEHI, ADGHI, ADEFI, ADEHI$\}$, a set of paths from point A to point I, with no backtracking

$C = \{$TT, TH, HT, HH$\}$, the ways in which two coins can be tossed

$D = \{$tuna, salmon, roast beef, ham, cheese$\}$, a set of sandwiches

$E = \{$A, B, C,$\ldots$, X, Y, Z$\}$, the capital letters of our alphabet

$F = \{\ \}$, the empty set

DEFINITION

If A is any set then $n(A)$ represents the number of elements in set A. $n(A)$ is called the **cardinal number**, or cardinality, of set A.

Referring to the sets above, $n(A) = 20$, $n(B) = 6$, $n(C) = 4$, $n(D) = 5$, $n(E) = 26$ and $n(F) = 0$.

(In this chapter you will only consider sets containing a finite number of elements, that is **finite sets**.)

In practice you will often also want to count elements that make up just part of some larger set X. Such partial sets are called **subsets** of X. The larger set is often referred to as the **universal set** or simply as the **universe**. The relationship between a universal set U and some subset A of U (written symbolically $A \subseteq U$ and read "A is a subset of U") is shown pictorially, in what is called a Venn diagram.

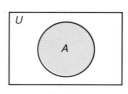

$A \subseteq U$

Referring to the universal sets *A, B, C, D, E* listed on page 4, some sample subsets of these universes are listed below.

R = {2, 4, 6, . . .,20}, the set of even numbers to 20, $R \subset A$

S = {ABEHI, ABEFI, ADEHI, ADEFI},
    the set of paths that pass through
    point *E*, $S \subset B$

T = {HH, TT}, the set of ways in which two coins can come up the same way, $T \subset C$

W = {tuna, salmon}, the set of fish sandwiches, $W \subset D$

X = {A, E, I, O, U}, the set of vowels, $X \subset E$

For each subset of *A* in a universe there is a related subset called the **complement** of *A*.

DEFINITION   If *A* is a subset of a universe *U* then *A′* is the complement of *A*, that is, the subset of elements in *U* that are not in subset *A*.

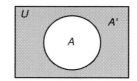

For counting purposes this means
$n(A) + n(A') = n(U)$.

Compare the following complements with their corresponding subsets listed above.

R′ = {1, 3, 5,. . ., 17, 19}, the set of odd numbers to 20

$n(R') = 10, n(R) = 10$

S′ = {ABCFI, ADGHI}, the set of paths
    that do not pass through E

$n(S') = 2, n(S) = 4$

T′ = {HT, TH}, the ways two coins can come up differently

$n(T') = 2, n(T) = 2$

W′ = {roast beef, ham, cheese}, all non-fish sandwiches

$n(W') = 3, n(W) = 2$

X′ = {B, C, D, F,. . ., X, Y, Z}, the set of consonants

$n(X') = 21, n(X) = 5$

When trying to count the elements of some subset *A* it is often easier to count the elements that are *not* in *A*, and then make use of the fact that $n(A) = n(U) - n(A')$ to calculate the number of elements in *A*.

Example 1   How many paths from point A to point I do not pass through point C?

Solution   Consider the number of paths that *do* pass through point C.

There is only one such path ABCFI.
On page 4 you found that
there were six paths from A to I.
Therefore, the number of paths that do not pass through point C
is (6 − 1) or 5.   ■

It is often the case that you will want to count elements related to more than one subset.

DEFINITION   If *A* and *B* are two sets, the intersection of *A* and *B*, written *A* ∩ *B*, is the set of elements common to both sets.

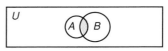

Should two sets have no elements in common, that is if *A* ∩ *B* = { } or *n*(*A* ∩ *B*) = 0, the two sets are called **disjoint**.

DEFINITION   If *A* and *B* are two sets, the union of *A* and *B*, written *A* ∪ *B*, is the set of elements in set *A or B or* both.

Example 2   Given a deck of 52 playing cards,
a) how many cards are red face cards?
b) how many are either red cards or face cards?

Solution   a) Here you are attempting to count the number of cards in the intersection of the subset of red cards, *R*, and the subset of face cards, *F*, namely,
R ∩ F = { J♡, Q♡, K♡, J◇, Q◇, K◇}
$n(R \cap F) = 6$
There are six red face cards in a full deck.

b) Here you are attempting to count the number of cards in the union of the two previously defined sets *R* and *F*. Refer to the illustration of *R, F* on the right. You should notice that the number of elements in the union of the two sets is the total number of elements in both sets *less the number of elements in their intersection*.

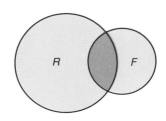

The number of elements in the intersection is *subtracted*, since the number is twice counted in the total $n(F) + n(R)$.

$$n(R \cup F) = \underset{n(R)}{26} + \underset{n(F)}{12} - \underset{n(R \cap F)}{6}$$

Simplifying, you can conclude that in a full deck there are 32 cards that are either red cards or face cards. ■

The last example leads to the following rule for counting the number of elements in the union of two sets.
For any two sets A and B

PROPERTIES

$$n(A \cup B) = n(A) + n(B) - n(A \cap B)$$

$$n(A \cup B) = n(A) + n(B), \text{ if } A \text{ and } B \text{ are disjoint.}$$

The next example illustrates the counting of objects in the union of three sets.

Example 3   In a class of 33 students,
  22 take Finite Math
  24 take Calculus
  20 take Algebra
  17 take Finite Math and Calculus
  17 take Algebra and Calculus
  13 take Finite Math and Algebra and
  12 take all three.
How many students in the class take at least one math course?

Solution   Let F = {students taking Finite Math}
  C = {students taking Calculus}
  A = {students taking Algebra}
Finding the number of students taking at least one math course is equivalent to calculating $n(F \cup C \cup A)$, the number of students in the union of the three sets.

The sets F, C and A determine seven disjoint subsets $R_1, R_2, R_3, R_4, R_5, R_6, R_7$.

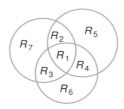

The solution to this problem lies in calculating the number of elements in each of these sets.

$$n(F \cup C \cup A) = n(R_1) + n(R_2) + n(R_3) + n(R_4) + n(R_5) + n(R_6) + n(R_7)$$
$$(R_1) = \{\text{students taking all three courses}\}$$
$$n(R_1) = 12, \text{ from the given information}$$

Also, $R_1 \cup R_2 = \{\text{students taking both Finite Math and Calculus}\}$

$$n(R_1 \cup R_2) = n(R_1) + n(R_2) \qquad\qquad R_1 \text{ and } R_2 \text{ are disjoint}$$
$$17 = 12 + n(R_2)$$
$$n(R_2) = 5$$

Similarly, it can be shown
$$n(R_3) = 1$$
$$\text{and } n(R_4) = 5$$

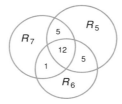

Also, $C = R_1 \cup R_2 \cup R_4 \cup R_5$
where $n(C) = n(R_1) + n(R_2) + n(R_4) + n(R_5)$
$$24 = 12 \quad + 5 \quad\quad + 5 \quad\quad + n(R_5)$$
$$n(R_5) = 2$$

Similarly it can be shown that
$$n(R_6) = 2$$
$$\text{and } n(R_7) = 4$$

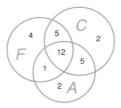

$$n(F \cup C \cup A) = n(R_1) + n(R_2) + \ldots + n(R_7)$$
$$= 12 + 5 + 1 + 5 + 2 + 2 + 4$$
$$= 31$$
31 of 33 students take at least one math course. ■

1.1 Exercises

Questions 1-6 refer to the following sets:
the universal set

U = {the first twenty natural numbers}
and the subsets

A = {the odd numbers to 19, inclusive}

B = {the even numbers to 20, inclusive}

C = {all 2-digit numbers to 20, inclusive}.

1. List the elements in each set, indicating the cardinality of each set.

2. Sketch a Venn diagram to illustrate the relationship between each pair, or triple, of the sets listed below.
   a) A, B c) A, C
   b) B, C d) A, B, C

3. Describe each of the following sets in words.
   a) A' c) $A \cap C$ e) $A \cup C$
   b) $A \cup B$ d) $(A \cup C)'$ f) $A' \cap C'$

4. List the elements in each of the sets described in question 3, indicating the cardinality of each set.

5. Which sets are disjoint?

6. Redefine sets A, B and C as subsets of your own invention. Keep the same universal set. Answer questions 1-5 where they pertain to your new subsets.

7. Refer to the Venn diagram to the right when evaluating each expression below. The number of elements in each region is shown in the diagram.

   a) $n(A)$ d) $n(A \cup B)$ g) $n(A \cap B)'$
   b) $n(B)$ e) $n(A')$ h) $n(U \cap B)$
   c) $n(A \cap B)$ f) $n(B')$ i) $n(U)$

8. In your own words, justify the formula $n(A \cup B) = n(A) + n(B) - n(A \cap B)$.

9. Use the accompanying diagram to help you evaluate each of the following values.
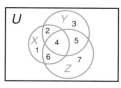
   a) $n(X)$ e) $n(X' \cap Z)$
   b) $n(Y)$ f) $n(Y \cap Z)$
   c) $n(Z)$ g) $n(X' \cup Y)$
   d) $n(X' \cap Y)$ h) $n(U)$

10.
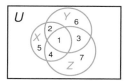
   Determine each of the following numbers.
   a) $n(X')$ g) $n(X' \cup X)$
   b) $n(Y')$ h) $n(X' \cup Y)$
   c) $n(Z')$ i) $n(X \cup Z)$
   d) $n(X' \cap X)$ j) $n(U \cap X)$
   e) $n(X \cap Y)$ k) $n(U \cup X)$
   f) $n(X \cap Z)$ l) $n(X' \cap Y' \cap Z')$

11. One hundred people have a cold, seventy-two people are absent and fifty people are absent with a cold. How many people are absent or have a cold?

12. 54 people were polled about their vacationing habits.
    25 vacationed in western Canada,
    31 vacationed in central Canada,
    28 vacationed in eastern Canada,
    11 vacationed in eastern and western Canada,
    10 vacationed in eastern and central Canada,
    17 vacationed in western and central Canada,
    and 4 vacationed in all three regions.
    How many people vacationed in at least one of these regions? How many did not?

13. Invent a problem of your own similar to question 12 and solve it.

1.2 The Fundamental Counting Principle

The person in the picture on the right is using a money machine to make a withdrawal from her savings account. After inserting her card, she must type in her personal password. The password she types in can be any 'word' from four to six letters in length. This password is a security measure that guards against possible misuse of her card should the card become lost or stolen. A thief trying to use the card would be faced with trying to find the correct password out of over three hundred million passwords. The exact number of possible passwords, $n(P)$, is 321 254 128.

You can be quite certain that no one has ever individually counted or listed all of the passwords referred to above.

The **fundamental counting principle** was used to carry out the calculation of $n(P)$. The development of this important counting technique follows.

Example 1   Feeling hungry, you look in the refrigerator for sandwich makings. You see a choice of salmon or roast beef and three kinds of bread, rye, white, and brown. List the sandwich combinations available to you.

Solution   The sandwich combinations can be set out in a tree diagram.

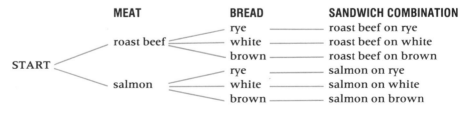

You can make six different sandwiches. ■

In the preceding example there were two sets to consider, M = {roast beef, salmon} and B = {rye, white, brown}.

The sandwich combinations created from the elements of the two sets M and B stem from what is called the **Cartesian product** of sets M and B.

DEFINITION

If A and B are any two sets, the Cartesian product, $A \times B = \{(x,y) \mid x \in A \text{ and } y \in B\}$.

The definition of Cartesian product above can be interpreted in a less abstract manner.

If A lists the ways in which some task can be performed and B lists the ways a second task can be performed, then $A \times B$ lists all ways in which the first task followed by the second task can be performed.

Example 2

Use a tree diagram to find all pairs in $B \times M$. Sets B and M are the breads and meats of Example 1.

Solution

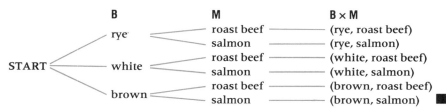

Note, in general $M \times B \neq B \times M$.

Example 3

Referring to the last example, determine $n(M \times B)$ and $n(B \times M)$.

Solution

Counting the ordered pairs in $M \times B$ and $B \times M$, $n(M \times B) = n(B \times M) = 6$.

PROPERTY

In general, $n(M \times B) = n(B \times M)$.

The important thing to notice in Example 3 is that
$$n(M \times B) = n(M) \times n(B)$$
$$= 2 \quad \times 3 \quad = 6$$
In general, the number of pairs in the Cartesian product of two sets is the product of the number of elements in each of the two sets, that is,
$$n(A \times B) = n(A) \times n(B)$$
This can be restated in the form of the fundamental counting principle.

RULE

If task A can be conducted in s ways and task B can be conducted in t ways then task A followed by task B can be conducted in st different ways.

Example 4   Select at random a province of Canada and then select at random a provincial capital city.
a) How many province-city pairs can be selected?
b) How many of these selections are correct pairings?
c) How many are incorrect pairings?

Solution   a) There are 10 provinces from which to choose. For each selection of a province, there are 10 cities which may be chosen. Thus by the fundamental counting principle there are 10×10 or 100 province-city pairs selectable.
b) 10 of these are correct pairings.
c) 90 of these are incorrect pairings. ■

The definition of a Cartesian product can be extended to include more than two sets.

DEFINITION   If A_i, $i = 1, 2, 3, \ldots, n$ are any n sets, the Cartesian product
$A_1 \times A_2 \times A_3 \times \ldots \times A_n = \{(x_1, x_2, x_3, \ldots, x_n) \mid x_i \subset A_i, i = 1, 2, 3, \ldots, n\}$

Example 5   Use a tree diagram to list all the ordered triples in $A \times B \times C$ where $A = \{\text{burger, hotdog}\}$, $B = \{\text{fries, chips}\}$, $C = \{\text{pop, milk, water}\}$.

Solution

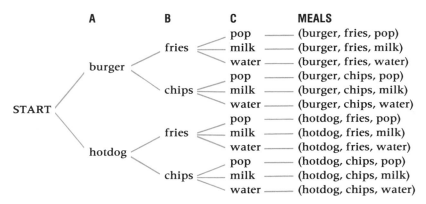

Notice in the last example that
$$n(A \times B \times C) = n(A) \times n(B) \times n(C)$$
$$= 2 \quad \times \quad 2 \quad \times \quad 3 \quad = 12$$

This suggests the following important extension of the fundamental counting principle, the **generalized** fundamental counting principle.

If n tasks $A_1, A_2, A_3, \ldots, A_n$ can be conducted in $a_1, a_2, a_3, \ldots, a_n$ ways respectively, then the n tasks can be conducted, in order, in $a_1 a_2 a_3 \ldots a_n$ different ways.

Example 6   The Joneses are in the process of decorating their guest bedroom. They want to paper, paint and carpet this room. At the moment they have selected six possible wallpaper patterns, seven paint colors and four carpets. From how many decorating combinations can the Joneses choose?

Solution   Assume each decorating combination is made up of one selection from each of the three sets.
Number of combinations = no. of wallpaper choices × no. of paint choices
× no. of carpet choices
= 6 × 7 × 4 = 168
The Joneses have 168 decorating combinations from which to choose.   ■

Example 7   Alpha/numeric information is translated into binary code for computer processing. Each digit and alphabetic character is assigned an eight-digit binary code, such as 01000111. How many different eight-digit binary codes are possible?

Solution   (It is important first to see that there are eight tasks involved in this example. The task in each case is the assigning of 0 or 1 to one of the eight slots of an eight-digit binary code.)

The eight tasks can be carried out in order in
2 × 2 × 2 × 2 × 2 × 2 × 2 × 2 or 2^8 or 256 ways.

There are 256 different eight-digit binary codes available for translating alpha/numeric information.   ■

The next example, in addition to using the fundamental counting principle, makes use of our knowledge of the union of several sets.

Example 8   Recall the person using a money machine, at the beginning of this section. Verify the statement made in the introduction to this section.
"The exact number of possible passwords, $n(P)$, is 321 254 128."

Solution   Let A, B and C be the sets of four, five, and six letter passwords respectively.
Keeping in mind that each letter in a password can be any of 26 different letters,
$n(A) = $ 26 × 26 × 26 × 26 $=$ 456 976
$n(B) = $ 26 × 26 × 26 × 26 × 26 $=$ 11 881 376
$n(C) = $ 26 × 26 × 26 × 26 × 26 × 26 $=$ 308 915 776
$P = A \cup B \cup C$ and A, B and C are disjoint sets
$n(P) = n(A \cup B \cup C) = n(A) + n(B) + n(C)$ $=$ 321 254 128.   ■

1.2 Exercises

1. In your own words, state the fundamental counting principle.

2. How many identical briefcases could be uniquely identified by two stick-on initials?

3. Canadian radio stations have four-letter call signs each beginning with a C. Determine the largest possible number of Canadian radio call signs.

4. Until the mid 1980's the Ministry of Transportation and Communications of Ontario issued car licence plates with numbers that consisted of three letters followed by three numbers. By the mid 80's the Ministry ran out of plate numbers, so they switched to issuing plates with three digits followed by three letters. How many license plates of the new design will the ministry be able to issue before they have to invent yet another numbering system?

5. Explain why using the fundamental principle of counting will not alone correctly answer the following. "Pizzas can be made with cheese, pepperoni, ham, olives, mushrooms or peppers as toppings. How many different 2-topping pizzas can be made?"

6. The Peppler family have a new baby girl. They want to give her a first name after her mother, grandmother or favorite aunt and a middle name from a 'short list' of five other names. How many such name combinations are the Pepplers able to select from?

7. How many different telephone numbers can a given area code have, if the first digit cannot be a zero?

8. A combination consists of three different numbers in the form 'a-right/b-left/c-right'. How many different combinations are possible for the lock shown on the right?

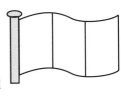

9. a) Mail delivery is speeded up through the use of postal codes. One postal code can target a letter as close as a given building or part of a street. Calculate the maximum number of postal codes possible given their present form of construction.

   b) Compare this number with the number of United States five-digit ZIP codes.

10. In how many ways can the flag to the right be colored if you have ten colors to choose from? The only restriction imposed is that no two adjacent regions can have the same color.

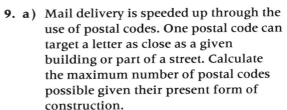

11. Given the same number of colors and restrictions as in question 10, calculate the number of unique color combinations possible for each of the following flag configurations.

a)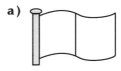

c)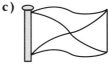

b)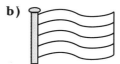

d)

12. In how many ways can a coin come up if tossed once? twice? three times? four times? five times? ten times? *n* times?

13. Refer to the diagram on the right. How many difference paths take you from point *A* to point *D* via points *B* and *C*?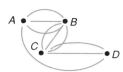

14. Three dice are tossed.
   a) In how many ways can the dice come up?
   b) In how many ways can the dice each come up a different number?
   c) In how many ways will the dice come up with at least two of the numbers the same?

15. Answer question 14 reading "tetrahedral dice" in place of the word "dice" (The number on a tetrahedral die is the number on the 'down' face).

16. Below is given a 'jargon generator'. You use it by selecting one word, in order, from columns 1, 2 and 3. The resulting phrase is a convincing sounding piece of jargon. How many phrases can be constructed using this jargon generator?

column 1	column 2	column 3
quasi	permanent	behaviour
semi	affordable	product
tentatively	stoical	acceptance
ongoing	temperate	wonderment
differentiated	aberrant	attainment
polymorphous		
inconsequential		

(Create your own jargon generator.)

17. A paint store owner mixes his own paint colors for his customers. He has three 'base' paints to which he adds one or more of thirty different tints. He can vary the amount of any one tint ten ways. How many different paints can he mix that each makes use of one tinting color? that makes use of two tinting colors?

18. Reread the introduction on page 2 and verify the conclusions made about Barb and Gary.

19. A fully stocked shoe store carries 100 styles of shoes in eight sizes and three colors. Estimate the value of the stock of shoes in the store.

20. A Morse code signal, (an example of a binary code) invented by the American, Samuel Morse, in 1838, is a sequence of one to four dots or dashes. How many possible Morse code signals are there?

21. In 1833 Louis Braille invented a writing system for the blind based on a rectangular set of six raised or flat dots on paper. Examples are shown below.

a	b	c	d	e	f	g	h	i	j
k	l	m	n	o	p	q	r	s	t
u	v	w	x	y	z				

How many different configurations of bumps and flats can be made? Are there enough different configurations to encode all commonly used alpha-numeric symbols?

22. A person tries to splice the two wires shown on the right together again. In how many ways can the two ends be matched up?

23. How many incorrect matchings would there have been in question 22 had there been 10 wires to match up? (Thank goodness for color coded wires!)

24. Estimate an upper limit on the number of words we have available to us. Justify your estimate.

25. Here you see one 'MUSIC' path. How many different MUSIC paths are there in the configuration?

26. How many different paths would there be through 'COUNTING', set up in a configuration similar to the one in question 25?

27. Four different sandwiches are distributed at random into the four lettered boxes shown.

a) In how many different ways can the sandwiches be placed in the boxes?
b) In how many different ways can the sandwiches be placed in the boxes if you are restricted to placing only one sandwich in each box?
c) How many of the sandwich placements in part a) have more than one sandwich in each box?

28. Try question 27 again, only this time use four sandwiches and five boxes.

29. a) In how many ways can a rectangle of dimension 3 × 1 be placed on a rectangular grid of dimension 7 × 1 so that the squares of the rectangle coincide exactly with the squares of the grid?

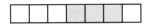

b) What would your answer have been if the rectangle had dimension a × 1 and the grid dimension b × 1, where a and b are natural numbers and a ⩽ b?

30. a) In how many ways can a rectangle of dimension 3 × 1 be placed on a rectangular grid of dimension 7 × 5?

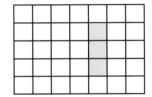

b) What would your answer have been if the rectangle had dimension a × 1 and the grid dimension b × c, where a, b and c are natural numbers with a ⩽ b and a ⩽ c?

31. a) In how many ways can a rectangular prism of dimension 3 × 1 × 1 be embedded in a block of dimension 7 × 5 × 6?

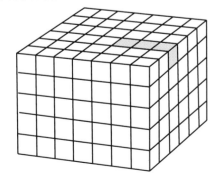

b) What would your answer have been if the rectangular prism had dimension a × 1 × 1 and the block dimension b × c × d, where a, b, c and d are natural numbers with a ⩽ b, c and d?

1.3 Arrangements

A Scrabble player with the seven letters E, I, O, B, C, M and N is faced with the challenge of trying to start the game by using all (or some) of these letters to spell a word of seven or fewer letters.

In this and similar situations the focus is on 'arranging' a given set of objects amongst themselves.

Consider the positions occupied by the objects.

The first letter position of the word can be occupied by any one of the seven letters.

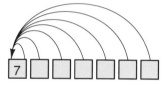

The second letter position of the word can be occupied by any one of the remaining six letters.

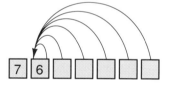

At this point we are considering all possible two-letter arrangements that can be constructed from the seven given letters. Applying the fundamental counting principle, we can say that there are 7×6 or 42 pairs. This set of 42 letter pairs, {EI, IE, EO, OE, EB, BE, EC, CE, EM, ME, EN, NE, IO, OI, IB, BI, IC, CI, IM, MI, IN, NI, OB, BO, OC, CO, OM, MO, ON, NO, BC, CB, BM, MB, BN, NB, CM, MC, CN, NC, MN, NM} is called the set of '2-arrangements of the 7 different letters'.

To each of the above 7×6 ordered pairs of letters, a third letter can be appended from the remaining five letters. The resulting three letter words, called '3-arrangements of 7 letters', number $(7 \times 6) \times 5$.

Summarizing the above and arguing in similar fashion, the number of
1-arrangements of 7 letters $= 7 = 7$
2-arrangements of 7 letters $= (7) \times 6 = 42$
3-arrangements of 7 letters $= (7 \times 6) \times 5 = 210$
4-arrangements of 7 letters $= (7 \times 6 \times 5) \times 4 = 840$
5-arrangements of 7 letters $= (7 \times 6 \times 5 \times 4) \times 3 = 2520$
6-arrangements of 7 letters $= (7 \times 6 \times 5 \times 4 \times 3) \times 2 = 5040$
7-arrangements of 7 letters $= (7 \times 6 \times 5 \times 4 \times 3 \times 2) \times 1 = 5040$.

Notice in the above that,
• each answer is a product of consecutive natural numbers,

• each product is made up of a number of factors equal to the number of
  letters in the arrangement,

• the first factor in the product equals the number of letters available from
  which to choose.

This pattern suggests an answer to the general question,
"How many r-arrangements are there of n different objects?"

Answer:
The number of r-arrangements of n objects $= n(n - 1)(n - 2)\ldots(n - r + 1)$.

$$\longleftarrow r \text{ factors} \longrightarrow$$

We will use the following notation when dealing with arrangements of
objects:

$P(n,r)$ will stand for the number of r-**arrangements** of n different objects.

Note: $_nP_r$ is another often used alternative notation for $P(n,r)$.

Example 1   Interpret and then evaluate each of the following: $P(4,3)$, $P(3,4)$, $P(n,2)$,
$P(6,6)$.

Solution $P(4,3)$ stands for the number of 3-arrangements of 4 objects.
$P(4,3) = 4 \times 3 \times 2 = 24$.

$P(3,4)$ has no meaning. (You cannot arrange more objects than there are
objects available to choose from.)

$P(n,2)$ stands for the number of 2-arrangements of n objects.
$P(n,2) = n(n - 1)$.

$P(6,6)$ stands for the number of 6-arrangements of 6 objects.
$P(6,6) = 6 \times 5 \times 4 \times 3 \times 2 \times 1 = 720$. ■

Example 2   In how many ways can five pictures in a line be arranged amongst themselves?

Solution   This question is equivalent to finding the number of 5-arrangements of 5 objects.
$P(5,5) = 5 \times 4 \times 3 \times 2 \times 1 = 120$
The pictures can be arranged amongst themselves in 120 ways.   ■

Example 3   Three of the nine numbered balls in the bowl at the right are withdrawn at random and set out in the order drawn. How many different three-digit numbers can be drawn?

Solution   This question is equivalent to asking for the number of 3-arrangements of 9 objects.
$P(9,3) = 9 \times 8 \times 7 = 504$
504 different three-digit numbers can be drawn.   ■

Example 4   a) How many batting orders are possible for a nine member baseball team?
b) How many batting orders are possible if the pitcher (usually the worst hitter) must bat last?

Solution   a) The question is equivalent to asking, "How many 9-arrangements of 9 objects are there?"
$P(9,9) = 9 \times 8 \times 7 \times 6 \times 5 \times 4 \times 3 \times 2 \times 1 = 362\ 880$
There are 362 880 batting orders possible.
b) This question is very similar to a) with one restriction.
As a rule of thumb, where restrictions are placed on an arrangement, consider the restriction first.
The ninth batting position can be filled in only one way (with the pitcher).
The first eight positions can be filled in $P(8,8)$ ways.
Using the fundamental counting principle,
the number of batting orders = $P(8,8) \times 1$
$= 8 \times 7 \times 6 \times 5 \times 4 \times 3 \times 2 \times 1 \times 1$
$= 40\ 320.$ ■

1.3 Exercises

1. Describe three everyday situations that involve arrangements of some set of objects.

2. Describe in your own words what a '2-arrangement of 3 objects' means; what an 's-arrangement of t objects' means.

3. List all the 2-arrangements of the symbols. $\{+ - \times\}$. List all the 3-arrangements.

4. Use a tree diagram to list all the 4-arrangements of the letters A, B, C, D.

5. Calculate.
   a) $P(2,2)$ e) $P(100,2)$ i) $P(5,3)$
   b) $P(3,2)$ f) $P(n,2)$ j) $P(30,3)$
   c) $P(4,2)$ g) $P(3,3)$ k) $P(5,5)$
   d) $P(20,2)$ h) $P(4,3)$ l) $P(4,5)$

6. Which is largest, $P(20,1)$, $P(20,10)$ or $P(20,20)$?

7. Which is smallest, $P(7,3)$, $P(4,3)$ or $P(10,3)$?

8. Arrange in order from smallest to largest, $P(100,1)$, $P(10,2)$ $P(7,3)$, $P(5,4)$.

9. Determine the values of n and r for each of the following to be true.
   a) $P(n,r) = 6 \times 5 \times 4 \times 3 \times 2 \times 1$
   b) $P(n,r) = 8 \times 7 \times 6$
   c) $P(n,r) = 510 \times 509 \times 508 \times 507$
   d) $P(n,r) = a(a - 1)(a - 2)$
   e) $P(n,r) = 9 \times 8 \times 7 \times 6 \times 5 \times 4 \times 3$
   f) $P(n,r) = 7.25$

10. Students are asked to solve the quadratic equation $ax^2 + bx + c = 0$ where the coefficients a, b and c can be any value 1, 2, 3, 4 or 5, no two the same. How many different quadratic equations would the students have to solve?

11. Consider the letters of the word HEXAGON.
    a) In how many ways can the letters of the word HEXAGON be arranged amongst themselves?
    b) In how many ways can the vowels of HEXAGON be arranged amongst themselves?
    c) How many arrangements of the letters of HEXAGON begin with an H?
    d) How many arrangements of letters of HEXAGON begin with a vowel? with a consonant?
    e) How are the two answers in part d) related?

12. A computer program is written that generates every arrangement of the letters AEIOLNPRSTY. The program checks each arrangement against a comprehensive set of English words in its memory in an attempt to find any words that have these eleven letters. If each search takes 0.01 s, how much computer time will be required to make a complete search of all arrangements? (Can you make up an eleven letter word from these letters?)

13. a) In how many orders can eight horses finish a race, with no ties in any position?
    b) In how many ways can these horses place 1st, 2nd and 3rd, that is, win, place and show?

14. a) Determine the number of ways five people can occupy five seats.
    b) Determine the number of ways five people can occupy seven seats.

15. You are given the word FIELD.
    a) How many 5-arrangements of these letters are possible?
    b) How many 5-arrangements start with the letter F?
    c) How many 5-arrangements begin with a vowel?
    d) How many 5-arrangements begin with a consonant?
    e) How many 5-arrangements begin and end with a vowel?
    f) How many 5-arrangements begin and end with a consonant?

1.4 Arrangements and Factorial Notation

Working with arrangements, you frequently meet products such as

$5 \times 4 \times 3 \times 2 \times 1$
$9 \times 8 \times 7 \times 6 \times 5 \times 4 \times 3 \times 2 \times 1$
$20 \times 19 \times 18 \times 17 \times 16$

For example, all of the letters ABCDE can be arranged amongst themselves in $P(5,5) = 5 \times 4 \times 3 \times 2 \times 1 = 120$ ways.

To more easily write and work with such products, **factorial notation** is introduced.

$1! = 1 = 1$
$2! = 2 \times 1 = 2$
$3! = 3 \times 2 \times 1 = 6$
$4! = 4 \times 3 \times 2 \times 1 = 24$
$5! = 5 \times 4 \times 3 \times 2 \times 1 = 120$
$6! = 6 \times 5 \times 4 \times 3 \times 2 \times 1 = 720$
$7! = 7 \times 6 \times 5 \times 4 \times 3 \times 2 \times 1 = 5040$
$n! = n(n - 1)(n - 2)\ldots \times 4 \times 3 \times 2 \times 1$

With this notation you could now say that the letters ABCDE can all be arranged amongst themselves in $P(5,5) = 5!$ ways.

In general, $P(n,n) = n!$ ($n!$ is read "n factorial").

Example 1

In how many different orders could 20 people line up in front of the ticket window of a theatre?

Solution

This question is equivalent to asking for the number of 20-arrangements of 20 objects.
$P(20, 20) = 20!$
This answer could be left in factorial form, as you would not be expected to write out or calculate the product of the 20 factors involved in 20!.

If an approximation is required, use the factorial key on your scientific calculator.

There are approximately 2 432 900 000 000 000 000 or 2.433 quintillion ways of having 20 people line up for a show!   ■

$P(n,r)$, that is, the number of r-arrangements of n objects, can also be given in factorial form.

Example 2   Express $P(10,4)$ in factorial form.

Solution $P(10,4) = 10 \times 9 \times 8 \times 7$

$$= \frac{10 \times 9 \times 8 \times 7 \times (6 \times 5 \times 4 \times 3 \times 2 \times 1)}{(6 \times 5 \times 4 \times 3 \times 2 \times 1)}$$

$$= \frac{10!}{6!} \quad \blacksquare$$

Example 3   Express $P(n,r)$ in factorial form.

Solution   Recall that $P(n,r)$ is a product of r consecutive natural numbers, the largest being n.

$$P(n,r) = n(n - 1)(n - 2)\ldots(n - r + 1)$$

This product is not $n!$ as it is missing the remaining $n - r$ consecutive natural factors, the largest being $(n - r)$. Multiplying and dividing the expression for $P(n,r)$ by these missing factors,

$$P(n,r) = \frac{n(n - 1)(n - 2)\ldots(n - r + 1)[(n - r)(n - r - 1)\ldots 3 \times 2 \times 1]}{[(n - r)(n - r - 1)\ldots 3 \times 2 \times 1)]}$$

$$P(n,r) = \frac{n!}{(n - r)!} \quad \blacksquare$$

Example 4   Assign a value to 0!

Solution   Since $P(n,r) = \dfrac{n!}{(n - r)!}$

$$P(n,n) = \frac{n!}{(n - n)!}$$

$$= \frac{n!}{0!}$$

But you know $P(n,n) = n!$
Thus 0! must be assigned the value 1.
$0! = 1$ ■

Example 5   In how many ways can the vertices of the figure on the right be labelled with distinct capital letters of the alphabet?

Solution   The above question is equivalent to asking for the number of 6-arrangements (6 vertices) of 26 objects (letters in the alphabet).

$$P(26,6) = \frac{26!}{20!} = 1.657\ 656 \times 10^8$$

There are approximately 166 million ways of labelling the figure!   ■

1.4 Exercises

1. Evaluate each of the following expressions. (Calculate with and without a calculator.)

   a) $5!$

   b) $\dfrac{10!}{9!}$

   c) $\dfrac{20!}{18!}$

   d) $\dfrac{10!}{10 \times 9!}$

2. Why is factorial notation called factorial notation?

3. Give two reasons why factorial notation was invented.

4. Why do some people refer to a 'factorial explosion'?

5. Simplify each of the following expressions.

   a) $\dfrac{n!}{(n-1)!}$

   b) $\dfrac{a!}{(a-2)!}$

   c) $\dfrac{(a-1)!}{(a-2)!}$

   d) $\dfrac{(a+1)!}{(a-1)!}$

6. Express each of the following in factorial notation.

   a) $P(7,7)$

   b) $P(7,5)$

   c) $P(m,m)$

   d) $P(a,b)$

7. Invent a problem to correspond with each of the answers below.

   a) $10!$

   b) $\dfrac{6!}{3!}$

   c) $\dfrac{52!}{47!}$

   d) $\dfrac{6!}{4!}$

8. In how many zeros will the number equalling $10!$ end?

9. What is the largest factorial your calculator will evaluate before giving an error message?

10. Show how the definition $n! = n \times (n-1)!$ can be used to find $5!$.

11. What value does your calculator assign to $0!$?

12. Express $P(n,n)$ in factorial notation and show that your answer is equivalent to $n!$.

13. Use your calculator, where possible, to find approximations for each expression given below.

    a) $20!$

    b) $\dfrac{16!}{8!}$

    c) $P(100,20)$

    d) $P(15,15)$

    e) $P(52,13)$

    f) $P(31,15)$

14. One of the three numbers shown below is equal to $11!$. Find which one it is without calculating the value $11!$.
    39 916 000, 39 916 850, 39 916 800

15. For which values of n will $n! > 2n$?

16. One simple way to code a message is to replace each letter of the alphabet with a different letter of the alphabet.
    For example, using
    original alphabet:
    ABCDEFGHIJKLMNOPQRSTUVWXYZ
    replacement alphabet:
    CDJKMZXYPOLNABFGHIQSTRVWUE
    the message 'HI THERE' becomes
    'YP SYMIM'. How many different codes of this type are there?

17. a) Show that there are no primes between $5! + 2$ and $5! + 5$, inclusive.

    b) In general, why are there no primes between $n! + 2$ and $n! + n$, inclusive? (You can use this idea to generate a long sequence of consecutive composite numbers.)

James Stirling (1692-1770) was an English mathematician. He is best known for discovering a formula that approximates the values of factorials.

18. How well does Stirling's formula $\sqrt{2\pi n}\ n^n e^{-n}$ approximate $n!$? Try some sample values for n.

19. Prove
$$\frac{1}{(a-1)!\ n!} + \frac{1}{a!\ (n-1)!} = \frac{a+n}{a!\ n!}$$

MAKING

Information, Please

One name that has been used to describe the latter part of the twentieth century is the Age of Information. You live in a world which has a telephone network involving over half a billion telephones. Radio signals from space probes come to earth and are converted into breath-taking photographs of the planets. Television, radio, newspapers, magazines, and books disseminate staggering quantities of the abstraction known as information.

Modern society depends on the rapid and accurate transmission of huge volumes of information. Many of the technological advances which help the world to cope with information flow have as their theoretical underpinning a branch of probability theory known as *information theory*.

Information theory is concerned with the likelihood of the transmission of messages. The theory is concerned with how much of a message will be received when one looks at the probabilities of transmission failure, distortion, and accidental additions of information called "noise". Information theory also shows the theoretical maximum amount of information that can be transmitted in a given situation. This is useful for communication engineers who wish to know just how much information can be transmitted if the information is properly coded and packed before transmission.

The components of an information transmission are sketched in the diagram below.

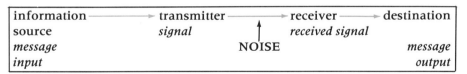

There is no such thing as perfect transmission of information. Information is lost, distorted or added in the transmission process. What is important in communication is ensuring the receiver has enough information in the output message to determine the contents of the input message within specified limits of accuracy.

Communication engineers, armed with the probabilities of loss, distortion and noise, can work to optimize the transmission of information. That is, for a given transmission channel, what is the greatest transmission rate of information which will permit the reception of messages with an acceptable level of error?

Information theory began with the work of one remarkable person, Claude Shannon. He is an American engineer/applied mathematician who has done research for the Bell Telephone Laboratories, and other important work in the fields of computing machines, cryptography and communications. It was Shannon, in papers written in 1938 and 1949, who demonstrated how Boolean algebra could be applied to switching circuits and hence, computers. It was Shannon who coined the term "bit" for binary digit which is so common in computer jargon today.

Shannon's most significant contribution, however, may have been his invention of information theory. He first presented his theory in the 1948 research paper *The Mathematical Theory of Communication*.

Information theory has changed the manner in which man regards information. Prior to Shannon's paper, many were aware of the problems being caused by the increasing flow of information over the available transmission channels, but information was a vague, unquantified concept which defied engineering analysis. Shannon showed how to deal with information in much the same way a physicist might deal with thermal engineering. His work paved the way for many rapid and significant advances in telecommunications.

Here are two interesting aspects of information theory.
The equation used to identify the average amount of information which can be transmitted in a given situation is a sum of probabilities. The equation is identical in form to an equation describing the motion of particles due to random collisions. The probability theory in information theory is identical to that used in statistical mechanics (mentioned in the opener to chapter 7).

Another interesting concept in information theory is redundancy. Because of the nature of the message being transmitted, it is sometimes possible to recode the message so that the recoded message takes less information than the original message, and so that there is still a high probability that the message can be understood. For example, because of the statistical frequency of letters in English, the average information per letter in an English message is about 1 bit. Information theory states that English is about 80% redundant. A message in English can be efficiently recoded, transmitted and accurately decoded using far less information than the original.

N THR WRDS, NGLSH CN B WRTTN MR CMPCTLY ND STLL B NDRSTD!

In Search of a Computer Program

As natural number n increases, $n!$ gets very big very quickly, as evidenced by the value for 100! shown below.

100! = 93 326 215 443 944 152 681 699 238 856 266 700 490 715
        968 264 381 621 468 592 963 895 217 599 993 229 915
        608 941 463 976 156 518 286 253 697 920 827 223 758
        251 185 210 916 864 900 000 000 000 000 000 000 000

Write a computer program that will accept any natural number, n, up to 100 as input, and print out n and the value for $n!$.
One digit in the given value for 100! is incorrect.

Can you find it?

(Hint: You do not need to generate 100! on a computer to find the error.)

In Search of One Hundred Natural Numbers

Use each digit 1, 2, 3, 4, once, the symbol ! at least once, and some of the symbols $+$, $-$, $\times$, $\div$, and brackets, to generate each of the first 100 natural numbers.

For example,

$$1 = 1 + 2 + 4 - 3!$$
$$2 = \frac{4!}{3!} - 2 \times 1$$
$$3 = 4! \div 2^3 \times 1$$
$$4 = 4! \div (1 \times 2 \times 3)$$
$$\vdots$$
$$10 = 1! + 2! + 3 + 4$$
$$\vdots$$
$$100 = (3! - 2)(4! + 1)$$

1.5 Arrangements with Like Elements

Up to this point in your investigation of arrangements you have considered counting arrangements of 'different' objects. Figure 1 below is a typical situation, where you see the various ways three different people can be arranged in a line to have a group picture taken. The picture can be composed in $P(3,3) = 3! = 6$ ways.

figure 1

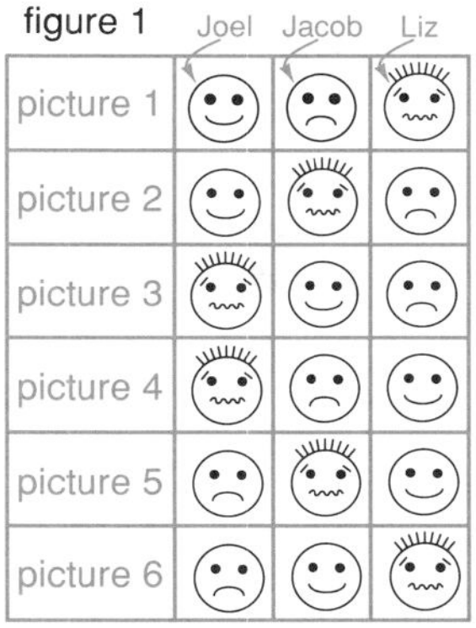

	Joel	Jacob	Liz
picture 1	😊	😐	😮
picture 2	😊	😮	😐
picture 3	😮	😊	😐
picture 4	😮	😐	😊
picture 5	😐	😮	😊
picture 6	😐	😊	😮

figure 2

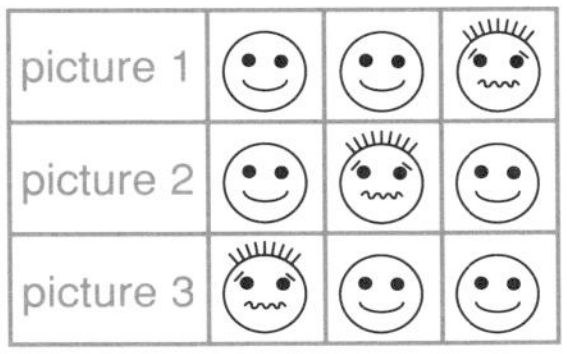

picture 1	😊	😊	😮
picture 2	😊	😮	😊
picture 3	😮	😊	😊

Had Joel and Jacob been identical twins the result would have been what is presented in figure 2. Notice that there are half as many arrangements in figure 2 as there are in figure 1.

Notice that picture 1 in figure 2 corresponds to pictures 1 and 6 in figure 1: Liz is in the same position and the two twins rearranged amongst themselves. The same can be said for picture 2 in figure 2 and pictures 2 and 5 in figure 1; also for picture 3 in figure 2 and pictures 3 and 4 in figure 1.

Had there been five people in the picture, with three of them identical triplets, the above illustration would have started in the following way.

figure 1

figure 2

In this case, each picture in figure 2 would correspond with 3! pictures in figure 1. The triplets would be pictured arranged amongst themselves in $P(3,3)$ ways while the position of the other two people would remain fixed.

Figure 1 would contain $P(5,5)$ or 5! pictures, 3! times the number in figure 2.

These results can be used to deduce that there would be $\frac{5!}{3!}$ or 5×4 or 20 different arrangements in figure 2.

In general, n objects, s of which are identical, can be arranged amongst themselves in $\frac{n!}{s!}$ ways.

The same argument can be applied over and over again for a set of n objects in which s_1 are alike of one kind, s_2 are alike of another kind,..., and s_k are alike of another kind.

RULE	The number of n-arrangements of n such objects $= \dfrac{n!}{s_1! s_2! s_3! \ldots s_k!}$

Example 1   In how many distinct ways can all of the letters of the word SASKATCHEWAN be arranged amongst themselves?

Solution   Total number of letters $= 12$
Number of S's $= 2$
Number of A's $= 3$

Total number of 12-arrangements $= \dfrac{12!}{2!3!} = 39\ 916\ 800$

All of the letters of the word SASKATCHEWAN can be arranged amongst themselves in 39 916 800 ways.   ■

Example 2   Toss a coin eight times.
a) In how many ways can the eight coin tosses come up?
b) How many of the ways in a) have heads being tossed four out of eight times?

Solution   a) Each toss can come up in one of two ways, heads or tails, Using the fundamental counting principle.
Number of outcomes after eight tosses
$= 2 \times 2 \times 2 \times 2 \times 2 \times 2 \times 2 \times 2 = 256$.

b) Think of the eight tosses of a coin as eight cards. In the case of heads being tossed four times, then four cards have H's written on them and four cards have T's.
Now the question becomes, "In how many ways can all eight cards be arranged amongst themselves, with four alike of one kind (H's) and four alike of a second kind (T's)?"

Number of arrangements $= \dfrac{8!}{4!4!} = 70$

70 of the 256 sets of eight tosses come up heads as often as tails.   ■

1.5 Exercises

1. Why are there fewer distinct 4-arrangements for the set of objects {A, A, B, C} than for the set of objects {A, B, C, D}?

2. Arrange the sets listed below in the order of having fewest 5-arrangements to most 5-arrangements.

$A = \{*, \checkmark, \varnothing, +, +\}$ $B = \{a, b, c, d, e\}$
$C = \{1, 2, 2, 2, 3\}$ $D = \{*, *, +, +, -\}$
$E = \{a, a, a, a, b\}$ $F = \{1, 1, 1, 2, 2\}$

3. Calculate the number of 5-arrangements for each of the sets listed in question 2.

4. Calculate the number of ways you can arrange the letters of each of the underlined words in this sentence.

5. In which word will you find the greatest number of arrangements of all of its letters: BINGO, AARDVARK or DEEDED?

6. How many different five-digit numbers can be made with the digits 23233?

7. Six coins are tossed, and the results noted.
  a) Calculate the number of ways each outcome can occur. Put your results in a copy of the table below.

Outcomes	0H	1H	2H	3H	4H	5H	6H
Number							

  b) Which configuration of heads is most likely to occur?

8. In how many different ways can you stack the coins shown on the right?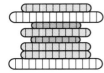

9. A team finishes a twenty game season with a record of 12 wins, 6 losses and 2 ties. In how many different orders could this have occurred?

10. A painter has enough paint to paint three offices white, three cream and four blue. In how many ways can these 10 offices be painted?

11. Invent a combinatorics problem to correspond with each of the answers given below.

  a) $\dfrac{6!}{2!}$ **c)** $\dfrac{12!}{4!8!}$

  b) $\dfrac{10!}{2!2!}$ **d)** $\dfrac{6!}{2!2!2!}$

12. A hobbyist strings 12 beads on a leather thong to make a necklace. Two of the beads are identical spheres and another four of the beads are identical cubes. The rest of the beads are identical cylinders.
  a) How many different 12-bead necklace patterns can be fashioned?
  b) How many of the patterns counted in part a) have the necessary symmetry about the centre of the pattern to make an acceptable necklace pattern?

13. You are at intersection A. You want to walk to intersection B. Calculate the number of different routes possible, that take you from A to B along the street network shown. Assume you walk in northerly or easterly directions only.

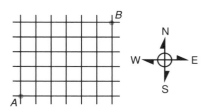

14. How many numbers greater than 3 000 000 can be formed from the digits 1, 2, 3, 3, 4, 4, 4?

1.6 Counting Subsets

In a well-known lottery game a player selects six numbers from 1 to 49 inclusive. Should all six of the player's numbers be drawn, in any order, that player will in all likelihood become an instant millionaire.

In situations such as the one above, the focus is on *selecting* a subset of objects from some larger set of objects (and not on the arranging of these objects amongst themselves as in previous sections of this chapter). In such situations the order in which the objects are selected is not important.

Refer to the six lottery numbers selected, {7, 22, 33, 41, 45, 48} as a '6-subset of 49 objects'.

Compare this 6-subset with the 6-arrangements of 7, 22, 33, 41, 45, 48. There is only one 6-subset containing the numbers 7, 22, 33, 41, 45, 48 while there are 6! 6-arrangements containing the same six numbers.

It is instructive to ask two related questions concerning the lottery ticket.

Q1: "How many 6-arrangements of the 49 numbers are there?" and

Q2: "How many 6-subsets of the 49 numbers are there?"

The answer to the first question is $P(49,6) = \dfrac{49!}{(49-6)!} = \dfrac{49!}{43!}$.

Each 6-number selection or subset you are trying to account for in the second question has been counted 6! times over in the first question.

This implies that the answer to the first question is 6! times larger than the answer to the second question.

Therefore, the lottery player can select a 6-subset of 49 numbers in $\dfrac{P(49,6)}{6!}$ ways, that is $\dfrac{49!}{(49-6)!6!}$ ways. This works out to 13 983 816 ways of selecting the six numbers.

The same kind of argument can be used to answer the general question, "How many *r*-subsets of *n* objects are there?"

The number of *r*-subsets of *n* objects is $\dfrac{P(n,r)}{r!}$

Proof: The number of r-arrangements of n objects is $P(n,r)$ or $\dfrac{n!}{(n-r)!}$

Each r-subset of n objects has been counted $r!$ times in the count $P(n,r)$.

Therefore the number of r-arrangements of n objects, $P(n,r)$, is $r!$ times larger than the number of r-subsets of n objects, that is,

the number of r-subsets of n objects $= \dfrac{P(n,r)}{r!}$

The symbol $C(n,r)$ is introduced to represent the number of r-subsets of n objects. $\dbinom{n}{r}$ and $_nC_r$ are other common notations for this.

Read $C(49,6)$, for example, as "the number of 6-subsets of 49 objects" or more simply as "49 choose 6".

RULE

Thus, $C(n,r) = \dfrac{P(n,r)}{r!}$ or $C(n,r) = \dfrac{n!}{(n-r)!r!}$

Example 1 Interpret and then evaluate $C(6,4)$, $C(4,6)$, $C(n,2)$, $C(10,r)$.

Solution $C(6,4)$ represents the number of 4-subsets of 6 objects.

$C(6,4) = \dfrac{6!}{(6-4)!4!} = \dfrac{6 \times 5 \times (4!)}{2!(4!)} = \dfrac{6 \times 5}{2} = 15.$

$C(4,6)$ has no meaning as you cannot select more objects (6) than are objects in the set (4).

$C(n,2)$ represents the number of 2-subsets of n objects.

$C(n,2) = \dfrac{n!}{(n-2)!2!} = \dfrac{n(n-1)(n-2)!}{2!(n-2)!} = \dfrac{n(n-1)}{2}.$

$C(10,r)$ represents the number of r-subsets of 10 objects.

$C(10,r) = \dfrac{10!}{(10-r)!r!}.$ ∎

Example 2   Deal out five cards from a full deck of 52 cards.

a) How many different five-card hands are possible?

b) How many of the five-card hands are made up of spades?

Solution   a) The number of five-card hands $= C(52,5) = \dfrac{52!}{(52-5)!5!} = \dfrac{52!}{47!5!}$

There are 2 598 960 different five-card hands possible.

b) Note that there are only 13 spades in a full deck of cards.
The number of five-card spade hands $= C(13,5)$
$$= \dfrac{13!}{(13-5)!5!} = \dfrac{13!}{8!5!} = 1287$$
There are 1287 five-card spade hands possible.   ■

Example 3   How many different line segments are determined by the labelled points in the diagram on the right?

Solution   Any two of the labelled points determines one of the line segments to be counted. (Note, for example, that segment AD and segment DA are one and the same. Order is not important here).
There are eight labelled points and any selection of two of them determines one line segment.

Therefore, the number of segments $= C(8,2) = \dfrac{8!}{(8-2)!2!} = \dfrac{8!}{6!2!} = \dfrac{8 \times 7}{2}$
$$= 28$$
The eight points determine 28 line segments.   ■

Example 4   Your name, along with nine others, is put in a hat. Four names are drawn at random to determine the winners of four identical prizes.
a) How many different selections of four names are possible?
b) In how many of the selections in part a) will your name appear?
c) In how many of the selections in part a) will your name not appear?

Solution a) 4 of 10 names can be selected in $C(10,4)$ ways.

$$C(10,4) = \frac{10!}{(10-4)!4!} = \frac{10}{6!4!} = 210$$

The four names can be drawn out of the hat in 210 ways, ignoring the order in which they are drawn.

b) Break the problem into two tasks, the number of ways your name can be selected and the number of ways the remaining three names can be selected.

Your name can be selected in $C(1,1)$ ways.

From the remaining 9 names, the remaining 3 names can be selected in $C(9,3)$ ways.

Applying the fundamental counting principle the two tasks can be performed simultaneously in $C(1,1) \times C(9,3)$ ways.

$$C(1,1) \times C(9,3) = 1 \times \frac{9!}{(9-3)!3!} = \frac{9!}{6!3!} = 84.$$

There are 84 selections in which your name appears.

c) Of the 210 selections, 84 contain your name and the remaining 126 do not. ■

Example 5 In a small drama class of 15 students, 8 students are to be selected to be actors in a play, 4 are to be selected as stage hands and the rest selected to the make-up team. In how many ways can the drama class be divided up to put on the play?

Solution Break the problem into three separate tasks, finding

A, the number of ways the actors can be selected,

S, the number of ways the stage crew can be selected (having selected the actors) and

M, the number of ways the remaining students can be selected to the make-up team.

$A = C(15,8);\ \ S = C(7,4);\ \ M = C(3,3).$

Applying the fundamental counting principle, the class can be divided up in $A \times S \times M$ ways.

$$A \times S \times M = C(15,8) \times C(7,4) \times C(3,3)$$
$$= \frac{15!}{(15-8)!8!} \times \frac{7!}{(7-4)!4!} \times \frac{3!}{(3-3)!3!}$$
$$= \frac{15!\ 7!}{7!\ 8!\ 3!\ 4!} = 225\ 225$$

The drama class can be divided in 225 225 ways. (It is left to the reader to verify that the same answer results if the order in which the various groups are counted is changed.) ■

Some applications involving arrangements require working with subsets first.

Example 6

A class consists of 15 boys and 17 girls. Two boys and two girls from this class are to be selected to fill the positions of chairperson, vice-chairperson, secretary, and treasurer of a school club. In how many ways can these people be selected to the four positions?

Solution

The two boys can be selected in $C(15,2)$ ways.
For each of these pairs of boys the girls can be selected in $C(17,2)$ ways.
Therefore the boys and girls can be selected in a total of $C(15,2) \times C(17,2)$ ways.

Each foursome can then be arranged through the four offices in 4! ways.
Therefore the four people can be selected to the four positions in

$$
\begin{aligned}
C(15,2) \times C(17,2) \times 4! &= \frac{15!}{(15-2)!2!} \times \frac{17!}{(17-2)!2!} \times 4! \\
&= \frac{15!}{13!2!} \times \frac{17!}{15!2!} \times 4! \\
&= \frac{(15 \times 14) \times (17 \times 16) \times 4!}{2!2!} \\
&= 342\ 720
\end{aligned}
$$

The four students can be selected to office in 342 720 ways. ■

Example 7

How many five-letter 'words' contain three different consonants and two different vowels?

Solution

If you consider the English alphabet with 21 consonants and 5 vowels, then
3 consonants may be chosen in $C(21,3)$ ways, and
2 vowels may be chosen in $C(5,2)$ ways.
Each of these 5-letter combinations can be arranged in 5! ways.
Therefore the number of possible 'words' is

$$
\begin{aligned}
C(21,3) \times C(5,2) \times 5! &= \frac{21!}{18!3!} \times \frac{5!}{3!2!} \times 5! \\
&= \frac{(21 \times 20 \times 19) \times (5 \times 4) \times 5!}{3!2!} \\
&= 1\ 596\ 000
\end{aligned}
$$

There are 1 596 000 such five-letter 'words'. ■

1.6 Exercises

1. Explain the differences between $P(n,r)$ and $C(n,r)$.

2. Ten problems follow. Identify those problems in which order is important and those problems in which order is not important.

   a) How many five-digit numbers can be formed using all of the digits 1, 2, 3, 4, 5?
   b) In how many ways can six runners finish a race (no ties)?
   c) Three of five people are chosen to go on a trip. In how many ways can they be chosen?
   d) Five people go to a hockey game. They can buy three seat tickets and two 'standing room only' tickets. In how many ways can the three seat tickets be distributed?
   e) A bridge hand consists of 13 of 52 cards. How many different bridge hands are there?
   f) Any three points determine a triangle. How many different triangles can be determined by the six points shown?

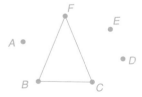

   g) (This question also refers to the diagram in f).) How many different straight line paths start from point A, pass through each of the other labelled points once, and return to point A?
   h) You want to order a medium-sized three topping pizza. There are eight toppings available. How many different pizzas can you order?
   i) Ten people shake hands with each other. How many handshakes take place?
   j) There are ten widgets on a shelf, one of which is defective. You buy five of the widgets at random. How many different selections of five widgets contain only good widgets? How many selections contain the defective widget?

3. a) Which number is larger, $P(10,3)$ or $C(10,3)$? How many times larger?
   b) Which is larger, $P(n,r)$ or $C(n,r)$? How many times larger?

4. Describe three everyday situations that involve choosing objects where order does not count.

5. Evaluate.
   a) $C(8,3)$ d) $C(n,1)$
   b) $C(10,5)$ e) $C(n,2)$
   c) $C(3,8)$ f) $C(n,(n-1))$

6. Which is largest, $C(5,4)$, $C(6,3)$, $C(7,2)$ or $C(8,1)$?

7. Evaluate, without the use of a formula or factorials.
   a) $C(1000,0)$ c) $C(1000,999)$
   b) $C(1000,1)$ d) $C(1000,1000)$
   What reasoning did you use?

8. Find the value(s) of n for which $C(6,n)$ takes on its largest value; its smallest value.

9. Find the value(s) of n for which $C(7,n)$ takes on its largest value; its smallest value.

10. Solve each of the problems listed in question 2.

11. Invent a different combinatorics problem to match each answer given below.
    a) $C(10,4)$ b) $C(8,3)$ c) $C(6,2)$

12. The 'C' in the notation stands for 'combination'. Look up the meaning of the word 'combination'. Why is it appropriate to use the word 'combination' in this context?

13. **a)** How many different pairs of cards can be drawn from a full deck of 52 cards? (A 'pair' means any two cards, here.)

    b) How many of these pairs contain only face cards, that is, jacks, queens or kings?

    c) How many of the pairs contain no face cards?

    d) How many of the pairs contain at least one face card?

14. **a)** How many diagonals are there in an a decagon?

    b) Prove that the number of diagonals in an n-gon is $\dfrac{(n^2 - 3n)}{2}$. Test this formula on several polygons of your choice.

    c) Use the formula in part b) to find the fewest number of sides a polygon must have to contain at least 1000 diagonals.

15. How many triangles can be constructed which have their vertices on the points given at the right?

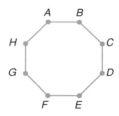

16. **a)** On the right you see a collection of eight points, no three collinear, that is, no three lying on the same straight line. If lines are drawn between each pair of these points, how many points of intersection would there be?

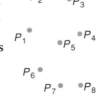

    b) What would your answer have been in part a) if there had been n points to start with? Test your answer for small sets of points.

17. **a)** In how many ways can ten people be divided up into two teams of five?

    b) In how many ways can 14 people be divided into three groups of five, five and four people?

18. Two students worked on the following question. "Five students go into a theatre that has 20 empty seats. In how many different ways can the five people be assigned their seat by the usher?"
Student A responded
$20 \times 19 \times 18 \times 17 \times 16$.
Student B responded $C(20,5) \times 5!$
They were both correct in their answers but they each attacked the problem differently. Explain how each student reasoned to her/his answer.

19. **a)** Give a non-algebraic common sense argument to show that
$C(1000,995) = C(1000,5)$.

    b) Prove that $C(n,r) = C(n,n - r)$.

20. **a)** How many different line segments start and end on one of the labelled points?

       •———•———•———•———•———•———•
       A B C D E F G

    b) Use your approach in part a) and the fundamental counting principle to determine the total number of rectangles in the grid.

21. **a)** Show that a set of ten objects can be partitioned into one group of two, one group of three, and one group of five, in $\dfrac{10!}{2!3!5!}$ ways.

    b) Prove that a group of n objects can be partitioned into groups of a, b, c and d, where $a + b + c + d = n$, in $\dfrac{n!}{a!b!c!d!}$ ways.

22. Four children have 20 different bubble gum baseball cards to divide evenly amongst themselves. In how many different ways can the cards be evenly shared?

In Search of an Understanding of Poker

Of the $C(52,5)$ different five-card hands that can be dealt in a game of poker, calculate the number of hands of each type illustrated below. The type of hand that occurs less often beats a hand that occurs more often. Verify that the hands have been listed in ascending order of strength.

Hand	Example	Number
five different (not in sequence or same suit)		
one pair		
two pair		
three of a kind		
straight		
flush		
full house		
four of a kind		
straight flush		
royal flush		

1.7 Power of a Set

In how many ways can you 'decorate' this hamburger?
The set of hamburger 'fixings',
F = {onions, ketchup, lettuce, mustard, pickles, tomatoes, cheese, relish}.

To give an answer to the above question it will be necessary to count up all possible selections that can be made from set F. The selections can range from 0-subsets (a plain hamburger) to 8-subsets ('the works') of set F.

Solving this problem is equivalent to determining the total number of subsets of F including the empty set and set F itself. The set of all subsets of F is known as the **power set** of F and is denoted $\mathcal{P}(F)$.
$$n[\mathcal{P}(F)] = C(8,0) + C(8,1) + C(8,2) + C(8,3) + C(8,4)$$
$$+ C(8,5) + C(8,6) + C(8,7) + C(8,8)$$
$$= 1 + 8 + 28 + 56 + 70 + 56 + 28 + 8 + 1$$
$$= 256$$

There are 256 ways of 'decorating' the hamburger.

An equivalent way of determining the number of subsets in the power set of F is to look at each element in set F and say there are two ways of selecting it, that is, taking the item or not taking the item.
Using the fundamental counting principle,
$$n[\mathcal{P}(F)] = 2 \times 2 \times 2 \times 2 \times 2 \times 2 \times 2 \times 2 = 2^8 = 256$$
In general, if a set A contains n different elements,
$$n[\mathcal{P}(A)] = C(n,0) + C(n,1) + C(n,2) + \ldots + C(n,n-1) + C(n,n) = 2^n$$
(Remember this number includes both the empty set and the set A itself. Be prepared in an application of this rule to reduce this number by 1 or 2 if one or both of these sets are to be excluded.)

Example 1 How many sums of money can be made up from the following coins: 1¢, 5¢, 10¢, 25¢, 50¢, $1?

Solution Each subset of the six coins generates a unique sum of money.
If the zero sum is not to be counted then the empty set is not to be counted.

Number of sums of money $= 2^6 - 1$
$$= 64 - 1$$
$$= 63$$

63 different sums of money can be made up from the six coins. ■

Example 2 How many different sums of money can be made up from the following set of coins: 3 pennies, 4 nickels, 1 quarter and 1 fifty cent piece?

Solution Using an extension of the 'take it or leave it' strategy employed in this section, you can argue as follows.
The number of pennies can be selected in 4 ways, that is 0, 1, 2 or 3 of them can be selected.
For each selection of pennies, the number of nickels can be selected in 5 ways, that is 0, 1, 2, 3, or 4 of them.
The other two coins can each be selected in two ways as before.
Applying the fundamental counting principle to the above, the number of non-zero sums of money $= 4 \times 5 \times 2^2 - 1 = 79$. ■

The last example leads to the following generalization.
If a set A contains n objects, a alike of one kind, b alike of another kind, c alike of another kind, with the remaining $(n - a - b - c)$ objects different, then the total number of subsets in A,
$n[\mathcal{P}(A)] = (a + 1)(b + 1)(c + 1)2^{n-a-b-c}$

Example 3 Find the number of subsets of $\{1, 1, 2, 2, 3, 3, 3, 4, 4, 4, 4, 5, 6, 7\}$.

Solution $n[\mathcal{P}\{1, 1, 2, 2, 3, 3, 3, 4, 4, 4, 4, 5, 6, 7\}]$
$$= (2 + 1)(2 + 1)(3 + 1)(4 + 1)(2^{14-2-2-3-4})$$
$$= 3 \times 3 \times 4 \times 5 \times 2^3$$
$$= 1440$$

There are 1440 subsets. ■

1.7 Exercises

1. List all the subsets of set {A , B , C}.

2. Calculate the number of subsets of each set listed below.
   a) {a, b, c, d, e}
   b) {0, 1, 2, 3}
   c) {S, S, S, S, S, S}

3. How many elements are in each set with the following number of subsets?
   a) 2   c) 8   e) 2^9
   b) 4   d) 64   f) $5 \times 3 \times 2^4$

4. Calculate.
   a) $n[\mathcal{P}\{a, e, i, o, u\}]$
   b) $n[\mathcal{P}\{\text{letters of the alphabet}\}]$
   c) $n[\mathcal{P}\{S, U, B, S, E, T, S\}]$
   d) $n[\mathcal{P}\{1, 2, 2, 3, 3, 3, 4, 5, 6\}]$

5. A stamp collector wishes to complete a set of stamps. The full set is shown below. How many different selections of stamps does the collector have to choose from?

6. How many different masses can be constructed from the following set of masses? 32 g, 16 g, 8 g, 4 g, 2 g, 1 g.

7. Pepi's Pizzeria offers ten different toppings on their pizzas.
   a) How many different three-topping pizzas can be ordered at Pepi's?
   b) How long would it take you to try all the possible pizzas you could order from Pepi's, if you ate one every day?

8. Car options available to a certain car buyer are as follows: air conditioning, turbo engine, AM/FM radio, special handling package and special trim package. How many different option combinations are available to the customer?

9. Henry Ford, inventor of the modern production line, boasted of his Model T Ford that you could have any colour you wanted just so long as it was black. Estimate the number of cars of a given make that can be built today that are unique in some obvious way.

10. A gardener has six tulips, four daffodils, eight crocus and two iris to choose from to make a flower bouquet. How many different flower combinations are available for the bouquet?

11. How long would it take a computer to generate all possible words that can be constructed from a set of seven different letters? Assume the computer can generate a different word every 0.01 s.

12. a) List all of the non-empty subsets of {2, 3, 5}.
    b) Treat each subset in a) as a set of factors of a number. List the numbers associated with each of these subsets.
    c) How are the numbers in b) related to the largest number listed in b)?
    d) A number x is composed of the following prime factors, 2, 2, 3, 3, 5, 7. Calculate the value of x and determine the number of divisors of this number.
    e) Write 300 as a product of primes and then determine the number of divisors of 300.

13. A tenant of an apartment building was robbed. The thief gained entry to the apartment by 'picking the lock' on the door. The tenant reacted by putting ten different keyed-locks on his door. He was robbed a second time, by the same thief, who simply picked all ten locks. When the shaken tenant phoned the locksmith to complain, the locksmith told him the solution was simple: leave some of the locks unlocked! Explain in detail the locksmith's reasoning.

Summary

- **Cardinal number or cardinality of a set:** If A is a set of objects and $n(A)$ represents the number of objects in the set, $n(A)$ is the cardinal number of A.
- **Finite set:** a set containing a finite number of objects
- **Universal set:** That set for which all other sets under consideration are subsets.
- **Empty set:** the set containing no elements, written { }
- **Subset of a set:** Set A is a subset of set B if all other objects in set A are objects in set B. A subset is written $A \subset B$. The empty set is defined to be a subset of all sets.

$A \subseteq B$

- **Complement of a set:** If set A is a subset of some universal set U then A', the complement of set A, is the set of objects that are in U but not in A.

- **Intersection of sets:** If A and B are two sets, the set of objects common to both A and B, written $A \cap B$, is called the intersection of A and B.

$A \cap B$

- **Disjoint sets:** two sets with no elements in common

$A \cap B = \{\}$

- **Union of sets:** If A and B are two sets, the union of A and B, written $A \cup B$, is the set of objects in set A or B or both.

$A \cup B$

  $n(A \cup B) = n(A) + n(B) - n(A \cap B)$
  (If A and B are disjoint,
  $n(A \cup B) = n(A) + n(B)$)
- **The fundamental counting principle:** If task A can be conducted in m ways and task B can be conducted in n ways then task A followed by task B can be conducted in mn different ways.
- **The generalized fundamental counting principle:** If n tasks $A_1, A_2, \ldots, A_n$ can be conducted, in order, in $a_1, a_2, \ldots, a_n$ different ways respectively, then the n tasks can be conducted, in order, in $a_1 a_2 \ldots a_n$ different ways.
- **r-arrangements of n objects:** $P(n,r) = n(n - 1)(n - 2)\ldots(n - r + 1)$

$$= \frac{n!}{(n - r)!}$$

- **Factorial notation:** $n! = n(n - 1)(n - 2)\ldots \times 3 \times 2 \times 1, n \in \mathbf{N}.\ (0! = 1)$

- **Arrangement with like objects:** For a set of n objects, s_1 alike of one kind, s_2 alike of another kind,$\ldots s_n$ alike another kind, the number of n-arrangements equals $\dfrac{n!}{s_1! s_2! s_3! \ldots s_n!}$

- **r-subsets of n objects:** $C(n,r) = \dfrac{P(n,r)}{r!} = \dfrac{n!}{(n-r)! \, r!}$

- **Power set:** The set of all subsets of a set A, $\mathcal{P}(A)$.
  If set A contains n different objects, $n[\mathcal{P}(A)] = 2^n$.
  If set A contains n objects, a alike of one kind, b alike of another kind and c alike of another kind, with $n - a - b - c$ objects different, then $n[\mathcal{P}(A)] = (a+1)(b+1)(c+1)2^{n-a-b-c}$

Inventory

True or False?
1. The set of natural numbers is an example of a finite set.
2. If $A = \{2, 4, 6, 8, 10\}$ then $n(A) = 5$.
Refer to the sets listed below when answering questions 3-9.
Universal set $U = \{1, 2, 3, 4, 5\}$ and subsets $A = \{\text{even numbers}\}$
$$B = \{x \mid x < 3\}$$
$$C = \{\text{prime numbers}\}$$

3. $A' = \{1, 3, 5\}$.
4. $A \cup B = \{1, 2, 4, 5\}$.
5. $A \cap B = \{2\}$.
6. Sets A and C are disjoint.
7. $B \subseteq C$.
8. $n[\mathcal{P}(U)] = 2^5$.
9. $n(A \cup C) = 4$.
10. The letters ABCD can be arranged 24 different ways.
11. $5! = 5 \times 4!$.
12. $0! = 0$.
13. $\dfrac{40!}{8!} = 5!$.
14. $P(10,3) = 720$.
15. $C(100,20) = \dfrac{100!}{80!20!}$.
16. $C(8,3) = C(8,5)$.
17. The letters AABCCC can all be arranged amongst themselves in $\dfrac{6!}{2!3!}$ ways.
18. $P(10,6) < C(10,6)$.
19. With three different notes chosen from do, re, mi, fah, so, lah, ti, do, you can make 56 different three-note tunes.
20. You can buy a set of three records from a selection of 10 different records in 120 different ways.

Review Exercises

1. You are given a universal set
   $U = \{A, B, C, D, E, F, G, H, I, J\}$
   and two associated subsets,
   $A = \{\text{vowels}\}$ and
   $B = \{\text{symmetrical letters}\}$.
   Identify the following sets and numbers.
   a) A' d) $A \cup B$ g) $n[\mathcal{P}(U)]$
   b) B' e) $A \times A$ h) $n(A \cap B)$
   c) $A \cap B$ f) $n(U \times U)$ i) $n(A' \cup B)$

2. Thirty students take Calculus, twenty-seven take Geography and ten students take both. How many students take Calculus or Geography?

3. Forty students are on either the tennis team or the badminton team. Eighteen students are on the tennis team and twenty-six students are on the badminton team. How many students are on both teams?

4. A magazine poll sampling 100 people gives the following results.
   17 read magazine A
   18 read magazine B
   14 read magazine C
    8 read magazines A and B
    7 read magazines A and C
    9 read magazines B and C
    5 read all three magazines
   a) Place the above information in a Venn diagram.
   b) How many of the people polled do not read any of the three magazines?
   c) How many people read just magazine A? just magazine B? just magazine C?
   d) How many of the people read at least one of the magazines?

5. State in your own words the fundamental counting principle.

6. In how many different ways can a person answer a 10-question True-False test?

7. Each question in a 10-question multiple choice test has four possible answers. In how many ways can a person answer such a test?

8. How many different descriptions of a person can be created using one description from each column in the table shown below?

Height	Age	Weight	Hair
short	child	thin	brown
medium	teen	normal	black
	middle-aged		red
tall	old	heavy	blond

9. A contestant spins the wheel, shown on the right, four times. Calculate the number of ways each of the following outcomes can occur.

   a) The contestant wins a prize each time.
   b) The contestant wins a different prize each time.
   c) The contestant does not win anything.

10. A particular stereo receiver has three dials for adjusting the mix of bass, mid-range and treble sounds. How many different sound adjustments can be made? Look carefully at the diagram on the right.

11. Some (foolish) person starts a chain letter by sending a letter to three people. The recipients of these letters are instructed to continue the chain by sending a copy of the letter to each of three others. How many letters would have been mailed out altogether after the tenth mailing, if nobody had broken the chain? Estimate the money wasted on postage.

12. A person decides to go for an eight block walk starting at point *A*, facing north. At each intersection the person may go right, left or straight ahead. How many different routes can the walk take?

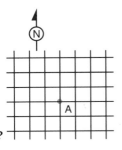

13. In how many ways can the objects in each set listed below be arranged amongst themselves?
    a) {1, 2, 3}   d) {S, H, A, K, E, S, P, E, A, R, E}
    b) {B, A, C, O, N}   e) {*, *, *, *, #}
    c) {E, U, L, E, R}   f) {*, *, *, *, #, #, #}

14. a) What does $P(a,b)$ represent?
    b) What does $C(c,d)$ represent?

15. a) Which is larger, $P(9,2)$ or $C(9,2)$? How many times larger?
    b) Which is larger, $P(a,b)$ or $C(a,b)$? How many times larger?

16. Evaluate
    a) 5!
    b) $\dfrac{20!}{19!}$
    c) 0!
    d) $P(6,3)$
    e) $P(8,8)$
    f) $C(12,10)$
    g) $C(7,7)$
    h) $C(n,0)$
    i) $C(n,n)$
    j) $C(n,1)$
    k) $C(n,n-1)$
    l) $\dfrac{P(1\ 000\ 000,3)}{C(1\ 000\ 000,3)}$

17. Calculate the number of different 5-digit numbers you can make with the five digits 1, 2, 3, 4, 5, in each of the following cases.
    a) Each digit must be different.
    b) Digits can be repeated.
    c) The number must be an even number, with no repeated digits.
    d) The number is greater than 40 000, with no repeated digits.

18. A coin is tossed eight times and the outcomes are HHTHTTTT.
    a) How many other outcomes are possible?
    b) How many outcomes have tails coming up five times?
    c) How many outcomes have heads coming up three times?

19. Your name, along with 19 others, is placed in a hat. Three of the names are drawn at random.
    a) How many different selections of three names are possible?
    b) How many of the selections in a) include your name?
    c) How many of the selections in a) do not include your name?

20. Twenty students make up a student's council.
    a) In how many ways can a president and vice-president be selected from the council?
    b) In how many ways can the three positions, president, vice-president, and secretary/treasurer be filled by members of the council?
    c) In how many ways can an 'executive committee' of three be selected from the student council? Why is this number smaller than the answer to part b)?

21. In lottery *A* you have to pick four of forty numbers, in any order, to win the grand prize. In lottery *B* you have to pick three of sixty numbers, in any order, to win the grand prize. In which lottery is it easier to be a grand prize winner?

22. Five boys and five girls line up for a group picture.
    a) In how many ways can they line up?
    b) In how many ways can they line up if the boys and girls are in alternate positions?

23. a) Invent and solve a combinatorics problem in which order is not important.
    b) Invent and solve a combinatorics problem where order is important.

24. Five cards are dealt from a deck of fifty-two cards.
    a) How many different hands can be dealt?
    b) How many hands will contain all face cards?
    c) How many hands will contain no face cards?
    d) How many hands will contain only spades or clubs?
    e) How many hands will contain only hearts?

25. How many subsets are there in each of the following sets?
    a) $\{A, B, C, D, E\}$
    b) $\{1, 2, 3, 4, 5, 6\}$
    c) $\{*, *, *, +, +\}$
    d) $\{*, *, +, +, +, +, s, g, h\}$

26. A person walks out of a store having purchased some of the six books she had been looking for. How many different purchases could she have made?

27. In how many ways can eight people be assigned to two four-person teams?

28. a) Use the fact that $3960 = 2^3 \times 3^2 \times 5 \times 11$ to determine the number of divisors of 3960.
    b) How many numbers will divide into one million?

29. In the card game of Euchre, only twenty-four cards are used, the 9's, 10's jacks, queens, kings and aces.
    a) In how many ways can one five-card hand be dealt?
    b) In how many ways can two five-card hands be dealt?
    c) In how many ways can four five-card hands be dealt?

30. In how many ways can ten people be paired?

31. A team finished the year with 10 wins, 4 losses and 2 ties. In how many different orders of wins, losses and ties could this have occurred?

32. What can you conclude about sets A, B and C, if $n(A \cup B \cup C) = n(A) + n(B) + n(C)$?

33. In your own words and with reference to a Venn diagram, justify the counting formula,
$$n(A \cup B \cup C) = n(A) + n(B) + n(C)$$
$$- n(A \cap B) - n(A \cap C)$$
$$- n(B \cap C) + n(A \cap B \cap C)$$

34. You have a formula for determining the number of elements in the union of two sets and a similar formula for counting the number of a elements in the union of three sets. Suggest a formula for determining $n(A \cup B \cup C \cup D)$. Test your formula.

35. The letter 'P' in the notation $P(n,r)$ stands for the word 'permutation'. Look up the meaning of this word and verify its appropriateness in this context.

36. "The values of $C(n,r)$ for a given value of n, and $r = 0, 1, 2, 3, \ldots, n$, are symmetrical about $\frac{n}{2} + 1$." Give an example to demonstrate the validity of this statement.

37. An urn contains 20 balls: five red ones, seven blue ones and eight white ones. Four of the balls are selected at random. How many different selections of four balls are possible, without regard to order? (Calculate and then sum the number of different selections for each of the following cases:
    case 1 all alike,
    case 2 three alike and one different,
    case 3 two alike of one colour and two alike of another,
    case 4 two alike and two different.)

CHAPTER TWO

Probability

"The probability of rain is 60%."

"My team has a better chance to win than your team."

"Luke won $2 000 000 in the lottery even though his chance of winning was one in a million."

"I just tossed five heads in a row. There is not much chance that the next toss will be heads."

"There are supposed to be thunderstorms today. I don't think I will take a chance on playing golf."

"Twenty people besides me applied for that job. I do think it is unlikely that I will be hired."

"Twenty people besides me applied for that job advertised by my aunt. I think it is likely that I will be hired."

You are flying in a three-engine jet plane. The probability that any one of the jet engines will fail is 0.0001. You wonder what the chance is that one, two or three of the engines will fail during your flight.

You are driving on a street that has three traffic lights. The probability that you will be stopped by any one light is 0.4. You wonder what the chance is that you will get through the three lights without stopping.

You are writing
a multiple choice test.
Every question has
five choices,
only one of which
is correct. You have
no idea how to answer
three of the questions.
How likely are you
to get one, two, or three
of these three questions
correct if you
guess the answer?

If a dark-haired
mother and father
have a particular type
of gene then the
probability that
any child that
they have will be
light-haired is 0.25.
Such a couple decides
to have three children.
What is the chance
that all three will
have light hair?

All of the above examples are situations that can be described using the theory of probability. Some of the words used such as "chance", "likely", and "unlikely" are very vague. Yet expressions such as "the probability that any one of the jet engines will fail is 0.0001" give very exact information. In this chapter and in chapter 7 you will learn to apply the theory of probability to examples such as these.

2.1 Experimental Probability

You are given a bag containing five colored stones: red, yellow, black, green and white. You take out one stone without looking in the bag. You wonder what your chance is of selecting a white stone. You decide to perform an experiment to check on your chance of selecting a white stone.

The experiment consists of taking one stone out of the bag, observing its color, then returning the stone to the bag. You repeat this experiment twenty times and find that the white stone was selected seven times. Since the *relative frequency* of obtaining a white, that is, the ratio of the number of white stones selected to the total number of stones selected, is

$\frac{7}{20} = 0.35 = 35\%$, you conclude that your chance, or probability, of getting

a white is 35%. This is an example of *experimental* probability.

You try the experiment again, only this time you perform the same experiment of taking out a stone then putting it back, 300 times. You observe that the number of white stones is 48. The relative frequency is

now $\frac{48}{300} = 16\%$, which is equivalent to a 16% chance of getting a white.

Once again you repeat the experiment until you have made 800 draws from the bag, obtaining 158 white. Now the relative frequency

$\frac{158}{800} \doteq 19.8\%$. As the number of trials increases, you note that the relative

frequency seems to be getting closer and closer to the (intuitive) value of 20%.

Here are some other examples of experimental probability.

Example 1   You toss a coin thirty times in a row. The coin comes up heads eighteen times. Calculate the experimental probability of obtaining a head when the coin is tossed.

Solution   The experimental probability of obtaining a head is the relative frequency

of a head which is $\frac{18}{30} = 0.6 = 60\%$.   ∎

Example 2   A single die is rolled sixty times in a row and the number (that is, the number of dots) appearing on the up face is observed. The results are recorded below.

Number on the Die	1	2	3	4	5	6
Occurrences	7	12	11	10	8	12

a) Find the experimental probability of rolling a 5 using the die.
b) Find the experimental probability of rolling a 4 using the die.
c) Find the experimental probability of rolling a 7 using the die.
d) Find the experimental probability of rolling a number less than 7 using the die.

Solution   a) In the experiment, a 5 was rolled eight times out of the sixty rolls. Thus, the relative frequency of a 5 is $\frac{8}{60}$. Hence the experimental probability is $\frac{8}{60} \doteq 0.13 = 13\%$.

b) In the experiment, a 4 was rolled ten times out of the sixty rolls. Thus, the experimental probability of rolling a 4 is $\frac{10}{60} \doteq 0.17 = 17\%$.

c) In the experiment, no 7 was rolled out of the sixty rolls. The experimental probability of obtaining a 7 is $\frac{0}{60} = 0 = 0\%$.

d) In the experiment, every number rolled was less than 7, in the sixty rolls. The experimental probability of obtaining a number less than 7 is $\frac{60}{60} = 1 = 100\%$. ■

Example 2 demonstrates that the probability of an event occurring is a number between 0 and 1. **An occurrence that is *impossible* has a probability of 0. An occurrence that is *certain* to occur has a probability of 1.**

The following line diagram indicates the range of probabilities and its relationship with some words used to describe probabilities.

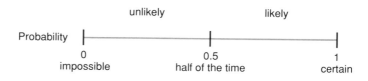

2.1 Exercises

1. The probability of something happening falls somewhere on the following probability scale.

    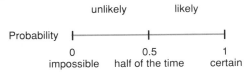

    What probability words from the scale would you use to describe the chance of each of the following occurrences?
    a) winning two million dollars in a lottery
    b) the sun rising tomorrow
    c) touching the back of your neck with your nose
    d) tossing a head with a quarter
    e) tossing a head with a two-headed coin
    f) tossing a tail with a two-headed coin
    g) tossing five coins at the same time and having each come up heads
    h) having supper tonight
    i) getting your homework done tonight
    j) rolling a die and having a number less than six occur on the up face

2. For each of the following weather predictions state a probability word that best describes the situation.
    a) The probability of snow today is 60%.
    b) The probability of rain tomorrow is 20%.
    c) The probability of rain today is 100%.
    d) The probability of a dust storm today is 0%.

3. a) Give two examples of occurrences that have a probability of 0.
    b) Give two examples of occurrences that have a probability of 1.
    c) Give two examples of occurrences whose probability can be described by the word *unlikely*.
    d) Give two examples of occurrences whose probability can be described by the word *likely*.
    e) Give two examples of occurrences whose probability can be described by the word *certain*.
    f) Give two examples of occurrences whose probability can be described by the word *impossible*.

4. You toss a coin forty times in a row. The coin comes up heads twenty-four times. Calculate the experimental probability of obtaining a head when the coin is tossed.

5. A single die is rolled sixty times in a row and the number (that is, the number of dots) appearing on the up face is observed. The results are recorded below.

Number on die	1	2	3	4	5	6
Occurrences	7	12	11	10	8	12

    a) Find the experimental probability of rolling a 1 using the die.
    b) Find the experimental probability of rolling a 6 using the die.
    c) Find the experimental probability of rolling a 9 using the die.
    d) Find the experimental probability of rolling a number greater or equal to 1 using the die.

6. A company that manufactures computer chips says that there is a 90% chance that a chip it makes will not work. Is this an experimental probability? Explain.

7. Perform an experiment to determine the experimental probability of
    a) obtaining a head when you toss a coin.
    b) rolling a 7 with two dice.
    c) selecting a red king when you select a single card from a deck of 52 playing cards.
    d) tossing three heads when you toss three coins, one after the other.

2.2 Sample Spaces and Events

Consider the experiment of rolling a single die and observing the number on the up face. You wonder what the relative frequency of rolling a 5 would be. Throwing a die and rolling a 5 means that exactly 5 dots appear on its up face. In this experiment the number on the up face can be 1, 2, 3, 4, 5 or 6.

In probability, each repetition of an experiment is called a **trial**. The possible results of each trial are **outcomes**. In the experiment of rolling a single die and observing the number of the up face, a trial is the rolling of the die and the six possible outcomes are rolling a 1, rolling a 2, rolling a 3,..., rolling a 6.

The universal set of all possible outcomes for an experiment is a **sample space** S for the experiment. In the experiment of rolling a die, $S = \{1, 2, 3, 4, 5, 6\}$.

Any subset of a sample space is an **event**, E, for the sample space. In the experiment of rolling a die and looking for a 5 on the up face, $E = \{5\}$.

An event that consists of only one outcome is a **simple event**.
$n(S)$ is the number of outcomes in the sample space S.
$n(E)$ is the number of outcomes of the event E, which is a subset of the sample space S.
Note that $n(S)$ is also the number of simple events in S.

The following examples will help you to clarify the meanings of sample space and event.

Example 1 An experiment consists of rolling a single die and observing the up face.
  a) List a sample space S.
  b) List the event E, "the die has 3 on its up face".
  c) List the event F, "the die has a number less than five on its up face".
  d) List the event G, "the die does not have a number less than five on its up face".
  e) Find $n(S)$, $n(E)$, $n(F)$, and $n(G)$.

Solution a) $S = \{1, 2, 3, 4, 5, 6\}$
  b) $E = \{3\}$
  c) $F = \{1, 2, 3, 4\}$
  d) $G = \{5, 6\}$
  e) $n(S) = 6$, $n(E) = 1$, $n(F) = 4$, $n(G) = 2$ ■

In Example 1 you should observe that event G is the **complement** of event (or set) F in the sample space. Observe that $n(F) + n(G) = n(S)$. Recall the following from section 1.1.

If events E and H are complements in the sample space S, then H is written "*not E*" or E' and $n(E) + n(\text{not } E) = n(S)$.

Example 2 Three coins are tossed and the outcome, whether the coin landed heads or tails, is noted in each case.

a) Use a tree diagram to list the sample space S for the experiment.

b) List the event E_1, "three heads occur".

c) List the event E_2, "a head and two tails occur".

d) List the event E_3, "two coins are the same and the third is different".

e) Find the following: $n(S)$, $n(E_1)$, $n(E_2)$ and $n(E_3)$.

Solution a)

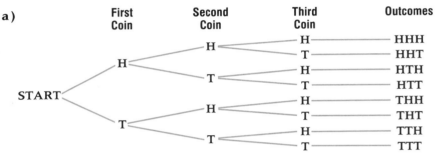

$\therefore$ $S = \{\text{HHH, HHT, HTH, HTT, THH, THT, TTH, TTT}\}$

b) $E_1 = \{\text{HHH}\}$

c) $E_2 = \{\text{HTT, THT, TTH}\}$

d) $E_3 = \{\text{HHT, HTH, HTT, THH, THT, TTH}\}$

e) $n(S) = 8$, $n(E_1) = 1$, $n(E_2) = 3$, $n(E_3) = 6$ ■

Example 3 For the purpose of a certain opinion poll, people are classified as young, middle-aged, or senior, and as male or female. The experiment is to select a person at random, and note the age and sex of the person. List the sample space consisting of the ordered pairs (age, sex).

Solution The sample space is {(young, male), (young, female), (middle-aged, male), (middle-aged, female), (senior, male), (senior, female)}. ■

Example 4 An experiment consists of selecting video tapes one after the other, without replacement, and testing them until either two defective tapes are found, or four tapes have been tested.

   a) Draw a tree diagram for this experiment, indicating all possible outcomes in the sample space.

   b) List the event E consisting of all outcomes where exactly one defective tape is tested.

   c) List the event F consisting of all outcomes where exactly one acceptable tape is tested.

Solution   D represents that a tape was defective.
A represents that a tape was acceptable.

a)

First Test	Second Test	Third Test	Fourth Test	Outcomes

The set in the right hand column listing all of the outcomes will be the sample space S.

b) $E = \{$DAAA, ADAA, AADA, AAAD$\}$

c) $F = \{$DAD, ADD$\}$ ■

Example 5 An experiment consists of rolling two dice, one red and one white, and noting the number appearing on the up faces. List the sample space of the experiment.

Solution The red die can come to rest in one of six different ways. With each of these ways the white die can come to rest in six different ways. Thus, by the counting principle of section 1.2, the two dice can come to rest in $6 \times 6 = 36$ different ways. The sample space will have 36 simple events or outcomes in it. This sample space is represented by the following table where the ordered pair (r,w) indicates that the number on the red die is r and on the white die is w.

		Number On The White Die				
Number On The Red Die	1	2	3	4	5	6
1	(1,1)	(1,2)	(1,3)	(1,4)	(1,5)	(1,6)
2	(2,1)	(2,2)	(2,3)	(2,4)	(2,5)	(2,6)
3	(3,1)	(3,2)	(3,3)	(3,4)	(3,5)	(3,6)
4	(4,1)	(4,2)	(4,3)	(4,4)	(4,5)	(4,6)
5	(5,1)	(5,2)	(5,3)	(5,4)	(5,5)	(5,6)
6	(6,1)	(6,2)	(6,3)	(6,4)	(6,5)	(6,6)

Note: The sample space for Example 5 can be used for rolling two dice that are indistinguishable. The outcomes (1,3) and (3,1), for instance, could be distinguished in a variety of ways: roll one die on the left and the other on the right, roll one die first and the other one later, or even roll one die two times. The key to this sample space is that there are 36 equally likely outcomes, where each outcome can be represented by an ordered pair (a,b) with $a \in \{1, 2, 3, 4, 5, 6\}$ and $b \in \{1, 2, 3, 4, 5, 6\}$.

Example 6 Two dice are rolled. Use the sample space of Example 5 to list the following events. State the number of elements in each event.

a) The sum of the up faces is six.

b) A number greater than four appears on either or both dice.

Solution Let E be the event "the sum of the up faces is six" and F the event "a number greater than four appears either on one or both dice". Then E and F can be listed using the sample space, S, from Example 5.
a) $E = \{(1,5), (2,4), (3,3), (4,2), (5,1)\}$
$n(E) = 5$.

b) $F = \{(1,5), (1,6), (2,5), (2,6), (3,5), (3,6),$
$(4,5), (4,6), (5,5), (5,6), (6,5), (6,6),$
$(6,1), (5,1), (6,2), (5,2), (6,3), (5,3),$
$(6,4), (5,4)\}$
$n(F) = 20$

2.2 Exercises

1. An experiment consists of rolling a single die and observing the up face.
   a) List a sample space S.
   b) List the event E "the die has 5 on its up face".
   c) List the event F "the die has a number greater than four on its up face".
   d) List the event G "the die does *not* have a number greater than four on its up face".
   e) Count to find $n(S)$, $n(E)$, $n(F)$ and $n(G)$.

2. A basketball player takes three free shots from the foul line; the outcome is noted each time as a hit H or a miss M.
   a) Use a tree diagram to list the sample space S for this experiment.
   b) List the event E_1 "three misses occur".
   c) List the event E_2 "two hits and a miss occur".
   d) List the event E_3 "there are more hits than misses".
   e) Count to find the following: $n(S)$, $n(E_1)$, $n(E_2)$ and $n(E_3)$.

3. Four coins are tossed and the outcome noted in each case.
   a) Use a tree diagram to list a sample space for this experiment.
   b) List the event E_1 "three tails and one head occur".
   c) List the event E_2 "two heads and two tails occur".
   d) List the event E_3 "there are more tails than heads".
   e) Count to find the following: $n(S)$, $n(E_1)$, $n(E_2)$ and $n(E_3)$.

4. A coin is tossed and a die is rolled.
   a) Draw a tree diagram and list a sample space S for the experiment.
   b) List the event E consisting of all outcomes in which the coin is heads and the number on the die is even.
   c) Count to find $n(S)$ and $n(E)$.

5. An experiment consists of testing a batch of calculators one after the other, without replacement, until either two defective calculators are found or three calculators have been tested.
   a) Draw a tree diagram for this experiment indicating all possible outcomes in the sample space.
   b) List the event E consisting of all outcomes where exactly one defective calculator is tested.
   c) List the event F consisting of all outcomes where exactly two acceptable calculators are selected.

6. An experiment consists of rolling two dice and observing the up faces.
   a) List a sample space S of the experiment.
   b) List the event E "the sum of the numbers is three".
   c) List the event F "a number less than four appears on either die or on both dice".
   d) Count to find the values of $n(S)$, $n(E)$ and $n(F)$.

7. A single card is drawn from a deck of 52 playing cards. The value and suit of the card is noted.
   a) List the event E that the card will be red.
   b) List the event F that the card will be a red face card.
   c) List the event G that the card will be a card showing an odd number of clubs.

8. Automobile engines are to be tested for compression and timing. The compression can be too low (L), too high (H), or correct (C). The result of the timing can be off (O) or accurate (A).
   a) Draw a tree diagram for this experiment indicating all possible outcomes in the sample space.
   b) List the event E that the timing is accurate.

9. A box contains three white balls and two red balls.
   a) List the sample space for an experiment where one ball is drawn at random and the color is noted. Consider the balls W_1, W_2, W_3, and R_1, R_2.
   b) List the event from part a), that one red ball is drawn at random.
   c) Draw a tree diagram and list the sample space for an experiment where two balls are picked at random from this box with no replacement of the first ball.
   d) List the event in part c) where two white balls are picked.

10. An experiment is performed where a die is rolled and an observation is made as to whether or not the outcome is even or odd. List the sample space for this experiment.

11. In an experiment a coin is tossed, a die is rolled and a card is selected from among the thirteen spades.
   a) Describe in words an outcome from a sample space S for this experiment.
   b) List four outcomes that belong to the sample space.
   c) How many simple events are there in the sample space?

12. A coin is tossed and two dice are rolled. The coin is noted as heads or tails, and the numbers on the up faces of the dice are observed.
   a) List four members of the sample space for this experiment.
   b) How many simple events are contained in this sample space?

13. Five balls, numbered 1 to 5, are in a bag. One ball is drawn and not replaced. Then a second ball is drawn. The number on each ball is noted.
   a) Use ordered pairs of numbers to list the sample space S for this experiment.
   b) List the event E "the numbers on both balls are even".

c) List the event F "the product of the numbers on the balls is four".
   d) List the event G "the numbers on the balls are both even, and the product of the number is four".
   e) Count to find $n(S)$, $n(E)$, $n(F)$ and $n(G)$.

14. A box contains four balls marked separately 1, 2, 3 and 4. A bag contains three balls lettered separately a, b and c. An experiment is performed where one ball is taken from the box then one ball from the bag. Number and letter are noted.
   a) Use ordered pairs (number, letter) to list a sample space S for this experiment.
   b) List the event E "the first ball is odd numbered".
   c) List the event F "the second ball is marked with a vowel".
   d) List the event G "the first ball is odd numbered, and the second ball is marked with a vowel".

15. A survey is made of families that have four children. Boys and girls in each family are noted, in order of birth.
   a) Use a tree diagram to list the sample space S of all possible outcomes for a family of four children.
   b) How many of the outcomes in the sample space correspond to the event that a family has two girls and two boys?

16. An experiment is performed in a laboratory using four trained rats and one untrained rat in the same cage. A rat is removed from the cage. It is observed whether the rat is trained or untrained. Then the rat is put into another cage. Two more rats are removed from the first cage. Each rat is observed for training and then put in the second cage.
   a) List six outcomes that belong to a sample space S. Label the trained rats T_1, T_2, T_3 and T_4.
   b) How many simple events are contained in S?

2.3 Uniform Probability Models

An experiment is performed of rolling a fair die and observing the number of dots on the up face. There are six possible outcomes. The sample space $S = \{1, 2, 3, 4, 5, 6\}$. You should have an intuitive feeling that each outcome is as likely to happen as any other outcome. The outcomes are described as **equally likely**.

Another experiment is performed in which one card is chosen from a 52-card deck of playing cards and the suit noted. There are four possible outcomes. The sample space $S = \{$diamond, heart, spade, club$\}$. Again, each outcome is equally likely.

Consider a third experiment in which a student is chosen at random from a class of 25 girls and 15 boys and the gender noted. There are two possible outcomes. The sample space $S = \{$girl, boy$\}$. In this sample space the outcomes are *not* equally likely.

The concept of equally likely outcomes is undefined. As the previous three examples show, the concept can be illustrated. Yet the concept can not be defined with mathematical precision. But, it is possible to explain in what circumstances two events in a sample space will be equally likely.

Two events E and F in a sample space S are equally likely if and only if the probability of event E is equal to the probability of event F.

Suppose S is a sample space that models an experiment consisting of k equally likely outcomes so that $S = \{s_1, s_2, s_3, \ldots, s_k\}$.

Let E be an event in S. If the probability of an event E is abbreviated $P(E)$, then $P(E)$ is defined as follows.

DEFINITION $P(E) = \dfrac{n(E)}{n(S)}$, where

$n(S) = $ the number of equally likely outcomes in the sample space S and
$n(E) = $ the number of outcomes in the event E which is a subset of the sample space S.

Unless it is otherwise stated or implied, you can assume that all outcomes are equally likely.

Because the outcomes in S are equally likely, the probabilities of each simple event $\{s_i\}$, $i = 1,2,3,\ldots,k$ are equal. Thus, $P(\{s_1\}) = P(\{s_2\}) = P(\{s_3\}) = \ldots = P(\{s_k\})$. Since the probability of each simple event $\{s_i\}$ remains constant at $\dfrac{n(\{s_i\})}{n(S)} = \dfrac{1}{n(S)}$, the probability is uniform throughout the sample space S. Hence, the model is known as a **uniform probability model**.

<table>
<tr><td></td><td>A uniform probability model is a sample space associated with an experiment such that each simple event is equally probable.</td></tr>
</table>

The probabilities in a uniform probability model have certain properties.

The Range Property

Because event E is a subset of S, $n(E) \leq n(S)$.

Thus, $P(E) = \dfrac{n(E)}{n(S)} \leq \dfrac{n(S)}{n(S)}$, that is, 1.

If $E = \{\ \}$, then $n(E) = 0$, and $P(E) = \dfrac{0}{n(S)} = 0$.

If $E = S$, then $n(E) = n(S)$, and $P(E) = 1$.

This leads to the following range property of $P(E)$.

PROPERTY

$0 \leq P(E) \leq 1$

If $E = \{\ \}$, then E cannot occur. E is an impossible event. Thus, P (impossible event) = 0.

If $E = S$, then E always occurs. E is a certain event. Thus, P (certain event) = 1.

The Complement Property

From section 2.2, you know the following.

If events E and H are complements in the sample space S, then H is written "not E" or E' and

$n(E) + n(\text{not } E) = n(S)$.   ①

Divide ① by $n(S)$, where $n(S) \neq 0$.

Thus, $\dfrac{n(E)}{n(S)} + \dfrac{n(\text{not } E)}{n(S)} = \dfrac{n(S)}{n(S)}$

which simplifies to

PROPERTY

$P(E) + P(\text{not } E) = 1$ which can be written $P(\text{not } E) = 1 - P(E)$

The "or" Property

In section 1.1 you learned that for any two sets E and F

$n(E \cup F) = n(E) + n(F) - n(E \cap F)$

Divide each term by $n(S)$. Thus

$\dfrac{n(E \cup F)}{n(S)} = \dfrac{n(E)}{n(S)} + \dfrac{n(F)}{n(S)} - \dfrac{n(E \cap F)}{n(S)}$

which can be simplified to

$P(E \cup F) = P(E) + P(F) - P(E \cap F)$.

Now an event is in $E \cup F$ whenever the event is *either* in E *or* F or in both E and F.

For this reason, $P(E \cup F)$ is written $P(E \text{ or } F)$.

Likewise, an event is in $E \cap F$ whenever the event is in E *and* the event is also in F.

For this reason, $P(E \cap F)$ is written $P(E \text{ and } F)$.
This gives the "or" property of probability.

PROPERTY

$P(E \text{ or } F) = P(E) + P(F) - P(E \text{ and } F)$

In section 1.1, where sets E and F are disjoint, that is, have no elements in common, $n(E \cap F) = 0$. In the context of probability, E and F are called **mutually exclusive** events. This means E and F contain no common outcomes. Thus $n(E \cap F) = 0$ and $P(E \text{ and } F) = 0$.

PROPERTY

For mutually exclusive events, $P(E \text{ or } F) = P(E) + P(F)$.

Example 1   Two dice are rolled and the numbers on the up faces are noted. Find the probability of the following events.

a) The sum of the numbers is seven.

b) The sum of the numbers is three.

c) A 2 appears on an up face.

Solution   You will need to use the table for two dice in section 2.2, on page 54. The sample space S contains 36 equally likely outcomes, thus $n(S) = 36$.

a) The event where the sum is seven is
$E = \{(1,6), (2,5), (3,4), (4,3), (5,2), (6,1)\}$.
Thus, $n(E) = 6$.
Therefore, P (the sum of the numbers is seven) is
$$P(E) = \frac{n(E)}{n(S)} = \frac{6}{36} = \frac{1}{6}.$$

b) The event where the sum is three is
$F = \{(1,2), (2,1)\}$.
Thus, $n(F) = 2$.
Therefore, P (the sum of the numbers is three) is
$$P(F) = \frac{n(E)}{n(S)} = \frac{2}{36} = \frac{1}{18}.$$

c) The event where a 2 appears on an up face is
$H = \{(1,2), (2,2), (3,2), (4,2), (5,2), (6,2), (2,1), (2,3), (2,4), (2,5), (2,6)\}$.
Thus, $n(H) = 11$.

Therefore, P (a 2 appears on an up face) is $P(H) = \dfrac{n(H)}{n(S)} = \dfrac{11}{36}$.   ■

Example 2 Two dice are rolled and the numbers on the up faces are noted. Find the probability of the following events.

a) The sum of the numbers is seven *or* the sum of the numbers is three.

b) A 2 appears on an up face *or* the sum of the numbers is seven.

Solution **a)** Let E, F and H represent the same events as in Example 1.

Thus, $P(E) = \frac{1}{6}$, $P(F) = \frac{1}{18}$, and $P(H) = \frac{11}{36}$.

P (the sum of the numbers is seven *or* the sum of the numbers is three)
is $P(E$ or $F) = P(E) + P(F) - P(E$ and $F)$.
Also, $E \cap F = \{\ \}$, and $n(E \cap F) = 0$

$P(E$ and $F) = \frac{0}{36} = 0$, that is,

the events E and F are mutually exclusive.

Thus, $P(E$ or $F) = \frac{1}{6} + \frac{1}{18} - 0 = \frac{3}{18} + \frac{1}{18} = \frac{4}{18}$, or $\frac{2}{9}$.

b) *Method 1*

P (a 2 appears on an upface *or* the sum of the numbers is seven)
$= P(H$ or $E) = P(H) + P(E) - P(H$ and $E)$

where $P(H) = \frac{11}{36}$, and $P(E) = \frac{1}{6}$.

Also, the event $H \cap E = \{(5,2), (2,5)\}$.

Thus, $n(H \cap E) = 2$, and $P(H$ and $E) = \frac{2}{36} = \frac{1}{18}$.

Therefore, $P(H$ or $E) = \frac{11}{36} + \frac{1}{6} - \frac{1}{18} = \frac{(11 + 6 - 2)}{36} = \frac{15}{36}$.

Method 2

The event needed is $H \cup E$ which can be listed directly as
$\{(1,2), (2,2), (3,2), (4,2), (5,2), (6,2), (2,1), (2,3), (2,4), (2,5), (2,6), (1,6),$
$(3,4), (4,3), (6,1)\}$.
Thus, $n(H \cup E) = 15$, and

$P(H$ or $E) = \frac{n(H \cup E)}{n(S)} = \frac{15}{36}$. ∎

Example 3 A single card is drawn from a deck of 52 playing cards, and the suit and face value noted.

a) What is the probability that the card will be either black or a face card?

b) What is the probability that the card will *not* be either black or a face card?

Solution   **a)** For this experiment of selecting a single card, there are 52 possible outcomes, the 52 cards in the deck. Thus, $n(S) = 52$.

Let B and F represent the events "black" and "face", respectively. There are 13 clubs and 13 spades, thus the number of black cards is $26 = n(B)$. Thus, $P(B) = \dfrac{26}{52}$.

There are 4 kings, 4 queens and 4 jacks. Thus, the number of face cards is $12 = n(F)$. Thus, $P(F) = \dfrac{12}{52}$.

Also, there are 6 black face cards in a deck, 3 clubs and 3 spades. Thus, $n(B \cap F) = 6$. Thus, $P(B \text{ and } F) = \dfrac{6}{52}$.

Therefore, the probability that the card drawn will be either black or a face card is $P(B \text{ or } F) = P(B) + P(F) - P(B \text{ and } F)$

$$= \frac{26}{52} + \frac{12}{52} - \frac{6}{52}$$

$$= \frac{32}{52} = \frac{8}{13}.$$

b) The probability that the card drawn will *not* be either black or a face card is $P(not(B \text{ or } F)) = 1 - P(B \text{ or } F)$

$$= 1 - \frac{8}{13} = \frac{5}{13}. \quad \blacksquare$$

Example 4   The owner of a fast food store received 25 applications from people applying for the position of manager. Of these 25 people, 15 have worked for this store before, 8 have a high school diploma, and 5 have both worked for the store before and have a high school diploma. What is the probability that a person selected at random from the applicants has worked for the store before or has a high school diploma?

Solution   Let B represent the set of people who have worked for the store before and D represent the set who have a high school diploma.

Thus, $n(B) = 15$, $n(D) = 8$, $n(B \cap D) = 5$, and $n(S) = 25$.
Therefore, $P(B \text{ or } D) = P(B) + P(D) - P(B \text{ and } D)$

$$= \frac{15}{25} + \frac{8}{25} - \frac{5}{25} = \frac{18}{25}. \quad \blacksquare$$

Odds in Favor

Sometimes probability statements are given in terms of *odds*. Odds are a comparison of the probability of an event E, and the probability of the complement of the event, *not E*.

DEFINITION   The odds in favor of an event E is the ratio $\dfrac{P(E)}{P(not\ E)}$.

Example 5   The weather report for tomorrow indicates that there is a 40% chance of snow. What are the odds in favor of there being snow tomorrow?

Solution   Let E be the event "it will snow tomorrow".
Then $P(E) = 40\% = 0.4$
Therefore, $P(not\ E) = 1 - P(E) = 1 - 0.4 = 0.6$
Thus, the odds in favor of there being snow tomorrow
$$= \frac{P(E)}{P(not\ E)}$$
$$= \frac{0.4}{0.6} = \frac{2}{3}$$
The odds in favor of snow tomorrow are 2 to 3 or 2:3.   ■

Note that sometimes the *odds against* an event are quoted. If the odds in favor of an event E are $a:b$, then the odds against event E are $b:a$. In Example 4, the odds against there being snow tomorrow are 3 to 2, or 3:2.

2.3 Exercises

1. **a)** An experiment consists of tossing a coin and noting the up side. Find the probability of a head coming up.

   b) An experiment consists of rolling a die and noting the number on the up face. Find the probability of a 4 coming up.

   c) An experiment consists of selecting one card from a deck of 52 playing cards and noting the color of the card. What is the probability of the card being red?

   d) A bag contains 100 coins which have the same shape and mass but exactly one of the coins is a gold coin. Without looking in the bag, you put your hand in and take out one coin. What is the probability that the coin you draw will be gold?

   e) Suppose the bag of 100 coins in part d) contained exactly five gold coins. What is the probability that the coin you draw will be gold?

   f) On a multiple-choice exam you do not know the answer to question 17. There are five possible answers. You guess an answer. What is the probability that your guess will be correct?

   g) Julietta enters a race to be run on an eight-lane track. There are seven other contestants. What is the probability that Julietta will be assigned the inside lane if the lanes are assigned randomly?

   h) A business marketing group is asked to design a market test for a new product. The product can be tested in any one of the five cities: Montreal, Halifax, Vancouver, Toronto or Orillia. If the city is selected at random, what is the probability that the city chosen will be Orillia?

2. An experiment consists of rolling a single die, and noting the number on the up face. Calculate the probability of the following events.
   a) event E "the die has 5 on its up face"
   b) event F "the die has a number greater than four on its up face"
   c) event G "the die does *not* have a number greater than four on its up face"

3. In question 2, what are the odds in favor of the die having a number greater than four on its up face?

4. Two dice are rolled and the numbers on the up faces are noted. Find the probability of the following events.
   a) the sum of the numbers is seven
   b) the sum of the numbers is ten
   c) a 4 appears as one of the numbers
   d) the sum of the numbers is seven *or* the sum of the numbers is ten
   e) a 4 appears as one of the numbers *or* the sum of the numbers is ten

5. In question 4 what are the odds in favor of the event in part a)? in part d)?

6. A single card is drawn from a deck of 52 playing cards and the suit and face value noted.
   a) What is the probability that the card will be either red or a face card?
   b) What is the probability that the card will *not* be either red or a face card?
   c) What are the odds in favor of the card being either red or a face card?

7. Three coins are tossed and the outcome noted in each case.
   a) Find the probability that all three will be heads.
   b) Find the probability that two will be heads and one tails.

8. 3 000 000 000 tickets have been sold in a lottery. One ticket chosen at random will win the first prize of $1 million dollars, ten tickets will win a second prize of $100 000, 50 tickets will win a third prize of $10 000, and 1000 tickets will win a fourth prize of $1000. Find the probability that a randomly chosen ticket will win
   a) one million dollars.
   b) $10 000 or more.
   c) nothing.

9. A coin is tossed and a die is rolled. Find the probability of each of the following events.
   a) the event E, consisting of all outcomes in which the coin is heads *and* the number on the die is even
   b) the event F, consisting of all outcomes in which the coin is heads *or* the number on the die is even

10. The compression and the timing of automobile engines are to be tested. The compression can be too low (L), too high (H), or correct (C). The result of the timing can be off (O) or accurate (A). Assume each outcome is equally likely. Find the probability of the event that the timing is accurate. See 2.2 Exercises, question 8.

11. A box contains three white balls and two red balls. A single ball is picked at random from the box.
   a) Find the probability that the ball is red.
   b) Find the odds in favor of the ball not being red. See 2.2 Exercises, question 9.

12. Using the box in question 11, two balls are picked at random with no replacement of the first ball. Find the probability that two white balls are picked.

13. A student feels that the probability of passing her driver's test is 90%, the probability of selling her bicycle is 60%, and the probability of passing the test and also selling her bicycle is 55%. Find the probability that she will pass the test *or* sell her bicycle.

14. The wine cellar of your chateau contains 250 bottles of red bordeaux, 200 bottles of red burgundy, 150 bottles of white bordeaux and 100 bottles of white burgundy. You ask a guest to collect a bottle from the cellar, but the light goes out so he must choose a bottle at random, without being able to see the label. He is too nervous to take the time to select any particular shape of bottle. Find the probability that the bottle contains a burgundy or a white wine.

15. A company that manufactures flashlights knows that 3% of its daily production have defective bulbs, 5% have defective batteries, and 2% have both defective bulbs and defective batteries. A flashlight is selected at random from the daily production. What is the probability that the flashlight will have a defective bulb or a defective battery?

16. a) The odds that it will snow tomorrow are two to three. What is the probability that it will snow tomorrow?
   b) The odds in favor of an event are a to b. Show that the probability of the event is $\dfrac{a}{(a+b)}$.

17. A newspaper article quotes the odds of winning a lottery as a million to one. Yet the odds in favor of winning the lottery are one to a million. Discuss this apparent discrepancy.

18. In a large sample of families in Canada, it was found that 80% of the husbands and 60% of the wives were employed outside the home. In 53% of the cases, both husband and wife were employed outside the home. Assume that the sample is representative of the whole population of Canada.
   a) What is the probability that at least one spouse is employed outside the home?
   b) What is the probability that neither spouse is employed outside the home?

2.4 Probability and Combinatorics

The counting techniques that you learned in chapter 1 are very useful in probability problems.

Example 1   A bag contains six white balls and four red balls. You randomly select three balls at the same time.

a) What is the probability that exactly two will be white?

b) What is the probability that all three will be white?

c) What is the probability that *at least one* of the three will be white?

Solution   **a)** There are 10 balls in the bag and you will select 3 of these 10. Thus, a sample space consists of all possible selections of 3 balls out of 10. But the number of ways of selecting 3 balls from 10 balls is $C(10,3)$. Therefore, $n(S) = C(10,3)$

$$= \frac{10!}{7!3!}$$

$$= 120.$$

There are 120 possible equally likely outcomes in the sample space, S. Let E be the event of selecting exactly two white balls. You must select two white balls and one red ball. There are six white and four red from which to choose. Thus there are $C(6,2)$ ways of choosing the two white balls and $C(4,1)$ ways of choosing the red one. Therefore,

$$n(E) = C(6,2) \times C(4,1)$$

$$= \frac{6!}{2!4!} \times \frac{4!}{3!1!} = 60.$$

Thus, $P(E) = \dfrac{n(E)}{n(S)} = \dfrac{60}{120} = \dfrac{1}{2}.$

The probability of selecting exactly two white balls from the bag is $\dfrac{1}{2}$.

b) Let G be the event that all three selected are white. Three white balls must be selected from six in $C(6,3)$ ways and no red balls from four in $C(4,0)$ ways.

$$n(G) = C(6,3) \times C(4,0)$$

$$= 20 \times 1 = 20$$

Thus $P(G) = \dfrac{n(G)}{n(S)} = \dfrac{20}{120} = \dfrac{1}{6}.$

The probability of selecting three white balls is $\dfrac{1}{6}$.

c) Let F be the event in which at least one white ball is selected out of the three.

Then (*not F*) is the event that *no* white ball is selected out of the three. Thus, $P(F) = 1 - P(not\ F)$.

If no white ball is selected, then all three balls must be red. Thus, $n(not\ F)$ is the number of ways of selecting three red balls from four red balls, namely, $C(4,3) = 4$.

Therefore, $P(not\ F) = \dfrac{n(not\ F)}{n(S)}$

$$= \frac{4}{120} = \frac{1}{30}$$

$$\text{and } P(F) = 1 - \frac{1}{30} = \frac{29}{30}.$$

Thus, the probability of selecting at least one white ball in the three drawn from the bag is $\dfrac{29}{30}$. ■

An alternative solution for part c) is to calculate the probability of selecting at least one white ball directly as:

P (selecting exactly one white ball) $+ P$ (selecting exactly two white balls) $+ P$ (selecting exactly three white balls)

$$= \frac{C(6,1) \times C(4,2)}{120} + \frac{C(6,2) \times C(4,1)}{120} + \frac{C(6,3) \times C(4,0)}{120}$$

$$= \frac{36}{120} + \frac{60}{120} + \frac{20}{120}$$

$$= \frac{116}{120} = \frac{29}{30}.$$

Example 2   A manufacturer of calculators would like to separate defective calculators from calculators that are acceptable. Through an error, a shipment of twelve calculators is sent out containing three defective calculators and nine acceptable calculators. A customer buys five of these calculators, without testing them.

a) What is the probability that all five will be acceptable?

b) What is the probability that two will be defective and three acceptable?

Solution   a) The sample space S consists of all events in which 5 calculators are selected from 12 calculators. Thus,
$n(S) = C(12,5) = 792$.
Let E be the event of selecting 5 acceptable calculators and no defective calculators. Since there are 9 acceptable calculators and 3 defective calculators,

$$n(E) = C(9,5) \times C(3,0) = 126.$$

Thus, $P(E) = \dfrac{126}{792}$ or $\dfrac{7}{44}$.

The probability of all five calculators being acceptable is $\dfrac{7}{44}$.

b) Let F be the event of selecting two defective and three acceptable calculators. The number of ways of selecting 2 defective calculators out of 3 is $C(3,2) = 3$.

Also, the number of ways of selecting 3 acceptable calculators out of 9 is $C(9,3) = 84$.

Thus, $n(F) = 3 \times 84$ or 252, and

$$P(F) = \dfrac{252}{792} \text{ or } \dfrac{7}{22}.$$

The probability of the customer getting two defective and three acceptable calculators is $\dfrac{7}{22}$. ∎

Example 3   In the game of poker, a hand of five cards is dealt to each player from a shuffled deck of 52 playing cards.

a) Find the probability of a hand containing a spade flush, that is, all five cards are spades.

b) Find the probability of a hand containing a full house of three kings and two fives.

Solution   **a)** The sample space consists of all possible selections of 5 cards from 52 cards.

Thus, $n(S) = C(52,5)$

$$= \dfrac{52!}{47!5!} \text{ or } 2\ 598\ 960.$$

If H is the event "spade flush" then H consists of all possible selections of 5 cards from 13 spades.

Thus, $n(H) = C(13,5) \qquad = 1287$ and

$$P(H) = \dfrac{1287}{2\ 598\ 960} \doteq 0.000\ 495.$$

The probability of a spade flush is 0.000 495.

b) Let E be the event that the 5 cards form a full house of 3 kings and 2 fives. There are $C(4,3)$ ways of choosing the 3 kings from the 4 kings in a deck. There are $C(4,2)$ ways of selecting the 2 fives from the 4 fives in a deck.

Thus, $n(E) = C(4,3) \times C(4,2)$

$$= 4 \times 6 \text{ or } 24,$$

and $P(E) = \dfrac{24}{2\ 598\ 960} \doteq 0.000\ 009\ 23.$ ∎

2.4 Exercises

1. A bag contains six white balls and four red balls. You take out three balls at the same time.
   a) What is the probability that *exactly two* of the balls will be red?
   b) What is the probability that *all three* will be red?
   c) What is the probability that *at least one* ball of the three will be red?

2. A bag contains five white balls, three green balls and eight red balls. You take out two balls at the same time.
   a) What is the probability that the two will be green?
   b) What is the probability that the two will be red?

3. A manufacturer of microwave ovens wishes to separate defective microwave ovens from microwave ovens that are acceptable. Through an error, a shipment of nine microwave ovens is sent out containing two defective microwave ovens and seven acceptable microwave ovens. A customer buys two of these microwave ovens, without testing them.
   a) What is the probability that the two will be acceptable?
   b) What is the probability that one will be defective and one acceptable?

4. Three cards are selected at random from a set of seven cards. Two of the cards are marked with the words "you win", and five with the words "try again".
   a) What is the probability that exactly one of the cards is a winning card?
   b) What is the probability that no card is a winning card?

5. Your name, along with nine others, is put in a hat. Four names are drawn at random to determine the winners of four identical prizes. What is the probability that your name will appear?

6. Your brother is saving labels from soup cans. He removes labels from three cans of pea soup, from five cans of vegetable soup and from four cans of onion soup. He neglects to indicate the contents on the unlabeled cans. You need two cans of onion soup to make your special stew. What is the probability that two cans selected at random will both contain onion soup?

7. You are hired to do quality control for a light bulb manufacturer. You decide to test five out of every 100 bulbs manufactured. To check the effectiveness of your testing, you take a sample of 100 good bulbs and replace two of these with defective bulbs. What is the probability of finding at least one defective bulb in the testing of this batch of 100?

8. A basket contains twelve red apples and eight green apples. Four apples are selected at random from the basket. Find the probability of each of the following events.
   a) all four apples will be red
   b) all four apples will be green
   c) three apples will be red and one green
   d) more apples will be green than red

9. In the game of poker, a hand of five cards is dealt to each player from a shuffled deck of 52 playing cards.
   a) Find the probability of a hand containing a heart flush, that is, all five cards are hearts.
   b) Find the probability of a hand containing a full house of three jacks and two fours.
   c) Find the probability of a hand containing any full house, that is, three cards of one denomination and two cards of another denomination.
   d) Find the probability of a hand containing four of a kind, that is, exactly four of the cards have the same denomination.

e) Find the probability of a hand containing a straight, that is, five cards in sequence, not all the same suit, with ace high or low.

10. You need to visit your bank, the book store and the music shop. You make a random choice of the order in which you visit the three places. Find the probability of each of the following events.
    a) you visit your bank first
    b) you visit the music shop before the book store

11. You are hired by your local member of parliament to conduct a survey on unemployment, crime, taxes and mail delivery. You make up a question on each topic for your survey sheet. If the questions are arranged in random order on the sheet, find the probability of each of the following.
    a) the question about mail delivery will be first
    b) the question about mail delivery will be first and the question on crime will be second

12. There are five black mice and five white mice available for an experiment which requires three mice. A random selection is made from the set of ten mice. What is the probability that two black mice and one white mouse will be selected?

13. A Finite Mathematics class has 20 students, 13 of whom are girls and the rest boys. Five students are to be selected at random to present a research problem to the class. What is the probability of three girls and two boys being selected?

14. In a small drama class of 15 students, eight students are to be selected to be actors in a play, four are to be selected as stage hands and the rest selected to the make-up team. You are in the class. What is the probability you will be selected as an actor in the play?

15. You and four other students are able to purchase five tickets for a Stanley Cup play-off game. Three are seat tickets and two are 'standing room only' tickets. You select the first ticket at random. What is the probability that you will get a seat ticket?

16. You are doing some wordprocessing, and accidentally type three letters of the alphabet without noticing which ones you typed. What is the probability that the letters will be in alphabetical order from left to right?

17. You have 15 $5\frac{1}{2}$ inch computer discs. Five of these are for the Apple IIGS computer, and ten are for the ICON. A friend who owns an Apple IIGS takes four discs from your file box, at random. What is the probability that none of the discs will be for the Apple IIGS?

18. A provincial lottery distributes 500 000 tickets numbered 000 000 to 499 999. One of these six-digit numbers is then chosen at random. Prizes are awarded according to the number of digits that match, from left to right, as follows. A ticket matching all six winning digits pays $100 000. Tickets matching the first five digits pay $10 000. Tickets matching the first four digits pay $5 000. Find the probability of a ticket holder winning
    a) $100 000.
    b) $10 000 or more.
    c) $5 000 or more.

19. The president of a NATO country must appoint four of the country's twelve cabinet members to a highly sensitive NATO committee. Unknown to the president, two spies from a non-NATO country have infiltrated the cabinet. If the four chosen are selected at random, what is the probability that neither of the two spies will be chosen?

2.5 Independent Events

Suppose a fair coin is tossed and shows a head. The probability of getting a head on the next toss is $\frac{1}{2}$. The fact that the head was obtained on the first toss has no effect on the outcome of the second toss. Coin tosses are **independent events**, since the knowledge of the outcome of one toss does not help you to predict the outcome of the next toss. A coin has no memory.

Likewise, different rolls of a fair die are independent events. The fact that a four appears on a roll does not assist you in predicting which number will come up on the next roll.

On the other hand, the events "today is cloudy" and "today it will rain" are dependent events. If it is cloudy today you know that the chances of rain have increased.

Consider the following two experiments.
1. You roll a die.
2. You toss a coin.

These experiments are independent.

It is clear that the probability that you roll a 5 is $\frac{1}{6} = P(5)$, and the probability that you toss a head is $\frac{1}{2} = P(H)$.

Suppose you perform the combined experiment of rolling the die and also tossing the coin. What is the probability that you roll a 5 *and* toss a head, that is, $P(5 \text{ and } H)$?

The sample space S of this combined experiment is
$S = \{(1,H), (2,H), (3,H), (4,H), (5,H), (6,H),$
$\quad (1,T), (2,T), (3,T), (4,T), (5,T), (6,T)\}.$

Therefore, $n(S) = 12$.
The event that you will roll a 5 and toss a head is $E = \{(5,H)\}$.
Hence, $n(E) = 1$.

Thus, $P(5 \text{ and } H) = \dfrac{n(E)}{n(S)} = \dfrac{1}{12}$.

Observe that $P(5) \times P(H) = \dfrac{1}{6} \times \dfrac{1}{2} = \dfrac{1}{12}$.

PROPERTY

In general, if E and F are independent events then
$P(E \text{ and } F) = P(E) \times P(F)$.

Example 1 You have two boxes. The first box contains five red balls and three white balls. The second box contains four black balls and seven green balls. One ball is selected at random from each box. What is the probability that the balls chosen will be white, and black?

Solution Let W be the event "a white is drawn" and B be the event "a black is drawn".

Therefore, $P(W) = \dfrac{3}{8}$ and $P(B) = \dfrac{4}{11}$.

What happens in the first box does not influence what occurs in the second box. Thus, the events are independent, and

$$P(W \text{ and } B) = P(W) \times P(B) = \frac{3}{8} \times \frac{4}{11} = \frac{3}{22}.$$

The probability of a white being chosen from the first box and a black from the second is $\dfrac{3}{22}$. ∎

Example 2 A calculator requires a keyboard assembly and a logic circuit. A manufacturer tests the finished product and finds that the probability of a defective keyboard assembly is 0.05, while the probability of a defective logic circuit is 0.02. What is the probability that a finished calculator will have both a satisfactory keyboard assembly and logic circuit? (Assume the condition of the keyboard is independent of the condition of the logic circuit.)

Solution Let K be the event that a keyboard assembly is satisfactory and L be the event that a logic circuit is satisfactory.
Thus, the probability that a finished calculator will have both a satisfactory keyboard assembly and logic circuit is $P(K \text{ and } L)$.
But $P(K \text{ and } L) \quad = P(K) \times \quad P(L)$
Now $P(K) = 1 - P(not\ K) = 1 - 0.05 = 0.95$
Also $P(L) = 1 - P(not\ L) = 1 - 0.02 = 0.98$
Thus, $P(K \text{ and } L) \quad = 0.95 \times \quad 0.98 \quad = 0.931$

Thus, the probability that a finished calculator will have both a satisfactory keyboard assembly and logic circuit is $0.931 = 93.1\%$. ∎

Example 3

Spinner A

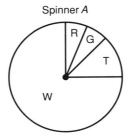

Spinner B

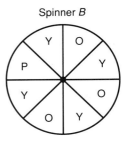

Spinner *A* on the left is $\frac{1}{16}$ red, $\frac{3}{4}$ white, $\frac{1}{8}$ turquoise, and $\frac{1}{16}$ green.

Spinner *B* on the right is divided into eight equal parts, four of which are colored yellow, three colored orange and one colored purple.

The spinners are fair, that is, the spinning needle has an equal chance of stopping at any point on the circumference of the circle.

Find the probability of each of the following when both spinners are set in motion.

a) a white on spinner *A and* a yellow on spinner *B*

b) a white on spinner *A or* a yellow on spinner *B*

Solution

a) Let *W* be the event "white on spinner *A*" and *Y* be the event "yellow on spinner *B*".
The probability of a white on *A* and a yellow on *B* is $P(W$ and $Y)$. Since *W* and *Y* are independent, then
$$P(W \text{ and } Y) = P(W) \times P(Y).$$
Now $P(W) = \frac{3}{4}$ and $P(Y) = \frac{4}{8}$.
Thus, $P(W \text{ and } Y) = \frac{3}{4} \times \frac{4}{8} = \frac{3}{8}$.
The probability of a white on spinner *A and* a yellow on spinner *B* is $\frac{3}{8}$.

b) The probability of a white on spinner *A or* a yellow on spinner *B* is
$$P(W \text{ or } Y) = P(W) + P(Y) - P(W \text{ and } Y)$$
$$= \frac{3}{4} + \frac{1}{2} - \frac{3}{8} = \frac{7}{8}.$$
The probability of a white on *A* or a yellow on *B* is $\frac{7}{8}$. ∎

2.5 Exercises

1. The probability that you win a lottery is 0.000 0001 while the probability that you become the Prime Minister of Canada is 0.000 003. Find the probability that you win a lottery *and* become Prime Minister of Canada.

2. According to the current insurance statistics of your city, the probability of your house burning down is 0.0003, while the probability of a theft from your house is 0.0006. Find the probability that this year your house will burn down *and* there will be a theft from your house.

3. You have two boxes. The first box contains six red balls and four white balls. The second box contains five black balls and six green balls. One ball is selected at random from each box. What is the probability that the balls chosen will be white, and black?

4. A walkman requires an amplifier and a tape circuit. A manufacturer tests the finished product and finds that the probability of a defective amplifier is 0.08 while the probability of defective tape circuit is 0.03. What is the probability that a finished walkman will have both a satisfactory amplifier and a satisfactory tape circuit? (Assume the condition of the amplifier is independent of the condition of the tape circuit.)

5.

Spinner *A* on the left is $\frac{1}{8}$ red, $\frac{3}{8}$ white, $\frac{1}{4}$ turquoise and $\frac{1}{4}$ green.

Spinner *B* on the right is divided into eight equal parts, three of which are colored yellow, two colored orange and three colored purple.

The spinners are fair, that is, the spinning needle has an equal chance of stopping at any point on the circumference of the circle.

Find the probability of each of the following when both spinners are set in motion.

a) a white on spinner *A and* a yellow on spinner *B*

b) a white on spinner *A or* a yellow on spinner *B*

c) a green on spinner *A or* a purple on spinner *B*

6. a) What is the probability of tossing a coin five times and having heads come up each time?

b) You toss a coin five times and each time the coin comes up heads. What is the probability that the coin will come up heads again on the next toss?

7. What is the probability of throwing two sevens in a row with a pair of dice?

8. a) You are given two decks of playing cards and asked to draw one card from each deck. What is the probability that both cards will be spades?

b) You are given two decks of playing cards and asked to draw two cards from each deck. What is the probability that the four cards selected will be spades?

9. In the U.S. Venus probe, two independent mechanical systems must both function in order that the probe make a successful landing. Officials at NASA estimate that under actual landing conditions, the probability of one system functioning is 80%, and of the other, 70%. What is the probability of a successful landing?

10. Six slips of paper, with a different digit from 1 to 6 printed on each, are placed in a box. The papers are well mixed. One slip is drawn and replaced. The papers are well mixed, and a second slip is drawn. Find the probability of each of the following.
    a) the first is marked with an odd number and the second with an even
    b) the first is marked with a four and the second with a number less than four
    c) both slips are marked with an even number

11. The chips used in a calculator contain several thousand components each of which is subject to failure. A certain type of calculator uses chip *A* and chip *B*. Chip *A* has a 90% chance of being defective, while chip *B* has an 80% chance of being defective. One chip of each kind is selected. Find the probability of each of the following.
    a) both chips are defective
    b) chip *A* is defective while chip *B* is not defective
    c) neither chip is defective
    d) at least one chip is defective

12. Two traffic lights operate independently of each other. The probability of being stopped at the first light is 0.2 and the probability of being stopped at the second is 0.6. Find the probability of each of the following.
    a) you will stop at both lights
    b) you will go through both lights
    c) you will be stopped at the first but not at the second light

13. Hospitals contain backup generators in case of power failure. A hospital has two backup generators each of which has a 2% probability of failure. Only one generator is needed to supply emergency power. What is the probability that the backup system will work in the case of a power failure?

14. You are flying in a three-engine jet plane. The probability that any one of the jet engines will fail is 0.0001. What is the probability that all three of the engines will fail during flight?

15. You are writing a multiple choice test. Every question has five choices, only one of which is correct. You have no idea how to answer three of the questions. What is the probability that you will get all three of these three questions correct if you guess the answers?

16. If a dark-haired mother and father have a particular type of gene then the probability that any child that they have will be light-haired is 0.25. Such a couple decides to have three children. What is the probability that all three children will have light hair?

17. Three people on your hockey team have calculated their respective probabilities of scoring a goal when each makes a shot on goal. Elizabeth scores 40% of the time, Jessica 50%, and Adel 35%. In a game, all three shoot independently on goal. Calculate the following probabilities.
    a) all three will not score
    b) at least one will score

18. You enter a contest in which one ball must be drawn from each of three bags. The first bag contains three green balls and two red balls. The second bag contains five green balls and three red balls. The third bag contains two green balls and four red balls. You win if you select exactly two green balls. What is the probability that you will win?

In Search of Non-uniform Probability Models

In a uniform probability distribution on a sample space containing n outcomes, each outcome is assigned the probability $\frac{1}{n}$. If an event in the sample space has k outcomes, that event is assigned the probability $\frac{k}{n}$.

But outcomes of experiments do not always occur with the same relative frequency. In such cases, a uniform probability model is unsuitable.

Suppose that you are in charge of buying merchandise for a clothing store. You wish to purchase T-shirts that come in four different sizes and six different colors. Thus, you must buy $4 \times 6 = 24$ different kinds of T-shirts. You will need to decide on the relative frequency of sales or the probability of a customer buying each one of these T-shirts. It should be clear that the 24 T-shirts will not all sell equally well. Thus, the probability model you will use will not be uniform. Suppose, for example, red is popular color this year and most of your customers are usually of medium size. Then you might assign a probability of P(medium red) = 0.6. Whereas, if grey is unpopular and very few customers are extra extra large, then an assignment P(extra extra large grey) = 0.05 could be reasonable.

Example 1 A customer comes into your clothing store described above. What is the probability the customer will make the following purchases? (Assume the purchase of any T-shirt is independent of the purchase of any other T-shirt.)

a) a medium red and extra extra large grey

b) a medium red or an extra extra large grey

Solution The "and" property and the "or" property and the "complement" property of probability hold for non-uniform probability models.

a) P(a medium red and an extra extra large grey)
   $= P$(a medium red) $\times P$(an extra extra large grey)
   $= 0.6 \times 0.05 = 0.03$

b) P(a medium red or an extra extra large grey)
   $= P$(a medium red) $+ P$(an extra extra large grey)
   $\quad -P$(a medium red and an extra extra large grey)
   $= 0.6 + 0.05 - 0.03 = 0.62$ ∎

Example 2   You go into a ski rental shop for a pair of skis. The shop has Rossignols and Fischers in the length of ski you need. There are twice as many Fischers as Rossignols. One half the Rossignols have Look bindings while three-quarters of the Fischers have Look bindings. The attendant picks one pair of these skis at random. What is the probability that you will get a pair of skis with Look bindings?

Solution   Let R be the event Rossignols are selected. Let F be the event Fischers are selected. Let L be the event the skis have Look bindings.

A reasonable non-uniform probability model would be the following:

$P(R) = \dfrac{1}{3}$, $P(F) = \dfrac{2}{3}$, $P(L$ given $R) = \dfrac{1}{2}$, and $P(L$ given $F) = \dfrac{3}{4}$.

The tree diagram will help you to calculate the probability. Note that the probability of an outcome is marked on the branch leading to the outcome.

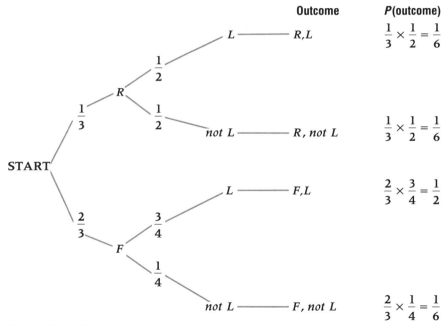

	Outcome	P(outcome)
	R, L	$\dfrac{1}{3} \times \dfrac{1}{2} = \dfrac{1}{6}$
	R, not L	$\dfrac{1}{3} \times \dfrac{1}{2} = \dfrac{1}{6}$
	F, L	$\dfrac{2}{3} \times \dfrac{3}{4} = \dfrac{1}{2}$
	F, not L	$\dfrac{2}{3} \times \dfrac{1}{4} = \dfrac{1}{6}$

The probability of getting skis with Look bindings
$= P(R,L) + P(F,L)$
$= \dfrac{1}{6} + \dfrac{1}{2} = \dfrac{2}{3}.$ ∎

Activities

1. As a sales representative for a large company, you are assigned a company car each week. The motor pool has three times as many Volvos as Mercedes. Half the Volvos and three-quarters of the Mercedes are air-conditioned. Assignments of cars are made at random.

    a) Draw a tree diagram and assign probabilities to each outcome.

    b) Find the probability that the car assigned to you next week will be air-conditioned.

2. You prefer to ski when it is snowing and the temperature is above 10°C. You can go skiing on only one of the next two days, Monday or Tuesday. You phone Environment Canada and obtain the following information.

    On Monday, the probability of snow is 40%, and the probability the temperature will be above 10°C is 70%.

    On Tuesday, the probability of snow is 80%, and the probability the temperature will be above 10°C is 10%.

    One of the two days is selected at random. What is the probability that it will be snowing and the temperature will be above 10°C?

3. The Motor Vehicle Department in your city has found that the probability of a person passing the test for a driver's licence on the first try is 75%. The probability that a person who fails on the first test will pass on the second try is 80%. The probability that a person who fails both of the first two tests will pass on the third is 70%.

    Find the probability of each of the following for a person taking the test.

    a) the person fails the first and second test

    b) the person will require at least two tries to pass

2.6 Conditional Probability

You are playing a game in which you and a friend each draw a ball at random from a bag containing four differently colored balls, red, yellow, green, and white. Each of you draws one ball, with your friend drawing first. The winner is not determined until after you have drawn. You win if you draw a red or a white ball. Your friend wins if you draw a yellow or a green ball.

The sample space S of the game is made up of ordered pairs "fm" where f is the color your friend picks and m is the color you pick. Thus, $S = \{RY, RG, RW, YR, YG, YW, WR, WY, WG, GR, GY, GW\}$ and $n(S) = 12$.

If A is the event that you win and F is the event your friend wins, then $A = \{RW, YR, YW, WR, GR, GW\}$ and $F = \{RY, RG, YG, WY, WG, GY\}$, Thus, $n(A) = n(F) = 6$.

The game is fair because $P(A) = P(F) = \dfrac{6}{12} = \dfrac{1}{2}$.

Suppose your friend has just drawn and has a white ball. What is the probability that you will win now? This type of probability is called a **conditional probability**. The condition is that your friend has drawn a white ball. To emphasize that this is a conditional probability, P(you win now) is described as P(you win on condition that your friend drew a white ball). If B is the event that your friend drew a white ball, and A is again the event that you win, then the probability that you win now is called $P(A$ on the condition that B occurred) or $P(A$ given $B)$. What is the probability of A given B?
Consider the following set diagram for the game.

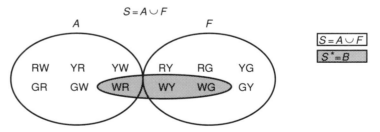

$$S = A \cup F$$

To find $P(A$ given $B)$ you must consider the reduced sample space S^* consisting only of the elements in $B = \{WR, WY, WG\}$.
For this reduced sample space, $n(S^*) = n(B) = 3$.

The event A given B consists only of the outcomes in A that are also in B. Thus, A given $B = A \cap B = \{WR\}$ and $n(A$ given $B) = 1$.

Hence, $P(A$ given $B) = \dfrac{n(A \text{ given } B)}{n(S^*)} = \dfrac{1}{3}$.

If you divide the numerator and denominator of the last fraction by $n(S) = 12$, you can relate $P(A$ given $B)$ to $P(A$ and $B)$ and $P(B)$.

This division gives $P(A$ given $B) = \frac{\frac{1}{12}}{\frac{3}{12}}$. ①

But $\frac{1}{12} = \frac{n(A \cap B)}{n(S)} = P(A$ and $B)$.

Also, $\frac{3}{12} = \frac{n(B)}{n(S)} = P(B)$.

Hence, from equation ① you obtain

$P(A$ given $B) = \frac{P(A \text{ and } B)}{P(B)}$.

This result can be demonstrated to be true for any sets A and B, and is actually chosen as the definition of $P(A$ given $B)$.

DEFINITION $P(A$ given $B) = \dfrac{P(A \text{ and } B)}{P(B)}$

Example 1   A bag contains white balls, a red ball and blue balls. There are three white balls, each marked differently with a one, two or three. The red ball is marked with a four. There are four blue balls, each marked differently with a five, six, seven or eight.

A ball is selected at random from the bag.
a) What is the probability that the ball chosen is white?
b) If the ball chosen is known to be marked with an odd number, what is the probability that the ball is white?

Solution   **a)** $n(S) =$ the number of balls $= 8$.
If E is the event that a white ball is chosen, then $n(E) = 3$.

Thus, $P(E) = \dfrac{3}{8}$.

The probability that the ball chosen is white is $\dfrac{3}{8}$.

b) Let A be the event that an odd number is chosen.

Therefore, $n(A) = 4$, and $P(A) = \dfrac{4}{8}$.

The probability that the ball chosen is white, given that the ball is marked with an odd number, is

$P(E$ given $A) = P\dfrac{(E \text{ and } A)}{P(A)}$.

But $E \cap A = \{$white 1, white 3$\}$, so $n(E \cap F) = 2$.

Hence, $P(E$ and $A) = \dfrac{2}{8}$.

Thus, $P(E$ given $A) = \dfrac{2}{8} \div \dfrac{4}{8} = \dfrac{1}{2}$.

Thus, the probability that the ball chosen is white, given that the ball is marked with an odd number, is $\dfrac{1}{2}$.   ■

Example 2 A chocolate bar manufacturer makes bars that are advertised to have a mass of 120 g. A quality control test indicates that the probability is 0.65 that the mass is 120 g, the probability is 0.20 that the mass is less than 120 g, and the probability is 0.15 that the mass is greater than 120 g.

A bar is selected at random and found not to have a mass of 120 g. Find, correct to 2 decimal places, the probability that this bar will have a mass of less than 120 g.

Solution Let E be the event that a bar selected has a mass of 120 g.
Let L be the event that a bar selected has a mass of less than 120 g.
Let G be the event that a bar selected has a mass of more than 120 g.
Then the probability required is

$$P(L \text{ given } not \ E) = \frac{P(L \text{ and } not \ E)}{P(not \ E)}.$$

But L and $not \ E = L$, so $P(L \text{ and } not \ E) = P(L) = 0.20$.
Also, $P(not \ E) = 1 - P(E) = 1 - 0.65 = 0.35$.

Therefore, $P(L \text{ given } not \ E) = \dfrac{0.20}{0.35} \doteq 0.571 = 0.57$ correct to 2 decimal

places.
Therefore, given the bar does not have the correct mass, the probability is 0.57 that this bar will have a mass of less than 120 g. ■

Example 3 You play a game of rolling two dice. You win the game if you roll a five before you roll a seven. You continue to roll until either a five or seven appears. What is the probability that you will win the game?

Solution Let E be the event a 5 is rolled, and F be the event a 7 is rolled. Then, the required probability is
$P(E \text{ given } B)$ where $B = E \cup F$
But $E = \{(1,4), (2,3), (3,2), (4,1)\}$
    $F = \{(1,6), (2,5), (3,4), (4,3), (5,2), (6,1)\}$.
Thus, $n(E) = 4$, $n(F) = 6$, $n(B) = 4 + 6 = 10$, and $n(S) = 36$.

Since $E \cap B = E$, therefore $P(E \text{ and } B) = P(E) = \dfrac{4}{36}$ and $P(B) = \dfrac{10}{36}$.

Thus, $P(E \text{ given } B) = \dfrac{P(E \text{ and } B)}{P(B)} = \dfrac{P(E)}{P(B)} = \dfrac{4}{36} \div \dfrac{10}{36} = \dfrac{4}{10} = \dfrac{2}{5}$.

Therefore, the probability of rolling a five before a seven is $\dfrac{2}{5}$. ■

The "and" Property of Conditional Probability
From the definition of conditional probability

$P(A \text{ given } B) = \dfrac{P(A \text{ and } B)}{P(B)}$, which can be rewritten as

$P(A \text{ and } B) = P(A \text{ given } B) \times P(B)$

PROPERTY

Example 4   A bag contains four white balls, three red balls and five blue balls. A ball is selected and *not* put back. Then a second ball is selected. Find the probability that both balls are white.

Solution   Because the first ball is not replaced, the selection of the second ball is dependent on the selection of the first ball. Let A be the event "a white ball is selected on the first draw", and B be the event "a white ball is selected on the second draw". Then the probability of two whites is
$P(A \text{ and } B) = P(A) \times P(B \text{ given } A)$.
Since there are four white balls to be chosen from among twelve balls,
$$P(A) = \frac{4}{12}.$$
After the event A has occurred, there are only 3 white balls among the remaining eleven. Thus, $P(B \text{ given } A) = \dfrac{3}{11}$.

Thus, $P(A \text{ and } B) = \dfrac{4}{12} \times \dfrac{3}{11} = \dfrac{1}{11}$.

The probability of getting two white balls without replacement is $\dfrac{1}{11}$. ■

Definition of Independent Events
Now that you understand the definition of *conditional* events, you can give a meaningful definition of *independent* events.

DEFINITION   Events E and F are independent if $P(E \text{ given } F) = P(E)$.

This statement indicates that event F taking place has no effect on whether or not the event E occurs.

Thus, the conditional events statement
$P(A \text{ and } B) = P(A \text{ given } B) \times P(B)$
becomes the independent events statement obtained in section 2.5,
namely, $P(A \text{ and } B) = P(A) \times P(B)$

Do not confuse the ideas of *mutually exclusive* events and *independent* events. Events E and F are mutually exclusive if $E \cap F = \{ \ \}$.
For example, if a family has only one child, the only possible events are
$B = \{boy\}$ and $G = \{girl\}$.
These two events are mutually exclusive.
They are *not* independent. If a family with only one child has a boy, the probability that it has a girl is 0. Thus, $P(G \text{ given } B) = 0$, whereas $P(G) = \dfrac{1}{2}$.
Since $P(G \text{ given } B) \neq P(G)$, the events are not independent.

2.6 Exercises

1. A bag contains white balls, a red ball and blue balls. There are four white balls, each marked differently with a one, two, three and four. The red ball is marked with a five. There are five blue balls, each marked differently with a six, seven, eight, nine or ten. A ball is selected at random from the bag.
   a) What is the probability that the ball chosen is blue?
   b) If the ball chosen is known to be marked with an odd number, what is the probability that the ball is blue?

2. Two dice are rolled and the numbers on the up faces are observed. Find the probability of each of the following events.
   a) Exactly one die shows a 5, given the sum is seven.
   b) The sum of the numbers is seven, given that exactly one die shows a 5.
   c) The sum of the numbers is seven, given that at least one die shows a 5.

3. A nail manufacturer makes nails that are advertised to have a length of 15 cm. A quality control test indicates that the probability is 0.71 that the length is 15 cm, the probability is 0.18 that the length is less than 15 cm, and the probability is 0.11 that the length is more than 15 cm. Find, correct to 2 decimal places, the probability that a randomly selected nail that does not have a length of 15 cm will have a length of less than 15 cm.

4. You play a game of rolling two dice. You win the game if you roll a four before you roll a seven. You continue to roll until either a four or seven appears. What is the probability that you will win the game?

5. Two students are selected at random from a group consisting of five girls and three boys. Find the probability that both students are girls, given that at least one is a girl.

6. A single die is rolled. Find the probability of rolling each of the following.
   a) a two, given the number rolled is odd
   b) a four, given the number rolled is even
   c) an even number, given the number rolled is a 6

7. Two cards are drawn from a deck of 52 playing cards without any replacement. Find the probability of each of the following.
   a) the second card is a club given the first one is a club
   b) both cards are clubs
   c) the second card is black given the first one is a spade

8. A bag contains six green balls, and three black balls. A ball is selected and *not* put back. Then a second ball is selected. Find the probability of each of the following.
   a) both balls are green
   b) both balls are black
   c) the second ball is green, given the first one is black
   d) the first ball is black and the second one is green
   e) one ball is black and the other one is green

9. Your class has won a homeroom contest and is rewarded with a pizza feast of twelve pizzas. Among the pizzas, two pizzas have bacon and anchovies, three pizzas have bacon and onions, three pizzas have green peppers and anchovies and four pizzas have green peppers and onions. You select two of the pizzas at random.
   a) What is the probability that both pizzas have anchovies given that both have bacon?
   b) What is the probability that one pizza has anchovies and the other has onions given that both have bacon?

10. Three gamblers roll a die, in turn. The one who first rolls a 4 wins. What are their respective chances of winning on the first throw?

11. You have tickets to a rock concert. Three tickets are in the first row, two tickets are in the second row and four tickets are in the third row. You select two tickets at random to give to a friend. You notice that one of the the tickets is not in the first row but you do not look at the other ticket. Find the probability of each of the following.
    a) both tickets are in the second row
    b) both tickets are in the third row

12. In your Finite Mathematics class, five students have programmable calculators, four have non-programmable calculators and one has no calculator. Three students are selected at random from among these ten. All three have exactly the same type of calculator. What is the probability that all three have programmable calculators?

13. The research branch of a pharmaceutical company did a study on the effect of a new painkilling drug.
    500 people were tested. 250 were given the new drug, while 250 were given a placebo. The results were as follows.

	Felt better	Felt no better	Total
Given new drug	185	65	250
Given placebo	115	135	250
Total	300	200	500

    a) What is the probability that a patient, selected at random, felt better after taking the new drug?
    b) What is the probability that a patient, selected at random, received the placebo, given that she or he felt better?

14. Three gamblers toss a coin. The first one who tosses a tail wins. Show that the probability of the the first gambler winning is $\dfrac{1}{2} + \dfrac{1}{16} + \dfrac{1}{128} + \dots$

15. Four cards are drawn from a deck of 52 playing cards without any replacement. Find the probability of each of the following.
    a) all cards are hearts
    b) all cards are hearts given the first two are hearts
    c) all cards are spades given the fourth was a diamond

16. A car insurance company examines the accident records of its policy holders for the past few years. It is found that 9.1% of the policy holders generally have had at least one accident, and 2.3% have had at least two accidents. What is the probability that a randomly selected policy holder, who has already had one accident during the present year, will have another accident this year?

17. a) Events A and B are such that $P(A$ given $B) = \dfrac{1}{2}$ and $P(A) = \dfrac{2}{3}$. Are the events A and B independent? Explain.
    b) Events G and H are such that $P(G) = \dfrac{1}{3}$, $P(H) = \dfrac{3}{5}$ and $P(G$ and $H) = \dfrac{1}{5}$. Prove that events G and H are independent.
    c) Events E and F are such that $P(E$ given $F) = \dfrac{1}{2}$, $P(F$ given $E) = \dfrac{1}{3}$ and $P(E$ and $F) = \dfrac{1}{5}$.
    Are the events E and F independent? Explain.

In Search of a Solution to the Birthday Problem

Suppose that you try the following experiment in your classroom. You ask each student to name the month and the day of the month that the student was born. What do you think the probability would be that at least two students in your class have the same birthday?

Before reading any further try the experiment in your class.

Perhaps you were surprised at the result. In a class of 25 students the probability that at least two students will have the same birthday is 56.9%, that is, the odds are better than even money that there will be a match.

Most people think of the facts that there are 365 days in a year and only 25 people to fit into the days, so they reason that the probability must be small.

Why is the probability of at least two students in a class of 25 having the same birthday greater than 50%?

To understand this problem it is well to consider a smaller class, say one with three students in the class.

P(at least two students will $= 1 - P$(no two students will
    have the same birthday)   have the same birthday).   ①

Now the first student was born on a particular day of 365 days, so that

P(first student was born) $= \dfrac{365}{365}.$

If the second student was born on a different day than the first, then there are only 364 days on which the second student could have been born. Thus,

P(second student was born on a different day $= \dfrac{364}{365}.$
    than the first student)

If the third student was born on a different day than the first and second students, then there are only 363 days on which the third student could have been born. Thus,

P(third student was born on a different day $= \dfrac{363}{365}.$
    than the first student and the second student)

Since the three births are independent,
P(no two students of three students will $= \left(\dfrac{365}{365}\right)\left(\dfrac{364}{365}\right)\left(\dfrac{363}{365}\right).$
    have the same birthday)

From ①,

P(at least two students will have the same birthday) $= 1 - P$(no two students will have the same birthday)

$= 1 - \left(\dfrac{365}{365}\right)\left(\dfrac{364}{365}\right)\left(\dfrac{363}{365}\right)$

$= 1 - 0.991\ 795\ 8341$

$= 0.008\ 204\ 1659$ or about 0.83%.

By using a similar argument you should show that for a class of 10 students,

P(at least two of the 10 students will have the same birthday)

$= 1 - P$(no two of the 10 students will have the same birthday)

$= 1 - \left(\dfrac{365}{365}\right)\left(\dfrac{364}{365}\right)\left(\dfrac{363}{365}\right)\left(\dfrac{362}{365}\right)\left(\dfrac{361}{365}\right)\left(\dfrac{360}{365}\right)\left(\dfrac{359}{365}\right)\left(\dfrac{358}{365}\right)\left(\dfrac{357}{365}\right)\left(\dfrac{356}{365}\right)$

$= 1 - 0.883\ 051\ 8223 = 0.116\ 948\ 1777$ or about 12%.

Explain why for a class of n students,

P(at least two of the n students have the same birthday)

$= 1 - P$(no two of the n students will have the same birthday)

$= 1 - \left(\dfrac{365}{365}\right)\left(\dfrac{364}{365}\right)\left(\dfrac{363}{365}\right)\cdots\left(\dfrac{365-n+1}{365}\right)$.

Activities

1. Write a computer program to evaluate
   P(at least two of the n students will have the same birthday)
   for any whole number value of n.

2. Use your computer program from question 1 or your calculator to verify the following.

Number of students	Probability that at least two students will have the same birthday
5	2.7%
10	11.7%
15	25.2%
20	41.1%
25	56.9%
30	70.6%
35	81.4%
40	89.9%
50	97.0%
60	99.4%

MAKING

Petals Around the Rose

There is a game and a mathematical secret society that is making headway throughout Canada and the United States. There are even chapters of the society in Switzerland. The name of the game and of the society is *Petals Around the Rose*. Once this game enters a school, the game spreads like wildfire in and outside the mathematics classrooms. Members of the society are called *potentates*. The organizer of the society in a school is the *chief potentate*.

The game is quite simple. A potentate knows the secret that gives the answer for any roll of five dice.

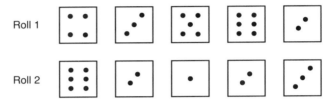

For roll 1 the answer is 6, while in roll 2 the answer is 2.

The potentate rolls the five dice and informs you that the potentate can tell you three things.

1. "The name of the game is *Petals Around the Rose*, and the name is important."
2. "The answer for any roll is an even number."
3. "The answer for the roll is ＿＿＿". (The blank is filled by the number represented by the roll.)

No potentate may ever reveal the method the potentate uses to obtain the answer in number 3. This is a very important regulation of the society. Indeed, every potential potentate must promise never to reveal this secret before she or he may become a member of the society.

Here are some more examples. Can you discover the secret?　　Answer

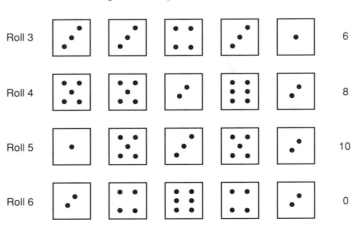

Do you see the pattern? Remember if you do, do not tell anyone else! The amazing thing about this game is that some people see how to get the answer in only three or four rolls. Others struggle for days before the truth finally dawns upon them. Even mathematics teachers and high school principals have problems seeing the pattern involved. Why not try to become a member of the society before your teacher does? No matter what happens, persevere. One person went five years before figuring out how to get the answer.

Now try the next examples. The answers for these are found at the end of this Making Connections.

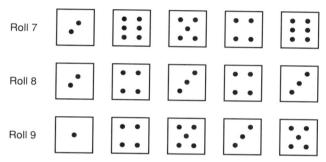

Be aware that the game is very addictive. You may discover that you will have difficulty finding time to eat or do your homework while you are working on your solution to the game. Indeed, once you are a member of the society, people will be pestering you to give your time to test them. Here are some more to try.

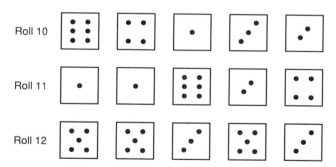

Perhaps you are now a potentate because you can predict the answer to any roll of five dice. If you are, then you may enrol others into the society as potentates. Anyone you test who can give the correct answer to six successive rolls of the dice can be enrolled as a potentate. You can make up certificates for your school society to give to those who have become potentates.

Good luck!

Answers:

roll 7: **4**; roll 8: **4**; roll 9: **10**; roll 10: **2**; roll 11: **0**; roll 12: **16**.

Summary

In probability, each repetition of an experiment is called a *trial*.

The possible results of each trial are *outcomes*.

Unless otherwise stated or implied, you can assume that all outcomes are *equally likely*.

The set of all possible outcomes for an experiment is a *sample space*, S, for the experiment.

Any subset of a sample space is an *event* for the sample space.

Any event that consists of only one outcome is a *simple event*.

The probability of the event E is abbreviated P(E)

$$P(E) = \frac{n(E)}{n(S)}$$

where $n(E)$ = the number of outcomes in E,

and $n(S)$ = the number of possible *equally likely* outcomes in a sample space, S.

A *uniform probability model* is a sample space associated with an experiment such that each simple event is equally probable.

Properties of Probability

- $0 \leqslant P(E) \leqslant 1$
  $P(\text{impossible event}) = 0$, $P(\text{certain event}) = 1$.

- If events E and H are complements in the sample space, S, then H is written *not E* or E' and
  $P(E) = P(not\ E) = 1$ or $P(not\ E) = 1 - P(E)$.

- $P(E\ or\ F) = P(E) + P(F) - P(E\ and\ F)$
  where the event (E or F) consists of all events that are either in E or in F or in both E and F, and where the event (E and F) consists of all events that are both in E and also in F.
  Whenever E and F are *mutually exclusive* events, that is, E and F have no outcomes in common, then $P(E\ and\ F) = 0$, and $P(E\ or\ F) = P(E) + P(F)$.

- $P(E\ given\ F)$ is the *conditional* probability that the event E will occur, provided the event F has already occurred.
  $P(E\ given\ F) = \dfrac{P(E\ and\ F)}{P(F)}$ which is equivalent to
  $P(E\ and\ F) = P(E\ given\ F) \times P(F)$. ①

- E and F are *independent* events if $P(E\ given\ F) = P(E)$.
  If E and F are independent events then
  $P(E\ and\ F) = P(E) \times P(F)$. ②
  Properties ① and ② are called the **"and"** properties.

- The odds in favor of an event E is the ratio $\dfrac{P(E)}{P(not\ E)}$.

Inventory

Answer the following by filling in the blanks.

1. P(certain event) = _____. P(impossible event) = _____.

2. $P(E)$ can never be larger than _____ or never smaller than _____.

3. If a single die is rolled, and the number on the up face is observed, then $n(S)$ = _____.

4. If two dice are rolled, and the numbers on the up faces are observed, then $n(S)$ = _____.

5. If a coin is tossed, and the up face is noted as heads or tails, then $n(S)$ = _____.

6. If three coins are tossed, and the up faces are noted as heads or tails, then $n(S)$ = _____.

7. If a card is drawn from a deck of playing cards, and the face value and suit is noted, then $n(S)$ = _____.

8. If E is the event that a sum of seven appears on the up faces when two dice are rolled, then $n(E)$ = _____.

9. $P(E) = 0.3$, then $P(not\ E)$ = _____.

10. $P(E) = 0.3$, $P(F) = 0.2$, and $P(E\ and\ F) = 0.1$, then $P(E\ or\ F)$ = _____.

11. $P(E) = 0.3$ and $P(F) = 0.2$, and E and F are independent events, then $P(E\ and\ F)$ = _____.

12. $P(F) = 0.5$ and $P(E\ and\ F) = 0.2$, then $P(E\ given\ F)$ = _____.

13. $P(E) = 0.3$. The odds in favor of event E are _____.

14. If events E and F are independent, and $P(E\ given\ F) = 0.4$, $P(E\ and\ F) = 0.08$, then $P(E)$ = _____ and $P(F)$ = _____.

Review Exercises

1. A single die is rolled. Find the probability of each of the following events.
   a) a six appears on the up face
   b) a three appears on the up face
   c) a three does not appear on the up face
   d) an eight appears on the up face
   e) a number less than eight appears on the up face
   f) a six appears on the up face or a three appears on the up face
   g) a six appears on the up face and a three appears on the up face

2. Two dice are rolled. Find the probability of each of the following events.
   a) the sum on the up faces is four
   b) the sum on the up faces is seven
   c) the sum on the up faces is not seven
   d) the sum on the up faces is four or the sum on the up faces is seven
   e) a three appears on at least one die
   f) a three appears on at least one die and the sum of the up faces is four
   g) a three appears on at least one die or the sum of the up faces is four

3. A single card is selected at random from a deck of playing cards. Find the probability of each of the following events.
   a) the card is black
   b) the card is black *and* a jack
   c) the card is black *or* a jack

4. An experiment consists of testing calculators one after the other, without replacement, until either two defective calculators are found or four calculators are tested.
   Calculate the probability of each of the following events.
   a) the event *E* consisting of all outcomes where exactly one defective calculator is tested
   b) the event *F* consisting of all outcomes where exactly two acceptable calculators are selected

5. Six balls are selected from a bag, at random and without replacement. Before the selection the bag contained eight red balls and nine yellow balls. Find the probability of each of the following events.
   a) exactly four of the balls are red
   b) at least four of the balls are red

6. On a cold winter morning your car has a 60% chance of starting while your parents' car has a 90% chance of starting. Find the probability of each of the following.
   a) neither car will start
   b) both cars will start
   c) either both cars will start or neither car will start
   d) exactly one of the cars will start

7. Two dice are rolled and the numbers on the up faces are noted. Find the odds in favor of the following events.
   a) the sum of the numbers is twelve
   b) one number is a three and the other is a six

8. Three coins are tossed and the outcome noted in each case.
   a) Find the probability that all three will be tails.
   b) Find the probability that two will be tails and one heads.
   c) Find the probability that two will be alike and one different.

9. A bag contains four white balls, two green balls and three red balls. You take out two balls at the same time.
   a) What is the probability that the two will be green?
   b) What is the probability that the two will be red?

10. You have two boxes. The first box contains three red balls and four white balls. The second box contains six black balls and five green balls. One ball is selected at random from each box. What is the probability that the balls chosen will be red, and black?

11. Four cards are selected at random from a set of eight cards. Three of the eight cards are marked with the words "100 dollars", and five with the words "fifty cents".
   a) What is the probability that exactly one of the cards wins $100?
   b) What is the probability that no card wins $100?

12. You have seven tickets to a Blue Jays game. Three tickets are in the left field stands, two are behind the plate and two are near first base. Two tickets are selected at random for your sisters. You notice that one of the tickets is not behind the plate. Find the probability that both tickets are near first base.

13. Two pets are selected at random from a group consisting of four dogs and two cats. Find the probability that both pets are cats, given that at least one is a cat.

14. You play a game of rolling two dice. You win the game if you roll a 2 before you roll a 6. You continue to roll until either a 2 or 6 appears. What is the probability that you will win the game?

15. The results at a university in Ontario indicate that 30% of students entering the university fail by the end of the first year. If a student survives the first year, he or she will have an 82% chance of graduating. Find the probability that a student entering first year will graduate.

16. A Canadian city has a morning and an evening newspaper. 35% of the city's population read the morning paper, 48% read the evening one, and 15% read both. If a person reads the morning paper, what is the probability that that person also reads the evening paper?

17. You and a friend are tossing coins. Each of you tosses a coin three times. What is the probability that each of you tosses the same number of heads?

18.
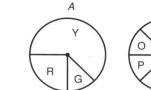

Spinner A on the left is $\frac{1}{4}$ red, $\frac{5}{8}$ yellow and $\frac{1}{8}$ green.

Spinner B on the right is divided into eight equal parts, two of which are colored white, five colored orange and one colored purple. The spinners are fair.
Find the probability of each of the following when both spinners are set in motion.
   a) a yellow on spinner A *and* a purple on spinner B
   b) a yellow on spinner A *or* a purple on spinner B

19. What is the probability of throwing two 5's in a row with a pair of dice?

20. A bag contains white balls, a red ball and blue balls. There are four white balls, each marked differently with a one, two, three, or four. The red ball is marked with a five. There are five blue balls, each marked differently with a six, seven, eight, nine or ten. Three balls are selected at random without replacement. Find the probability that the balls will be of different colors, each marked with an odd number.

21. You perform an experiment in which you toss a coin and then take a single step. If the coin is heads you move one step forward. If the coin is tails you move one step backwards. You toss the coin six times. You always move from your new position. Find the probability of being in each of the following positions after the sixth toss.
   a) at your starting point
   b) two steps from your starting point
   c) four steps from your starting point

CHAPTER THREE

Matrices

Getting to school or work each morning is one of the first tasks you do. If you live too far away to walk or cycle, you have to decide whether to drive a car or motorcycle, or whether to take public transportation. In most cities in Canada the roads are getting more and more congested with traffic each year. The city authorities and various levels of government have to plan many years ahead where and when new roads should be built to accommodate the expected increase in traffic. The transportation authorities also have to decide where and when to increase public transportation facilities. To make better decisions in these areas, planners need to be able to forecast how many people will be driving to work and how many will be going by public transportation in five years' time.

There are many factors that have to be taken into consideration. These include changes in the numbers of people working in the city and changes in people's transportation habits. Gasoline prices can rise, causing some people to switch from driving to work to using transit. The transportation company can increase its fares, causing people to make the change from using transit to driving to work.

A sociologist is studying this trend. She has discovered in her research that, within the next year, 85% of current transit passengers will continue to take public transportation while 15% intend to drive to work. 92% of present drivers will continue to drive to work but 8% plan to switch to public transportation. In a particular city, 42 000 people drive to work each day and 65 000 use transit. If the working population does not increase in size, how many people will be driving to work in three years? How many people will be using public transit in five years? In the long run, will there be so many cars on the road that the city will become one big traffic jam? As you will see in this chapter, these questions can be answered by using matrices.

3.1 Introduction to Matrices

A supplier of personal computers has three warehouse locations in Ontario: Weston, Guelph and Kingston. Supplies of monitors, printers, disk drives and keyboards are maintained in each of these locations. The number of each item at each location can be summarized in a chart.

City	Monitors	Printers	Disk Drives	Keyboards
Weston	24	32	48	27
Guelph	42	38	70	50
Kingston	19	26	34	25

You can record this information in a rectangular array called a **matrix**. A matrix is usually given a capital letter name.

Here, let $A = \begin{bmatrix} 24 & 32 & 48 & 27 \\ 42 & 38 & 70 & 50 \\ 19 & 26 & 34 & 25 \end{bmatrix} \begin{matrix} 1 \\ 2 \\ 3 \end{matrix}$ rows

$\begin{matrix} 1 & 2 & 3 & 4 \end{matrix}$
columns

Each number in this array is an **element** of the matrix. For example, 24 is an element of the matrix A. The **dimension** of a matrix is $m \times n$, where m is the number of **rows** and n is the number of **columns**. Therefore, the dimension of A is 3×4, where 3 is the number of rows and 4 is the number of columns. The dimension of a matrix is also called the order of the matrix.

To identify the rows and columns within a matrix, number the columns from left to right and the rows from top to bottom. In the matrix A above, the second row is 42 38 70 50. These numbers represent the numbers of monitors, printers, disk drives and keyboards, respectively, that are stored in the warehouse in Guelph. The third column of the matrix A is 48
70
34.

These numbers represent the number of disk drives stored in each of the warehouses at Weston, Guelph and Kingston, respectively.

If you want to refer to a particular element in matrix A, for example the number of disk drives in the Guelph warehouse, use notation $a_{23} = 70$. The subscripts 2 and 3 indicate the element is in *row* 2 and *column* 3. Observe that the first subscript refers to the row while the second subscript indicates the column.

The letter a shows that the element belongs to the matrix A.

DEFINITION

Two matrices A and B are equal if they have the same dimensions, $m \times n$, and if $a_{ij} = b_{ij}$ for all i, j, such that $1 \leqslant i \leqslant m$, $1 \leqslant j \leqslant n$, $i, j \in$ N. The elements a_{ij} and b_{ij} are **corresponding elements**.

Example

For the matrices

$$A = \begin{bmatrix} 6 & 1 & 12 \\ 7 & -1 & -12 \\ 8 & 0 & 5 \\ 9 & 4 & 2 \end{bmatrix} \quad B = \begin{bmatrix} 6 & 1 & 12 \\ 7 & -1 & -12 \\ 8 & 0 & 5 \end{bmatrix} \quad C = \begin{bmatrix} -6 & 1 & 12 \\ 7 & -1 & -12 \\ 8 & 0 & 5 \end{bmatrix}$$

a) write the dimension of A.

b) list the elements in the third row of A.

c) list the elements in the third column of A.

d) which element is indicated by b_{23}? by b_{32}?

e) explain why A and B are not equal.

f) explain why B and C are not equal.

Solution

$$A = \begin{bmatrix} 6 & 1 & 12 \\ 7 & -1 & -12 \\ 8 & 0 & 5 \\ 9 & 4 & 2 \end{bmatrix} \begin{matrix} \text{row 1} \\ \text{row 2} \\ \text{row 3} \\ \text{row 4} \end{matrix} \qquad A = \begin{bmatrix} 6 & 1 & 12 \\ 7 & -1 & -12 \\ 8 & 0 & 5 \\ 9 & 4 & 2 \end{bmatrix}$$
$$\text{col 1 ~ col 2 ~ col 3}$$

a) A has 4 rows   and   3 columns
   The dimension of A is 4×3.

b) The elements in the third row of A are $\{8, 0, 5\}$.

c) The elements in the third column of A are $\{12, -12, 5, 2\}$.

d) $B = \begin{bmatrix} 6 & 1 & 12 \\ 7 & -1 & -12 \\ 8 & 0 & 5 \end{bmatrix} \begin{matrix} 1 \\ 2 \\ 3 \end{matrix}$ $B = \begin{bmatrix} 6 & 1 & 12 \\ 7 & -1 & -12 \\ 8 & 0 & 5 \end{bmatrix} \begin{matrix} 1 \\ 2 \\ 3 \end{matrix}$
$$\quad\quad 1 \quad 2 \quad 3 \quad\quad\quad\quad\quad\quad\quad 1 \quad 2 \quad 3$$
$$\quad\quad b_{23} = -12 \quad\quad\quad \text{and} \quad\quad\quad b_{32} = 0$$

e) The dimension of A is 4×3, and B is 3×3. Matrices cannot be equal if their dimensions are not equal.

f) $b_{11} \neq c_{11}$, therefore B and C are not equal. Two matrices B and C are equal only if they are of the same dimension, *and* each element of B equals the corresponding element of C. ■

3.1 Exercises

Use these tables and the corresponding matrices to complete questions 1-5.

Table 1. Manufacturing costs of cars at three plants.

Model	Plant 1	Plant 2	Plant 3
Bug	$4500	$5000	$4750
Dart	$9850	$8900	$10 000
Sportville	$12 000	$11 500	$11 000

$$A = \begin{bmatrix} 4500 & 5000 & 4750 \\ 9850 & 8900 & 10\ 000 \\ 12\ 000 & 11\ 500 & 11\ 000 \end{bmatrix}$$

Table 2. American League baseball standings.
East Division

Teams	Won	Lost	Fraction Won	Runs For	Runs Against
Milwaukee	8	2	0.800	66	40
New York	6	4	0.600	54	51
Toronto	5	4	0.556	37	40
Baltimore	5	5	0.500	46	58
Detroit	4	5	0.444	42	29
Boston	4	5	0.444	37	43
Cleveland	1	8	0.111	45	66

$$B = \begin{bmatrix} 8 & 2 & 0.800 & 66 & 40 \\ 6 & 4 & 0.600 & 54 & 51 \\ 5 & 4 & 0.556 & 37 & 40 \\ 5 & 5 & 0.500 & 46 & 58 \\ 4 & 5 & 0.444 & 42 & 29 \\ 4 & 5 & 0.444 & 37 & 43 \\ 1 & 8 & 0.111 & 45 & 66 \end{bmatrix}$$

Table 3. Sale prices.

Item	Price
Gym shorts	$4.95
Rugger shorts	$6.95
Twill pants	$9.95
Plaid shirts	$9.95

$$C = \begin{bmatrix} 4.95 \\ 6.95 \\ 9.95 \\ 9.95 \end{bmatrix}$$

Table 4. Movie times.

Fantasia	1:30	3:30	5:15	7:30	9:15

$$D = [1:30\ 3:30\ 5:15\ 7:30\ 9:15]$$

1. Copy and complete the table.

Matrix	Number of Rows	Number of Columns	Dimension	Number of Elements
A				
B				
C				
D				

2. Determine which of the matrices fits each description.
   a) a square matrix, dimension $k \times k$
   b) a row matrix, dimension $1 \times k$
   c) a column matrix, dimension $k \times 1$

3. Identify the precise location of each item of information.
   a) the cost of manufacturing Darts at each plant
   b) the price of rugger shorts
   c) the time of the last show of Fantasia
   d) the statistics about the Toronto baseball team

4. Describe how each of the matrices would change under the following conditions.
   a) matrix A if an additional plant making Bugs, Darts, and Sportvilles were opened
   b) matrix B if New York played Cleveland, and New York won by 8 runs to 6
   c) matrix C if all the sale prices were reduced by a dollar, but the store had sold out of plaid shirts
   d) matrix D if the cinema became a four-plex showing three other movies in addition to Fantasia

5. Explain what each element or set of elements represents.
   a) column 2 of matrix A
   b) element b_{34}

c) column 5 of matrix B

d) element c_{31}

e) element d_{12}

f) row 1 of matrix A

6. What are the possible orders of a matrix which has 18 elements?

7. A matrix X has order $m \times n$.
   a) How many elements are there in X?
   b) How many rows are there in X? How many columns?
   c) If you remove one row from X, what is its order?
   d) If you remove one row and one column from X, how many elements will the matrix now contain?

8. If $\begin{bmatrix} x & 3 & -4 \\ 2 & y & z \end{bmatrix} = \begin{bmatrix} 5 & a & b \\ c & 7 & 8 \end{bmatrix}$
   determine the values of a, b, c, x, y, and z.

9. If matrix A is equal to matrix B, what can you say about the orders of these matrices?

10. Matrix A is a matrix of dimension $m \times n$. State any restrictions on the values of m and n if A is a column matrix.

11. Repeat question 10 if A is a row matrix.

12. Repeat question 10 if A is a square matrix.

13. Write a matrix that represents some information that you know.
    Explain what the elements in the first row represent.
    Explain what the elements in the first column represent.

14. A square $n \times n$ matrix M is *symmetric*, if $m_{ij} = m_{ji}$, for values of i and j between 1 and n. Determine which of the following matrices are symmetric.
    a) $A = \begin{bmatrix} 2 & 4 \\ 4 & 3 \end{bmatrix}$
    b) $B = \begin{bmatrix} 1 & 2 & 3 \\ -2 & 0 & -4 \\ -3 & 4 & 5 \end{bmatrix}$

c) $C = \begin{bmatrix} 1 & 2 & 3 \\ 2 & 5 & 4 \\ 3 & 4 & 0 \end{bmatrix}$ e) $E = \begin{bmatrix} 2 & 0 & 3 \\ 0 & 4 & 1 \\ 3 & 1 & 0 \\ 4 & 0 & 1 \end{bmatrix}$

d) $D = \begin{bmatrix} 2 & 3 \\ -3 & 2 \end{bmatrix}$ f) $F = \begin{bmatrix} 1 & 0 & 0 & 0 \\ 0 & 1 & 0 & 0 \\ 0 & 0 & 1 & 0 \\ 0 & 0 & 0 & 1 \end{bmatrix}$

15. The following chart gives the baseball standings for the National League, East Division.

Team	Won	Lost	Fraction won	Runs for	Runs Against
New York	8	2	0.800	46	32
St. Louis	7	2	0.778	36	21
Pittsburgh	4	4	0.500	30	29
Chicago	3	5	0.375	32	26
Montreal	2	5	0.286	23	35
Philadelphia	1	8	0.111	30	56

This data can be represented by the matrix, M, where

$$M = \begin{bmatrix} 8 & 2 & 0.800 & 46 & 32 \\ 7 & 2 & 0.778 & 36 & 21 \\ 4 & 4 & 0.500 & 30 & 29 \\ 3 & 5 & 0.375 & 32 & 26 \\ 2 & 5 & 0.286 & 23 & 35 \\ 2 & 8 & 0.200 & 30 & 54 \end{bmatrix}$$

a) What is the dimension of M?

b) What does the data in row 4 represent?

c) What does the data in column 3 represent?

d) What does element m_{43} represent?

e) In which row and column is the number of runs scored against Chicago?

f) Write the new matrix M if Montreal played St. Louis, and won by 10 runs to 1.

MAKING

Game Theory

Few mathematical theories developed in the twentieth century have generated as much interest or caused as much controversy as the theory of games. The theory of games draws heavily from probability theory and matrix theory, but is a distinct mathematical field of itself.

Some of the seminal ideas of game theory were introduced in the 1920's. The theory itself was first completely presented in the massive work *Theory of Games and Economic Behavior* in 1944. The authors were John von Neumann and Oskar Morgenstern. Morgenstern was an economist and von Neumann was one of the most brilliant mathematicians of the twentieth century.

The theory of games is a mathematical analysis of situations involving the rational behaviour of two or more people whose interests are in conflict. The theory is sometimes thought of as the applied mathematics of economic and social behaviour.

Originally the theory had as many critics as proponents. Economists and social scientists felt that the theory tried to deal with phenomena that were too varied and complex for a single theory. But even in criticizing the theory, these scientists began to use the language and concepts of the theory of games.

John von Neumann

The language of the theory of games is evocative. Without developing the theory here, we can still look at some of concepts.

A *strategy* is a behaviour that one or more of the persons can adopt.

A *two-person*, *zero-sum* game is a situation where the winnings of one person exactly equal the losses of the other. Von Neumann proved the famous minimax theorem for such games. The minimax theorem states that for each player a strategy exists that minimizes the maximum loss the other player can impose on the first.

The study of non-zero-sum games are of importance in situations such as labor disputes where labor and management can choose behaviours which allow both sides to 'win'.

Mixed strategies occur when a player chooses his actions at random, but with certain probabilities that a particular action will be chosen.

The *Shapley-Shubik power index* gives a measure of a stockholder's voting influence when the number of shares held in a company is the only consideration.

Does anyone take game theory seriously in practical considerations? The yacht *Stars and Stripes*, winner of the America's Cup sailing competition in 1987, was designed partially using the results of game theory.

3.2   Addition and Scalar Multiplication of Matrices

In the first section of this chapter you met the matrix A which represented the numbers of computer components that were stored at three warehouses.

City	Monitors	Printers	Disk Drives	Keyboards
Weston	24	32	48	27
Guelph	42	38	70	50
Kingston	19	26	34	25

$$A = \begin{bmatrix} 24 & 32 & 48 & 27 \\ 42 & 38 & 70 & 50 \\ 19 & 26 & 34 & 25 \end{bmatrix}$$

If the manufacturer of the components makes a delivery of components to each of the warehouses, the additional stock is given in the chart below.

City	Monitors	Printers	Disk Drives	Keyboards
Weston	10	12	25	15
Guelph	20	24	44	25
Kingston	12	15	28	10

This can be represented by the matrix Q, where

$$Q = \begin{bmatrix} 10 & 12 & 25 & 15 \\ 20 & 24 & 44 & 25 \\ 12 & 15 & 28 & 10 \end{bmatrix}$$

The updated inventory in each warehouse can be found by adding corresponding elements of the matrices A and Q to form a new matrix, T

$$A + Q = \begin{bmatrix} 24 + 10 & 32 + 12 & 48 + 25 & 27 + 15 \\ 42 + 20 & 38 + 24 & 70 + 44 & 50 + 25 \\ 19 + 12 & 26 + 15 & 34 + 28 & 25 + 10 \end{bmatrix}$$

$$T = \begin{bmatrix} 34 & 44 & 73 & 42 \\ 62 & 62 & 114 & 75 \\ 31 & 41 & 62 & 35 \end{bmatrix}$$

If stock is now taken out of the warehouses for delivery to stores, the quantities removed can be represented by another 3×4 matrix, D.

$$D = \begin{bmatrix} 14 & 16 & 30 & 12 \\ 15 & 20 & 32 & 10 \\ 10 & 8 & 24 & 12 \end{bmatrix}$$

The inventory remaining in the warehouse can be found by subtracting corresponding elements of matrix D from those of matrix T to form another matrix, S.

$$T - D = \begin{bmatrix} 34 - 14 & 42 - 16 & 73 - 30 & 42 - 12 \\ 62 - 15 & 62 - 20 & 114 - 32 & 75 - 10 \\ 31 - 10 & 41 - 8 & 62 - 24 & 35 - 12 \end{bmatrix}$$

$$S = \begin{bmatrix} 20 & 26 & 43 & 30 \\ 47 & 42 & 82 & 65 \\ 21 & 33 & 38 & 23 \end{bmatrix}$$

S is also a 3×4 matrix.

DEFINITION

Two matrices are added by adding their corresponding elements. Two matrices are subtracted by subtracting their corresponding elements.

PROPERTY

Two matrices A and B can be added or subtracted only if the dimension of A equals that of B.

Suppose that the management of the company foresees a great demand for personal computers in the near future and instructs that the inventory of each component in each warehouse be doubled. If the inventory in each warehouse is given by matrix S, then the new inventory will be given by adding another matrix S to the original matrix S.

$$S + S = \begin{bmatrix} 20 & 26 & 43 & 30 \\ 47 & 42 & 82 & 65 \\ 21 & 33 & 38 & 23 \end{bmatrix} + \begin{bmatrix} 20 & 26 & 43 & 30 \\ 47 & 42 & 82 & 65 \\ 21 & 33 & 38 & 23 \end{bmatrix}$$

$$= \begin{bmatrix} 40 & 52 & 86 & 60 \\ 94 & 84 & 164 & 130 \\ 42 & 66 & 76 & 46 \end{bmatrix}$$

This matrix is $2S$. Obviously, the matrix $2S$ can also be formed by multiplying each element of matrix S by 2.

$$2S = 2 \begin{bmatrix} 20 & 26 & 43 & 30 \\ 47 & 42 & 82 & 65 \\ 21 & 33 & 38 & 23 \end{bmatrix}$$

$$= \begin{bmatrix} 2 \times 20 & 2 \times 26 & 2 \times 43 & 2 \times 30 \\ 2 \times 47 & 2 \times 42 & 2 \times 82 & 2 \times 65 \\ 2 \times 21 & 2 \times 33 & 2 \times 38 & 2 \times 23 \end{bmatrix}$$

$$= \begin{bmatrix} 40 & 52 & 86 & 60 \\ 94 & 84 & 164 & 130 \\ 42 & 66 & 76 & 46 \end{bmatrix}$$

DEFINITION

Multiplying each element of a matrix by the same real number is called **scalar multiplication** of a matrix. The real number is called a **scalar**.

Example   Given

$$A = \begin{bmatrix} 1 & 3 \\ 2 & -4 \end{bmatrix}$$

$$B = \begin{bmatrix} 2 & 0 & 3 \\ 1 & 5 & 9 \end{bmatrix}$$

$$C = \begin{bmatrix} 4 & 7 \\ -3 & 2 \end{bmatrix}$$

determine the following, if possible.

a) $A + B$ c) $5B$

b) $A - C$ d) $2A + 3C$

Solution   a) Since A is a 2×2 and B is a 2×3 matrix, it is impossible to form $A + B$ because A and B do not have the same dimensions.

b) $A - C$
$$= \begin{bmatrix} 1 & 3 \\ 2 & -4 \end{bmatrix} - \begin{bmatrix} 4 & 7 \\ -3 & 2 \end{bmatrix}$$
$$= \begin{bmatrix} 1 - 4 & 3 - 7 \\ 2 - (-3) & -4 - 2 \end{bmatrix}$$
$$= \begin{bmatrix} -3 & -4 \\ 5 & -6 \end{bmatrix}$$

c) $5B$
$$= 5 \begin{bmatrix} 2 & 0 & 3 \\ 1 & 5 & 9 \end{bmatrix}$$
$$= \begin{bmatrix} 5 \times 2 & 5 \times 0 & 5 \times 3 \\ 5 \times 1 & 5 \times 5 & 5 \times 9 \end{bmatrix}$$
$$= \begin{bmatrix} 10 & 0 & 15 \\ 5 & 25 & 45 \end{bmatrix}$$

d) $2A + 3C = 2 \begin{bmatrix} 1 & 3 \\ 2 & -4 \end{bmatrix} + 3 \begin{bmatrix} 4 & 7 \\ -3 & 2 \end{bmatrix}$
$$= \begin{bmatrix} 2 \times 1 & 2 \times 3 \\ 2 \times 2 & 2 \times (-4) \end{bmatrix} + \begin{bmatrix} 3 \times 4 & 3 \times 7 \\ 3 \times (-3) & 3 \times 2 \end{bmatrix}$$
$$= \begin{bmatrix} 2 \times 1 + 3 \times 4 & 2 \times 3 + 3 \times 7 \\ 2 \times 2 + 3 \times (-3) & 2 \times (-4) + 3 \times 2 \end{bmatrix}$$
$$= \begin{bmatrix} 14 & 27 \\ -5 & -2 \end{bmatrix}$$

3.2 Exercises

1. Given

$$A = \begin{bmatrix} 12 & 15 & 10 \\ 11 & 20 & 14 \end{bmatrix}$$

$$B = \begin{bmatrix} -7 & -3 & 5 \\ 8 & 4 & 2 \end{bmatrix}$$

$$C = \begin{bmatrix} 2 & 4 \\ 3 & 8 \\ 6 & 7 \end{bmatrix}$$

determine the following, if possible.

a) $A + B$ d) $4C$

b) $A - B$ e) $3A - 5B$

c) $A + C$ f) $2A + 3B$

2. Given

$$M = \begin{bmatrix} 2 & 4 \\ -3 & 7 \end{bmatrix}$$

$$N = \begin{bmatrix} 5 & 11 \\ 0 & -3 \end{bmatrix}$$

$$P = \begin{bmatrix} 20 \\ 49 \\ -12 \end{bmatrix}$$

$$Q = \begin{bmatrix} 15 \\ -20 \\ 34 \end{bmatrix}$$

form the following, if possible.

a) $3M$ e) $\dfrac{1}{2}Q$

b) $2N$ f) $5P + \dfrac{1}{2}Q$

c) $3M - 2N$

d) $5P$ g) $M - P$

3. Given

$$A = \begin{bmatrix} -1 & 3 & 5 \\ 8 & 0 & -2 \end{bmatrix}$$

$$B = \begin{bmatrix} 0 & 11 \\ 1 & 3 \end{bmatrix}$$

$$C = \begin{bmatrix} 2 & 5 \\ 3 & 4 \end{bmatrix}$$

form the following, if possible.

a) $B - C$ c) $A + B$

b) $4A$ d) $4B - 3C$

4. Given

$F = [6 \quad 8 \quad 10]$ and

$$G = \begin{bmatrix} 1 \\ 0.1 \\ 1.1 \end{bmatrix}$$

find the following.

a) $\dfrac{1}{2}F$ c) $0.1F$

b) $10G$ d) $0.1G$

5. The production of Bugs, Darts, and Sportvilles in three plants for the first six months of this year are given by the chart below.

Car Models	Plant 1	Plant 2	Plant 3
Bugs	200	250	300
Darts	150	175	200
Sportvilles	40	20	30

The production figures for the last six months of this year are given in the chart below.

Car Models	Plant 1	Plant 2	Plant 3
Bugs	180	200	250
Darts	120	150	185
Sportvilles	60	32	40

Represent the production figures for the whole of this year by means of a suitable matrix.

6. The management of the automobile company producing Bugs, Darts, and Sportvilles (see question 5) decides to increase production in the first six months of next year by 10% from the figures for the first six months of this year. Express the production figures for the first six months of the next year by a suitable matrix. Round off each element to the nearest whole number.

7. The cost of producing the cars referred to in questions 5 and 6 are given by the matrix A.

$$A = \begin{bmatrix} 4500 & 5000 & 4750 \\ 9850 & 8900 & 10\,000 \\ 12\,000 & 11\,500 & 11\,000 \end{bmatrix}$$

A new productivity deal with the union results in a 20% reduction in costs; express the new production costs by means of a suitable matrix.

8. The statistics of the CFL Eastern Division at the beginning of the season are given by the chart below.

City of Team	Games Played	Games Won	Games Lost	Games Tied	Points For	Points Against
Toronto	1	1	0	0	21	20
Ottawa	1	1	0	0	20	11
Winnipeg	1	0	1	0	11	20
Hamilton	1	0	1	0	20	21

    a) Form a matrix, M, to represent the above statistics.

    b) Winnipeg plays Ottawa and ties the game 32–32; Toronto plays Hamilton and loses 12–19. Form a matrix, B, to represent the statistics for these two new games only.

    c) What matrix should be formed to represent the standings of the teams after the games in b)? Form this matrix.

9. If $\begin{bmatrix} 2 & 3 & -7 \\ c & 7 & d \end{bmatrix} + 5\begin{bmatrix} 4 & a & b \\ 2 & f & 5 \end{bmatrix} = \begin{bmatrix} p & 18 & 18 \\ 7 & 17 & 0 \end{bmatrix}$

determine a, b, c, d, f and p.

10. Given

$$A = \begin{bmatrix} 1 & -2 \\ -3 & 4 \end{bmatrix}$$

$$B = \begin{bmatrix} 0 & 1 \\ 2 & 3 \end{bmatrix}$$

show that

    a) $2A + 3A = 5A$

    b) $2(3A) = 6A$

    c) $A + B = B + A$

    d) $2(A + B) = 2A + 2B$

11. The square matrix A is "magic": the sum of the numbers in each row, column and diagonal is 15.

$$A = \begin{bmatrix} 4 & 9 & 2 \\ 3 & 5 & 7 \\ 8 & 1 & 6 \end{bmatrix}$$

    a) Calculate

$$A + k\begin{bmatrix} 1 & 1 & 1 \\ 1 & 1 & 1 \\ 1 & 1 & 1 \end{bmatrix}$$

       for $k = 3$, $k = 2$ and $k = 7$.

    b) Explain why the three matrices in part a) are also "magic".

    c) Choose three values for the scalar d. Calculate the sum

$$A + d\begin{bmatrix} 0 & 1 & -1 \\ -1 & 0 & 1 \\ 1 & -1 & 0 \end{bmatrix}$$

       for each value of d.

    d) Explain why the magic sum in c) is the same as the original magic sum.

    e) Find another matrix M which gives the same magic sum as matrix A when you form the sum $A + kM$, for any scalar k.

12. Determine $a, b,$ and c if

$$a\begin{bmatrix} 1 & 1 & 1 \\ 1 & 1 & 1 \\ 1 & 1 & 1 \end{bmatrix} + c\begin{bmatrix} -1 & 1 & 0 \\ 1 & 0 & 1 \\ 0 & -1 & 1 \end{bmatrix}$$
$$+ b\begin{bmatrix} 0 & 1 & -1 \\ -1 & 0 & 1 \\ 1 & -1 & 0 \end{bmatrix} = \begin{bmatrix} 8 & 3 & 4 \\ 1 & 5 & 3 \\ 6 & 7 & 2 \end{bmatrix}$$

13. Given

$$P = \begin{bmatrix} 7 & 4 \\ -1 & 2 \end{bmatrix} \qquad Q = \begin{bmatrix} -6 & -9 \\ 1 & 2 \end{bmatrix}$$

find X where $P + X = Q$.

14. Let $Z_{m \times n}$ be an $m \times n$ matrix, where each element is zero.

    a) If $A = \begin{bmatrix} a & b & c \\ d & e & f \end{bmatrix}$ find the additive inverse, $-A$, of A such that $A + (-A) = Z_{2 \times 3}$.

    b) If B is 4×5, what is $B + Z_{4 \times 5}$?

    c) If $P + Q = R$, show that $P = R + (-Q)$.

3.3 Multiplication of Matrices

Kirk has to go to the store on his way home from school, to help his mother. On Monday he bought one dozen eggs, two loaves of whole wheat bread and four litres of milk. This data can be expressed in the form of a matrix A, where

$$A = [1 \quad 2 \quad 4].$$

A is a row matrix with the first element representing the quantity of eggs, the second element representing the quantity of bread and the third element representing the quantity of milk.

If eggs cost \$1.25/dozen, bread \$1.50/loaf and milk \$1.00/L, the prices of these items can be represented by a column matrix C, where

$$C = \begin{bmatrix} 1.25 \\ 1.50 \\ 1.00 \end{bmatrix}$$

To calculate the amount of money that Kirk spent, you need to multiply the quantity of each item bought by the corresponding price, and then add the products together.

Total spent = $\$(1 \times 1.25 + 2 \times 1.50 + 4 \times 1.00)$
             = \$8.25

In terms of the matrices A and C
total spent in dollars = AC

$$= [1 \quad 2 \quad 4] \begin{bmatrix} 1.25 \\ 1.50 \\ 1.00 \end{bmatrix}$$

In order to multiply a row matrix such as A by a column matrix such as C, first check that matrix A has the same number of elements in its row as matrix C has in its column.
Multiply the first elements of A and C, the second elements of A and C, and so on.
Then add these products.

$$AC = [1 \times 1.25 + 2 \times 1.50 + 4 \times 1.00]$$
$$= [8.25]$$

The result is the 1×1 matrix $AC = [8.25]$.

On Wednesday, Kirk bought three loaves of bread and six litres of milk. On Friday he bought two dozen eggs, five loaves of bread and eight litres of milk.

The shopping Kirk did on the three days, Monday, Wednesday and Friday can be represented by the matrix, B, below.

$$B = \begin{bmatrix} 1 & 2 & 4 \\ 0 & 3 & 6 \\ 2 & 5 & 8 \end{bmatrix} \begin{matrix} \text{Monday} \\ \text{Wednesday} \\ \text{Friday} \end{matrix}$$
$$\begin{matrix} \downarrow & \downarrow & \downarrow \\ E & B & M \end{matrix}$$

To calculate the amount spent each day, you multiply matrix B by matrix C as shown below.

Total spent each day = BC
in dollars

$$= \begin{bmatrix} 1 & 2 & 4 \\ 0 & 3 & 6 \\ 2 & 5 & 8 \end{bmatrix} \begin{bmatrix} 1.25 \\ 1.50 \\ 1.00 \end{bmatrix}$$

$$= \begin{bmatrix} 1 \times 1.25 + 2 \times 1.50 + 4 \times 1.00 \\ 0 \times 1.25 + 3 \times 1.50 + 6 \times 1.00 \\ 2 \times 1.25 + 5 \times 1.50 + 8 \times 1.00 \end{bmatrix} \begin{matrix} \text{Monday} \\ \text{Wednesday} \\ \text{Friday} \end{matrix}$$

$$= \begin{bmatrix} 1.25 + 3.00 + 4.00 \\ 0 \quad + 4.50 + 6.00 \\ 2.50 + 7.50 + 8.00 \end{bmatrix}$$

$$= \begin{bmatrix} 8.25 \\ 10.50 \\ 18.00 \end{bmatrix}$$

Thus Kirk spent $8.25 on Monday, $10.50 on Wednesday and $18.00 on Friday.

In matrix multiplication the elements of *a row from the matrix on the left* are multiplied by the matching elements of *a column from the matrix on the right*. The products thus formed are *added* to form an element of the product matrix.

If Kirk had shopped at a discount store he could have obtained the eggs for $1.10/dozen, the bread for $0.99/loaf and the milk for $0.78/L. You can combine these prices with the original prices in matrix C to form a new matrix, D, shown below.

$$D = \begin{bmatrix} 1.25 & 1.10 \\ 1.50 & 0.99 \\ 1.00 & 0.78 \end{bmatrix}$$

If you multiply matrix D by matrix B in a similar way, you will obtain a 3×2 matrix which gives you the cost of the three days shopping at both stores.

$$\begin{bmatrix} 1 & 2 & 4 \\ 0 & 3 & 6 \\ 2 & 5 & 8 \end{bmatrix} \begin{bmatrix} 1.25 & 1.10 \\ 1.50 & 0.99 \\ 1.00 & 0.78 \end{bmatrix}$$

$$= \begin{bmatrix} 1 \times 1.25 + 2 \times 1.50 + 4 \times 1.00 & 1 \times 1.10 + 2 \times 0.99 + 4 \times 0.78 \\ 0 \times 1.25 + 3 \times 1.50 + 6 \times 1.00 & 0 \times 1.10 + 3 \times 0.99 + 6 \times 0.78 \\ 2 \times 1.25 + 5 \times 1.50 + 8 \times 1.00 & 2 \times 1.10 + 5 \times 0.99 + 8 \times 0.78 \end{bmatrix}$$

$$= \begin{bmatrix} 8.25 & 6.20 \\ 10.50 & 7.65 \\ 18.00 & 13.39 \end{bmatrix} \begin{matrix} \text{Monday} \\ \text{Wednesday} \\ \text{Friday} \end{matrix}$$

Cost at   Cost at
regular   discount
store   store

Notice how the product matrix was formed. To create, for example, the element in the first row and the second column, you would: multiply the first element of row one of B by the first element of column two of D, the second element of row one in B by the second element of column two in D, and so on. Then, add all of these products.

You have seen three matrix multiplications in this section.

$$AC = \begin{bmatrix} 1 & 2 & 4 \end{bmatrix} \begin{bmatrix} 1.25 \\ 1.50 \\ 1.00 \end{bmatrix} = \begin{bmatrix} 8.25 \end{bmatrix}$$

$$BC = \begin{bmatrix} 1 & 2 & 4 \\ 0 & 3 & 6 \\ 2 & 5 & 8 \end{bmatrix} \begin{bmatrix} 1.25 \\ 1.50 \\ 1.00 \end{bmatrix} = \begin{bmatrix} 8.25 \\ 10.50 \\ 18.00 \end{bmatrix}$$

$$BD = \begin{bmatrix} 1 & 2 & 4 \\ 0 & 3 & 6 \\ 2 & 5 & 8 \end{bmatrix} \begin{bmatrix} 1.25 & 1.10 \\ 1.50 & 0.99 \\ 1.00 & 0.78 \end{bmatrix} = \begin{bmatrix} 8.25 & 6.20 \\ 10.50 & 7.65 \\ 18.00 & 13.39 \end{bmatrix}$$

The dimensions of each of the matrices in these products are as follows:

$$\begin{matrix} A & C & = & AC \\ (1 \times 3) & (3 \times 1) & & (1 \times 1) \\ B & C & = & BC \\ (3 \times 3) & (3 \times 1) & & (3 \times 1) \\ B & D & = & BD \\ (3 \times 3) & (3 \times 2) & & (3 \times 2) \end{matrix}$$

In general, you can multiply two matrices X and Y, with X on the left of Y, only if their dimensions satisfy the condition: the number of columns in X must equal the number of rows in Y.

$$\begin{array}{ccc} X & Y & = & Z \\ (p \times q) & (q \times r) & & (p \times r) \end{array}$$

In other words, if X has the dimension $p \times q$ then Y must have the dimension $q \times r$.
The resulting product matrix Z, will be of the dimension $p \times r$.

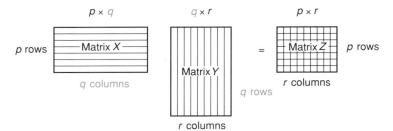

To form the element z_{ij} of the product matrix $Z = XY$, you multiply the element x_{ik} of the ith row of the $p \times q$ matrix X by the matching element y_{kj} of the $q \times r$ matrix Y for $k = 1$ to $k = q$. Add the products so formed.

$$\begin{bmatrix} x_{11} & x_{12} \dots x_{1j} \dots x_{1q} \\ x_{21} & x_{22} \dots x_{2j} \dots x_{2q} \\ \vdots & \vdots \quad \vdots \quad \vdots \\ x_{i1} & x_{i2} \dots x_{ij} \dots x_{iq} \\ \vdots & \vdots \quad \vdots \quad \vdots \\ x_{p1} & x_{p2} \dots x_{pj} \dots x_{pq} \end{bmatrix} \begin{bmatrix} y_{11} & y_{12} \dots y_{1j} \dots y_{1r} \\ y_{21} & y_{22} \dots y_{2j} \dots y_{2r} \\ \vdots & \vdots \quad \vdots \quad \vdots \\ y_{i1} & y_{i2} \dots y_{ij} \dots y_{ir} \\ \vdots & \vdots \quad \vdots \quad \vdots \\ y_{q1} & y_{q2} \dots y_{qj} \dots y_{qr} \end{bmatrix} = \begin{bmatrix} z_{11} & z_{12} \dots z_{1j} \dots z_{1r} \\ z_{21} & z_{22} \dots z_{2j} \dots z_{2r} \\ \vdots & \vdots \quad \vdots \quad \vdots \\ z_{i1} & z_{i2} \dots z_{ij} \dots z_{ir} \\ \vdots & \vdots \quad \vdots \quad \vdots \\ z_{p1} & z_{p2} \dots z_{pj} \dots z_{pr} \end{bmatrix}$$

Example

If $A = \begin{bmatrix} 2 \\ 4 \\ 6 \end{bmatrix}$, $B = \begin{bmatrix} 0 & 5 & 7 \\ 3 & -1 & 8 \end{bmatrix}$, $C = \begin{bmatrix} -3 & 1 \\ -4 & 10 \end{bmatrix}$, and $I = \begin{bmatrix} 1 & 0 \\ 0 & 1 \end{bmatrix}$

evaluate the following products, if possible. State the dimension of each matrix in the product and the dimension of the resulting matrix.

a) BA **b)** CB **c)** AB **d)** C^2 **e)** B^2 **f)** CI **g)** IC

Solution

a) Since B is a 2×3 matrix and A is a 3×1 matrix, it is possible to form the product BA. The dimension of BA will be 2×1.

$$\begin{aligned} BA &= \begin{bmatrix} 0 & 5 & 7 \\ 3 & -1 & 8 \end{bmatrix} \begin{bmatrix} 2 \\ 4 \\ 6 \end{bmatrix} \\ &= \begin{bmatrix} 0 \times 2 + & 5 \times 4 + 7 \times 6 \\ 3 \times 2 + (-1) \times 4 + 8 \times 6 \end{bmatrix} \\ &= \begin{bmatrix} 62 \\ 50 \end{bmatrix} \end{aligned}$$

b) C is a 2 × 2 matrix and B is a 2 × 3 matrix. Therefore, the product CB can be formed and will have the dimension 2 × 3.

$$CB = \begin{bmatrix} -3 & 1 \\ -4 & 10 \end{bmatrix} \begin{bmatrix} 0 & 5 & 7 \\ 3 & -1 & 8 \end{bmatrix}$$

$$= \begin{bmatrix} (-3) \times 0 + 1 \times 3 & (-3) \times 5 + 1 \times (-1) & (-3) \times 7 + 1 \times 8 \\ (-4) \times 0 + 10 \times 3 & (-4) \times 5 + 10 \times (-1) & (-4) \times 7 + 10 \times 8 \end{bmatrix}$$

$$= \begin{bmatrix} 3 & -16 & -13 \\ 30 & -30 & 52 \end{bmatrix}$$

c) A is a 3 × 1 matrix with one column and B is a 2 × 3 matrix with two rows. Therefore, it is not possible to form a product AB, since the number of columns in A is not equal to the number of rows in B.

Try it.
$$\begin{bmatrix} 2 \\ 4 \\ 6 \end{bmatrix} \begin{bmatrix} 0 & 5 & 7 \\ 3 & -1 & 8 \end{bmatrix} = \begin{bmatrix} 2 \times 0 + ? \times 3 \\ 4 \times 5 + ? \times (-1) \\ 6 \times 7 + ? \times 8 \end{bmatrix} \quad \text{Cannot be done.}$$

d) C is a 2 × 2 matrix, so product CC can be formed and will have the dimension 2 × 2.

$$C^2 = \begin{bmatrix} -3 & 1 \\ -4 & 10 \end{bmatrix} \begin{bmatrix} -3 & 1 \\ -4 & 10 \end{bmatrix}$$

$$= \begin{bmatrix} (-3) \times (-3) + 1 \times (-4) & (-3) \times 1 + 1 \times 10 \\ (-4) \times (-3) + 10 \times (-4) & (-4) \times 1 + 10 \times 10 \end{bmatrix}$$

$$= \begin{bmatrix} 5 & 7 \\ -28 & 96 \end{bmatrix}$$

e) B is a 2 × 3 matrix, therefore product BB cannot be formed. The number of columns in B is not the same as the number of rows in B. You will note that only square matrices can be squared, that is, multiplied by themselves.

f) $CI = \begin{bmatrix} -3 & 1 \\ -4 & 10 \end{bmatrix} \begin{bmatrix} 1 & 0 \\ 0 & 1 \end{bmatrix}$

$$= \begin{bmatrix} (-3) \times 1 + 1 \times 0 & (-3) \times 0 + 1 \times 1 \\ (-4) \times 1 + 10 \times 0 & (-4) \times 0 + 10 \times 1 \end{bmatrix}$$

$$= \begin{bmatrix} -3 & 1 \\ -4 & 10 \end{bmatrix}$$

g) $IC = \begin{bmatrix} 1 & 0 \\ 0 & 1 \end{bmatrix} \begin{bmatrix} -3 & 1 \\ -4 & 10 \end{bmatrix}$

$$= \begin{bmatrix} 1 \times (-3) + 0 \times (-4) & 1 \times 1 + 0 \times 10 \\ 0 \times (-3) + 1 \times (-4) & 0 \times 1 + 1 \times 10 \end{bmatrix}$$

$$= \begin{bmatrix} -3 & 1 \\ -4 & 10 \end{bmatrix}$$

Note that in parts f) and g), $CI = IC = C$.

$I = \begin{bmatrix} 1 & 0 \\ 0 & 1 \end{bmatrix}$ is the 2 × 2 **identity matrix**.

DEFINITION

An identity matrix I is a square matrix, with ones in the main diagonal and zeros elsewhere. If I is of order $n \times n$, and A is any $n \times n$ matrix, then $AI = IA = A$.

3.3 Exercises

1. The matrices P and Q are multiplied to form the matrix R where $PQ = R$. If the dimensions of P, Q and R are $4 \times a$, $3 \times b$ and $c \times 7$, respectively, determine a, b and c.

2. If $M = \begin{bmatrix} 3 & 5 & 6 \\ 0 & 1 & 2 \end{bmatrix}$, $P = \begin{bmatrix} 12 & 10 \\ 8 & 7 \end{bmatrix}$

   and $S = \begin{bmatrix} 11 \\ 4 \\ -3 \end{bmatrix}$

   determine the following products, if possible. State the dimension of each matrix in the product and the dimension of the resulting matrix.
   a) PM c) SM
   b) MS d) P^2 where $P^2 = PP$

3. a) If $T = \begin{bmatrix} 3 & -7 \\ 5 & 2 \end{bmatrix}$ and $S = \begin{bmatrix} 4 & -8 \\ 1 & 6 \end{bmatrix}$
      determine the products TS and ST.
   b) Does ST equal TS?

4. a) IF $K = \begin{bmatrix} 2 & 5 \\ 3 & 4 \end{bmatrix}$ and $I = \begin{bmatrix} 1 & 0 \\ 0 & 1 \end{bmatrix}$

      determine the products KI and IK.
   b) What do you notice about the products KI and IK and the matrix K?
   c) Choose any other 2×2 matrix, Z. Determine the products ZI and IZ.

5. a) If $I = \begin{bmatrix} 1 & 0 & 0 \\ 0 & 1 & 0 \\ 0 & 0 & 1 \end{bmatrix}$ and

      $A = \begin{bmatrix} 3 & 6 & 2 \\ 4 & 1 & 0 \\ -6 & 2 & 5 \end{bmatrix}$

      determine IA and AI.
   b) What do you notice about the products AI and IA and the matrix A in part a)? I is the 3×3 identity matrix.
   c) Choose any other 3×3 matrix Q. Determine the products QI and IQ.

6. a) Write the 4×4 identity matrix.
   b) Multiply the 4×4 identity matrix on the left and right by any other 4×4 matrix. What do you notice about your results?

7. If both AB and BA can be formed what can you say about the orders of A and B?

8. If S^2 can be formed, what can you say about the order of the matrix S?

9. For the matrix $S = \begin{bmatrix} 2 & 5 \\ 1 & 3 \end{bmatrix}$
   form the products S^2, S^3 and S^4.

10. The following table shows the medal standings of four school teams participating in a track meet.

Team	Gold	Silver	Bronze
Kingswood	16	25	18
Silversprings	14	20	26
St. Anne's	13	18	10
P.K. Fletch	11	14	16

   A gold medal is worth three points.
   A silver medal is worth two points.
   A bronze medal is worth one point.
   Use matrix multiplication to calculate each team's total point count.

11. The production costs of manufacturing three stereo components by four different companies are given in the chart below.

Company	Speakers	Turntables	Amplifers
KYZ Company	$57.50	$40.00	$65.75
Matazuhi	$45.60	$45.00	$67.95
Cross-Smith	$52.80	$43.50	$62.15
Able-Ready	$55.00	$38.95	$70.25

   Use matrix multiplication to determine the cost of manufacturing twenty-five speakers, thirty turntables and thirty-six amplifiers by each of the companies.

12. Use the production cost data from question 11 and matrix multiplication to determine the cost of manufacturing one hundred speakers, ninety turntables and eighty-five amplifiers by each of the manufacturers.

13. In 3.1 Exercises, the costs of producing three types of automobile, Bugs, Darts and Sportvilles, at three plants were given in a chart.

Car Model	Plant 1	Plant 2	Plant 3
Bug	$4500	$5000	$4750
Dart	$9850	$8900	$10 000
Sportville	$12 000	$11 500	$11 000

Multiply the matrices below. What does the resulting product matrix mean?

$$\begin{bmatrix} 4\ 500 & 5\ 000 & 4\ 750 \\ 9\ 850 & 8\ 900 & 10\ 000 \\ 12\ 000 & 11\ 500 & 11\ 000 \end{bmatrix} \begin{bmatrix} 20 \\ 30 \\ 10 \end{bmatrix}$$

14. Use the matrices

$$X = \begin{bmatrix} 1 & 0 \\ 3 & 4 \end{bmatrix} \text{ and } Y = \begin{bmatrix} 0 & 1 \\ 3 & 5 \end{bmatrix}$$

to determine whether the following statements are true for matrices.
a) $X^2 - Y^2 = (X - Y)(X + Y)$
b) $(X + Y)^2 = X^2 + 2XY + Y^2$
c) $(X - Y)^2 = X^2 - 2XY + Y^2$

15. Choose any three square matrices A, B and C and use them to show that $(AB)C = A(BC)$.

16. The message HELP can be represented by the numbers 8 5 12 16. These numbers can be arranged as a matrix

$$M = \begin{bmatrix} 8 & 5 \\ 12 & 16 \end{bmatrix}.$$

This matrix M can be encoded by multiplying M on the left by the matrix E, where

$$E = \begin{bmatrix} 4 & -1 \\ -7 & 2 \end{bmatrix}$$

Evaluate the product $C = EM$.

17. Multiply the matrix C (formed in question 16) on the left by the matrix.

$$D = \begin{bmatrix} 2 & 1 \\ 7 & 4 \end{bmatrix}$$

18. In the introduction to this chapter, you read about a city in which 65 000 people took public transit to work and 42 000 people drove. This information can be represented by the matrix

$$P = \begin{bmatrix} 65\ 000 \\ 42\ 000 \end{bmatrix}.$$

A survey showed that 85% of the transit passengers were intending to continue travelling by transit and 15% were going to start driving to work. 92% of the car drivers were going to continue to drive to work and 8% were going to switch. This information can be represented by the matrix T, where

$$T = \begin{bmatrix} 0.85 & 0.08 \\ 0.15 & 0.92 \end{bmatrix}.$$

a) Evaluate the matrix product TP.
b) What does the product matrix TP represent?

19. The matrix

$$I = \begin{bmatrix} 1 & 0 \\ 0 & 1 \end{bmatrix}$$

is the 2×2 identity matrix. Two 2×2 matrices, A and B, that satisfy the condition $AB = I$ are called **inverse matrices**. Determine which of the following pairs of matrices are inverse matrices.

a) $X = \begin{bmatrix} 3 & 5 \\ 1 & 2 \end{bmatrix}$ $Y = \begin{bmatrix} 2 & -5 \\ -1 & 3 \end{bmatrix}$

b) $P = \begin{bmatrix} 4 & 3 \\ 1 & 2 \end{bmatrix}$ $Q = \begin{bmatrix} 2 & -3 \\ -1 & 4 \end{bmatrix}.$

20. For most pairs of square matrices A and B, $AB \neq BA$. For each pair of matrices in question 19, prove that $AB = BA$. Matrices that have this property are called **commutative matrices**.

In Search of a Computer Program to Multiply Matrices

Multiplying matrices of any order larger than 2×2 is a tedious and error-prone task.

To form the matrix product AB the following steps are necessary.

1. Input the dimensions of A and B.
2. Check that the matrices can be multiplied.
3. Input the values of the elements of A and B.
4. To form the ijth term of the product matrix, multiply the elements of the ith row of A by the matching elements of the jth column of B and sum these products.
5. Repeat step 4 for all rows i of A and all columns j of B.
6. Print the product matrix.

The following is a computer program in BASIC that will perform matrix multiplication.

```
100   REM PROGRAM TO MULTIPLY MATRICES
110   PRINT "STATE THE DIMENSION OF MATRIX A"
120   INPUT M,N
130   PRINT "STATE THE DIMENSIONS OF MATRIX B"
140   INPUT P,Q
150   IF N = P THEN GOSUB 200
160   IF N > < P THEN GOSUB 600
170   STOP
180   :
200   REM SUBROUTINE TO MULTIPLY MATRICES A AND B
210   FOR I = 1 TO M
220   : FOR J = 1 TO N
230   : : PRINT "TYPE IN NEXT ELEMENT OF MATRIX A "
240   : : INPUT A(I,J)
250   : NEXT J
260   NEXT I
270   :
280   FOR I = 1 TO P
290   : FOR J = 1 TO Q
300   : : PRINT "TYPE IN THE NEXT ELEMENT OF MATRIX B"
310   : : INPUT B(I,J)
320   : NEXT J
330   NEXT I
340   :
350   FOR K = 1 TO Q
360   : FOR I = 1 TO M
370   : : FOR J = 1 TO P
380   : : : LET C(I,K) = C(I,K) + A(I,J) * B(J,K)
390   : : NEXT J
400   : NEXT I
```

```
410   NEXT K
420   :
430   PRINT "MATRIX A X MATRIX B = "
440   FOR I = 1 TO M
450   :FOR J = 1 TO Q
460   ::PRINT C(I, J) "    ";
470   :NEXT J
480   :PRINT
490   NEXT I
500   RETURN
510   :
600   REM SUBROUTINE IF N><P
610   PRINT "THE MATRICES CANNOT BE MULTIPLIED"
620   RETURN
630   END
```

1. What do M and N represent in line 120?
2. What do P and Q represent in line 140?
3. What does $A(I, J)$ represent in line 240?
4. What does $B(I, J)$ represent in line 310?
5. Which lines of the program actually calculate the elements of the product matrix?

Some calculators can perform matrix operations. Look up the instructions to your calculator and see if it has matrix operations. If you have access to a computer or a programmable calculator, use the above program (or a similar one) for matrix multiplication in some of the exercises that follow. Your school may have software available for matrix multiplication.

3.4 Matrices Used in Coding

When you were younger you probably tried to send 'secret messages' to your friends in code. Perhaps you used the code in which the letter A is represented by the number 1, B by 2 and so on. In this code, the message "Meet me Saturday" becomes 13 5 5 20 13 5 19 1 20 21 18 4 1 25. The problem with this code is that everyone knows it and can decipher your message. Governments and companies often need to send secret messages that cannot be decoded except by their own employees. Mathematicians have been extensively employed in devising codes. People who invent and decipher codes are called cryptographers. Here are some messages.

a) 5   1   19   25   3   15   4   5

b) 3   14   18   10   3   4   7   22   5   11   20   5   14   7

c) 94   85   102   51   134   120   143   75

Can you break the codes to reveal their meaning?
Using the "easy code" which replaces A by 1, and so on, should enable you to decode message a).

A variation of this code begins with 3 for A, 4 for B, and so on until 26 is reached for X. Then 1 is used for Y and 2 for Z.
Use this to decode message b).

This second method of coding is relatively easy to break for an experienced cryptographer, because it still retains the letter frequency of English.

To obtain a more difficult code, you must find some method of scrambling the letters in a complicated way. Cryptographers use matrices to provide such a code. First, an encoding matrix, E, and a decoding matrix, D, must be provided. Then the following steps are taken:

1. Write the letters of the message as numbers using 1 for A, 2 for B, and so on.

A	B	C	D	E	F	G	H	I	J	K	L	M
1	2	3	4	5	6	7	8	9	10	11	12	13
N	O	P	Q	R	S	T	U	V	W	X	Y	Z
14	15	16	17	18	19	20	21	22	23	24	25	26

2. Write the numbers obtained in step *1* as a matrix, M. The matrix must have a dimension that will enable it to be multiplied on the left by E.
3. Multiply M on the left by the encoding matrix, E. The numbers given by this product matrix are the encoded message.
4. The receiver of the message writes the encoded message as a matrix C and multiplies the matrix C on the left by the decoding matrix, D.
5. Finally, to read the message, the receiver takes the numbers in the last matrix and replaces 1 by A, 2 by B and so on.
   The encoder needs to know the details of the encoding process only, including the matrix E. The decoder needs to know the details of the decoding process only, including the matrix D.

Example 1   Encode the message MATH IS BEST using the encoding matrix

$$E = \begin{bmatrix} 3 & 4 \\ 2 & 3 \end{bmatrix}$$

Solution   *Step 1*   Translate the message into numbers using 1 for A and so on.

M	A	T	H		I	S		B	E	S	T
13	1	20	8		9	19		2	5	19	20

Step 2   The encoding matrix has two columns. To use it as a multiplier on the left, the message must be written as a matrix with two rows. Therefore, the message matrix is

$$M = \begin{bmatrix} 13 & 1 & 20 & 8 & 9 \\ 19 & 2 & 5 & 19 & 20 \end{bmatrix}$$

Step 3   Multiply E by M.

$$EM = \begin{bmatrix} 3 & 4 \\ 2 & 3 \end{bmatrix} \begin{bmatrix} 13 & 1 & 20 & 8 & 9 \\ 19 & 2 & 5 & 19 & 20 \end{bmatrix}$$
$$= \begin{bmatrix} 115 & 11 & 80 & 100 & 107 \\ 83 & 8 & 55 & 73 & 78 \end{bmatrix}$$

Therefore, the encoded message is 115 11 80 100 107 83 8 55 73 78.   ■

Example 2   Show that the coded message in Example 1 can be decoded using the decoding matrix

$$D = \begin{bmatrix} 3 & -4 \\ -2 & 3 \end{bmatrix}$$

Solution   *Step 1.*   The decoding matrix, D, has two columns. To use D as a multiplier on the left, the message must be written as a matrix with two rows.

Thus, $C = \begin{bmatrix} 115 & 11 & 80 & 100 & 107 \\ 83 & 8 & 55 & 73 & 78 \end{bmatrix}$

Step 2. C is then multiplied on the left by D.

$$DC = \begin{bmatrix} 3 & -4 \\ -2 & 3 \end{bmatrix} \begin{bmatrix} 115 & 11 & 80 & 100 & 107 \\ 83 & 8 & 55 & 73 & 78 \end{bmatrix}$$
$$= \begin{bmatrix} 13 & 1 & 20 & 8 & 9 \\ 19 & 2 & 5 & 19 & 20 \end{bmatrix}$$

Step 3.   The numbers from step 2 recreate the original message MATH IS BEST when 1 is replaced by A, 2 by B and so on.

Note that if the message has an odd number of letters you can complete the message matrix with zeros.

It is easy to invent an encoding matrix, E. But how can you find the corresponding decoding matrix, D?

The coded message, C, is the product of E on the left and the message matrix M.

$$C = EM$$

When you multiply C on the left by the decoding matrix, D, you want to obtain the message matrix, M. Therefore, the decoding matrix, D, must satisfy

$$DC = M$$

Since $C = EM$,

$$D(EM) = M$$

or $(DE)M = M$

If this equation is to be true for all messages, M, then DE must be the identity matrix $I = \begin{bmatrix} 1 & 0 \\ 0 & 1 \end{bmatrix}$ or $DE = I$. ■

Example 3   Find the decoding matrix, D, if the encoding matrix is $E = \begin{bmatrix} 4 & -3 \\ -1 & 1 \end{bmatrix}$.

Solution   Suppose the decoding matrix is

$$D = \begin{bmatrix} a & b \\ c & d \end{bmatrix}.$$

Then $DE = I$ or $\begin{bmatrix} a & b \\ c & d \end{bmatrix} \begin{bmatrix} 4 & -3 \\ -1 & 1 \end{bmatrix} = \begin{bmatrix} 1 & 0 \\ 0 & 1 \end{bmatrix}$

Multiplying $\begin{bmatrix} 4a - b & -3a + b \\ 4c - d & -3c + d \end{bmatrix} = \begin{bmatrix} 1 & 0 \\ 0 & 1 \end{bmatrix}$

Equating corresponding matrix elements

$$4a - b = 1 \quad ① \qquad\qquad 4c - d = 0 \quad ③$$
$$-3a + b = 0 \quad ② \qquad\qquad -3c + d = 1 \quad ④$$

Equations ① and ② can be solved for a and b by elimination or substitution to give $a = 1$ and $b = 3$.

Similarly, equations ③ and ④ can be solved for c and d to give $c = 1$ and $d = 4$. Therefore, the decoding matrix

$$D = \begin{bmatrix} 1 & 3 \\ 1 & 4 \end{bmatrix} \quad ■$$

DEFINITION   Matrices that satisfy the condition $DE = I$ are called **inverse** matrices. D is the inverse of E and is sometimes written E^{-1}. E is the inverse of D and can be written as D^{-1}.

3.4 Exercises

1. Encode the message FINITE MATH IS GREAT using each of the given encoding matrices.

   a) $E_1 = \begin{bmatrix} 1 & -1 \\ -2 & 3 \end{bmatrix}$

   b) $E_2 = \begin{bmatrix} 2 & 5 \\ 1 & 3 \end{bmatrix}$

   c) $E_3 = \begin{bmatrix} 1 & -3 \\ -3 & 10 \end{bmatrix}$

2. Use the decoding matrix, D, to decode the following messages, where

   $D = \begin{bmatrix} 5 & 7 \\ 2 & 3 \end{bmatrix}$

   a) $\begin{array}{cccc} -60 & -97 & 44 & 70 \end{array}$

   b) $\begin{array}{ccccc} -69 & -9 & -120 & -80 & 45 \\ 52 & 8 & 87 & 58 & -30 \end{array}$

   c) $\begin{array}{cccccc} -6 & -124 & -81 & -102 & -95 & 36 \\ 7 & 89 & 59 & 75 & 70 & -24 \end{array}$

3. a) Find the decoding matrices for each of the encoding matrices in question 1.

   b) Check that the decoding matrices that you have found in part a) of this question do in fact decode the message that you encoded in question 1.

4. Messages can be encoded by matrices that are of different dimension from 2×2.

   a) How many rows should your message matrix have if you use a 3×3 encoding matrix?

   b) Encode the message VACATIONS using the encoding matrix E.

   $E = \begin{bmatrix} 1 & 0 & 1 \\ 4 & 4 & 3 \\ -4 & -3 & -3 \end{bmatrix}$

   c) Show that you can decode the result using D.

   $D = \begin{bmatrix} -3 & -3 & -4 \\ 0 & 1 & 1 \\ 4 & 3 & 4 \end{bmatrix}$

5. Show that the encoding matrix

   $E = \begin{bmatrix} 2 & 8 \\ 1 & 4 \end{bmatrix}$

   has no decoding matrix.

6. You can also encode a message matrix M by multiplying M on the right by an encoding matrix E. The message C is given by $C = ME$. If

   $E = \begin{bmatrix} 2 & 3 \\ 1 & 2 \end{bmatrix}$

   a) how many columns should the message matrix M have?

   b) Use E and multiplication on the right to encode the message VIVA CANADA. (Hint. Write the numbers of the message down the first column in order and then down the second column.)

   c) Find the decoding matrix D corresponding to E.

   d) Use matrix multiplication by D on the right to decode the coded message of part b).

   e) If you used the matrix E given in part a) of this question and matrix multiplication on the left, would you obtain the same coded message C? Justify your answer.

7. Any 2×2 encoding matrix E can be written as

   $E = \begin{bmatrix} a & b \\ c & d \end{bmatrix}$

   a) Determine the corresponding decoding matrix

   $D = \begin{bmatrix} x & y \\ z & w \end{bmatrix}$

   in terms of a, b, c and d.

   b) State a condition that a, b, c and d must satisfy for E to have a decoding matrix.

8. Use the rule you determined in question 7 to write decoding matrices for the following encoding matrices, if possible.

   a) $\begin{bmatrix} 2 & 5 \\ 6 & 10 \end{bmatrix}$ c) $\begin{bmatrix} 3 & 6 \\ -2 & -4 \end{bmatrix}$

   d) $\begin{bmatrix} 3 & -4 \\ -1 & 2 \end{bmatrix}$ d) $\begin{bmatrix} 3 & -7 \\ -2 & 5 \end{bmatrix}$

In Search of Inverse Matrices

In Section 3.4 you used the encoding matrix

$$E = \begin{bmatrix} 1 & 2 & 1 \\ 2 & 3 & 1 \\ -2 & 0 & 1 \end{bmatrix}$$

To find the corresponding decoding matrix, D, you are looking for a matrix such that $DE = I$.

$$\text{Let } D = \begin{bmatrix} a & b & c \\ d & e & f \\ g & h & i \end{bmatrix}$$

$$DE = \begin{bmatrix} a & b & c \\ d & e & f \\ g & h & i \end{bmatrix} \begin{bmatrix} 1 & 2 & 1 \\ 2 & 3 & 1 \\ -2 & 0 & 1 \end{bmatrix} = \begin{bmatrix} 1 & 0 & 0 \\ 0 & 1 & 0 \\ 0 & 0 & 1 \end{bmatrix}$$

Multiplying

$$\begin{bmatrix} a + 2b - 2c & 2a + 3b & a + b + c \\ d + 2e - 2f & 2d + 3e & d + e + f \\ g + 2h - 2i & 2g + 3h & g + h + i \end{bmatrix} = \begin{bmatrix} 1 & 0 & 0 \\ 0 & 1 & 0 \\ 0 & 0 & 1 \end{bmatrix}$$

Equating corresponding elements of each matrix

$a + 2b - 2c = 1$ ①	$2a + 3b = 0$ ②	$a + b + c = 0$ ③
$d + 2e - 2f = 0$ ④	$2d + 3e = 1$ ⑤	$d + e + f = 0$ ⑥
$g + 2h - 2i = 0$ ⑦	$2g + 3h = 0$ ⑧	$g + h + i = 1$ ⑨

Equations ①, ② and ③ can be solved to give $a = 3, b = -2, c = -1$.
Equations ④, ⑤ and ⑥ can be solved to give $d = -4, e = 3, f = 1$.
Equations ⑦, ⑧ and ⑨ can be solved to give $g = 6, h = -4, i = -1$.
Therefore, the decoding matrix D is

$$\begin{bmatrix} 3 & -2 & -1 \\ -4 & 3 & 1 \\ 6 & -4 & -1 \end{bmatrix}$$

Try these.

1. Find the decoding matrix for

$$\begin{bmatrix} 3 & 1 & -4 \\ -4 & -1 & 6 \\ -2 & -1 & 3 \end{bmatrix}$$

2. Prove that the matrix

$$\begin{bmatrix} 1 & 0 & 2 \\ 3 & 2 & 4 \\ 2 & 1 & 3 \end{bmatrix}$$

does not have a decoding matrix.

Matrices can also be used to represent equations. The equations

$$3x - 7y = 5$$
$$-2 + 5y = 4$$ ①

can be written as

$$\begin{bmatrix} 3 & -7 \\ -2 & 5 \end{bmatrix} \begin{bmatrix} x \\ y \end{bmatrix} \begin{bmatrix} 5 \\ 4 \end{bmatrix}$$ ②

You can multiply each side of this matrix equation by any 2×2 matrix M.

$$M \begin{bmatrix} 3 & -7 \\ -2 & 5 \end{bmatrix} \begin{bmatrix} x \\ y \end{bmatrix} = M \begin{bmatrix} 5 \\ 4 \end{bmatrix}$$ ③

If matrix M can be chosen so that

$$M \begin{bmatrix} 3 & -7 \\ -2 & 5 \end{bmatrix} = \begin{bmatrix} 1 & 0 \\ 0 & 1 \end{bmatrix}$$

then the matrix equation ③ would become

$$\begin{bmatrix} 1 & 0 \\ 0 & 1 \end{bmatrix} \begin{bmatrix} x \\ y \end{bmatrix} = M \begin{bmatrix} 5 \\ 4 \end{bmatrix}$$

$$\text{or} \begin{bmatrix} x \\ y \end{bmatrix} = M \begin{bmatrix} 5 \\ 4 \end{bmatrix}$$

and the original equations ① would be solved.

Thus, $M \begin{bmatrix} 3 & -7 \\ -2 & 5 \end{bmatrix} = \begin{bmatrix} 1 & 0 \\ 0 & 1 \end{bmatrix}$

Therefore, M must be the inverse matrix for the matrix

$$\begin{bmatrix} 3 & -7 \\ -2 & 5 \end{bmatrix}$$

In 3.4 Exercises, question 8d, you found that the inverse matrix for

$$\begin{bmatrix} 3 & -7 \\ -2 & 5 \end{bmatrix} \text{ is } \begin{bmatrix} 5 & 7 \\ 2 & 3 \end{bmatrix}$$

Therefore, using this matrix for M in ③ gives

$$\begin{bmatrix} 5 & 7 \\ 2 & 3 \end{bmatrix} \begin{bmatrix} 3 & -7 \\ -2 & 5 \end{bmatrix} \begin{bmatrix} x \\ y \end{bmatrix} = \begin{bmatrix} 5 & 7 \\ 2 & 3 \end{bmatrix} \begin{bmatrix} 5 \\ 4 \end{bmatrix}$$

$$\text{or} \quad \begin{bmatrix} 1 & 0 \\ 0 & 1 \end{bmatrix} \begin{bmatrix} x \\ y \end{bmatrix} = \begin{bmatrix} 53 \\ 22 \end{bmatrix}$$

Therefore, $x = 53$ and $y = 22$.

Now try these.

3. Find the inverse matrix for

$$\begin{bmatrix} 3 & -5 \\ -1 & 2 \end{bmatrix} \text{ and use it to solve the equations}$$
$$3x - 5y = 2$$
$$-x + 2y = 3$$

4. Use the decoding matrix D determined on page 118 to solve the equations

$$x + 2y + z = 4$$
$$2x + 3y + z = 3$$
$$-2x \quad\quad + z = -3$$

3.5 Matrices Used in Networks

When you plan a trip by airplane you look at the route maps of an airline. You often find that you cannot travel directly to your destination. You will probably wish to minimize the number of changes of airplanes. Matrices can be used to help you solve this problem.

The airline you are considering has flights between various cities as shown in the diagram below.

This diagram can be simplified to a diagram of points and lines.

A network matrix can be constructed using this diagram. The rows and columns of the matrix represent the points Y, B, W, O and C. If there is a direct link between two cities, 1 is placed in the appropriate location in the matrix. If there is no direct link between two cities, 0 is placed in the appropriate location. Zeros are placed on the main diagonal line corresponding to the first row and first column, and so on, because it is considered that there is no direct link from a city to itself, for example, from Ottawa to Ottawa. The network matrix A is shown below.

$$A = \begin{bmatrix} 0 & 1 & 0 & 0 & 1 \\ 1 & 0 & 0 & 0 & 1 \\ 0 & 0 & 0 & 0 & 1 \\ 0 & 0 & 0 & 0 & 1 \\ 1 & 1 & 1 & 1 & 0 \end{bmatrix} \begin{matrix} Y \\ B \\ W \\ O \\ C \end{matrix}$$

$$Y \quad B \quad W \quad O \quad C$$

There are, however, indirect routes between the cities. Let us look at the product of matrix A with itself.

$$
\overset{A}{\begin{bmatrix} 0 & 1 & 0 & 0 & 1 \\ 1 & 0 & 0 & 0 & 1 \\ 0 & 0 & 0 & 0 & 1 \\ 0 & 0 & 0 & 0 & 1 \\ 1 & 1 & 1 & 1 & 0 \end{bmatrix}}
\overset{A}{\begin{bmatrix} 0 & 1 & 0 & 0 & 1 \\ 1 & 0 & 0 & 0 & 1 \\ 0 & 0 & 0 & 0 & 1 \\ 0 & 0 & 0 & 0 & 1 \\ 1 & 1 & 1 & 1 & 0 \end{bmatrix}}
=
\overset{A^2}{\begin{bmatrix} 2 & 1 & 1 & 1 & 1 \\ 1 & 2 & 1 & 1 & 1 \\ 1 & 1 & 1 & 1 & 0 \\ 1 & 1 & 1 & 1 & 0 \\ 1 & 1 & 0 & 0 & 4 \end{bmatrix}}
$$

What does the matrix A^2 represent?
Consider the number 1 in the first row and second column of A^2, the position representing Yellowknife/Brandon.

This number was formed by multiplying the elements of the first row of A by the elements in the second column of A.

$$
[0\ 1\ 0\ 0\ 1]\begin{bmatrix} 1 \\ 0 \\ 0 \\ 0 \\ 1 \end{bmatrix}
\begin{array}{ccccc}
Y & B & W & O & C \\
= 0 \times 1 & +1 \times 0 & +0 \times 0 & +0 \times 0 & +1 \times 1 \\
= 0 & +\ 0 & +\ 0 & +\ 0 & +\ 1 \\
\text{no} & \text{no} & \text{no} & \text{no} & \text{link} \\
\text{link} & \text{link} & \text{link} & \text{link} & \text{to} \\
\text{to Y} & \text{to B} & \text{to Y} & \text{to Y} & \text{Y and B} \\
 & & \text{or B} & \text{or B} &
\end{array}
$$

Each 0 in the sum indicates the absence of a direct link between a city and Brandon, or between a city and Yellowknife, or absence of direct links between a city and both Yellowknife and Brandon.
Each 1 indicates that a city has both a direct route to Yellowknife *and* a direct route to Brandon.
Therefore a route exists from Yellowknife to Brandon via Calgary.

Consider the second row of the matrix A^2, 1   2   1   1   1.
The first 1 tells you that you there is one indirect route from Yellowknife to Brandon via one other city. Looking at the route map, you see that you can travel from Yellowknife to Brandon via Calgary. The 2 tells you that there are two indirect routes from Brandon and back to Brandon again via one other city each time. From the route map you can see that this can be done via Yellowknife or Calgary.

Thus the matrix A^2 represents the number of indirect routes from one city to another via *one* other city.

Now let us look at the matrix A^3.

$$A^3 = \begin{bmatrix} 2 & 3 & 1 & 1 & 5 \\ 3 & 2 & 1 & 1 & 5 \\ 1 & 1 & 0 & 0 & 4 \\ 1 & 1 & 0 & 0 & 4 \\ 5 & 5 & 4 & 4 & 2 \end{bmatrix} \begin{matrix} Y \\ B \\ W \\ O \\ C \end{matrix}$$

$$\quad\quad Y \quad B \quad W \quad O \quad C$$

This matrix indicates the number of indirect routes from one city to another via *two* intermediary cities.

For example, the 3 in the second row indicates that there are three indirect routes from Yellowknife to Brandon using two intermediary points.

From the route map you can see that you can travel
Yellowknife-Calgary-Yellowknife-Brandon or
Yellowknife-Brandon-Calgary-Brandon or
Yellowknife-Brandon-Yellowknife-Brandon.
(No reasonable person would want to undertake any of these particular journeys as a way of going from Yellowknife to Brandon when a direct route is available!)

Similarly, the matrix A^k represents the number of routes between each pair of cities with k-1 intermediate points.

Example 1   Five oil tankers are in the North Atlantic. By reason of various equipment faults and weather conditions, some of the tankers are unable to communicate directly with each other. The possible communications paths are shown in the diagram. (The arrowheads indicate the direction or directions in which messages can pass.) One tanker can be used to pass on a message from another tanker. For various reasons, any communication involving more than one relay point is considered undesirable.

Determine whether all the tankers can communicate with each other, using at most one relay point.

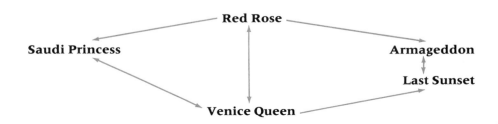

Solution   First set up a communication matrix, C, for this situation. Notice that the matrix C is not symmetric, since some of the communication links are one-way only.

FROM

TO

	Red Rose	Saudi Princess	Venice Queen	Armageddon	Last Sunset	
Red Rose	0	1	1	1	0	
Saudi Princess	0	0	1	0	0	
Venice Queen	1	1	0	0	1	$= C$
Armageddon	0	0	0	0	1	
Last Sunset	0	0	0	1	0	

The number of two-stage paths is given by C^2.

$$C^2 = \begin{bmatrix} 0 & 1 & 1 & 1 & 0 \\ 0 & 0 & 1 & 0 & 0 \\ 1 & 1 & 0 & 0 & 1 \\ 0 & 0 & 0 & 0 & 1 \\ 0 & 0 & 0 & 1 & 0 \end{bmatrix} \begin{bmatrix} 0 & 1 & 1 & 1 & 0 \\ 0 & 0 & 1 & 0 & 0 \\ 1 & 1 & 0 & 0 & 1 \\ 0 & 0 & 0 & 0 & 1 \\ 0 & 0 & 0 & 1 & 0 \end{bmatrix}$$

$$= \begin{bmatrix} 1 & 1 & 1 & 0 & 2 \\ 1 & 1 & 0 & 0 & 1 \\ 0 & 1 & 2 & 2 & 0 \\ 0 & 0 & 0 & 1 & 0 \\ 0 & 0 & 0 & 0 & 1 \end{bmatrix}$$

A 0 indicates that there is no two-stage path.
(For example, from Red Rose to Armageddon.)
A 1 indicates that there is one two-stage path.
(For example, from Saudi Princess to Red Rose.)
A 2 indicates that there are two two-stage paths.
(For example, from Red Rose to Last Sunset.)
Since the numbers in C give the number of direct, or one-stage, communication links and the numbers in matrix C^2 give the number of two-stage communication links, then the sum of these two matrices, $C + C^2$, will show all the one- or two-stage communication links.

$$C + C^2 = \begin{bmatrix} 0 & 1 & 1 & 1 & 0 \\ 0 & 0 & 1 & 0 & 0 \\ 1 & 1 & 0 & 0 & 1 \\ 0 & 0 & 0 & 0 & 1 \\ 0 & 0 & 0 & 1 & 0 \end{bmatrix} + \begin{bmatrix} 1 & 1 & 1 & 0 & 2 \\ 1 & 1 & 0 & 0 & 1 \\ 0 & 1 & 2 & 2 & 0 \\ 0 & 0 & 0 & 1 & 0 \\ 0 & 0 & 0 & 0 & 1 \end{bmatrix}$$

$$= \begin{bmatrix} 1 & 2 & 2 & 1 & 2 \\ 1 & 1 & 1 & 0 & 1 \\ 1 & 2 & 2 & 2 & 1 \\ 0 & 0 & 0 & 1 & 1 \\ 0 & 0 & 0 & 1 & 1 \end{bmatrix}$$

$$
\begin{array}{c c}
 & \begin{array}{c c c c c} \text{RR} & \text{SP} & \text{VQ} & \text{A} & \text{LS} \end{array} \\
\begin{array}{c} \text{RR} \\ \text{SP} \\ \text{VQ} \\ \text{A} \\ \text{LS} \end{array} &
\left[\begin{array}{c c c c c}
1 & 2 & 2 & 1 & 2 \\
1 & 1 & 1 & 0 & 1 \\
1 & 2 & 2 & 2 & 1 \\
0 & 0 & 0 & 1 & 1 \\
0 & 0 & 0 & 1 & 1
\end{array} \right]
\end{array}
$$

A 0 in this matrix indicates that there are no direct, or no two-stage, communication links.
(For example, from Saudi Princess to Armageddon.)
A 1 indicates that there is one direct or one two-stage link.
(For example, from Venice Queen to Red Rose.)
A 2 indicates that there are two possible direct or two-stage links.
(For example, from Red Rose to Venice Queen.)
Therefore the following tankers cannot communicate using at most one relay point: Saudi Princess to Armageddon;
Armageddon to Red Rose, Saudi Princess, or Venice Queen;
Last Sunset to Red Rose, Saudi Princess, or Venice Queen.   ■

A similar matrix method can be applied to determine the best team in a round robin tournament.

Example 2   Four teams play in a tournament with the following results.
West Rouge beat Scarborough B and St. John's, but lost to East York A.
St. John's beat Scarborough B and East York A.
Scarborough B beat East York A.
Which is the best team?

Solution   The following diagram shows the results; the arrows point to the loser.

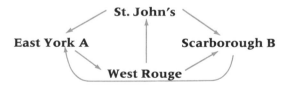

A matrix, D, can be set up to show these results.

$$
\begin{array}{c c}
 & \hspace{2.5em} \text{BEAT} \\
 & \begin{array}{c c c c} \text{WR} & \text{SB} & \text{EY} & \text{SJ} \end{array} \\
\begin{array}{c} \text{WR} \\ \text{SB} \\ \text{EY} \\ \text{SJ} \end{array} &
\left[\begin{array}{c c c c}
0 & 1 & 0 & 1 \\
0 & 0 & 1 & 0 \\
1 & 0 & 0 & 0 \\
0 & 1 & 1 & 0
\end{array} \right] = D
\end{array}
$$

The 1 in the first row and second column indicates that West Rouge beat Scarborough B. Another way of expressing this is to say that West Rouge dominated over Scarborough B.
For this reason, D is sometimes called a **dominance matrix**.

What does the matrix D^2 represent?

$$D^2 = \begin{bmatrix} 0 & 1 & 0 & 1 \\ 0 & 0 & 1 & 0 \\ 1 & 0 & 0 & 0 \\ 0 & 1 & 1 & 0 \end{bmatrix} \begin{bmatrix} 0 & 1 & 0 & 1 \\ 0 & 0 & 1 & 0 \\ 1 & 0 & 0 & 0 \\ 0 & 1 & 1 & 0 \end{bmatrix} = \begin{bmatrix} 0 & 1 & 2 & 0 \\ 1 & 0 & 0 & 0 \\ 0 & 1 & 0 & 1 \\ 1 & 0 & 1 & 0 \end{bmatrix}$$

The number 2 in the first row and third column was formed by multiplying the first row of D by the third column of D.

$$\text{WR} \quad [0 \quad 1 \quad 0 \quad 1] \begin{bmatrix} 0 \\ 1 \\ 0 \\ 1 \end{bmatrix} \begin{array}{l} = 0 \times 0 + 1 \times 1 + 0 \times 0 + 1 \times 1 \\ = \quad 0 \quad + \quad 1 \quad + \quad 0 \quad + \quad 1 \quad = 2 \\ \quad\quad\quad \text{WR} \quad\quad\quad \text{SB} \quad\quad\quad \text{EY} \quad\quad\quad \text{ST} \end{array}$$

EY

The 1 in this sum indicates that West Rouge beat a team and also that same team beat East York A. This is called a **two-stage dominance**. Therefore, the matrix D^2 gives the number of two-stage dominances between the teams.

One way of ranking the teams would be to add the rows of the matrix, D to obtain the number of wins that each team had scored.

$$D = \begin{bmatrix} 0 & 1 & 0 & 1 \\ 0 & 0 & 1 & 0 \\ 1 & 0 & 0 & 0 \\ 0 & 1 & 1 & 0 \end{bmatrix} \begin{array}{l} \text{sum of row 1} = 2 \\ \text{sum of row 2} = 1 \\ \text{sum of row 3} = 1 \\ \text{sum of row 4} = 2 \end{array}$$

Unfortunately, this does not give a very decisive result. If you take into account not only matrix D but also the two-stage dominances given by D^2, a clearer result is evident.

The **power rating** of a team can be defined as the sum of all its one- and two-stage dominances.

$$D + D^2 = \begin{bmatrix} 0 & 1 & 0 & 1 \\ 0 & 0 & 1 & 0 \\ 1 & 0 & 0 & 0 \\ 0 & 1 & 1 & 0 \end{bmatrix} \begin{bmatrix} 0 & 1 & 2 & 0 \\ 1 & 0 & 0 & 0 \\ 0 & 1 & 0 & 1 \\ 1 & 0 & 1 & 0 \end{bmatrix} = \begin{bmatrix} 0 & 2 & 2 & 1 \\ 1 & 0 & 1 & 0 \\ 1 & 1 & 0 & 1 \\ 1 & 1 & 2 & 0 \end{bmatrix} = S$$

	Matrix S				Power Rating
West Rouge	0	2	2	1	$0 + 2 + 2 + 1 = 5$
Scarborough B	1	0	1	0	$1 + 0 + 1 + 0 = 2$
East York A	1	1	0	1	$1 + 1 + 0 + 1 = 3$
St. John's	1	1	2	0	$1 + 1 + 2 + 0 = 4$

Higher power ratings indicate a stronger team. Therefore, the teams should be ranked in the following order.

West Rouge	first
St. John's	second
East York A	third
Scarborough B	fourth ∎

3.5 Exercises

1. Construct the communication matrix for each of the following diagrams.

a)

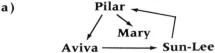

b)

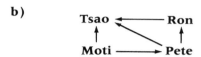

c)

d)

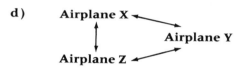

2. Construct a network diagram for each of the following network matrices.

a) $A = \begin{bmatrix} 0 & 1 & 1 \\ 0 & 0 & 1 \\ 1 & 1 & 0 \end{bmatrix}$

b) $B = \begin{bmatrix} 0 & 2 & 1 \\ 2 & 0 & 1 \\ 1 & 1 & 0 \end{bmatrix}$

c) $C = \begin{bmatrix} 0 & 1 & 0 & 1 \\ 1 & 0 & 1 & 0 \\ 0 & 1 & 0 & 0 \\ 0 & 0 & 0 & 0 \end{bmatrix}$

d) $D = \begin{bmatrix} 0 & 2 & 1 & 1 \\ 0 & 0 & 0 & 0 \\ 1 & 2 & 0 & 1 \\ 1 & 2 & 1 & 0 \end{bmatrix}$

e) $E = \begin{bmatrix} 0 & 1 & 1 & 0 & 2 \\ 0 & 0 & 1 & 2 & 0 \\ 1 & 0 & 0 & 1 & 0 \\ 0 & 2 & 1 & 0 & 0 \\ 2 & 0 & 1 & 1 & 0 \end{bmatrix}$

f) $F = \begin{bmatrix} 0 & 1 & 2 & 0 & 1 \\ 1 & 0 & 1 & 2 & 0 \\ 0 & 2 & 0 & 1 & 2 \\ 0 & 1 & 1 & 0 & 3 \\ 1 & 2 & 0 & 1 & 0 \end{bmatrix}$

3. a) What does a row of zeros in a network matrix imply for the corresponding network diagram?
   b) If the elements in the third row and the third column of a network matrix were all zeros, what would this imply for the third point in the corresponding network diagram?

4. Use the matrices of question 2 to evaluate the following.
   a) A^2
   b) A^3
   c) B^2
   d) B^3

5. What do the matrices you formed in question 4 represent for the networks in question 2?

6. For the tankers in Example 1 (page 122), determine whether all the tankers can communicate with each other using at most
   a) two relay points.
   b) three relay points.
   c) four relay points.

7. The following diagram illustrates the direct rail connections between various cities.

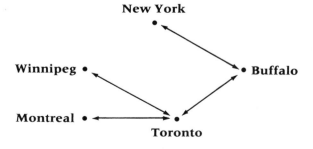

Use matrices to determine between which pairs of cities you can travel with at most one change of train.

8. The diagram below illustrates part of the chain of command of an oil company.

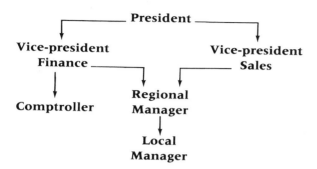

a) Construct the communication matrix C.
b) Construct and interpret the matrix C^2.

9. Ecologists are concerned about DDT contamination in the food chain shown below.

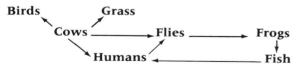

DDT has negligible effects if it passes through more than two intermediary species. When DDT is applied, both grasslands and humans are affected. Use matrix analysis to determine which of the above species is affected by DDT.

10. In a round robin squash match among four players the following results were recorded.
Terry beat Kim and Marc.
Marc beat Kim.
Craig beat Terry, Kim and Marc.
a) Construct a diagram and matrix for this tournament.
b) Rank the players using their power ratings.

11. A recent round robin baseball tournament produced these results.
Lions defeated Braves and Cheetahs, but lost to Dodgers and Hawks.
Braves lost to everyone except Cheetahs.
Cheetahs beat Dodgers only.
Dodgers defeated Lions and Braves and lost to Hawks.
There were no ties.

Use power ratings to rank the five teams.

3.6 Simple Markov Chains

In the introduction to this chapter, you read about a certain city in which 42 000 people drive to work and 65 000 use public transit. People's habits are changing. A new survey reveals the following statistics: 85% of current transit passengers will continue to use transit to go to work while 15% will switch to driving their car. 92% of car drivers will continue to drive, but 8% will switch to public transport.

Information obtained by such surveys is used by city planners to predict future situations based on present-day trends. A process, devised by the Russian mathematician Andrei Andreevich Markov, which allows the calculation of the probabilities of future events, can be adapted to solve the above and similar problems by using matrices.

The information in the survey can be expressed by the following matrix T, called a **transition matrix**.

$$\begin{array}{c} \text{From} \\ \begin{array}{cc} \text{Transit} & \text{Car} \end{array} \\ \text{To} \begin{array}{c} \text{Transit} \\ \text{Car} \end{array} \begin{bmatrix} 0.85 & 0.08 \\ 0.15 & 0.92 \end{bmatrix} = T \end{array}$$

In the matrix T, the first column represents the percentages of people who take public transit to work at the present time. The first row of the first column represents the percentage of the present public transit riders who intend to continue to take public transit to work. The second row of the first column represents the percentage of the present public transit riders who intend to change to driving their car to work. The second column represents the percentages of people who drive their car to work at the present time. The first row of the second column represents the percentage of present car drivers who intend switching to public transit. The second row of the second column represents the percentage of present car drivers who intend to continue to drive to work. Therefore, the first row of the matrix T, represents the percentages of present public transit and car users who intend to travel by public transit in the future.
The current ridership can be expressed as a 2×1 column matrix.

$$Z = \begin{bmatrix} 65\ 000 \\ 42\ 000 \end{bmatrix}$$

To find the number of people who will use public transit after the changes, you need to multiply the number of present public transit riders by 85% (0.85) and the number of present car drivers by 8% (0.08) and add these products. Therefore, the number of public transit riders will be
$0.85 \times 65\ 000 + 0.08 \times 42\ 000 = 58\ 610$.
Similarly, the number of car users will be
$0.15 \times 65\ 000 + 0.92 \times 42\ 000 = 48\ 390$.

These numbers are exactly the same as those given by multiplying the present ridership matrix, Z, by the transition matrix, T.

$$TZ = \begin{bmatrix} 0.85 & 0.08 \\ 0.15 & 0.92 \end{bmatrix} \begin{bmatrix} 65\ 000 \\ 42\ 000 \end{bmatrix} = \begin{bmatrix} 0.85 \times 65\ 000 + 0.08 \times 42\ 000 \\ 0.15 \times 65\ 000 + 0.92 \times 42\ 000 \end{bmatrix}$$

$$= \begin{bmatrix} 58\ 610 \\ 48\ 390 \end{bmatrix}$$

That is, there will be 58 610 people using public transportation and 48 390 people driving to work after the changes.

Notice that it is very important how you set up transition matrix, T. The first row must contain the percentages of people who will use transit after the transition process. The second row must contain the percentages of people who will drive their cars after the transition.

Example 1   Farmers think that 75% of their children will follow in their footsteps and be farmers too. City dwellers think that 95% of their children will work in the city and only 5% of their children will become farmers. Suppose that this does indeed happen and that the percentages do not change from generation to generation.

If the present number of farmers and non-farmers in a country is 20 000 and 80 000, respectively, determine the numbers of farmers and non-farmers that there will be in two generations.

Solution   You can set up a transition matrix T, to denote this process.

$$\begin{bmatrix} 0.75 & 0.05 \\ 0.25 & 0.95 \end{bmatrix} \quad \text{Farmers in the next generation} \\ \text{Non-farmers in the next generation}$$

To find the numbers of farmers and non-farmers after one generation, you would multiply the column matrix $\begin{bmatrix} 20\ 000 \\ 80\ 000 \end{bmatrix}$ by T, giving $T \begin{bmatrix} 20\ 000 \\ 80\ 000 \end{bmatrix}$.

To find the numbers of farmers and non-farmers after two generations you need to multiply this new column matrix by T, to give

$$T \left[T \begin{bmatrix} 20\ 000 \\ 80\ 000 \end{bmatrix} \right] \text{ or } T^2 \begin{bmatrix} 20\ 000 \\ 80\ 000 \end{bmatrix}$$

Therefore, matrix T^2 will represent the respective probabilities for the grandchildren of present-day citizens.

$$T^2 = \begin{bmatrix} 0.575 & 0.085 \\ 0.425 & 0.915 \end{bmatrix}$$

$$\begin{bmatrix} 0.575 & 0.085 \\ 0.425 & 0.915 \end{bmatrix} \begin{bmatrix} 20\ 000 \\ 80\ 000 \end{bmatrix} = \begin{bmatrix} 0.575 \times 20\ 000 + 0.085 \times 80\ 000 \\ 0.425 \times 20\ 000 + 0.915 \times 80\ 000 \end{bmatrix}$$

$$= \begin{bmatrix} 18\ 300 \\ 81\ 700 \end{bmatrix}$$

That is, after two generations there will be 18 300 farmers and 81 700 non-farmers, compared to 20 000 and 80 000 today. ∎

Example 2   Using the data from Example 1, and assuming the population of farmers and non-farmers continues to change in the same way from generation to generation, determine the ultimate proportion of farmers and non-farmers in the population.

Solution   Assume that the population tends to some fixed proportion of farmers and non-farmers as times goes on.

Let a% of the final population be farmers and b% be non-farmers.

Then $a + b = 100$ ①

Since this is the final proportion of farmers and non-farmers, no change will occur in the following generation.

Therefore,

$$T\begin{bmatrix} a \\ b \end{bmatrix} = \begin{bmatrix} a \\ b \end{bmatrix}$$

or $\begin{bmatrix} 0.75 & 0.05 \\ 0.25 & 0.95 \end{bmatrix} \begin{bmatrix} a \\ b \end{bmatrix} = \begin{bmatrix} a \\ b \end{bmatrix}$

Therefore, $0.75a + 0.05b = a$ ②

$0.25a + 0.95b = b$ ③

Solving equations ② and ③ gives

$a = \dfrac{100}{6}$ or $\dfrac{1}{6} \times 100$ and $b = \dfrac{500}{6}$ or $\dfrac{5}{6} \times 100$.

That is, $\dfrac{1}{6}$ of the population will be farmers and $\dfrac{5}{6}$ will not.   ■

Notice the assumptions implicit in this model.

  1. The rates of change remain the same.
  2. The actual events are the same as the results of the survey of opinions.
  3. There are no changes in the total population numbers.

The problems discussed above of the transit/car travellers and the farmers/non-farmers are examples of Markov processes.

PROPERTIES   A **Markov process** satisfies the three following conditions.

  1. There are a fixed number of states. For example, in the car/transit situation the problem was reduced to two states. People were either taking public transit to work or driving a car.
  2. At each stage, every element in the process must be in one of these states. In the transportation problem, no people were 'allowed' to walk or cycle to work.
  3. The probability of transferring from one state to another depends on the two states only and not on preceding transitions. For example, in the farmer/non-farmer problem, the probability of a child being a farmer depended only on his or her parents' occupation and not on his or her grandparents' occupation.

In the above examples, a 2×2 transition matrix was adequate for the problems presented. The following example shows the use of a 3×3 transition matrix.

Example 3   People in a city are classified according to their occupation into three groups: employed in industry, employed in small business and self-employed. Some of the people change their type of occupation from year to year. A survey determined that a person's occupation this year depends on her/his occupation last year, as shown in the table below.

Employment Last Year	Employment This Year	Percent
Industry	Industry	70
	Small business	20
	Self-employed	10
Small Business	Industry	30
	Small business	50
	Self-employed	20
Self-employed	Industry	30
	Small business	30
	Self-employed	40

a) Form a transition matrix to represent this process.

b) If there were 35 000 people employed in industry, 20 000 employed in small business and 12 000 self-employed last year, determine the numbers of people in each category this year.

Solution   **a)** The required matrix is T.

$$T = \begin{bmatrix} 0.70 & 0.30 & 0.30 \\ 0.20 & 0.50 & 0.30 \\ 0.10 & 0.20 & 0.40 \end{bmatrix}$$

row 1 represents the percentages of people employed in each category last year and who will be employed in industry this year

column 1 represents the percentages of people employed in industry last year

b) To determine the numbers of people in each category this year, you multiply the column matrix

$$\begin{bmatrix} 35\ 000 \\ 20\ 000 \\ 12\ 000 \end{bmatrix} \text{ on the left by } T. \quad \begin{bmatrix} 0.70 & 0.30 & 0.30 \\ 0.20 & 0.50 & 0.30 \\ 0.10 & 0.20 & 0.40 \end{bmatrix}\begin{bmatrix} 35\ 000 \\ 20\ 000 \\ 12\ 000 \end{bmatrix}$$

$$= \begin{bmatrix} 0.70 \times 35\ 000 + 0.30 \times 20\ 000 + 0.30 \times 12\ 000 \\ 0.20 \times 35\ 000 + 0.50 \times 20\ 000 + 0.30 \times 12\ 000 \\ 0.10 \times 35\ 000 + 0.20 \times 20\ 000 + 0.40 \times 12\ 000 \end{bmatrix} = \begin{bmatrix} 34\ 100 \\ 20\ 600 \\ 12\ 300 \end{bmatrix}$$

Therefore, this year there will be 34 100 people employed in industry and 20 600 in small business. 12 300 people will be self-employed. ■

3.6 Exercises

1. A student studying math this year has a 70% chance of taking math next year and a 30% chance of not taking math next year. A student not taking math this year has a 90% chance of not taking math next year and a 10% chance of taking math next year. 850 students took math this year and 240 did not.
   a) Write a transition matrix for this process.
   b) Use the transition matrix from part a) to predict the number of students taking math next year.

2. A survey revealed that 37% of the population smoke. Each year 15% of smokers quit and 5% of non-smokers start.
   a) Write a transition matrix for this process.
   b) Determine the percentage of smokers after one year.
   c) Determine the percentage of smokers after two years.

3. A town's pollution index is checked daily to see if the air is acceptable (A) or unacceptable (U). If the air is A, there is a 40% chance that tomorrow's air will also be A. If today's air is U, there is a 70% chance that tomorrow's air will be U. If today is U, predict the pollution condition after three days.

4. A survey of voter loyalty revealed the following results in one riding.

Will vote in next election	Voted in last election		
	Conservative	Liberal	NDP
Conservative	85%	15%	5%
Liberal	10%	75%	15%
NDP	5%	10%	80%

In the last election 25 786 voted Liberal, 23 070 voted Conservative and 15 604 voted NDP.
   a) Predict the results of the next election.
   b) What assumptions are you making when you make this forecast?
   c) What conditions might make the results of your predictions invalid?
   d) Use the transition matrix to predict the percentage of those who voted Liberal in the last election who will vote Liberal two elections from now.

5. A detergent company conducted a 'brand loyalty' survey about their new "Seawhite" laundry detergent. The following results were obtained. 70% of current users of "Seawhite" would buy it again when they next bought detergent. 30% of current users would switch to another brand. Of those presently using a different brand, 40% would try "Seawhite" next time. Determine how much of the market "Seawhite" can capture in the long run.

6. The buying patterns of new car buyers in the region of Halton were found to be:

Next car	Current car	
	Small	Large
Small	80%	40%
Large	20%	60%

Determine the long-term distribution of cars in Halton.

7. A sampling of workers' families done by a sociology student revealed the following trends:

NEXT GENERATION	CURRENT GENERATION	
	White Collar	Blue Collar
White Collar	100%	20%
Blue Collar	0%	80%

Find the long-term distribution of occupations.

Summary

- A matrix is a rectangular array of numbers that can be used to record information.

- elements, rows, columns, dimension (order) of a matrix

- equality of matrices

- addition, subtraction, and scalar multiplication of matrices

- multiplication of matrices:
  ($m \times n$ matrix) $\times$ ($n \times r$ matrix) = ($m \times r$ matrix)

- To form the ijth element of the product of two matrices, multiply the elements from the ith row of the matrix on the left by the matching elements from the jth column of the matrix on the right, and sum the products so formed.

- Matrices can be used in coding. If E is the encoding matrix, you need the inverse matrix D to decode the message, such that $DE = I$, where I is the identity matrix.

- An identity matrix is a square matrix with ones on the main diagonal and zeros elsewhere.

- Matrices can be used in network problems. If A is a network matrix, the product matrix A^k gives the number of routes, with $k - 1$ intermediate points, between two points in the network.

- Markov chains

- Matrices can be used in transition problems. If T is the transition matrix and Z is a column vector describing the original state, then $T^n Z$ gives the state after n transitions.

- If $T^n Z$ approaches a certain matrix Y as n gets large, then this limiting matrix Y can be determined by solving the following equations.
  sum of entries of $Y = 100\%$
  $$TY = Y$$

Inventory

Use the matrices
$$A = \begin{bmatrix} 2 & 4 & 6 \\ 0 & 3 & 7 \\ -1 & 5 & 8 \end{bmatrix} \quad B = [1 \quad 2 \quad 3] \quad C = \begin{bmatrix} 0 \\ 1 \\ 5 \end{bmatrix}$$
to answer questions 1-10 where possible.

1. The element $a_{31} =$ _____.
2. $a_{ij} = 7$ if $i =$ _____ and $j =$ _____.
3. Matrix _____ is a square matrix.
4. Matrix _____ is a column matrix.
5. The dimension of B is _____.
6. $5A =$ _____.
7. $2B - 3C =$ _____.
8. The dimension of the product AC is _____.
9. Can you form the product AB?
10. $BC =$ _____.
11. Use the matrix
    $$\begin{bmatrix} 2 & 3 \\ 1 & 2 \end{bmatrix}$$ to decode the message $-20 \quad -17 \quad -1 \quad 25 \quad 20 \quad 13 \quad 7 \quad -10$.
12. If E is an encoding matrix and D is a decoding matrix then
    a) $DE =$ _____.
    b) D and E are called _____ matrices.
13. The network matrix for the diagram below is

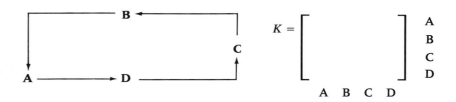

14. Using the network matrix, K, from question 13, you can obtain
    $$K^2 = \begin{bmatrix} 0 & 0 & 1 & 0 \\ 0 & 0 & 0 & 1 \\ 1 & 0 & 0 & 0 \\ 0 & 1 & 0 & 0 \end{bmatrix}$$
    Is it possible for each point in the diagram of question 13 to communicate with every other point, using a maximum of one relay point?
15. If T is a transition matrix and X is a column vector representing the present state, then TX represents the state after _____ transition(s).

Review Exercises

Use these tables and the corresponding matrices to answer questions 1-4.

Table 1

Name	Age	Height (cm)	Mass (kg)
Sue	15	162	48
Greg	18	185	75
Anna	16	150	52

$$A = \begin{bmatrix} 15 & 162 & 48 \\ 18 & 185 & 75 \\ 16 & 150 & 52 \end{bmatrix}$$

Table 2

Day	Mon	Tues	Wed	Thur	Fri	Sat	Sun
Temperature	17	20	24	26	21	19	23

$B = [17\ 20\ 24\ 26\ 21\ 19\ 23]$

Table 3

Type of Muffin	Cost/dozen (to bake)
Bran	$1.25
Blueberry	$1.50
Chocolate chip	$1.75

$$C = \begin{bmatrix} 1.25 \\ 1.50 \\ 1.75 \end{bmatrix}$$

1. Copy and complete this table.

Matrix	No. of Rows	No. of Columns	Dimension	No. of Elements
A				
B				
C				

2. Identify by row and column the precise location of each of the following.
   a) the heights of the students
   b) Greg's statistics
   c) the cost of 1 dozen chocolate chip muffins
   d) the temperature on Sunday

3. Explain the meaning and give the value of each of the following.
   a) a_{23} d) the first row of A
   b) b_{41} e) the first column of A
   c) c_{21} f) the second column of A

4. Describe how each of the matrices would change under the following conditions.
   a) Two more students were added to Table 1.
   b) The temperatures were recorded for two weeks in Table 2.
   c) The cost of making muffins goes up by 100%.

5. Use the matrices
$$X = \begin{bmatrix} 2 & 5 & 7 \\ -3 & 0 & 4 \end{bmatrix} \qquad Y = \begin{bmatrix} 1 & 5 \\ -2 & 3 \end{bmatrix}$$
$$Z = [9\ -2\ 4] \qquad W = \begin{bmatrix} 6 & -5 \\ 8 & -7 \end{bmatrix}$$
to evaluate the following, if possible.
   a) $2Y + 3W$ d) XZ
   b) $X - 4W$ e) Y^2
   c) YX f) WY

6. M, P and T are three matrices which satisfy $MP = T$. The dimensions of M, P and T are $a \times b, c \times d$ and $e \times f$, respectively. What equalities must be satisfied by a, b, c, d, e and f?

7. The following chart shows the number of items sold in an electronics store over a three week period.

	Stereos	TVs	VCRs	Computers
Week 1	5	3	8	2
Week 2	4	6	10	3
Week 3	6	4	9	1

The average cost of each item is given.
Stereos $950
TVs $750
VCRs $500
Computers $1500

Use matrix multiplication to determine the total receipts from sales for each week.

8. Encode the following messages using the encoding matrix $E = \begin{bmatrix} 3 & 5 \\ 1 & 2 \end{bmatrix}$.

a) MEET ME AT NINE
b) I LOVE YOU
c) THE CODE MUST BE BROKEN

9. Determine the decoding matrix, D, corresponding to the matrix, E, in question 8.

10. Use the decoding matrix D that you determined in question 9 to decode the following messages.

a)
```
73   73   75   52   26   29
26   19
```

b)
```
99   70   42   120  127  3
39   25   16   47   47   1
```

c)
```
103  79   98   89   85   117
39   40   54   103  38   28
39   35   30   45   15   15
19   41
```

11. A communication network for espionage agents has been set up as shown in the diagram below.

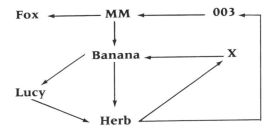

a) Construct the communication matrix M for this network.
b) Evaluate M^2, M^3 and M^4.
c) What information do you receive from the matrix M^3?
d) Are there any spies who cannot communicate with each other in two steps or less? Which ones?
e) If Banana is captured by the enemy, construct the new network matrix.
f) What information do you receive from the matrix M^4?

12. Several downtown streets have been made one-way as shown in the diagram below. The intersections are labelled A, B, C, D, E and F.

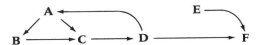

Is it possible to travel between each pair of intersections? If not, between which pairs of intersections is it not possible to travel?

13. A rat in a maze is continually faced with a choice of left (L) and right (R) turns. The rat can only recall his last turn. His behaviour on the next turn is described by the matrix A.

$$A = \begin{matrix} & \text{LAST TURN} \\ & \begin{matrix} \text{L} & \quad \text{R} \end{matrix} \\ \begin{bmatrix} 0.8 & 0.4 \\ 0.2 & 0.6 \end{bmatrix} & \begin{matrix} \text{L} \\ \text{R} \end{matrix} \end{matrix} \text{ NEXT TURN}$$

(The 0.2 means that a rat who turned left on his last turn has a 20% chance of turning right on the next turn.)

a) Determine the long term behaviour of the rat.
b) In the long term, how many left turns will he make out of 100 choices?

14. A small town has three variety stores, Corner Variety, 6-12 Store and Quik Serve. The town's residents were surveyed on August 1. It was found that $\frac{1}{4}$ of them shopped at Corner Variety, $\frac{1}{3}$ at the 6-12 Store and the rest at Quik Serve. Each month, Corner Variety keeps 90% of its customers and loses 10% of them to Quik Serve. The 6-12 Store is not well managed. Each month, it loses 10% of its customers to Quik Serve and 80% to Corner Variety. Quik Serve retains 40% of its customers each month, losing 10% to the 6-12 Store and the rest to Corner Variety. What proportion of the town's shoppers would you expect the 6-12 Store to have by October 1 of the same year?

15. A person is identified as a leader if he or she influences the behaviour of other members of a group. The diagram below shows the direct influences that people in a group have on one another.

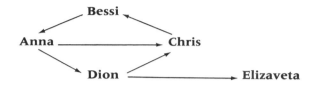

A dominance matrix, D, can be set up from this chart, as shown below.
Person below
influences

$$\begin{array}{c}\quad\quad A\ \ B\ \ C\ \ D\ \ E\\ \begin{array}{c}A\\B\\C\\D\\E\end{array}\left[\begin{array}{ccccc}0&0&1&1&0\\ & & & & \\ & & & & \\ & & & & \\ & & & & \end{array}\right]\end{array}$$

a) Complete the matrix D.
b) Evaluate the matrices D^2, D^3, D^4 and D^5.
c) The strength of a person's influence can be determined as the sum of the elements in the corresponding row in the power matrix P, where P is given by the formula
$$P = D + \frac{1}{2}D^2 + \frac{1}{3}D^3 + \frac{1}{4}D^4 + \frac{1}{5}D^5.$$
Determine the power rating for each of the people in this group.
d) The person with the highest rating is the leader. Who is the leader of this group?

16. Encode COMPUTERS ARE HERE by matrix multiplication on the right using the encoding matrix
$$\begin{bmatrix}1&2&1\\2&3&1\\-2&0&1\end{bmatrix}$$
(Hint. Write the letters of the message matrix across row 1 in order and then across row 2.)

17. Use the decoding matrix
$$\begin{bmatrix}3&-7\\-2&5\end{bmatrix}$$
and matrix multiplication on the right to decode the message c) on page 114.

18. The shifts in population to and from city, suburbs and country are as shown in the chart below.

		TO	
	City	Suburbs	Country
City	65%	30%	5%
Suburbs	20%	70%	10%
Country	20%	10%	70%

FROM (rows: City, Suburbs, Country)

This year's population distribution (in millions) is

City	Suburbs	Country
13	9	4

a) Could you use the matrix product
$$\begin{bmatrix}0.65&0.30&0.05\\0.20&0.70&0.10\\0.20&0.10&0.70\end{bmatrix}\begin{bmatrix}13\\9\\4\end{bmatrix}$$
to predict next year's population distribution?
b) If you answered yes to part a), justify your answer.
If you answered no to part a), what matrix product could be used to predict next year's population distribution?
c) Predict the population distribution after two years.

19. Aroma Coffee sells two different blends composed of Mocha, Jamaican and Kenyan beans as shown in matrix M.
%Mocha %Jamaican %Kenyan
$$M = \begin{bmatrix}25&50&25\\60&20&20\end{bmatrix}\begin{matrix}\text{Blend A}\\\text{Blend B}\end{matrix}$$
$$P = \begin{bmatrix}40&30\end{bmatrix}$$
       A B
The production matrix P shows how many kg are to be produced. Calculate the product matrix PM, and state what it represents.

CHAPTER FOUR

Solving Systems of Equations and Inequalities

A very common problem in business and industry is the minimizing of transportation costs when shipping commodities from warehouse to customer.

A manufacturer of TV sets has two warehouses, one in Manston and one in Picton. The Manston warehouse has 100 sets in stock and the Picton warehouse has 60.

Three retailers, Radio World, Cut-Price Stereo and TV City have put in orders for 50, 70 and 40 of the latest TV sets respectively.

The distances of the stores from the warehouses are shown in the diagram, in kilometres.

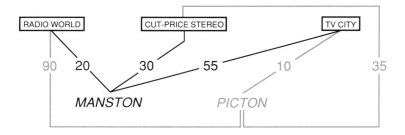

The cost of shipping one TV set 1 km is estimated to be \$0.50. The problem is to decide how many sets are to be shipped from each of the warehouses to each of the stores to minimize the transportation costs.

To solve this problem let the number of sets shipped from the Manston warehouse to Radio World, Cut-Price Stereo and TV City be represented by x, y and z respectively. Then the number of sets shipped to each of these retailers from Picton must be $50 - x$, $70 - y$ and $40 - z$. Since the total shipped from Manston must equal 100, you can write the equation
$x + y + z = 100$ ①
There are other restrictions on the values that x, y and z can take.
For example $0 \leqslant x \leqslant 50$, $0 \leqslant y \leqslant 70$, $0 \leqslant z \leqslant 40$.

Also x, y and z must be whole numbers.

The total cost is given by the expression below.
$$0.50(20x + 30y + 55z + 90(50 - x) + 35(70 - y) + 10(40 - z)) \quad ②$$

In this chapter you will learn how to minimize this expression.

Activities

1. Simplify the expression in ②.

2. Use equation ① to write the expression you obtained in **1** in terms of x and y only.

3. Take various values of x and y and evaluate the expression you have found. You can use the chart below.

x \ y	0	10	20	30	40	50	60	70
0								
10								
20								
30								
40								
50								

4.1 Mathematical Modelling

When a new airplane is designed, often a model of the proposed design is built. The model can then be tested in a wind tunnel. Modifications can be made to improve the performance of the model before the full-size version is built. This is an example of a *physical* model of a real life situation.

Many situations in the real world can be modelled by *mathematical* structures; in chapter 3, matrices were used. Other mathematical structures, such as relations and equations, also model real-life situations. The following examples illustrate this.

Example 1   A medium pizza costs $5 for a topping of tomato sauce and cheese plus $0.50 for each additional topping. Determine an expression for the cost, $C, of a pizza with n additional toppings.

Solution   The cost of one extra topping is $0.50, for two it is $2 \times \$0.50$ and so on. Therefore, the cost of n additional toppings is $n \times \$0.50$ or $\$0.50n$.

Since the cost of the basic pizza is $5, the cost $C, of the pizza with n toppings is given by
$C = 5 + 0.50n$

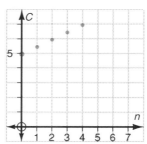

$C(n) = 5 + 0.50n$ is a **linear function** in the variable n.   ■

Example 2   The cost of renting a swimming pool for a private party for one hour depends on the number of people you invite. You need to have one lifeguard for every 20 people at your pool party. The cost of renting the pool with one lifeguard is $17.
You have to pay an additional $6 for each extra lifeguard. Determine an expression for cost, $C, of renting the pool for one hour as a function of n, the number of people at the party.

Solution   For 20 people or less, the cost is $17.
For any number of people from 21 to 40, the cost is $$(17 + 6)$.
For any number of people from 41 to 60, the cost is $$(17 + 2 \times 6)$.

This function can be defined as follows:

$C = 17, 1 \leqslant n \leqslant 20$

$C = (17 + 6), 21 \leqslant n \leqslant 40$

$C = (17 + 2 \times 6), 41 \leqslant n \leqslant 60$ and so on.

$C = (17 + 6k)$ where $20k + 1 \leqslant n \leqslant 20k + 20, k, n \in W$.

The graph of this function is shown below.

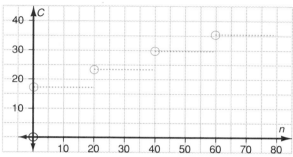

This function is called a **step function**. ■

Often you encounter situations where the price varies according to the quantity of goods that are bought.

Example 3 If you are ordering wedding invitations you find that it costs $2 each for the first 50 ordered, $1.50 each for the next 50 and $1 each for any in excess of 100.

Determine an expression for the cost, $C, of x wedding invitations.

Solution If $0 \leqslant x \leqslant 50$ the price of x wedding invitations is given by $C = 2x$.

If $50 < x \leqslant 100$, the cost of x wedding invitations is made up of two parts. The cost of the first 50 invitations, namely $50 \times \$2 = \$100$. The cost of the remaining $(x - 50)$ invitations, namely $(x - 50) \times \$1.50 = \$1.5(x - 50)$. Therefore, for $50 < x \leqslant 100$, $C = 100 + 1.5(x - 50)$.

If $x > 100$, the cost of the invitations includes the cost of the first 50 at $2 each, namely $100, the cost of the next 50 at $1.50 each, namely $75, and the cost of the remaining $(x - 100)$ at $1 each, namely $\$1(x - 100)$.

Therefore, for $x > 100$, the equation of this function is $C = 175 + (x - 100)$. The complete expression for this function is

$C = 2x, 0 \leqslant x \leqslant 50$

$C = 100 + 1.5(x - 50), 51 \leqslant x \leqslant 100$

$C = 175 + 1(x - 100), x > 100$. ■

This function is **piece-wise linear**.

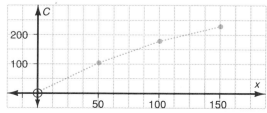

The functions discussed in Examples 1, 2 and 3 are functions of the whole numbers. The graphs of these functions consist of a series of dots. Such functions are known as **discrete** functions.

Example 4   The height h in metres of a rocket is given by the equation $h = 200x - 2x^2$ where x is the distance in metres from the point where it was fired. Determine the domain of x for this situation.

Solution   The height of the rocket must be greater than or equal to zero.
Therefore, $h \geqslant 0$.
The graph of the function $h = 200x - 2x^2$ is a parabola opening downwards.
The x-intercepts of the parabola are found by setting $h = 0$. This gives
   $200x - 2x^2 = 0$
$2x(100 - x) = 0$
Therefore, $x = 0$ and $x = 100$ are the x-intercepts.

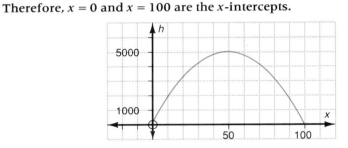

From the graph you can see that $h \geqslant 0$, if $0 \leqslant x \leqslant 100$.
Therefore, the domain for x is $\{x \in R \mid 0 \leqslant x \leqslant 100\}$.
This is a **non-linear continuous** function of the real variable x. ∎

Example 5   Chocolate bars cost 75 cents each and cans of pop cost 50 cents each at a local convenience store. Santos buys some of each and spends $4.25.
Maria buys the same quantities as Santos at a large discount store where chocolate bars are 60 cents each and pop is 50 cents a can.
Her bill is $3.80. Form a set of equations that model this situation.

Solution   The number of chocolate bars that each person buys is the same, but the equation does not say what this number is. It is unknown. You can represent this number by a variable, for example, x. In the same way you can represent the number of cans of pop by the variable y.
Therefore, the cost of x chocolate bars at 75 cents each is $75x$ cents.
The cost of y cans of pop at 50 cents each is $50y$ cents.
Since Santos' total bill is $4.25 or 425 cents, then
$75x + 50y = 425$ ①
It is important that both sides of this equation are expressed in cents.

A second equation, representing the cost of Maria's shopping, is
$60x + 50y = 380$ ②
Equations ① and ② model the situation. ∎

4.1 Exercises

1. Write equations to express the first quantity in terms of the second.
   a) the distance, d, in kilometres travelled in t hours at a speed of 60 km/h
   b) the price, $\$p$, of x hamburgers which cost $2 each
   c) the mass, m, in grams of v cm³ of a substance with a density of 2.5 gm/cm³
   d) the taxes, $\$t$, on a house with frontage x metres if the taxes are calculated as a fixed rate of $500 plus an additional rate of $50 per metre frontage

2. a) Sketch the graphs of each of the functions in question 1.
   b) Which of the functions in question 1 are continuous functions of a real variable and which are discrete functions?
   c) State any restrictions on the domains of the variables in question 1.

3. The cost of renting a school bus with its driver for a day is $200. Each bus will hold 70 students.
   a) Determine an expression for the cost, $\$c$, of renting the school buses needed for a ski trip as a function of the number, x, of students going on a trip.
   b) Sketch a graph of this function.
   c) Is the function used in part a) a step function or is it piece-wise linear?
   d) Is the function used in part a) a discrete function or a continuous function?

4. The cost of buying computer chips varies depending on the quantity you wish to purchase. For a particular chip the cost is $5 each for the first 40. For each chip in excess of 40 the cost is $3.50 each.
   a) Determine an expression for the cost, $\$c$, of buying x chips.
   b) Sketch the graph of this function.
   c) What is the domain of this function?

5. The cost of renting a car is $35 per day or part of a day plus 25 cents per km.
   a) Write an equation to express the cost, $\$c$, of renting a car for one day and driving x km.
   b) Write an equation to express the cost of renting a car for d days and driving 400 km.
   c) Write an equation to express the cost of renting a car for d days and driving x km.
   d) You rent the car and keep it in the garage all the time. Write an equation to express the cost of the car for h hours.
   e) Sketch a graph of the function in part d).
   f) You drive this car with a team of drivers at a constant rate of 60 km/h for 5 days across the country. Write an equation to express the cost of the car rental as a function of the hours, h, the car is used.
   g) Sketch a graph of the function in part f).
   h) How could you describe the graphs in e) and g)?

6. The temperature, T, in degrees C of a cup of coffee t seconds after it is poured is given (approximately) by the equation
   $$T = 20 + \frac{80}{t + 1}$$
   a) Use a table of values to sketch the graph of this function.
   b) What is the domain of t?
   c) Is this a continuous or a discrete function?

7. There is a sale of socks and ties at Barry's favorite store. All the socks are one price and all the ties are another price. If Barry buys six pairs of socks and two ties, his bill will be $45.50. If he buys five pairs of socks and three ties his bill will be $49.25. Form a set of equations to model this situation.

M A K I N G

Models for Inherited Human Characteristics

Many human characteristics, such as eye color, hair color, sex, ear lobe type, and tongue type, are inherited. Some of these characteristics can be illustrated and studied with relatively simple probability models. One such characteristic is tongue rolling. Some people can roll their tongues into a U-shape, and others cannot. Rolling is dominant over non-rolling. In figure 1, R stands for a rolling gene and n stands for a non-rolling gene.

Figure 1
Possible Results Relating to Tongue Rolling

		Female Parent (nn)	
		n	n
Male Parent (Rn)	R	Rn	Rn
	n	nn	nn

Each offspring from this union has a probability of $\frac{1}{2}$ of being a roller and each offspring also has a probability of $\frac{1}{2}$ of being a non-roller.

Sex-linked inheritance characteristics
Some people cannot distinguish certain colors or combinations of colors. Some types of color-blindness are red, green, red-green, blue-yellow, and complete color-blindness. Only about 1 percent of women are color-blind, but somewhere between 5 and 8 percent of men are color-blind.
It has been observed that a color-blind father may have a daughter with normal vision, and then this daughter may have a son in whom the trait of color-blindness reappears after having been missing for a generation. Inherited characteristics that behave in this way are called *sex-linked* characteristics.

The occurrence of sex-linked characteristics can be explained by assuming that X chromosomes contain genes that transmit certain characteristics and that Y chromosomes do not contain genes that transmit these characteristics. These genes, even though they are not dominant, will express themselves in male offspring because Y chromosomes, which males get and females do not get, contain no genes to prevent the expression of these sex-linked traits. A female would be color-blind only if the gene for color-blindness is carried by both of her X chromosomes. Models can be constructed to depict probabilities of color-blindness occurring in offspring. In these models, X denotes a chromosome with a normal gene for color vision, and X' denotes a chromosome with a gene for color-blindness. Normal color vision is dominant over color-blindness.

The following combinations are possible in regard to color-blindness.

XX: Normal female
XX': Carrier female
X'X': Color-blind female
XY: Normal male
X'Y: Color-blind male

Since there are three combinations relating to color-blindness that could exist in females and two combinations that could exist in males, there are $3 \times 2 = 6$ possible mating combinations. Figures 2 and 3 show two of these six possibilities. It is possible to conclude from figure 2 that none of the offspring from this union would be color-blind. All the female offspring however, would be carriers of the gene for color-blindness.

Figure 3 shows that half the males born of the union of a normal male and a female carrier can be expected to be color-blind, and half the females can be expected to be carriers of the gene for the color-blindness.

Figure 2
Possible Combinations of Offspring
Resulting from a Color-Blind Male
And a Normal Female

		Normal Female (XX)	
		X	X
Color-Blind Male (X'Y)	X'	XX'	XX'
	Y	XY	XY

Figure 3
Possible Combinations of Offspring
Resulting from a Normal Male
and a Carrier Female

		Carrier Female (XX')	
		X	X'
Normal Male (XY)	X	XX	XX'
	Y	XY	X'Y

Reflection and the construction of other tables would show that female offspring could be color-blind only if the father is color-blind *and* the mother is either color-blind or a carrier of the gene for color-blindness.

4.2 Solving Systems of Equations by Elimination

A record store is offering two different special deals. The first deal consists of three cassettes and two albums for $38. The second deal offers two cassettes and three albums for $37. How much is the company charging for each cassette and each album separately?

There are two stages in solving this problem. First, you should form a system of equations to model the situation. Second, the system of equations must be solved.

Example 1

Three cassettes and two albums cost $38. Three albums and two cassettes cost $37. Determine the cost of one cassette and one album.

Solution

Let $c represent the cost of one cassette and $a represent the cost of one album. Since the cost of three cassettes and two albums is $38
$$3c + 2a = 38 \qquad \text{①}$$
Similarly, since two cassettes and three albums cost $37
$$2c + 3a = 37 \qquad \text{②}$$
One way to solve these equations is to eliminate one of the variables. In order to eliminate a variable it is necessary to make the coefficients of that variable in both equations equal. So to eliminate the variable a you should multiply equation ① by 3 and equation ② by 2.

$3 \times$ ①	$9c + 6a = 114$	③
$2 \times$ ②	$4c + 6a = 74$	④

Subtracting equation ④ from equation ③ will eliminate a.
$$\text{③} - \text{④} \qquad 5c = 40$$
$$c = 8$$
You can now determine the value of a by substituting 8 for c in either equation ① or ②.
From ①
$$3(8) + 2a = 38$$
$$2a = 14$$
$$a = 7$$
Therefore, each cassette costs $8 and each album costs $7.

You can check this result by substituting the values for a and c into equation ②, the original equation that was *not* used to find a.
$$L.S. = 2c + 3a \qquad\qquad R.S. = 37$$
$$= 2(8) + 3(7) \text{ or } 37$$
$$L.S. = R.S.$$
Therefore, $a = 7$ and $c = 8$ is the correct solution. ∎

The method of elimination can be extended to solve a system of three equations in three unknowns.

Example 2 Solve the following system of equations.

$$2x - y + 3z = 0 \qquad ①$$
$$x + y - 2z = 1 \qquad ②$$
$$3x + 2y + 4z = -13 \qquad ③$$

Solution The first step is to eliminate one of the variables from two of the equations. Eliminate x from equations ① and ②.

$$
\begin{array}{rl}
 & 2x - y + 3z = 0 \qquad ① \\
2 \times ② & 2x + 2y - 4z = 2 \qquad ④ \\
① - ④ & -3y + 7z = -2 \qquad ⑤
\end{array}
$$

The next step is to form a second equation involving y and z only. In other words, you must eliminate x from another pair of the original equations. To eliminate x from equations ② and ③, multiply equation ② by 3.

$$
\begin{array}{rl}
3 \times ② & 3x + 3y - 6z = 3 \qquad ⑥ \\
 & 3x + 2y + 4z = -13 \qquad ③ \\
⑥ - ③ & y - 10z = 16 \qquad ⑦
\end{array}
$$

You have now reduced the original system of three equations, ①, ② and ③, in three unknowns, x, y and z, to a system of two equations, ⑤ and ⑦, in two unknowns, y and z.

$$-3y + 7z = -2 \qquad ⑤$$
$$y - 10z = 16 \qquad ⑦$$

These equations can be solved by the method of Example 1, as follows. To eliminate y from these equations you need to multiply equation ⑦ by 3.

$$3 \times ⑦ \qquad 3y - 30z = 48 \qquad ⑧$$

In this case since the coefficient of y in equation ⑤ is -3 and the coefficient of y in equation ⑧ is $+3$, it is necessary to *add* equations ⑤ and ⑧ to eliminate y.

$$⑤ + ⑧ \qquad -23z = 46 \qquad ⑨$$
$$z = -2$$

You can now find the value of y by substituting -2 for z in equation ⑤ or ⑦.

From ⑦

$$y - 10(-2) = 16$$
$$y + 20 = 16$$
$$y = -4$$

Now you can find the value of x by substituting the value of y and z into one of equations ①, ② or ③.

From ②

$$x + (-4) - 2(-2) = 1$$
$$x - 4 + 4 = 1$$
$$x = 1$$

Therefore, the solution is the ordered triple $(x,y,z) = (1,-4,-2)$. This solution can be checked by substituting into equations ① and ③. ∎

The process of solving three equations in three unknowns can be summarized as follows.

1. Eliminate the same variable from each of two pairs of the original equations so that you form two new equations in two unknowns.

2. Eliminate a second variable from the equations formed in step *1*.
   This gives you the value of one of the variables.

3. Substitute the value of the variable you have determined in *2* into one of the equations you formed in *1*.
   This gives you the value of the second variable.

4. Substitute the values of the two variables you have found into one of the original equations.
   This gives you the value of the third variable.

Your solution may be checked by substituting the values into each of the original equations.

The method of elimination can be extended to solve four equations in four unknowns, as shown in Example 3.

Example 3   Solve the following system of equations

$$
\begin{array}{ll}
x + y + z + t = 2 & \text{①} \\
2x - y - z + 2t = 7 & \text{②} \\
x + 2y - z - 3t = -7 & \text{③} \\
x - 3y + 4z - 2t = 0 & \text{④}
\end{array}
$$

Solution   *Step 1* Eliminate the same variable from each of three different pairs of equations.

Eliminate x in order to obtain three equations in three variables, y, z and t.

$$
\begin{array}{lll}
\text{①} - \text{③} & -y + 2z + 4t = 9 & \text{⑤} \\
\text{①} - \text{④} & 4y - 3z + 3t = 2 & \text{⑥} \\
2 \times \text{①} - \text{②} & 3y + 3z = -3 & \text{⑦}
\end{array}
$$

Step 2 Eliminate a second variable from two different pairs of the equations formed in step *1*.

Since ⑦ has no t term, choose ⑦ as one of the equations and eliminate t from ⑤ and ⑥.

$$
\begin{array}{lll}
& 3y + 3z = -3 & \text{⑦} \\
3 \times \text{⑤} - 4\text{⑥} & -19y + 18z = 19 & \text{⑧}
\end{array}
$$

Step 3 Eliminate one of the variables from the two equations formed in step *2*.

Eliminate z from ⑦ and ⑧.

$$
\begin{array}{ll}
6 \times \text{⑦} - \text{⑧} & 37y = -37 \\
& y = -1
\end{array}
$$

Step 4 Substitute into the equations formed in steps 2 and 1, and finally into one of the original equations to evaluate each variable.

Substituting in ⑦
$$3(-1) + 3z = -3$$
$$-3 + 3z = -3$$
$$z = 0$$

Substituting in ⑤
$$-(-1) + 2(0) + 4t = 9$$
$$1 + 4t = 9$$
$$t = 2$$

Substituting in ①
$$x + (-1) + (0) + (2) = 2$$
$$x = 1$$

These values can be checked by substituting
$x = 1, y = -1, z = 0$ and $t = 2$ into each of ② ③ ④.

② $L.S.\ 2(1) - (-1) - 0 + 2(2) = 7$ $R.S.\ 7$
$L.S. = R.S.$

③ $L.S.\ 1 + 2(-1) - 0 - 3(2) = -7$ $R.S.\ -7$
$L.S. = R.S.$

④ $L.S.\ 1 - 3(-1) + 0 - 2(2) = 0$ $R.S.\ 0$
$L.S. = R.S.$

Therefore the solution is $(x,y,z,t) = (1,-1,0,2)$.   ■

DEFINITION

Homogeneous equations are equations in which each term is of the same degree in the variables. Therefore, homogeneous *linear* equations have terms in which the variables are all of degree 1.

The following are examples of homogeneous linear equations:
$2x - 3y = 0$, $4x + 2y - 3z = 0$, $x + y + z - t = 0$.

Note that the constant term is zero.

Systems of homogeneous linear equations can be solved by elimination in exactly the same way as non-homogeneous systems.

4.2 Exercises

1. Solve the following systems of equations by elimination.
   a) $3x - 4y = 17$
      $2x - 3y = 12$
   b) $8x - 5y = -7$
      $2x + 3y = 10$
   c) $x + 3y + 4z = 3$
      $4x + y + 4z = 21$
      $2x - 2y - 3z = 8$
   d) $x - 5y + 3z = 26$
      $x + 8y + 2z = 6$
      $2x + 6y + z = 1$

2. A rectangular rug is 1 m longer than it is wide. If the perimeter of the rug is 12 m, find the area of the rug.

3. One litre of a 12% acid solution contains 120 mL of concentrated acid and 880 mL of water. How much pure water and how much 12% acid solution must be mixed together to obtain 16 L of a 9% acid solution?

4. A service station is hiring mechanics at $15 per hour, apprentice mechanics at $5 per hour and pump attendants at $3.50 per hour. A total of 12 people are hired. The sum of the number of apprentices and the number of pump attendants equals the number of mechanics. How many of each can be hired for a total of $114 per hour?

5. Solve the system of equations you formed in question 7 of 4.1 Exercises to determine the price of ties and socks in the sale.

6. Solve the system of equations formed in Example 5 in section 4.1 to determine the number of chocolate bars and cans of pop that Santos and Maria bought.

7. In two dimensions a linear equation such as $3x - 4y = 17$ represents a straight line. The solution of a system of two linear equations such as those in question 1 a) represents the point or points (if any) that are common to the two straight lines. In three dimensional geometry a linear equation in three variables x, y, z represents the points on a plane. To find the point or points (if any) that are common to the three planes, you must solve the system of their equations. Find the point of intersection of the three planes given by the equations below.
   $2x + 3y - z = 0$
   $x + 4y + 2z = -5$
   $2x - y - z = 4$

8. a) Solve the equations
      $ax + by = e$
      $cx + dy = f$
      in order to express x and y in terms of a, b, c, d, e and f.
   b) Is there always a solution to the equations in part a)?
   c) Write a computer program to solve the equations in part a).

9. Write a computer program to solve a system of three equations in three variables. It should contain the following steps.
   a) Ask the user the values of the coefficients in each equation.
   b) Display the three equations.
   c) Multiply one equation by a constant, where the user determines which equation and what constant is to be used.
   d) Subtract two equations.
   e) Repeat steps b) – d) until you eliminate two of the variables from the equations.
   f) Solve the equations by back-substitution.

10. In an electrical circuit, Kirchhoff's Law states that the sum of the IR products equals the e.m.f. where I is the current flowing through the resistor R. The e.m.f. is the voltage produced by the battery in the circuit. The currents I_1, I_2 and I_3 flow in a circuit shown below.

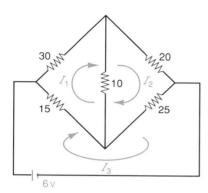

By going round each loop of the circuit and noting that the current flowing through the resistor 15 is $I_1 - I_3$, you can form the equations below.

$$30I_1 + 10(I_1 - I_2) + 15(I_1 - I_3) = 0$$
$$20I_2 + 25(I_2 - I_3) + 10(I_2 - I_1) = 0$$
$$15(I_3 - I_1) + 25(I_3 - I_2) = 6$$

Simplify these equations and then solve them by elimination, correct to 2 decimal places.

11. a) Write a program to solve three equations in three variables without any intermediate decisions being made by the user.

b) Test your program using the equations in question 1c).

c) Test your program again using the following equations.

$$2x - 3y + 4z = 10$$
$$x + y - z = 2$$
$$3x - 2y + 3z = 12$$

12. A scientist has a hypothesis that the temperature, t, of a substance at time x is given by a quadratic function $t = ax^2 + bx + c$. Find the values of the coefficients a, b and c so that the function $t = ax^2 + bx + c$ will fit the data below.

t	−20	4	10
x	1	3	4

13. Solve the following systems of equations by elimination.

a)
$$4x + 3y - 2z + t = 8$$
$$2x - 2y + z - 2t = 8$$
$$x + y + z + t = 0$$
$$3x - y + 4z - 3t = 14$$

b)
$$x + y + z + t = 3$$
$$2x + 3y - 4z + t = 14$$
$$3x - 5y + 2z - 3t = -13$$
$$4x + 2y - z - t = 2$$

14. Solve the following systems of homogeneous equations.

a)
$$2x + 3y = 0$$
$$3x - 2y = 0$$

b)
$$x + y + z = 0$$
$$2x - y + 5z = 0$$
$$x - y + 2z = 0$$

c)
$$x - y - z + 2t = 0$$
$$2x + y + z - t = 0$$
$$3x + 2y - z - t = 0$$
$$x - 3y + 2z + 3t = 0$$

15. Could you have foretold that the solutions you found in question 14 would be the solutions of all similar homogeneous systems? Explain.

In Search of a Vector Method for Solving Linear Systems

Column and row matrices are often called **vectors**.
Vectors of the same dimension can be added and subtracted.
All vectors can be multiplied by a scalar.

There is a special product of two vectors called the **dot product**.
For two vectors $[a \quad b \quad c]$ and $[u \quad v \quad w]$ the dot product is defined by

$$[a \quad b \quad c] \bullet \begin{bmatrix} u \\ v \\ w \end{bmatrix} = au + bv + cw.$$

Notice that the dot product of two vectors is a scalar.
You can show that the dot product of vectors satisfies the following
properties, where x, y and z are vectors and k is a scalar.
$$x \bullet y = y \bullet x; \quad x \bullet (ky) = k(x \bullet y); \quad x \bullet (y + z) = x \bullet y + x \bullet z$$

For a 2×1 vector such as $\begin{bmatrix} 3 \\ 2 \end{bmatrix}$, it is easy to find a vector such as $[-2, \quad 3]$

with the property that $[-2, \quad 3] \bullet \begin{bmatrix} 3 \\ 2 \end{bmatrix} = 0$. Such vectors are called
orthogonal.

A system of equations such as $2x + 3y = 8$
$$5x - 2y = 1 \text{ can be written as}$$
one vector equation $\quad \begin{bmatrix} 2 \\ 5 \end{bmatrix} x + \begin{bmatrix} 3 \\ -2 \end{bmatrix} y = \begin{bmatrix} 8 \\ 1 \end{bmatrix} \quad \circledast$

To solve this vector equation, "dot" the equation first with a vector that is
orthogonal to $\begin{bmatrix} 2 \\ 5 \end{bmatrix}$ and then with a vector that is orthogonal to $\begin{bmatrix} 3 \\ -2 \end{bmatrix}$.

Dotting equation $\circledast$ with $[-5 \quad 2]$ gives
$$[-5 \quad 2] \bullet \begin{bmatrix} 2 \\ 5 \end{bmatrix} x + [-5 \quad 2] \bullet \begin{bmatrix} 3 \\ -2 \end{bmatrix} y = [-5 \quad 2] \bullet \begin{bmatrix} 8 \\ 1 \end{bmatrix}$$
$$0x \qquad\qquad -19y = \qquad -38, \text{ that is, } y = 2$$

Dotting equation $\circledast$ with $[2 \quad 3]$ gives
$$[2 \quad 3] \bullet \begin{bmatrix} 2 \\ 5 \end{bmatrix} x + [2 \quad 3] \bullet \begin{bmatrix} 3 \\ -2 \end{bmatrix} y = [2 \quad 3] \bullet \begin{bmatrix} 8 \\ 1 \end{bmatrix}$$
$$19x \qquad\qquad + 0y = \qquad 19, \text{ that is, } x = 1$$
Therefore, the solution of equation $\circledast$ is $(x,y) = (1, 2)$.

Use the vector dot product to solve the following systems of equations.
1. **a)** $4x - 3y = 6$ **b)** $5x + y = 13$ **c)** $4x + 3y = 7$
       $x + y = 5$ $2x - 3y = -5$ $2x + 5y = 21$

2. How could you use the dot product to solve a system of three equations in three unknowns?

4.3 Using Matrices to Solve Systems of Equations

The method of elimination used in section 4.2 can be used to solve systems of four equations in four variables and systems involving even more variables. However, there is a need for a more systematic approach, particularly for large systems. One such method uses matrices.

The operations that you used to solve a system of equations by elimination were as follows.

• Two equations may be interchanged.

• Any equation may be multiplied by a non-zero number.

• Any equation may be replaced by the sum of that equation and a multiple of any other equation.

The resulting transformed system has the same solution set as the original.

DEFINITION   Systems of equations that have the same solution sets are **equivalent**.

The system of equations that you solved in Example 2 of section 4.2,

$$\begin{array}{rl} 2x - y + 3z = 0 & \text{①} \\ x + y - 2z = 1 & \text{②} \\ 3x + 2y + 4z = -13 & \text{③} \end{array}$$

can be represent by two matrices.
The coefficients of x, y and z in the three equations can be represented by the **coefficient matrix**

$$C = \begin{bmatrix} 2 & -1 & 3 \\ 1 & 1 & -2 \\ 3 & 2 & 4 \end{bmatrix}$$

A second matrix, A, where

$$A = \left[\begin{array}{ccc|c} 2 & -1 & 3 & 0 \\ 1 & 1 & -2 & 1 \\ 3 & 2 & 4 & -13 \end{array} \right]$$

is the **augmented matrix** of this system of equations.

Any operations which can validly be performed on the system of *equations* can also be performed on the *rows of this augmented matrix*. These three operations, known as **elementary row operations**, are stated below.

• Two rows of augmented matrix can be interchanged.

• Any row of the augmented matrix can be multiplied by a non-zero real number.

• Any row of the augmented matrix may be replaced by the sum of that row and a multiple of any other row.

The resulting transformed matrix will be the augmented matrix of a system which is equivalent to the original one.

Just before the process of back-substitution in Example 2 of section 4.2 was begun, the equations ①, ② and ③ had been transformed to the system

$$
\begin{aligned}
2x - y + 3z &= 0 \quad ① \\
y - 10z &= 16 \quad ⑦ \\
- 23z &= 46 \quad ⑨
\end{aligned}
$$

The augmented matrix of this new system of equations (formed by elimination) is B, where

$$
B = \left[\begin{array}{ccc|c}
2 & -1 & 3 & 0 \\
0 & 1 & -10 & 16 \\
0 & 0 & -23 & 46
\end{array}\right]
$$

Compare this with the original augmented matrix A where

$$
A = \left[\begin{array}{ccc|c}
2 & -1 & 3 & 0 \\
1 & 1 & -2 & 1 \\
3 & 2 & 4 & -13
\end{array}\right]
$$

The form of the matrix B is called **row-reduced echelon form** or row-reduced form. Once an augmented matrix is in this form it is clear that the corresponding equations can be easily solved by back-substituting.

The following are examples of row-reduced matrices:

$$
\left[\begin{array}{ccc|c}
1 & 2 & 6 & 0 \\
0 & 0 & 4 & 1 \\
0 & 0 & 0 & 0
\end{array}\right]
\qquad
\left[\begin{array}{ccc|c}
2 & 5 & 0 & 9 \\
0 & 1 & 4 & 0 \\
0 & 0 & 0 & 3
\end{array}\right]
$$

The criteria for a matrix being row-reduced are as follows.

PROPERTIES

Any zero rows occur last.
The first non-zero element in a row occurs anywhere to the right of the first non-zero element in the row above.

The following is not row-reduced. The last row has a non-zero element, 2, which is *not* to the right of the first non-zero element, 1, in the row above.

$$
\left[\begin{array}{ccc|c}
2 & 5 & 0 & 9 \\
0 & 1 & 4 & 0 \\
0 & 2 & 3 & 6
\end{array}\right]
$$

A system of equations can be solved by reducing the corresponding augmented matrix to row-reduced form by means of a sequence of elementary row operations.

Example   Solve the system of equations represented by the augmented matrix A.

$$A = \begin{bmatrix} 2 & -1 & 3 & | & 0 \\ 1 & 1 & -2 & | & 1 \\ 3 & 2 & 4 & | & -13 \end{bmatrix}$$

Solution   The first step is to create a zero in position a_{21}

First multiply row ② by 2.
$$\begin{bmatrix} 2 & -1 & 3 & | & 0 \\ 2 & 2 & -4 & | & 2 \\ 3 & 2 & 4 & | & -13 \end{bmatrix}$$

Then replace row ② by row ② – row ①.
$$\begin{bmatrix} 2 & -1 & 3 & | & 0 \\ 0 & 3 & -7 & | & 2 \\ 3 & 2 & 4 & | & -13 \end{bmatrix}$$

The next step is to create a zero in a_{31}.

Multiply row ③ by 2.
$$\begin{bmatrix} 2 & -1 & 3 & | & 0 \\ 0 & 3 & -7 & | & 2 \\ 6 & 4 & 8 & | & -26 \end{bmatrix}$$

Replace row ③ by row ③ – 3 × row ①.
$$\begin{bmatrix} 2 & -1 & 3 & | & 0 \\ 0 & 3 & -7 & | & 2 \\ 0 & 7 & -1 & | & -26 \end{bmatrix}$$

The final step is to create a zero in a_{32} without introducing non-zero numbers into a_{21} and a_{31}. This is achieved by multiplying row ③ by 3

$$\begin{bmatrix} 2 & -1 & 3 & | & 0 \\ 0 & 3 & -7 & | & 2 \\ 0 & 21 & -3 & | & -78 \end{bmatrix}$$

and then replacing row ③ by row ③ – 7 × row ②, to give B, the row-reduced echelon form of matrix A.

$$B = \begin{bmatrix} 2 & -1 & 3 & | & 0 \\ 0 & 3 & -7 & | & 2 \\ 0 & 0 & 46 & | & -92 \end{bmatrix}$$

The corresponding system of equations can be solved by re-writing the augmented matrix B as a system of equations and by using back-substitution.

$$2x - y + 2z = 0$$
$$3y - 7z = 2$$
$$46z = -92$$

Solving $46z = -92$,
$$z = -2$$

Substituting $z = -2$ in $3y - 7z = 2$,
$$3y - 7(-2) = 2$$
$$y = -4$$

Substituting $z = -2$ and $y = -4$ in $2x - y + 3z = 0$,
$$2x - (-4) + 3(-2) = 0$$
$$x = 1$$

Therefore, the solution is $(x, y, z) = (1, -4, -2)$.   ■

4.3 Exercises

1. Write the augmented matrix for each of the following systems of equations.

   a) $3x - 4y = 17$
       $2x - 3y = 12$

   b) $x + 3y + 4z = 3$
       $4x + y + 4z = 21$
       $2x - 2y - 3z = 8$

   c) $x + 2y - 2z + 4t = 5$
       $x - 2y + 2z - 2t = -5$
       $2x - 3y + z - t = -10$
       $3x + 4y - z - t = 6$

2. Write a system of equations that corresponds to each of the following augmented matrices.

   a) $\begin{bmatrix} 8 & 5 & | & -9 \\ 2 & 3 & | & 10 \end{bmatrix}$

   b) $\begin{bmatrix} 1 & -5 & 3 & | & 26 \\ 1 & 8 & 2 & | & 6 \\ 2 & 6 & 1 & | & 1 \end{bmatrix}$

   c) $\begin{bmatrix} 1 & -2 & 1 & 1 & | & 3 \\ 2 & 1 & -1 & 3 & | & 12 \\ 1 & 1 & 1 & 1 & | & 6 \\ 1 & -1 & 1 & -5 & | & -20 \end{bmatrix}$

3. Identify which of the following matrices are in row-reduced form.

   a) $\begin{bmatrix} 2 & 0 & | & 7 \\ 1 & 0 & | & 2 \end{bmatrix}$

   b) $\begin{bmatrix} 3 & -1 & 5 & | & 0 \\ 0 & 0 & 1 & | & 3 \\ 0 & 0 & 0 & | & 4 \end{bmatrix}$

   c) $\begin{bmatrix} 2 & 6 & 9 & | & 11 \\ 0 & 1 & 5 & | & 6 \\ 0 & 0 & 2 & | & 5 \end{bmatrix}$

   d) $\begin{bmatrix} 3 & 2 & | & 7 \\ 0 & 5 & | & 8 \end{bmatrix}$

   e) $\begin{bmatrix} 3 & 0 & 5 & | & -3 \\ 0 & 0 & 2 & | & 1 \\ 0 & 0 & 0 & | & 4 \end{bmatrix}$

   f) $\begin{bmatrix} 1 & 2 & 6 & | & -5 \\ 0 & 5 & 6 & | & 2 \\ 0 & 0 & 0 & | & 0 \end{bmatrix}$

4. Use matrices to solve the following systems of homogeneous equations.

   a) $2x - 3y = 0$
       $x + y = 0$

   b) $x + y - z = 0$
       $2x + 3y - z = 0$
       $3x - y + 4z = 0$

   c) $x - y + 2z + t = 0$
       $3x + y - z - 5t = 0$
       $x + 2y + z + 3t = 0$
       $2x - 3y - 5z - 2t = 0$

5. Solve the systems of equations in questions 1 and 2 by reducing the corresponding augmented matrices to row-reduced form.

6. Write a computer program to reduce a 3×4 augmented matrix to row-reduced form. It should contain the following steps.

   1. Ask the user to input the coefficients of the matrix.

   2. Display the matrix.

   3. Offer the user a choice of two operations *4* and *5*.

   4. Multiply one row of the matrix by a real number.

   5. Replace one row of the matrix by the sum of that row and a multiple of another row.

   6. Repeat steps *2*, *3*, *4*, *5* until the matrix is row-reduced.

7. Test your program from question 6 on the matrices in question 2.

8. Write a program to reduce a 3×4 augmented matrix to row-reduced form using steps *1* and *2* from question 6 and then no further input from the user. Test this program using the augmented matrix from question 2b).

9. Extend your program from question 6 to include the process of back-substitution to solve the corresponding system of equations. Test your program with the system of equations in question 1b).

4.4 Special Cases

A system of equations in two variables such as
$$2x + 3y = 7$$
$$3x - 2y = 4$$
can be represented by the graphs of two straight lines. The point of intersection of the lines, (2,1), corresponds to the solution of the system of equations, that is, $x = 2$ and $y = 1$.

Systems of equations that have at least one solution are said to be **consistent**.

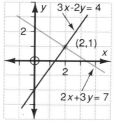

However, some systems of equations represent lines that do not meet. For example the system of equations
$$2x + 3y = 7$$
$$2x + 3y = 14$$
represents two parallel lines.

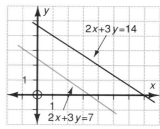

Consider how you would solve these equations either by elimination or by reducing the corresponding augmented matrix to row-reduced form.

To eliminate x you could subtract the two equations, giving $0y = 7$. This equation for y has no solution since division by zero is undefined.

To obtain a zero in the a_{21} position of the matrix $A = \begin{bmatrix} 2 & 3 & 7 \\ 2 & 3 & 14 \end{bmatrix}$
you need to replace row ② by row ② + $(-1) \times$ row ①.

This gives $\begin{bmatrix} 2 & 3 & 7 \\ 0 & 0 & 7 \end{bmatrix}$

A difficulty here occurs when you form the system of equations corresponding to this transformed matrix and try to perform back-substitution.
$$2x + 3y = 7$$
$$0y = 7$$

The second equation has *no solution*: *the last row of the row-reduced matrix has zeros in all the columns* that correspond to variables in the system of equations *but a non-zero value in the last column*.

The same difficulty would occur with a 3×3 system of equations corresponding to the row-reduced matrix A below.

$$A = \left[\begin{array}{ccc|c} 2 & 1 & 3 & 7 \\ 0 & 3 & 4 & -5 \\ 0 & 0 & 0 & 3 \end{array} \right]$$

Here the equation that corresponds to the third row is $0z = 3$ and this has no solution.

Systems of equations that have no solution are said to be **inconsistent**.

Example 1   Determine which of the following row-reduced augmented matrices correspond to systems that are inconsistent.

a) $\left[\begin{array}{cc|c} 2 & 4 & 7 \\ 0 & 2 & 0 \end{array} \right]$
c) $\left[\begin{array}{ccc|c} 3 & 0 & 0 & 5 \\ 0 & 4 & 1 & 0 \\ 0 & 0 & 0 & 3 \end{array} \right]$

b) $\left[\begin{array}{cc|c} 2 & 4 & 7 \\ 0 & 0 & 2 \end{array} \right]$
d) $\left[\begin{array}{ccc|c} 5 & -1 & 2 & 6 \\ 0 & 1 & 0 & 9 \\ 0 & 0 & 2 & 0 \end{array} \right]$

Solution   a) This matrix corresponds to the system

$$2x + 4y = 7$$
$$2y = 0$$

The second equation can be solved to give $y = 0$ and the value for y substituted into the first equation to determine x.

Therefore, the system corresponding to this matrix has a solution.

b) This matrix corresponds to the system

$$2x + 4y = 7$$
$$0y = 2$$

The second has no solution. Therefore, this system has no solution.

c) This matrix corresponds to the system

$$3x = 5$$
$$4y + z = 0$$
$$0z = 3$$

This last equation has no solution. Therefore, the corresponding system has no solution.

d) This matrix corresponds to the system

$$5x - y + 2z = 6$$
$$y = 9$$
$$2z = 0$$

These equations can be solved to give $z = 0$, $y = 9$, $x = 3$. Therefore, this system has a solution.   ■

PROPERTY

A system has *no solution* if the last non-zero row in the augmented row-reduced matrix consists of *zeros in every place except the last*.

A second difficulty occurs when you try to find the point of intersection of the lines given by the equations

$2x - y = 3$ ①
$4x - 2y = 6$ ②

To eliminate x from equations ① and ② add $(-2) \times$ equation ① to equation ② to obtain $0y = 0$. Any real value for y will satisfy this equation. If you look at the graphs of these two lines you see that the two different equations represent the same line, that is, the equations are consistent.

Any point on the line is a solution of this system. Therefore, there is no unique solution, but an infinite number of solutions.

Equation ① can be rearranged to give $x = \dfrac{y + 3}{2}$. Therefore, for any real value a, any point that can be represented by $\left(\dfrac{a + 3}{2}, a \right)$ is a solution of this system. The variable a in this solution is called the **parameter**.

Systems of equations that have an infinite number of solutions are said to be **consistent** and **dependent**. Systems that have a unique solution are said to be **consistent** and **independent**.

If you solve the system above by reducing the corresponding augmented matrix to row-reduced form, you obtain a similar result.

From equations ① and ② the augmented matrix is

$$\begin{bmatrix} 2 & -1 & | & 3 \\ 4 & -2 & | & 6 \end{bmatrix}$$

To obtain a zero in the a_{21} position, add $2 \times$ row ① to row ②. This gives

$$\begin{bmatrix} 2 & -1 & | & 3 \\ 0 & 0 & | & 0 \end{bmatrix}$$

This last row corresponds to the equation

$0y = 0$

which has any real number as the solution for y.

PROPERTY

A system has an *infinite number of solutions* if the last row of the augmented row-reduced matrix consists of *zeros in each place*.

Example 2   Determine which of the augmented row-reduced matrices correspond to a system that has an infinite number of solutions.

a) $\begin{bmatrix} 2 & 4 & | & 6 \\ 0 & 0 & | & 0 \end{bmatrix}$

c) $\begin{bmatrix} 1 & 3 & 7 & | & -2 \\ 0 & 1 & 5 & | & 0 \\ 0 & 0 & 1 & | & 0 \end{bmatrix}$

b) $\begin{bmatrix} 2 & 4 & | & 6 \\ 0 & 1 & | & 0 \end{bmatrix}$

d) $\begin{bmatrix} 2 & 0 & 1 & | & 4 \\ 0 & 2 & 0 & | & 0 \\ 0 & 0 & 0 & | & 0 \end{bmatrix}$

Solution   Since the last row of the matrices a) and d) consists of all zeros, these systems have an infinite number of solutions.   ■

Example 3   Reduce the following augmented matrices to row-reduced form and determine whether the corresponding systems have one, many or no solutions.

a) $A = \begin{bmatrix} 2 & 1 & 3 & | & 5 \\ 2 & 2 & 3 & | & 9 \\ 2 & 3 & 4 & | & 19 \end{bmatrix}$ b) $B = \begin{bmatrix} 1 & 7 & 9 & | & 9 \\ 2 & 6 & 6 & | & 8 \\ 2 & 10 & 12 & | & 16 \end{bmatrix}$ c) $C = \begin{bmatrix} 2 & 1 & 4 & | & 8 \\ 4 & 5 & 8 & | & 22 \\ 2 & 4 & 4 & | & 14 \end{bmatrix}$

Solution   a) Add $(-1) \times$ row ① to row ② and $(-1) \times$ row ① to row ③ to obtain zeros in a_{31} and a_{21} positions.

$\begin{bmatrix} 2 & 1 & 3 & | & 5 \\ 0 & 1 & 0 & | & 4 \\ 0 & 2 & 1 & | & 14 \end{bmatrix}$

Add $(-2) \times$ row ② to row ③ to complete the row-reduction.

$\begin{bmatrix} 2 & 1 & 3 & | & 5 \\ 0 & 1 & 0 & | & 4 \\ 0 & 0 & 1 & | & 6 \end{bmatrix}$

This system can be solved to give a unique solution for (x,y,z).

b) Add $(-2) \times$ row ① to row ② and $(-2) \times$ row ① to row ③ to obtain

$\begin{bmatrix} 1 & 7 & 9 & | & 9 \\ 0 & -8 & -12 & | & -10 \\ 0 & -4 & -6 & | & -2 \end{bmatrix}$

Add $(-0.5) \times$ row ② to row ③

$\begin{bmatrix} 1 & 7 & 9 & | & 9 \\ 0 & -8 & -12 & | & -10 \\ 0 & 0 & 0 & | & 3 \end{bmatrix}$

This last line corresponds to the equation $0z = 3$ which has no solution. Therefore, this system has no solution.

c) Add $-2 \times$ row ① to row ② and $-1 \times$ row ① to row ③ to obtain

$$\begin{bmatrix} 2 & 1 & 4 & | & 8 \\ 0 & 3 & 0 & | & 6 \\ 0 & 3 & 0 & | & 6 \end{bmatrix}$$

Subtracting row ② from row ③ gives

$$\begin{bmatrix} 2 & 1 & 4 & | & 8 \\ 0 & 3 & 0 & | & 6 \\ 0 & 0 & 0 & | & 0 \end{bmatrix}$$

The last line corresponds to the equation $0z = 0$, which is true for all values of z.

Therefore, this system has an infinite number of solutions. ∎

Example 4   The following row-reduced augmented matrices correspond to systems of equations which have an infinite solution set. Determine the most general form of the solution for each system.

a) $\begin{bmatrix} 2 & 3 & -1 & | & 8 \\ 0 & 2 & 5 & | & 10 \\ 0 & 0 & 0 & | & 0 \end{bmatrix}$

b) $\begin{bmatrix} 1 & 3 & 5 & 8 & | & 12 \\ 0 & 0 & 2 & 4 & | & 7 \\ 0 & 0 & 0 & 0 & | & 0 \\ 0 & 0 & 0 & 0 & | & 0 \end{bmatrix}$

Solution   **a)** This matrix corresponds to the system of equations

$$\begin{aligned} 2x + 3y - z &= 8 \quad ① \\ 2y + 5z &= 10 \quad ② \\ 0z &= 0 \quad ③ \end{aligned}$$

Equation ③ is true for all real values of z.

Equation ② may be rearranged to give y in terms of z as

$$y = \frac{10 - 5z}{2}$$

Substituting this expression for y into equation ① gives

$$2x + \frac{3(10 - 5z)}{2} - z = 8$$
$$4x + 30 - 15z - 2z = 16$$
$$4x = 17z - 14$$
$$x = \frac{17z - 14}{4}$$

Therefore, the most general form of the solution of this system is

$\left(\dfrac{17a - 14}{4}, \dfrac{10 - 5a}{2}, a \right)$ where a is the parameter

and can take any real value.

b) This matrix corresponds to the system of equations

$$x + 3y + 5z + 8t = 12 \quad ①$$
$$2z + 4t = 7 \quad ②$$
$$0z + 0t = 0 \quad ③$$
$$0t = 0 \quad ④$$

Equations ③ and ④ are true for all values of z and t.

Equation ② determines z, if t is given, as $z = \dfrac{7 - 4t}{2}$

Substituting $\dfrac{7 - 4t}{2}$ for z in equation ① gives

$$x + 3y + \frac{5(7 - 4t)}{2} + 8t = 12$$
$$2x + 6y + 35 - 20t + 16t = 24$$
$$2x + 6y \qquad\qquad - 4t = -11$$

Therefore, the most general form of the solution of this system is

$\left(\dfrac{-11 + 4b - 6a}{2}, a, \dfrac{7 - 4b}{2}, b \right)$ where a and b are parameters
that can take any real value. ■

The number of solutions of a system of linear equations can be summarized using the concept of the rank of a matrix.

DEFINITION

The **rank** of a matrix is the number of non-zero rows in the row-reduced form of the matrix.

Consider the row-reduced augmented matrices A, B and C below.

$$A = \begin{bmatrix} 1 & 3 & 5 & | & 7 \\ 0 & 4 & 1 & | & 9 \\ 0 & 0 & 2 & | & 4 \end{bmatrix} \quad B = \begin{bmatrix} 1 & 3 & 5 & | & 7 \\ 0 & 4 & 1 & | & 9 \\ 0 & 0 & 0 & | & 5 \end{bmatrix} \quad C = \begin{bmatrix} 1 & 3 & 5 & | & 7 \\ 0 & 4 & 1 & | & 9 \\ 0 & 0 & 0 & | & 0 \end{bmatrix}$$

Matrix	Rank of coefficient matrix	Rank of augmented matrix	Number of variables	Number of solutions
A	3	3	3	one
B	2	3	3	none
C	2	2	3	infinite

PROPERTIES

If the rank of the coefficient matrix equals the rank of the augmented matrix, the system is consistent and there is at least one solution.

If the ranks of the coefficient and augmented matrices *and* the number of variables are equal, the system is consistent and independent and there is a unique solution.

If the rank of the coefficient matrix is less than the rank of the augmented matrix, the system is inconsistent and there are no solutions.

If the rank of the coefficient matrix equals the rank of the augmented matrix but is less than the number of variables, the system is dependent and there are an infinite number of solutions.

If r = rank of the coefficient matrix = rank of the augmented matrix and n = number of variables, then $n - r$ is the number of parameters in the solution.

For homogeneous systems the last column in the augmented matrix consists of zeros. Therefore, the ranks of the coefficient and augmented matrices are equal for all homogeneous systems. This leads to the fact that all homogeneous systems have at least one solution, namely (0,0) or (0,0,0) or (0,0,0,0), as you have found in Exercises 4.2 question 14, and 4.3 question 4.

The following example shows that some homogeneous systems have an infinite number of solutions.

Example 5   Three children, Jim, Cathy and Peter are playing on a teeterboard. They discover that they can balance the teeterboard in three positions. If Jim and Cathy sit together 1 m from the centre, they balance Peter sitting 2 m from the centre on the opposite side. If j, c and p represent the weights of the three children, the law of the lever gives the equation
$j + c = 2p$ ①

If Jim and Peter sit together 1 m from the centre, they balance Cathy sitting 1.5 m from the centre on the opposite side. This can be represented by the equation
$j + p = 1.5c$ ②

If Jim sits 1.5 m from the centre and Cathy sits 1 m away from the centre on the opposite side they are balanced. This gives the equation
$1.5j = 1c$ ③

Solve the homogeneous system of equations ① ② ③ using matrices.

Solution The equations ① ② ③ can be rewritten as

$$j + \quad c - 2p = 0$$
$$j - 1.5c + \quad p = 0$$
$$1.5j - \quad c \qquad = 0$$

This system can be represented by the augmented matrix M, where

$$M = \begin{bmatrix} 1 & 1 & -2 & \bigm| & 0 \\ 1 & -1.5 & 1 & \bigm| & 0 \\ 1.5 & -1 & 0 & \bigm| & 0 \end{bmatrix}$$

This can be row-reduced in the following steps.

row① – row②
1.5 × row① – row③

$$\begin{bmatrix} 1 & 1 & -2 & \bigm| & 0 \\ 0 & 2.5 & -3 & \bigm| & 0 \\ 0 & 2.5 & -3 & \bigm| & 0 \end{bmatrix}$$

row② – row③

$$\begin{bmatrix} 1 & 1 & -2 & \bigm| & 0 \\ 0 & 2.5 & -3 & \bigm| & 0 \\ 0 & 0 & 0 & \bigm| & 0 \end{bmatrix}$$

This matrix corresponds to the equations

$$j + c - 2p = 0 \quad ④$$
$$2.5c - 3p = 0 \quad ⑤$$
$$0p = 0 \quad ⑥$$

Equation ⑥ implies that p can take any real value.

Equation ⑤ gives $c = 1.2p$ and equation ④ gives

$$j + 1.2p - 2p = 0$$

or $\qquad j = 0.8\,p$

Therefore, the general solution of the given system of homogeneous equations is $(j,c,p) = (0.8a, 1.2a, a)$ where a can be any real number. The information obtained from the teeterboard was not sufficient to determine the weights of the three children. It did tell us that their weights are in the ratio $0.8 : 1.2 : 1$. ■

Computer programs can solve systems of equations like those in this section. A program should give appropriate messages for one, none, or many solutions, and can be tested in the systems above, or in the next exercises.

4.4 Exercises

1. Determine the number of solutions of the systems corresponding to the following row-reduced augmented matrices.

a) $\begin{bmatrix} 1 & 5 & | & 8 \\ 0 & 2 & | & 0 \end{bmatrix}$

b) $\begin{bmatrix} 2 & -8 & | & 11 \\ 0 & 0 & | & 2 \end{bmatrix}$

c) $\begin{bmatrix} 1 & 0 & | & 8 \\ 0 & 0 & | & 0 \end{bmatrix}$

d) $\begin{bmatrix} 1 & 3 & 8 & | & 2 \\ 0 & 1 & 3 & | & 8 \\ 0 & 0 & 0 & | & 5 \end{bmatrix}$

e) $\begin{bmatrix} 2 & 0 & 5 & | & 0 \\ 0 & 1 & 0 & | & 0 \\ 0 & 0 & 0 & | & 0 \end{bmatrix}$

f) $\begin{bmatrix} 1 & 5 & -3 & | & 5 \\ 0 & 3 & 5 & | & 0 \\ 0 & 0 & 2 & | & 0 \end{bmatrix}$

g) $\begin{bmatrix} 1 & 3 & 5 & 8 & | & 12 \\ 0 & 4 & 2 & 1 & | & 8 \\ 0 & 0 & 1 & 0 & | & 0 \\ 0 & 0 & 0 & 0 & | & 0 \end{bmatrix}$

h) $\begin{bmatrix} 2 & 4 & 6 & 0 & | & 18 \\ 0 & 1 & 0 & 0 & | & 5 \\ 0 & 0 & 2 & 0 & | & 6 \\ 0 & 0 & 0 & 0 & | & 4 \end{bmatrix}$

i) $\begin{bmatrix} 1 & 5 & 7 & 9 & | & 22 \\ 0 & -2 & 6 & 2 & | & 2 \\ 0 & 0 & 4 & -3 & | & 1 \\ 0 & 0 & 0 & 5 & | & 5 \end{bmatrix}$

2. For each system in question 1 that has one solution, determine that solution.

3. For each system in question 1 that has an infinite number of solutions, determine the most general form of that solution.

4. Illustrate graphically the solutions to parts a), b), and c) of question 1.

5. Row-reduce the following augmented matrices to echelon form and then determine the number of solutions in each case.

a) $\begin{bmatrix} 2 & 4 & | & 8 \\ 1 & 6 & | & 8 \end{bmatrix}$

b) $\begin{bmatrix} 3 & -5 & | & -7 \\ -6 & 10 & | & 14 \end{bmatrix}$

c) $\begin{bmatrix} -1 & 8 & | & 5 \\ -2 & 16 & | & 20 \end{bmatrix}$

d) $\begin{bmatrix} 3 & 5 & -3 & | & 8 \\ 1 & -3 & 2 & | & 4 \\ 4 & 2 & -1 & | & 12 \end{bmatrix}$

e) $\begin{bmatrix} 4 & 1 & 2 & | & 5 \\ 1 & 3 & 0 & | & 9 \\ 6 & 7 & 2 & | & 10 \end{bmatrix}$

f) $\begin{bmatrix} 3 & 1 & 5 & | & -10 \\ -2 & 4 & 8 & | & -14 \\ 1 & 2 & 3 & | & -8 \end{bmatrix}$

g) $\begin{bmatrix} 2 & 4 & 5 & -1 & | & 8 \\ 0 & 3 & 0 & 4 & | & 1 \\ 1 & 5 & 6 & 0 & | & 11 \\ 3 & 12 & 11 & 3 & | & 20 \end{bmatrix}$

h) $\begin{bmatrix} 1 & 0 & 3 & 2 & | & 5 \\ 0 & 4 & 1 & -2 & | & 3 \\ 1 & 3 & 0 & 1 & | & 4 \\ 2 & 7 & 4 & 1 & | & 16 \end{bmatrix}$

6. For each system in question 5 that has one solution, determine that solution.

7. For each system in question 5 that has an infinite number of solutions, determine the most general form of that solution.

8. Illustrate graphically the solutions to parts a), b), and c) of question 5.

9. Write a computer program to solve a system of three equations in three variables. Make sure that your program will give appropriate messages for one, none, or many solutions. Test your program with the systems in question 5 d), e) and f). Modifications will be needed for special cases.

4.5   The Solution of m Equations in n Variables, where $m \neq n$

Up till now you have dealt with systems of equations in which the number variables and the number of equations were the same, that is 2 equations in 2 variables, 3 equations in 3 variables or 4 equations in 4 variables. In many real life applications the number of constraints on the variables, and hence the number of equations, is not the same as the number of variables.

Consider the case where the number, m, of equations is less than the number, n, of variables. Suppose three variables, x, y and z satisfy the equations

$$2x + 4y - 5z = 12$$
$$x + y + z = -10$$

A third equation may be formed, namely $0x + 0y + 0z = 0$, which is true for all values of x, y and z. This system can be solved by methods you have already learned.

An equation such as $0x + 0y + 0z = 0$ corresponds to a row of zeros in the augmented matrix.

If an augmented matrix for a system in four variables is

$$\begin{bmatrix} 2 & 1 & 5 & 7 & | & 9 \\ 0 & 3 & 1 & 5 & | & 6 \end{bmatrix}$$

you can add two rows of zeroes to this matrix to obtain a 4×4 matrix

$$\begin{bmatrix} 2 & 1 & 5 & 7 & | & 9 \\ 0 & 3 & 1 & 5 & | & 6 \\ 0 & 0 & 0 & 0 & | & 0 \\ 0 & 0 & 0 & 0 & | & 0 \end{bmatrix}$$

This system can then be solved by the usual methods.

A different situation arises when the number, m, of equations is greater than the number, n, of variables. The following example illustrates the situation with two variables.

Example   Determine the solution of the following systems, if possible, and illustrate graphically.

a) $2x + 3y = 5$
    $x - 2y = -1$
    $3x + 4y = 7$

b) $2x + 3y = 5$
    $x - 2y = -1$
    $3x + 4y = 10$

c) $2x + 3y = 5$
    $2x + 3y = 6$
    $x - 2y = -1$

Solution   Three linear equations represent the graphs of three straight lines. If the three lines pass through a common point of intersection there will be a solution to the system.

a) Use two of the equations to determine the point of intersection, if any, of these two lines.

The first two equations $2x + 3y = 5$
$$x - 2y = -1$$
can be solved to give $(1,1)$.

This solution must then be checked in the third equation
$$3x + 4y = 7$$
If $(x,y) = (1,1)$ then $L.S. = 3(1) + 4(1) = 7$ and $R.S. = 7$
Therefore, $L.S. = R.S.$

The solution $(1,1)$ satisfies all three equations. The corresponding lines pass through the common point $(1,1)$ as shown in diagram 1.

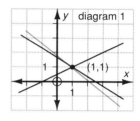

b) The system to be solved is
$$2x + 3y = 5$$
$$x - 2y = -1$$
$$3x + 4y = 10$$
The first two equations can be solved to determine the solution $(1,1)$. Checking this solution in the equation $3x + 4y = 10$ gives $3(1) + 4(1) = 7$ which is not equal to 10. Therefore, the solution of the first two equations is not a solution of the third one. This corresponds to the graphs of three lines which do not intersect at a common point, shown in diagram 2.

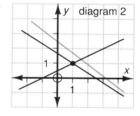

c) The system to be solved is
$$2x + 3y = 5$$
$$2x + 3y = 6$$
$$x - 2y = -1$$
Solving the equations $2x + 3y = 5$ by subtracting them
$$2x + 3y = 6$$
gives $0y = 1$ which has no solution. Therefore, the whole system has no solution. The graph of these lines shows two parallel lines. See diagram 3.   ■

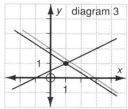

In general, if the number of equations, m, exceeds the number of variables, n, choose n of the equations and solve these. Then, if there is a solution for these equations, check it in the remaining equations.

4.5 Exercises

1. Determine the solutions of the following systems.

   a) $x - 3y = 10$
   $2x + 4y = 10$

   g) $x - 3y = 0$
   $-2x + 6y = 2$
   $2x + 4y = 10$

   b) $x - 3y = 0$
   $2x + 4y = 10$
   $x + 5y = 8$

   h) $x - 3y = 0$
   $-2x + 6y = 0$
   $3x - 9y = 0$

   c) $x - 3y = 0$
   $2x + 4y = 10$
   $x + 5y = 11$

   i) $x - 3y = 0$
   $2x + 4y = 10$
   $3x - 2y = 7$
   $4x + 5y = 17$

   d) $x - 3y = 0$
   $-2x + 6y = 0$

   j) $x - 3y = 0$
   $2x + 4y = 10$
   $3x - 2y = 7$
   $x + y = 6$

   e) $x - 3y = 0$
   $-2x + 6y = 2$

   k) $x - 3y = 0$
   $2x + 4y = 10$
   $-2x + 6y = 2$
   $x + y = 6$

   f) $x - 3y = 0$
   $-2x + 6y = 0$
   $2x + 4y = 10$

   l) $x - 3y = 0$
   $2x + 4y = 10$
   $-2x + 6y = 2$
   $x + 2y = 5$

2. Illustrate each part of question 1 graphically.

3. Write a computer program to solve a system of m equations in two variables, where $m = 1, 2, 3,$ or 4. Make sure that your program will give appropriate messages for one, none, or many solutions. Test your program with the systems in question 1.

4. Determine the solutions (if any) of the following systems.

   a) $2x - y + z = -2$
   $3x + y + 2z = 7$
   $x + y - z = 5$
   $x - y + 3z = -3$

   b) $x + y + z = 3$
   $2x - 3y + 5z = 4$
   $x + y - 3z = -2$
   $3x + 2y + 2z = 7$

5. Solve the following systems of equations.

   a) $x + 2y - 3z = 4$
   $2x + y + 4z = 2$

   b) $x - 3y + 4z + t = 1$
   $2x - y + z - 2t = 2$
   $3x + y - 2z + 3t = 3$

   c) $x + 3y = 4$

   d) $x + 3y + z = 5$

   e) $2x - 3y - z + t = 0$

   f) $3x + y + 2z - 5t = 3$
   $x - 2y + z + t = 1$

6. Write a computer program that will solve a system of m equations in three variables, where $m = 1, 2, 3,$ or 4. The program should give appropriate messages for one, none, or many solutions. Test your program with the systems in question 4.

7. Extend your program from question 6 to solve a system of m equations in n unknowns, where $1 \leqslant m \leqslant 4$ and $2 \leqslant n \leqslant 4$. Test your program with the systems in questions 5 b), 5 e) and 5 f).

8. Solve the following systems of homogeneous equations.

   a) $x + 2y = 0$
   $2x + 4y = 0$
   $-3x + 6y = 0$

   c) $x - 3y = 0$
   $2x + 4y = 0$
   $x + 2y = 0$

   b) $x + y + z = 0$
   $2x + y + 3z = 0$
   $3x + 4y + 2z = 0$
   $x - y + 3z = 0$

   d) $3x + y - 4z = 0$
   $-4x - y + 6z = 0$
   $-2x - y + 3z = 0$
   $3x + y - 5z = 0$

9. Illustrate graphically questions 8 a) and 8 c).

4.6 Systems of Linear Inequalities

If two numbers are represented by x and y, then the two statements
"The sum of two numbers is 10" and
"The sum of two number is greater than 10"
can be modelled algebraically and geometrically as follows.

The algebraic equation	the algebraic linear inequality
$x + y = 10$	$x + y > 10$
corresponds geometrically to the points on the line	corresponds geometrically to the points on the x-y plane that lie above the line $x + y = 10$

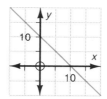
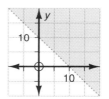

You have graphed regions that represent inequalities in earlier grades.

Example 1   Graph the system
$$y > 2x + 1$$
$$2x + y \leqslant 5$$

Solution   For the inequality $y > 2x + 1$ you should first draw the boundary line $y = 2x + 1$, using a table of values if necessary. This line will be broken because y cannot equal $2x + 1$.

To determine which side of the line is to be shaded, you can use a "test point". Any point that does not lie on the line is suitable. Choose (0,0). Substitute the values $x = 0$ and $y = 0$ into each side of the inequality $y > 2x + 1$ to obtain $y = 0$ and $2x + 1 = 2(0) + 1$, or 1.

Since 0 is not greater than 1, the test point, (0,0), does not satisfy the inequality $y > 2x + 1$. Therefore, the point (0,0) is not in the shaded region.

Therefore the required region will lie *above* the line $y = 2x + 1$, as shown in diagram 1.

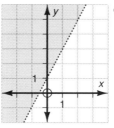
diagram 1

For the inequality $2x + y \leqslant 5$ you should first draw the boundary line $2x + y = 5$. This is a solid line this time, since $2x + 5$ can equal the value 5. You can again use the point (0,0) as a test point, since it does not lie on the line $2x + y = 5$.

Since $2(0) + (0) = 0$ which is less than 5, (0,0) lies in the shaded region. Therefore, the region to be shaded is *under* the line $2x + y = 5$, as shown in diagram 2.

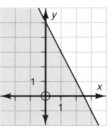

diagram 2

The final graph of the given system of inequalities is the *intersection* of the shaded regions in diagrams 1 and 2.
This is shown in diagram 3.

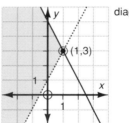

diagram 3

The coordinates of the point of intersection of the two lines $y = 2x + 1$ and $2x + y = 5$ can be found by solving the system of equations below.
$y = 2x + 1$
$2x + y = 5$
The point of intersection is (1,3).   ■

Example 2   A cross-country skier takes chocolate and raisins in her pack. She needs to carry at least 1000 calories. The chocolate has 5 calories per gram and the raisins have 3 calories per gram. The chocolate costs $1 for 100 grams and raisins cost $1.50 for 100 grams. She has only $3 to spend on snacks. Find a system of inequalities that describes the possible quantities of chocolate and raisins that she might take.

Solution   Let x represent the number of grams of chocolate and y represent the number of grams of raisins that she takes with her.
Then the total number of calories is $5x + 3y$.
Since she needs at least 1000 calories
$$5x + 3y \geqslant 1000 \quad \text{①}$$

This is one inequality that describes the quantities of chocolate and raisins. The cost of 100 g of chocolate is $1, therefore, the cost of 1 g is 1 cent. Therefore, the cost of x g of chocolate is x cents.

The cost of 100 g of raisins is $1.50, therefore the cost of 1 g is 1.5 cents.

Therefore, the cost of y g of raisins is $1.5y$ cents.

Since she has only $3 (= 300 cents) to spend, the total cost of the raisins and the chocolate must be less than or equal to 300.

Therefore, the second inequality is
$$x + 1.5y \leqslant 300 \quad \text{②}$$
x and y must also satisfy the inequalities $x \geqslant 0$ ③ and $y \geqslant 0$ ④.   ■

Example 3   Sketch the region defined by the inequalities in Example 2.

Solution   One method of sketching the lines is to find their x and y intercepts.
To find the x-intercept, put $y = 0$ into the equation.

To find the y-intercept, put $x = 0$ into the equation.

To graph the inequality $5x + 3y \geqslant 1000$, you must first draw the line $5x + 3y = 1000$. It will be a solid line with x-intercept 200 and y-intercept approximately 333. Using $(0,0)$ as a test point, you find that the shaded region lies above this line. To graph the inequality $x + 1.5y \leqslant 300$ you must first graph the line $x + 1.5y = 300$. This is a solid line with x-intercept 300 and y-intercept 200. Again using $(0,0)$ as a test point, you find the required region is below this line.

$x \geqslant 0$ represents points to the right of the y-axis,
$y \geqslant 0$ represents points above the x-axis.

The region defined by all four inequalities of Example 2 is the intersection of these four regions, as shown in the diagram.   ■

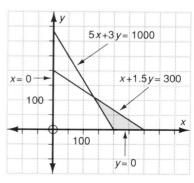

Example 4   A school board is hiring staff for a new elementary school. Each teacher is paid $25 000 per year and each teacher's aide is paid $15 000 per year. The total budget for teachers' and teacher's aides' salaries is $600 000 per year. There must be at least 12 teachers and at least one teacher's aide for each teacher. Determine the inequalities that must be satisfied by the numbers of teachers and numbers of teacher's aides.

Solution   Let t represent the number of teachers hired and a represent the number of aides hired.

Since there cannot be a negative number of either
$t \geqslant 0$ and $a \geqslant 0$.   ①

The total annual salary paid to t teachers and a aides is $25\ 000t + 15\ 000a$.

Since this must be less than $600\ 000$
$25\ 000t + 15\ 000a \leqslant 600\ 000$
or, dividing by 5000
$5t + 3a \leqslant 120$ ②

Since there must be at least 12 teachers
$t \geqslant 12$ ③

Since there must be least one teacher's aide for each teacher
$a \geqslant t$ ④

The inequalities ① ② ③ ④ must be satisfied by the number, t, of teachers and the number, a, of teacher's aides. ∎

Example 5   Sketch a graph of the region represented by the inequalities in Example 4.

Solution   First of all you need to decide which axis will represent the variable a and which will represent t. Plot t along the horizontal axis and a along the vertical axis.

Then the inequality $t \geqslant 0$ corresponds to points to the right of the vertical axis. The inequality $a \geqslant 0$ corresponds to points above the horizontal axis. The intersection of these two regions is shown in diagram 1.

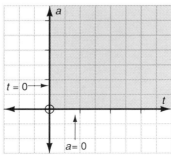

diagram 1

To sketch the region represented by
$$5t + 3a \leqslant 120 \qquad ②$$
first draw the boundary line,
$$5t + 3a = 120.$$
Then consider a test point.
Since the point (0,0) does not lie on
the line $5t + 3a = 120$, you use it as a
test point. Substitute the coordinates
(0,0) into ② to obtain
$$5(0) + 3(0) \leqslant 120$$
or $\qquad\qquad 0 \leqslant 120$

Since this is true, (0,0) lies in the
shaded region. Therefore,
the region given by the inequality ②
is shown in diagram 2.

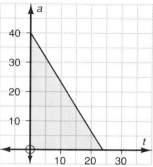

diagram 2

The graph of $t \geqslant 12$ consists of points
to the right of the vertical line $t = 12$,
as shown in diagram 3.

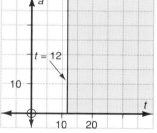

diagram 3

The graph of $a \geqslant t$ consists of
the points above the line $a = t$,
as shown in diagram 4.

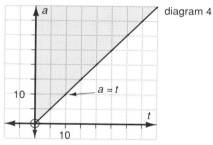

diagram 4

The intersection of these graphs
shown in diagram 5
shows the
possible values for t and a.
This is called the **feasible region**
for these variables.

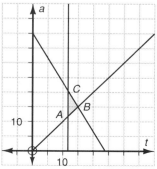

diagram 5

4.6 Exercises

1. Sketch the graph of the region represented by each of the following systems of linear inequalities.
   a) $x \geqslant 0$
      $y < 5$
      $y > x - 3$
   b) $y < 3x - 2$
      $y < 10 - x$
      $y \geqslant 0$
   c) $2x + 3y < 6$
      $2x + 3y \geqslant -6$

2. Find the vertices of all the regions in question 1.

3. Write an inequality to represent each of the following constraints.
   a) The time, t, taken must not exceed 5 s.
   b) The sum of the age, a, of the teacher and her years, y, of service must not exceed 90.
   c) The variables x, y and z must be non-negative.
   d) The speed, s, of the vehicle must not exceed the speed limit, p, by more than 10 km/h.
   e) The difference between the age of the mother, m, and the age of the child, d, does not exceed 50.

4. Draw sketch graphs to show the feasible regions for the variables in 3b), d) and e).

5. A mathematics contest paper consists of a part A with 6 questions worth 4 marks each and a part B with 4 questions worth 6 marks each.
   a) Choose variables to represent the numbers of questions that you attempt from each part of the paper and state any necessary restrictions on the variables.
   b) Write inequalities that express the following constraints. (Assume that you score full marks if you answer a question.) You must answer at least three questions from part A and at least two from part B. You want to obtain at least 36 points.
   c) Graph the feasible region.

6. Two types of condensed food for a camping trip are Camp-Grub and Pack-Rations. Each 100 g of the two foods contain the following nutrients.

	Vitamins	Calories	Protein	Carbo-hydrates
Camp-Grub	80 units	160	8 g	25 g
Pack-Rations	20 units	150	32 g	30 g

   a) Choose suitable variables for the amount of Camp-Grub and Pack-Rations that you take on the trip.
   b) Write inequalities to express the following, which are calculated for the whole trip.
      You need at least 3000 units of vitamins.
      You need no less than 15 000 calories.
      Your protein needs are at least 700 g.
      You need at least 3500 g of carbohydrates.
      The total weight of the rations must not exceed 15 kg.
   c) Plot a graph to show the feasible region formed by the inequalities from part b).
   d) Find the coordinates of the vertices of the feasible region.

7. Write a system of inequalities to represent each of the following regions sketched below.
   a)

   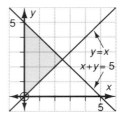

   b)

   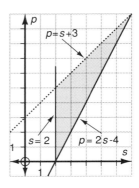

4.7 Formulation of Linear Programming Problems

Consider again the problem (that you met in Example 4 of section 4.6) of hiring teachers and teacher's aides for the new elementary school. The teachers are paid $25 000 annually and the teacher's aides are paid $15 000 annually. The total salary budget is $600 000 per year. The minimum number of teachers is 12 and there must be at least one teacher's aide for each teacher. If t represents the number of teachers hired and a the number of aides hired, the given constraints can be represented by the inequalities.

$t \geqslant 0; a \geqslant 0; 5t + 3a \leqslant 120; t \geqslant 12; a \geqslant t.$

Suppose you want to hire the greatest number of staff, teachers and teacher's aides together. This is a **linear programming** problem.

The problem is to find the maximum value that $t + a$ can take and still satisfy the given constraints.

The function $t + a$ is called the **objective function** for this problem.

A linear programming problem consists of optimizing (that is minimizing or maximizing) some function (the objective function) subject to various constraints. The problem is *linear* if the constraints and the objective function are represented by *linear* functions of the variables.

To formulate such a problem, you need to

1. specify the variables for the situation
2. express the constraints (or conditions) on the variables in terms of linear inequalities.
3. identify the objective function.

Example   A mining company has two mines. Takoma East and Takoma West. One shift of 100 miners at each of the mines produces lead, uranium and nickel ores in the following amounts.

Ore	Takoma East	Takoma West
Lead	2 tonnes	5 tonnes
Uranium	400 tonnes	300 tonnes
Nickel	500 tonnes	500 tonnes

The forecast demand for each of these ores for the next year is:

    900   tonnes of lead
100 000   tonnes of uranium
150 000   tonnes of nickel

How many shifts of 100 miners should be worked at each of the mines in the coming year to keep the salary bill to a minimum? Formulate this problem as a linear programming problem.

Solution   The first step is to identify the variables. The number of shifts worked at each mine determines the salaries and production of each ore. Therefore, let the number of shifts at Takoma East and Takoma West be represented by x and y respectively.

The second step is to list the inequalities that must be satisfied by x and y. Obviously $x \geqslant 0$ and $y \geqslant 0$.   ①

In order to provide 900 tonnes of lead
$$2x + 5y \geqslant 900$$ ②

In order to provide 100 000 tonnes of uranium
$$400x + 300y \geqslant 100\ 000$$
or $$4x + 3y \geqslant 1\ 000$$ ③

In order to provide 150 000 tonnes of nickel
$$500x + 500y \geqslant 150\ 000$$
or $$x + y \geqslant 300$$ ④

The salary bill will be proportional to the total number of shifts worked at the two mines, that is, $x + y$.

Therefore you have the third step.
The objective function is $x + y$.   ■

4.7 Exercises

Formulate each of the following situations as a linear programming problem. Be sure to specify the variables, express the constraints as inequalities and identify the objective function.

1. The Canadian Motor Company makes two models of economy car, the Beaver and the Moose. The company makes a profit of $400 on each Beaver that it sells and $300 on each Moose. The labour requirements for each car are given in the table below.

Car	Assembly	Finishing	Testing
Beaver	150 h	50 h	10 h
Moose	60 h	40 h	20 h

During each production run, there are 30 000 h available for assembly, 13 000 h for finishing and 5 000 h for testing. How many cars of each model should be made in order to maximize the profit of each production run?

2. An oil company operates two refineries, 1 and 2, which produce gasoline, heavy engine oil and kerosene in different proportions from each litre of crude oil supplied to the refinery. The proportions are shown in the table below.

	Refinery 1	Refinery 2
Gasoline	0.5	0.3
Heavy engine oil	0.3	0.3
Kerosene	0.2	0.4

The company has agreed to supply its customers with the following daily amounts.

50 000 L	gasoline
42 000 L	heavy engine oil
40 000 L	kerosene

Find the minimum volume of crude oil that is necessary to meet these demands.

3. Two machine operators, Pat and Frank, make bolts and nails. Pat can make 600 bolts and 400 nails per hour. Frank can make 1000 bolts and 400 nails per hour. Pat earns $15 per hour and Frank earns $20 per hour. For how many hours should each work to fill an order for 6000 bolts and 3200 nails at minimum cost?

4. Three stores A, B, and C are stocked from two warehouses X and Y. Each warehouse has 12 cartons of a particular item and each of three stores wants 8 cartons. The shipping cost per carton from warehouse to store are given in chart below. Determine the number of cartons to be shipped from each warehouse with minimum transportation cost.

Store Warehouse	A	B	C
X	$2	$2	$3
Y	$4	$3	$4

5. A manufacturer of two types of skis, beginner and racing, has a great demand for her product. She can sell all the skis she can make. Three machines are used in the manufacturing process for the times shown in the chart below.

	Machine Time		
Machine	1	2	3
Beginner	30 m	60 m	48 m
Racing	60 m	30 m	48 m

No machine may be operated for more than 8 h per day. The profit on beginner skis is $40 and on racing skis is $30. Find the number of each type of skis that should be manufactured for a maximum profit.

4.8 Solving Linear Programming Problems

Consider again the problem that you met (in sections 4.6 and 4.7) of hiring teachers and teacher's aides for the new elementary school. If t and a represent the numbers of teachers and teacher's aides respectively, the constraints that must be satisfied are:

$t \geqslant 0$; $a \geqslant 0$; $5t + 3a \leqslant 120$; $t \geqslant 12$; $a \geqslant t$.

These constraints correspond to a feasible region shown in the diagram.

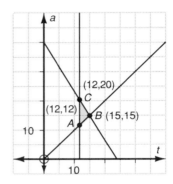

To find the maximum number of teachers and teacher's aides that can be hired, you need to find the maximum value that the objective function, $t + a$, can take for points in the feasible region.

Notice that

$t + a = c$, where c is a constant

represents a series of parallel lines with slope -1 and t and a intercepts equal to the constant value, c. Therefore, the problem is to find the maximum value for this constant c, so that the line $t + a = c$ intercepts the feasible region. The diagram below shows several of these lines.

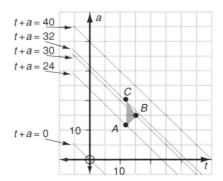

It is clear that the maximum value will occur at one of the vertices of the feasible region. Therefore, a quick way to solve this problem is to evaluate the quantity to be maximized, $t + a$, at each of the vertices.

At the vertex $A(12,12)$, $t + a = 24$

At the vertex $B(15,15)$, $t + a = 30$

At the vertex $C(12,20)$, $t + a = 32$

Therefore, the maximum number of teachers and teachers aides that can be hired is 32, 12 teachers and 20 teacher's aides.

To solve linear programming problems in two variables you need to take three steps.

1. Express the constraints (or conditions) on the variables in terms of linear inequalities.

2. Solve this system of inequalities graphically, to obtain the feasible region.

3. Evaluate the objective function at each of the vertices of the feasible region and select the optimum solution, which may be a maximum or a minimum.

Example 1

In Examples 2 and 3 of section 4.6, you met a cross-country skier who was taking x grams of chocolate and y grams of raisins with her. In order to have at least 1000 calories with her and spend at most \$3, the variables must satisfy the inequalities $x \geq 0$; $5x + 3y \geq 1000$; $x + 1.5y \leq 300$. Determine the quantities of chocolate and raisins that she should pack to keep the weight of food to a minimum.

Solution

The feasible region is shown in the diagram.

The vertices are the points

$A(300,0)$, $B(200,0)$, $C\left(\dfrac{400}{3}, \dfrac{1000}{9}\right)$.

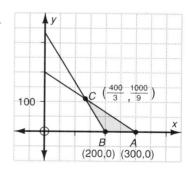

The weight of the food is $x + y$ grams. This is the objective function. Evaluating $x + y$ at each vertex gives the following results.

Point	$x + y$
$A(300,0)$	300
$B(200,0)$	200
$C\left(\dfrac{400}{3}, \dfrac{1000}{9}\right)$	$\dfrac{2200}{9} = 244.\dot{4}$

Therefore, she should take 200 grams of chocolate and no raisins. ∎

Example 2   In the Example in section 4.7, you met the mining company that produces lead, uranium and nickel at two mines, Takoma East and Takoma West. How many shifts of 100 miners should be worked at each of the mines in the coming year to keep the salary bill to a minimum?

Solution   Let the number of shifts worked at Takoma East and Takoma West be x and y respectively.

The inequalities that must be satisfied by x and y were determined in the previous section. They are:

$$
\begin{array}{rcll}
x & \geqslant & 0 & \text{①} \\
2x + 5y & \geqslant & 900 & \text{②} \\
4x + 3y & \geqslant & 1000 & \text{③} \\
x + y & \geqslant & 300 & \text{④}
\end{array}
$$

The next step is to draw the feasible region bounded by these inequalities and to find the vertices of this region. The vertices $A(0,333.\dot{3})$, $B(100,200)$, $C(200,100)$ and $D(450,0)$ are shown in the diagram.

The feasible region extends indefinitely in the first quadrant to the right and above the boundary lines.

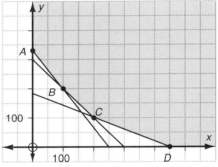

The salary will be proportional to the total number of shifts worked at the two mines, that is $x + y$. Therefore, the final step is to evaluate the objective function, $x + y$, at each of the vertices of the feasible region.

Vertex	$x + y$
$A(0,333.3)$	333.3
$B(100,200)$	300
$C(200,100)$	300
$D(450,0)$	450

Therefore, there are two vertices B and C which will provide a minimum value for $x + y$.

This surprising result becomes clearer if you look at the intersection of the lines $x + y = $ constant and the feasible region. These lines are parallel to the line BC which is part of the boundary of the feasible region.

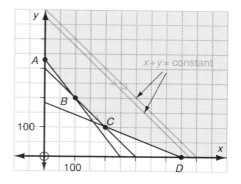

Any point on the line BC will also produce the same minimum value of 300 for $x + y$.

Therefore, the solution to this problem is that a total of 300 shifts should be worked at the two mines. The number of shifts at Takoma East should be between 100 and 200, and the remaining shifts should be worked at Takoma West. ■

Example 2 is an example of an ambiguous solution to a linear programming problem, because the conditions are not sufficient to determine a unique solution.

It will be useful and interesting to investigate further what happens in various cases.

Example 3   Assume that the salary bill in the two mines Takoma East and Takoma West is a minimum, that is $x + y = 300$. Determine the quantities of each of the ores mined if the following number of shifts are worked:

	a)	b)	c)	d)	e)
Takoma East	100	125	150	175	200
Takoma West	200	175	150	125	100

Solution   If x, y represent the number of shifts worked at Takoma East and Takoma West respectively, the amount of lead ore is $2x + 5y$, the amount of uranium is $400x + 300y$ and the amount of nickel is $500x + 500y$. Therefore

a) if $x = 100$ and $y = 200$ the amount of each ore is

lead	1 200	tonnes
uranium	100 000	tonnes
nickel	150 000	tonnes

b) if $x = 125$ and $y = 175$, you have

lead	1 125	tonnes
uranium	102 500	tonnes
nickel	150 000	tonnes

c) if $x = 150$ and $y = 150$, you have

lead	1 050	tonnes
uranium	105 000	tonnes
nickel	150 000	tonnes

d) if $x = 175$ and $y = 125$, you have

lead	975	tonnes
uranium	107 500	tonnes
nickel	150 000	tonnes

e) if $x = 200$ and $y = 100$, you have

lead	900	tonnes
uranium	110 000	tonnes
nickel	150 000	tonnes

Notice that each of these situations satisfies the conditions that the salary bill should be a minimum and that at least 900 tonnes of lead and 100 000 tonnes of uranium should be mined.

Since each of the points lies on the line $x + y = 300$ and the amount of nickel is given by $500x + 500y = 500(x + y)$, each choice produces exactly 150 000 tonnes of nickel.

The choice of exactly how many shifts should be worked at each mine, subject to the conditions stated in Example 2, might depend on the likelihood of being able to sell excess lead or uranium ore.

4.8 Exercises

1. Graph the feasible region determined by each of the following systems of inequalities.
   a) $y \geq 2x - 3$
      $x \geq 0$
      $y \leq x + 3$
   b) $x \geq 2$
      $2y \geq 3x - 6$
      $y \leq 7 - x$
   c) $x \geq 0, y \geq 0$
      $y \geq x$
      $y \leq 6 - x$

2. Find the maximum value of $x + y$ if x and y satisfy the constraints in question 1 a).

3. Find the maximum value of $3x + 2y$ if x and y satisfy the constraints in question 1 b).

4. Find the minimum value of $2x + y$ if x and y satisfy the constraints in question 1 c).

5. In the question about teachers and teacher's aides from the introduction to this section, find the minimum amount of money that the school board must spend on salaries in order to satisfy the given conditions. How many teachers and teacher's aides are hired in this case?

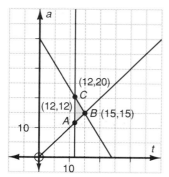

6. Use geometric linear programming to solve question 1 in 4.7 Exercises.

7. Use geometric linear programming to solve question 3 in 4.7 Exercises.

8. Use geometric linear programming to solve question 4 in 4.7 Exercises.

9. Use geometric linear programming to solve question 5 in 4.7 Exercises.

10. a) Use geometric linear programming to solve question 2 in 4.7 Exercises.
    b) Discuss the various amounts of crude oil that could be supplied to each of the two refineries 1 and 2, and the conditions under which one combination of amounts might be preferable to another.

11. A poster printing company makes two sizes of posters, 20 cm × 25 cm and 60 cm × 90 cm. There are 20 printers and 15 cutters. The time taken by the cutters and printers on each poster is as follows.

Size	Printer	Cutter
20 × 25	3 min	1.5 min
60 × 90	5 min	3 min

The machines run 18h/day. The profit on the posters is $1.50 each for the smaller ones and $3.00 for the larger ones. Determine the numbers of posters that should be produced each day for a maximum profit.

4.9 Solving Linear Programming Problems by Simplex Techniques

In section 4.8 you learned how to use geometric linear programming to find the optimum value of a linear combination of two variables that were subject to several linear constraints.

In this section you will learn a technique that will enable you to extend this process to the case where there are more than two variables. The technique is called the **simplex method.**

Example Determine non-negative values of x, y and z that maximize $M = 3x + 4y + 5z$ subject to the following constraints.

$$\left.\begin{array}{rcl} 2x + 3y & \leqslant & 8 \\ 2y + 5z & \leqslant & 10 \\ 3x + 2y + 4z & \leqslant & 15 \end{array}\right\} \ \text{①}$$

Solution To solve this problem you will need to introduce variables, u, v and w called **slack variables.** These variables are defined by the equations

$$\left.\begin{array}{rcl} 2x + 3y + u & = & 8 \\ 2y + 5z + v & = & 10 \\ 3x + 2y + 4z + w & = & 15 \end{array}\right\} \ \text{②}$$

Notice that u is the amount by which $2x + 3y$ is less than 8, v is the amount by which $2y + 5z$ is less than 10 and w is the amount that $3x + 2y + 4z$ is less than 15, in the original constraints ①.
Therefore, u, v and w must be non-negative.

The objective function $M = 3x + 4y + 5z$ together with the three equations in ② give a system of four linear equations in seven non-negative variables x, y, z, u, v, w and M.

$$\left.\begin{array}{rcl} 2x + 3y + u & = & 8 \\ 2y + 5z + v & = & 10 \\ 3x + 2y + 4z + w & = & 15 \\ -3x - 4y - 5z + M & = & 0 \end{array}\right\} \ \text{③}$$

This system of equations ③ can be solved by matrix techniques of section 4.3
The corresponding matrix is

$$\begin{array}{ccccccc} x & y & z & u & v & w & M \end{array}$$
$$\left[\begin{array}{ccccccc|c} 2 & 3 & 0 & 1 & 0 & 0 & 0 & 8 \\ 0 & 2 & 5 & 0 & 1 & 0 & 0 & 10 \\ 3 & 2 & 4 & 0 & 0 & 1 & 0 & 15 \\ -3 & -4 & -5 & 0 & 0 & 0 & 1 & 0 \end{array}\right] = A$$

The rank of the reduced matrix must be less than or equal to 4, which is less than the number of variables, 7. Therefore, four equations in seven unknowns have an infinite number of solutions.

One obvious solution is $x = 0$, $y = 0$, $z = 0$, $u = 8$, $v = 10$, $w = 15$ and $M = 0$.

It is also clear that this is not a maximum value for M.

The simplex process consists of three steps.

1. Since the coefficients of x, y and z in row 4 are all negative, increasing the value of x, y or z will necessitate an increase in M. You choose to increase the variable with the coefficient of largest magnitude in row 4, since for each increase of 1 of that variable, M will increase the most. Therefore, you choose to increase the value of z, since the coefficient of z in row 4 is -5.

2. The next step is to consider the restrictions on the size of z from the first three rows of the matrix. The first row does not involve z in this case. The second row corresponds to the equation
$2y + 5z + v = 10$
Since y, z and v are all non-zero, the largest possible value for z will occur when $y = v = 0$. Therefore $z \leqslant 2$.

Similarly row 3 corresponds to the equation
$3x + 2y + 4z + w = 15$
The largest possible value for z will occur when $x = y = w = 0$. Therefore,
$$z \leqslant \frac{15}{4} \text{ or } z \leqslant 3.75$$
Out of these two restrictions on z the stricter is that $z \leqslant 2$. This restriction on z comes from row 2.

Therefore, the element 5 in the *second* row (corresponding to the strictest restriction on z) and the *third* column (corresponding to the element which will change M the most) becomes the "pivot" for the reduction process, which is the next step of the simplex process.

3. The next step is to use elementary row operations on matrix A to put zeros in every element in the third column except for the second row.

$$\begin{array}{c} \\ \\ 4 \times \text{row } 2 - 5 \times \text{row } 3 \\ \text{row } 4 + \text{row } 2 \end{array} \begin{array}{ccccccc} x & y & z & u & v & w & M \\ \end{array} \\ \left[\begin{array}{ccccccc|c} 2 & 3 & 0 & 1 & 0 & 0 & 0 & 8 \\ 0 & 2 & 5 & 0 & 1 & 0 & 0 & 10 \\ -15 & -2 & 0 & 0 & 4 & -5 & 0 & -35 \\ -3 & -2 & 0 & 0 & 1 & 0 & 1 & 10 \end{array} \right] = A'$$

Looking at row 2, you see that $z = 2$ if $y = v = 0$. Using the value from row 1, $x = 0$ and $u = 8$ is one solution. Similarly, from row 3, $w = 7$ and from row 4, $M = 10$, which is an increase in the value of M.

This simplex process of three steps is repeated until there are no negative coefficients in row 4 of the matrix.

$$
\begin{array}{ccccccc}
x & y & z & u & v & w & M \\
\end{array}
$$

$$
\begin{bmatrix}
2 & 3 & 0 & 1 & 0 & 0 & 0 & | & 8 \\
0 & 2 & 5 & 0 & 1 & 0 & 0 & | & 10 \\
-15 & -2 & 0 & 0 & 4 & -5 & 0 & | & -35 \\
-3 & -2 & 0 & 0 & 1 & 0 & 1 & | & 10
\end{bmatrix}
$$

Using -15 in column 1 as a pivot gives

$$
\begin{array}{ccccccc}
x & y & z & u & v & w & M \\
\end{array}
$$

$$
\begin{array}{l}
15 \times \text{row } 1 + 2 \times \text{row } 3 \\
\\
\\
5 \times \text{row } 4 - \text{row } 3
\end{array}
\begin{bmatrix}
0 & 41 & 0 & 15 & 8 & -10 & 0 & | & 50 \\
0 & 2 & 5 & 0 & 1 & 0 & 0 & | & 10 \\
-15 & -2 & 0 & 0 & 4 & -5 & 0 & | & -35 \\
0 & -8 & 0 & 0 & 1 & 5 & 5 & | & 85
\end{bmatrix}
$$

Next, using 41 in column 2 as a pivot gives

$$
\begin{array}{ccccccc}
x & y & z & u & v & w & M \\
\end{array}
$$

$$
\begin{array}{l}
\\
41 \times \text{row } 2 - 2 \times \text{row } 1 \\
-41 \times \text{row } 3 - 2 \times \text{row } 1 \\
8 \times \text{row } 1 + 41 \times \text{row } 3
\end{array}
\begin{bmatrix}
0 & 41 & 0 & 15 & 8 & -10 & 0 & | & 50 \\
0 & 0 & 205 & -30 & 25 & 20 & 0 & | & 310 \\
615 & 0 & 0 & -30 & -180 & 225 & 0 & | & 1335 \\
0 & 0 & 0 & 120 & 105 & 125 & 205 & | & 3885
\end{bmatrix}
$$

The simplex process ends here, since all the coefficients in row 4 are positive.

From row 4, the maximum value for M occurs where $u = v = w = 0$

$$205M = 3885$$

$$M = \frac{777}{41}$$

From row 1, $41y = 50$ From row 2, $205z = 310$

$$y = \frac{50}{41} \qquad\qquad z = \frac{62}{41}$$

From row 3, $615x = 1335$

$$x = \frac{89}{41}$$

Therefore the maximum value of M is $\dfrac{777}{41}$, when $x = \dfrac{89}{41}$, $y = \dfrac{50}{41}$, and $z = \dfrac{62}{41}$

You can check that conditions are satisfied:

$$2x + 3y = \frac{328}{41} = 8 \leqslant 8$$
$$2x + 5z = 10 \leqslant 10$$
$$3x + 2y + 4z = 15 \leqslant 15 \quad \blacksquare$$

4.9 Exercises

1. Maximize $M = x + 2y + z$, using the simplex method, where x, y and z are non-negative, subject to the constraints:
$$x - y + 2z \leqslant 10 \qquad 2x + y + 3z \leqslant 12$$

2. A company in Scarborough assembles cars and trucks. The assembly is carried out in three departments: sheet metal stamping, engine assembly and final assembly. The number of person-hours required for assembling cars and trucks in each of the three departments are shown below.

	Sheet metal stamping	Engine assembly	Final assembly
Cars	50	50	25
Trucks	25	50	100

Each department has a capacity of 200 000 person-hours per year. Cars produce a profit of $600 each and trucks produce a profit of $1000 each. How many cars and trucks should be produced to gain a maximum possible profit?
a) Formulate this problem as a linear programming problem.
b) Introduce slack variables and identify the coefficient matrix, A.
c) Solve the problem using simplex techniques.

3. Ventris is planning to build and rent vacation cabins on a piece of property of area 200 m². The cabins must be completed in 14 days by 10 workers. There are two types of cabin, A and B. The details of each cabin are given in the chart.

	Cabin A	Cabin B
Time to Build	2 person-days	3 person-days
Area of land	25 m²	45 m²
Profit/month	$300	$400

Determine the numbers of each type of cabin to be built for a maximum profit.

4. In Toula's pizza store there are five options for pizza. You can order either a small, medium or large pizza on its own or you can order three small pizzas or two medium pizzas as a package. The ingredients needed for each pizza or package and the profit for each are given in the chart.

	Small	Medium	Large	3 small	2 medium
Flour	50 g	60 g	80 g	150 g	120 g
Toppings	15 g	18 g	20 g	30 g	30 g
Profit	$2	$3	$6	$4.50	$5

The store has 50 kg of flour and 15 kg of toppings. The staff has to produce a maximum of 1000 pizzas or pizza packages per day. Determine the numbers of pizzas and pizza packages it should produce each day for a maximum profit.

Summary

- modelling situations using linear, non-linear, piece-wise linear, step, discrete and continuous functions

- modelling situations using systems of linear equations

- solving systems of linear equations by means of elimination

- homogenous and non-homogeneous equations

- the augmented matrix of a system of equations

- reducing an augmented matrix to row-reduced echelon form, and hence solving the corresponding system of equations

- the rank of a matrix

Rank of coefficient matrix	Rank of augmented matrix	Number of variables	Number of solutions	Number of parameters (in solution)
c	a	n	none, if $c \neq a$	
c	a	n	one, if $c = a = n$	
c	a	n	an infinite number, if $c = a < n$	$n - a$

- using a calculator or computer to solve systems of equations

- solving m equations in n unknowns, where $m \neq n$

- writing inequalities to represent constraints in problems involving linear systems

- graphing systems of inequalities in two variables

- formulating linear programming problems

- solving problems using geometric linear programming

- solving linear programming problems using simplex techniques

Inventory

Questions 1-6 refer to graphs A, B and C below.

A.

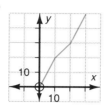

B.

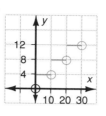

C.

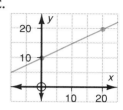

1. Graph _____ is a linear function.

2. Graph _____ is a step function.

3. Graph _____ is a piece-wise linear function.

4. The equation of graph A can be written as
   $y = 2x, \; 0 \leqslant x \leqslant$ _____
   $y =$ _____ $+ x, \; 10 < x \leqslant$ _____
   $y = 2x -$ _____ $, \; x >$ _____

5. The equation of graph B can be written as
   $y = 4n, \;$ _____ $\leqslant x < 10n, \; n \in N$

6. The equation of graph C can be written as
   $y =$ _____ $x +$ _____

7. The first step in solving the equations below, when not using matrices, is to form _____ equations in _____ variables by eliminating _____ from _____ pairs of the equations given.
   $2x + 3y - 4z = 7$
   $x - 2y + z = 11$
   $3x + y + 2z = 8$

8. The augmented matrix of the system of equations in question 7 is

   _____.

9. Which of the following augmented matrices are in row-reduced echelon form?

$$A = \begin{bmatrix} 2 & 4 & -1 & 8 \\ 0 & 2 & 0 & 6 \\ 0 & 1 & 1 & 0 \end{bmatrix} \quad B = \begin{bmatrix} 2 & 4 & -2 & 7 \\ 0 & 0 & 1 & 9 \\ 0 & 0 & 0 & 0 \end{bmatrix} \quad C = \begin{bmatrix} 3 & 5 & 1 & -3 \\ 0 & 3 & 7 & 2 \\ 0 & 0 & 7 & 14 \end{bmatrix}$$

10. State the rank of each of the row-reduced matrices in question 9.

11. If the number of trucks, t, is to be non-negative, then t _____ 0.

12. If the sum of the number of trucks, t, and the number of cars, c, is to be at least 50, then t_____ c_____ 50.

13. Copy the figure below and then shade in the region corresponding to the inequalities in questions 11 and 12.

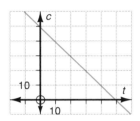

14. The graph below gives a feasible region for the variables x and y. Determine the minimum value for $2x + 3y$.

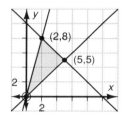

Questions 15-17 refer to the solution of the following linear programming problem using simplex techniques.

Maximize the function $4x + 7y + 6z + 4t$ subject to the constraints

$$\left.\begin{array}{r} 2x + 5y - 3z - 2t \leqslant 5 \\ 3x - 2y + 4z + 3t \leqslant 2 \\ x - 4y - 5z + 6t \leqslant 7 \\ x, y, z, t \geqslant 0 \end{array}\right\}①$$

15. Introduce suitable slack variables and transform the inequalities ① into equations.

16. Complete the coefficient matrix

$$A = \begin{bmatrix} x & y & z & t & u & v & w & M & \\ 2 & 5 & -3 & -2 & - & - & - & - & 5 \\ - & - & - & - & 0 & 1 & 0 & 0 & 2 \\ 1 & -4 & -5 & 6 & - & - & - & - & 7 \\ - & - & - & - & 0 & 0 & 0 & 1 & 0 \end{bmatrix}$$

17. Determine a feasible solution to begin the simplex method of solution.

Review Exercises

1. A sociologist has a theory that the number, n, of violent crimes in a city is related to the unemployment rate, r, by the formula
   $n = 15 + 600r$
   a) Sketch the graph of this function for $0 \leqslant r \leqslant 0.20$, in steps of 0.04.
   b) Describe this function as linear/non-linear, discrete/continuous.

2. For 8 h each day a laboratory technician prepares cell cultures for analysis. He needs 30 min to set up the equipment at the beginning of the day and 20 min to prepare each culture.
   a) Write an equation that relates the time, t, (in hours) that he has been working and the number, n, of cultures that he has prepared.
   b) Sketch the graph of this function.
   c) Is this graph discrete or continuous?
   d) What is the domain and range of this function?

3. A taxi company charges $1.00 for the first kilometre and $0.50 for each additional kilometre. Write an equation relating the cost, c, of a taxi ride and the distance, x, in kilometres, if the minimum charge is $1.00.

4. For a ride of 10 km the taxi company charges $5.50 for one person and $1.00 extra for each additional passenger.
   a) Write an equation relating the cost c of a ride of 10 km to the number, n, of passengers.
   b) Sketch the graph of this relation.
   c) Is this function discrete or continuous?
   d) What is a reasonable domain for this function?

5. Solve the following systems of equations by elimination.
   a) $2x + y = 6$
   $x - y = 0$

   b) $4x - 7y = 16$
   $6x + 4y = -5$

   c) $3x - 2y + 5z = -1$
   $2x + 5y - 4z = -9$
   $4x + 3y - 2z = -13$

   d) $5x - 4y - 6z = 21$
   $-2x + 3y + 4z = -15$
   $3x - 7y - 5z = 15$

   e) $4w + x + 2y - 3z = -16$
   $3w + 3x - y + 4z = 14$
   $5w + 4x + 3y - z = -10$
   $-w + 2x + 5y + z = -4$

6. Write the augmented matrices representing the systems of equations in question 5.

7. Solve the systems of equations in question 5 by reducing the corresponding augmented matrices to row-reduced echelon form.

8. The following reduced augmented matrix represents a system of equations.
   $$\begin{bmatrix} 1 & 2 & 3 & | & 4 \\ 0 & 3 & 4 & | & 2 \\ 0 & 0 & 0 & | & 3 \end{bmatrix}$$
   a) State the rank of the coefficient, and augmented, matrix.
   b) State the number of solutions.

9. Repeat question 8 for these matrices.
   a) $\begin{bmatrix} 2 & 3 & 1 & | & 5 \\ 0 & 1 & 4 & | & 6 \\ 0 & 0 & 0 & | & 2 \end{bmatrix}$ b) $\begin{bmatrix} 2 & 3 & 1 & | & 5 \\ 0 & 1 & 4 & | & 6 \\ 0 & 0 & 2 & | & 0 \end{bmatrix}$
   c) $\begin{bmatrix} 2 & 3 & 1 & | & 5 \\ 0 & 1 & 4 & | & 6 \\ 0 & 0 & 0 & | & 0 \end{bmatrix}$ d) $\begin{bmatrix} 2 & 3 & 1 & | & 5 \\ 0 & 0 & 0 & | & 0 \\ 0 & 0 & 0 & | & 0 \end{bmatrix}$

10. In the cases in question 9 where there are an infinite number of solutions, state the number of parameters that would be needed in the solution.

11. Solve the following systems of equations (if possible) by means of matrices.

a) $3x - y = 4$
   $6x - 2y = 3$

b) $x + 2y - z = 5$
   $2x + 3y - 3z = 8$
   $y + z = 2$

c) $x - y \qquad - 2t = 3$
   $2x - 2y + 2z - 2t = 4$
   $z + t = -1$
   $x - y + 2z \qquad = 1$

d) $2x + 4y = 8$
   $6x + 2y = 12$
   $4x - 2y = 4$

e) $2x - 3y + z = 0$
   $x - 2y - 3z = -4$
   $3x + y + 2z = 6$
   $x + y + z = 4$

f) $3x - 2y + z + 2t = 6$
   $2x + 4y - 2z + 3t = 2$

12. A plane flew into a head wind to a city 150 km away. The flight took 2.5 h. On the return trip the wind was with the plane and the speed of the wind was half that of the outward flight. The return trip took only 1 h. If the airspeed of the plane was constant, what was the speed of the wind on the outward flight?

13. Keith, Sarah and Peter find that they can balance a teeterboard in the two ways shown in the diagram below. If the sum of their weights is 126 kg, determine the weight of each child.

14. a) Using Kirchhoff's law for electric circuits that the sum of the IR products equals the e.m.f., show that the currents I_1, I_2 and I_3 flowing, as shown in the diagram below, satisfy the equations.
    $30(I_1 - I_3) + 20I_1 + 10(I_1 - I_2) = 0$
    $10(I_2 - I_1) + 40I_2 + 50(I_2 - I_3) = 0$
    $30(I_3 - I_1) + 50(I_3 - I_2) = 12$

   b) Simplify these equations and then solve them, correct to 2 decimal places.

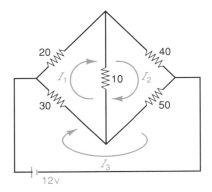

15. Solve the following systems of homogeneous equations.

a) $2x + 3y = 0$
   $4x - 6y = 0$

b) $x - y + z = 0$
   $3x + y - z = 0$
   $x + 3y - 3z = 0$

c) $2x + 3y + z = 0$
   $x - y + z = 0$
   $3x + y - 2z = 0$

16. An investor has $100 000 to invest in both common and preferred stock. She has decided that no more than 75% of the total should be invested in either type. More should be invested in common stock than in preferred stock.

a) Represent these choices by a set of linear inequalities.

b) Sketch a graph to represent these inequalities.

17. Graph the solution of each of the following systems of inequalities.

a) $x \geqslant 2$
$y \geqslant 3$
$x + y \leqslant 8$

b) $x + y \geqslant -2$
$x - 2y \leqslant 4$
$y - x \leqslant 4$
$x + y \leqslant 4$

18. Find the minimum value of $3x + 4y$ if x and y satisfy the system of inequalities in question 17a).

19. Find the maximum value of $5x - 2y$ if x and y satisfy the system of inequalities in question 17b).

20. The manufacturer of TV sets (in the introduction to this chapter) had 100 sets in the Manston warehouse and 60 sets in the Picton warehouse. Radio-World has ordered 50 sets, Cut-Price Stereo has ordered 70 sets and TV City has ordered 40 sets. The distances from the warehouses to each of the retailers is shown (in km) in the diagram below. It costs $0.50 per set per km to transport the sets. Use geometric linear programming to determine how many sets should be sent from each warehouse to each store to minimize the transportation costs.

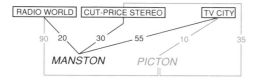

21. Dr. Nazerali works 8 h per day seeing up to 40 patients. She performs tests, which take 5 min, does complete medicals, which take 25 min, and has consultations, which take 20 min, each. A part-time assistant comes in for 2 h for each afternoon to do the filing. To file reports for tests takes 1 min, for medicals takes 5 min and for consultations takes 10 min, each. The tests, medicals and consultations earn a profit of $10, $30 and $40 respectively. Find how many of each the doctor should perform each day to maximize her profit.

22. The number of litres, L, of alcohol remaining in a vat is a quadratic function of the time, t, elapsed since the tap was opened. In other words, L can be expressed as $L = at^2 + bt + c$.
After 1, 2 and 3 minutes the amount of alcohol left is 38.4, 21.6 and 9.6 litres respectively

a) Use this information to write three equations for the coefficients a, b and c.

b) Write the augmented matrix corresponding to this system.

c) Use your calculator or computer to reduce this matrix to row-reduced echelon form.

d) Hence, find the values of a, b and c.

e) How long will it take the vat to empty?

23. Megan's math teacher gave the class a set of 25 homework problems with instructions to hand in at most 20 solutions.
The 18 problems in part A are worth 3 marks each
and the 7 problems in part B are worth 12 marks each.
Megan knows from the last such problem set that she takes on average 5 minutes to solve a 3 mark question and 15 minutes to solve a 12 mark one.
She can only manage to spend 2.5 h on this assignment.
How many problems from each section should she attempt to obtain the maximum score?
What is the maximum score that she can hope to get under these conditions?

a) Identify the variables in this problem.

b) Express the constraints as a set of linear inequalities.

c) Identify the objective function for this linear programming problem.

d) Solve this problem using geometric linear programming.

CHAPTER FIVE

The Binomial Theorem

If you toss a penny, the penny can come up either heads, H, or tails, T. Thus, there are two possible outcomes, namely H or T.

If you toss two pennies, the outcomes can be determined using the following tree diagram.

First penny	Second penny	Outcomes
H	H	HH
	T	HT
T	H	TH
	T	TT

START

If you toss three pennies, the following tree diagram will enable you to obtain the outcomes.

First penny	Second penny	Third penny	Outcomes
H	H	H	HHH
		T	HHT
	T	H	HTH
		T	HTT
T	H	H	THH
		T	THT
	T	H	TTH
		T	TTT

START

What would the outcomes be if you tossed fifty pennies? To answer this question you should examine, in a different manner, the outcomes for tossing one, two or three pennies.

Number of Pennies	Outcomes	Outcomes in abbreviated form
1	H T	H $H + T$ T
2	HH HT TH TT	H^2 HT $H^2 + 2HT + T^2$ TH T^2
3	HHH HHT HTH HTT THH THT TTH TTT	H^3 H^2T H^2T HT^2 $\quad H^3 + 3H^2T + 3HT^2 + T^3$ H^2T HT^2 HT^2 T^3

Observe that the abbreviated outcomes in the last column may be written as follows:

1 penny				H	+	T	=	$(H + T)^1$
2 pennies		H^2	+	2HT	+	T^2	=	$(H + T)^2$
3 pennies	H^3	+	$3H^2T$	+	$3HT^2$	+	T^3	=	$(H + T)^3$

From the above pattern, it appears that the abbreviate outcomes for tossing four pennies will be given by the expansion of $(H + T)^4$.

$$(H + T)^4 = (H + T)(H + T)^3 = H^4 + 4H^3T + 6H^2T^2 + 4HT^3 + H^4$$

By making a tree diagram for four pennies, show that $H^4 + 4H^3T + 6H^2T^2 + 4HT^3 + H^4$ is the abbreviated form for four pennies.

If you wish to determine the outcomes obtained when you toss fifty pennies, you would need to expand $(H + T)^{50}$. In this chapter, you will learn a simple way to do this.

5.1 An Investigation of the Expansion of $(a + x)^n$, $n \in W$

In the introduction to this chapter, you saw the need to be able to expand expressions like $(a + x)^2$, $(a + x)^3$, $(a + x)^4$, ... , $(a + x)^{50}$, where $a =$ H and $x =$ T. In previous grades, you learned that $(a + x)^2 = a^2 + 2ax + x^2$. In this section, you will use this result to calculate the expansions of $(a + x)^3$, $(a + x)^4$, and $(a + x)^5$. You will discover patterns that will enable you to obtain a shortcut for finding the terms of the expansion of $(a + x)^n$ for various values of $n \in W = \{0, 1, 2, 3, 4, ...\}$.

1. a) Use FOIL to show that $(a + x)(a + x) = a^2 + 2ax + x^2$.
    b) Expand $(a + x)^2$.

2. a) Complete $(a + x)(a^2 + 2ax + x^2)$
          $= a(a^2 + 2ax + x^2) + x(a^2 + 2ax + x^2)$
          $= \underline{\quad} + \underline{\quad} + \underline{\quad} + \underline{\quad} + \underline{\quad} + \underline{\quad}$
          $= a^3 + 3a^2x + 3ax^2 + x^3$
    b) Expand $(a + x)^3$.

3. Expand $(a + x)^4$ by using your result from question 2b) and the fact that $(a + x)^4 = (a + x)(a + x)^3$.

4. Use your results of question 3 to expand $(a + x)^5$.

5. Write each of the following without using brackets.
    a) $(a + x)^0$ b) $(a + x)^1$

6. Copy the following table. Use your results of questions 3 and 4 to fill in the blanks. To help you to see patterns note that x^0 and a^0 have been added to each row in the first and last terms respectively.

	Binomial	Expansion of $(a + x)^n$	Coefficients
$n = 0$	$(a + x)^0$	a^0x^0	1
$n = 1$	$(a + x)^1$	$a^1x^0 + a^0x^1$	1 1
$n = 2$	$(a + x)^2$	$a^2x^0 + 2a^1x^1 + a^0x^2$	1 2 1
$n = 3$	$(a + x)^3$	$a^3x^0 + 3a^2x^1 + 3a^1x^2 + a^0x^3$	1 3 3 1
$n = 4$	$(a + x)^4$	$a^4x^0 + \underline{\quad} + \underline{\quad} + \underline{\quad} + a^0x^4$	1 __ __ __ 1
$n = 5$	$(a + x)^5$	$a^5x^0 + \underline{\quad} + \underline{\quad} + \underline{\quad} + \underline{\quad} + a^0x^5$	1 __ __ __ __ 1

7. The triangle of coefficients in question 6 is called **Pascal's triangle** after the French mathematician, Blaise Pascal, who lived from 1623 to 1662.
    a) Describe a pattern that relates the numbers in one row of Pascal's triangle to the numbers in the *preceding* row. Check your pattern to see that it actually gives the numbers for rows $n = 4$ and $n = 5$, which are as follows.

        $n = 4$ 1   4   6   4   1
        $n = 5$ 1   5   10   10   5   1
    b) Write the numbers that you would expect to have in rows $n = 6$ and $n = 7$.

8. The following are the correct expansions of $(a + x)^n$ for $n = 0$ to $n = 5$.

$n = 0$ $(a + x)^0 =$ $\qquad\qquad a^0 x^0$

$n = 1$ $(a + x)^1 =$ $\qquad\qquad a^1 x^0 + a^0 x^1$

$n = 2$ $(a + x)^2 =$ $\qquad\qquad a^2 x^0 + 2a^1 x^1 + a^0 x^2$

$n = 3$ $(a + x)^3 =$ $\qquad\qquad a^3 x^0 + 3a^2 x^1 + 3a^1 x^2 + a^0 x^3$

$n = 4$ $(a + x)^4 =$ $\qquad\qquad a^4 x^0 + 4a^3 x^1 + 6a^2 x^2 + 4a^1 x^3 + a^0 x^4$

$n = 5$ $(a + x)^5 =$ $\qquad a^5 x^0 + 5a^4 x^1 + 10a^3 x^2 + 10a^2 x^3 + 5a^1 x^4 + a^0 x^5$

Examine the various patterns that appear in the above expansions then complete each of the following.

a) In row $n = 3$, the exponent of a begins with 3 then decreases by _____ going from left to right.

b) In each row the exponent of a _____ by 1 going from left to right.

c) The exponent of a in row $n = 6$ will start with _____ then _____ by 1 going from left to right.

d) In row $n = 4$, the exponent of x begins with 0 then increases by _____ going from left to right ending with the value _____ .

e) In each row the exponent of x _____ by 1 going from left to right.

f) The exponent of x in row $n = 6$ will start with _____ then _____ by 1 going from left to right ending with the value _____ .

g) In row $n = 4$, for each term
(the exponent of a) + (the exponent of x) = _____ .

h) In row $n = 6$, for each term
(the exponent of a) + (the exponent of x) will be _____ .

i) The number of terms in row $n = 3$ is _____ .

j) The number of terms in row $n = 6$ will be _____ .

9. In this question, you will use the patterns discovered in question 8 to guess the expansion of $(a + x)^6$.

a) The coefficients are the seven numbers in row $n = 6$ in Pascal's triangle. List these seven numbers.

b) State the value of (the exponent of a) + (the exponent of x) in row $n = 6$.

c) The first two terms in row $n = 6$ are $a^6 x^0 + 6a^5 x$. List the remaining five terms in order.

10. Use the patterns that you discovered in the previous questions to answer the following about the expansion of $(a + x)^k$.

a) The expansion of $(a + x)^k$ has _____ terms.

b) The first term is $a^k x^0$ and the last term is _____.

c) The exponent of a decreases by 1 going from _____ to _____ .

d) The exponent of x increases by _____ going from left to right.

e) For each term (the exponent of a) + (the exponent of x) = _____ , that is, the degree of each term is _____ .

f) The coefficients of terms can be obtained from the $(k + 1)$st row, $n =$ _____ of Pascal's triangle.

5.2 The Expansion of $(a + x)^n$ for $n \in W$

In Section 5.1 you investigated the expansion of $(a + x)^n$ for $n = 0, 1, 2, 3, 4, 5$ and guessed the expansions for $n = 6$ and $n = k$.

Several patterns appear in the expansion of $(a + x)^k$. These patterns can be summarized as follows.

1. The expansion of $(a + x)^k$ has $k + 1$ terms.
2. The first term is $a^k x^0$ and the last term is $a^0 x^k$.
3. The exponent of a decreases by 1 going from left to right.
4. The exponent of x increases by 1 going from left to right.
5. For each term (the exponent of a) + (the exponent of x) = k, that is, the degree of each term is k.
6. a) The coefficients of terms can be obtained from the $(k + 1)$st row, $n = k$ of Pascal's triangle.
    b) Each number in Pascal's triangle of coefficients is the sum of the adjacent numbers on each side of it in the row above.

Example   Use the six patterns above to obtain the expansion of $(a + x)^8$.

Solution   There are nine terms in the expansion of $(a + x)^8$.   Pattern 1

The nine terms of the expansion are
$a^8 x^0$, $a^7 x^1$, $a^6 x^2$, $a^5 x^3$, $a^4 x^4$, $a^3 x^5$, $a^2 x^6$, $a^1 x^7$, $a^0 x^8$.   Patterns 3, 4 and 5

The coefficients are obtained from row $n = 8$
in Pascal's triangle.   Pattern 6

To find row $n = 8$ using Pattern 6, you must write row $n = 5$ and then build up rows $n = 6$ and $n = 7$. For example, in row $n = 6$, the third term $15 = 5 + 10$, is the sum of the second and third terms of the previous row $n = 5$.

row $n = 5$			1		5		10		10		5		1	
row $n = 6$		1		6		15		20		15		6		1	
row $n = 7$	1		7		21		35		35		21		7		1
row $n = 8$	1	8		28		56		70		56		28		8		1

Combining the above, you obtain the following:

$$(a + x)^8 = a^8 x^0 + 8a^7 x^1 + 28a^6 x^2 + 56a^5 x^3 + 70a^4 x^4 + 56a^3 x^5 + 28a^2 x^6 + 8a^1 x^7 + a^0 x^8. \quad \blacksquare$$

5.2 Exercises

1. How many terms are there in the expansion of each of the following?
   a) $(a + x)^{12}$ b) $(a + x)^{30}$ c) $(a + x)^{39}$

2. State the first two terms and the last term in the expansion of $(a + x)^{30}$.

3. Supply the missing exponent for the following terms, without coefficients, in the expansion of $(a + x)^{18}$.
   a) $a^5 x^\blacksquare$ c) $a^\blacksquare x^7$
   b) $a^{10} x^\blacksquare$ d) $a^\blacksquare x^{15}$

4. In the expansion of $(a + x)^7$,
   a) list all eight terms, without coefficients,
   b) list all eight coefficients.
   c) Use a) and b) to write the full expansion.

5. Repeat question 4 for the expansion of
   a) $(a + x)^8$, having nine terms
   b) $(a + x)^9$, having ten terms
   c) $(a + x)^{10}$, having eleven terms
   d) $(a + x)^{11}$, having twelve terms
   e) $(a + x)^{12}$, having thirteen terms.

6. Extend Pascal's triangle to row $n = 12$.

7. In the expansion of $(m + k)^5$,
   a) list all six terms, without coefficients,
   b) list all the coefficients.
   c) Use a) and b) to write the full expansion.

8. Expand.
   a) $(a + k)^5$ c) $(w + b)^8$
   b) $(y + t)^4$ d) $(H + T)^6$

9. a) Expand $(a + x)^3$.
   b) Use the result in a) to expand $(2 + x)^3$.

10. a) Expand $(a + x)^4$
    b) Use the result in a) to expand $(a + 3)^4$.

11. a) Expand $(a + x)^5$.
    b) Use the result in a) to expand $(2k + 4)^5$.

12. a) Expand $(a + x)^7$.
    b) Use the fact that $(a - b)^7 = (a + (-b))^7$ to expand and simplify $(a - b)^7$.
    c) Expand and simplify $(3 - x)^7$.

13. The first four numbers in the row $n = 100$ of Pascal's triangle are:
    1, 100, 4950, 161 700.
    a) Write the first four terms in the expansion of $(a + x)^{100}$.
    b) Write the last three coefficients in the row $n = 101$ of Pascal's triangle.
    c) Write the last four terms of the expansion of $(a + x)^{100}$.

14. The first four terms of the expansion of $(a + x)^{90}$ are:
    $a^{90} + 90a^{89}x + 4005a^{88}x^2 + 129\ 495a^{87}x^3$.
    a) Write the first four coefficients in row $n = 90$ of Pascal's triangle.
    b) Write the last four coefficients in row $n = 90$ of Pascal's triangle.
    c) Write the last four terms in the expansion of $(a + x)^{90}$.

15. a) Expand $(H + T)^5$.
    b) Use the result in part a) to write the thirty-two different outcomes you would obtain in tossing five pennies.

5.3 A Proof of the Binomial Theorem

In 5.2 Exercises, you used Pascal's triangle to write the expansion of $(a + x)^n$ for $n = 8$ to 12. In order to use this method to find the expansion of $(a + x)^{100}$, you would need to write the rows of Pascal's triangle up to $n = 100$, a formidable and time consuming task! In this section, you will learn another way to find the expansion of $(a + x)^n$.

This result is called the **binomial theorem**.

In order to understand the expansion of $(a + x)^n$, you should consider the expansion of $(a + x)^3 = (a + x)(a + x)(a + x)$. To assist you in seeing what happens to each a and each x, replace
$(a + x)(a + x)(a + x)$ by
$(a_1 + x_1)(a_2 + x_2)(a_3 + x_3)$
where the subscripts distinguish the a's and x's in the three different factors.
$$(a + x)^3 = (a_1 + x_1)(a_2 + x_2)(a_3 + x_3)$$
$$= (a_1 + x_1)(a_2a_3 + a_2x_3 + x_2a_3 + x_2x_3)$$
$$= a_1a_2a_3 + a_1a_2x_3 + a_1x_2a_3 + a_1x_2x_3 + x_1a_2a_3 + x_1a_2x_3 + x_1x_2a_3 + x_1x_2x_3$$
Note the following facts about this equation.

1. The terms are of degree 3, namely the number of factors multiplied. Omitting the subscripts these terms are
   aaa, aax, axa, axx, xaa, xax, xxa, xxx.
2. Each term is obtained by selecting one letter, and only one letter, from each factor, then multiplying these letters together. (Each subscript occurs once, and only once, in each term.)
3. The expansion consists of all possible terms formed as in 2.

   These three facts are true for all expansions of $(a + x)^n$.

   By applying these three facts to the expansion of $(a + x)^4$, you will now be able to understand why the coefficients turn out to be as you guessed in section 5.1.

   For the expansion of $(a + x)^4$, you should consider the terms as
   $(a_1 + x_1)(a_2 + x_2)(a_3 + x_3)(a_4 + x_4)$.
1. Since there are four factors, the terms are of degree 4. Without the coefficients the terms are
   a^4, a^3x, a^2x^2, ax^3, x^4, that is a^4x^0, a^3x^1, a^2x^2, a^1x^3, a^0x^4.
2. Each term is obtained by selecting one, and only one, letter, either an a or an x, from each of the four factors, then multiplying these letters together.
   For a^4x^0, you select no x's and four a's from the four factors. Recall from chapter 1 that this can be done in $C(4,0)$ ways.
   Since $C(4,0) = 1$, a^4x^0 occurs only once in the expansion.
   For a^3x^1, you select an x from one factor and an a from each of the remaining three factors. This can be done in $C(4,1)$ ways.
   Since $C(4, 1) = 4$, a^3x^1 occurs four times in the expansion.

For a^2x^2, you select an x from each of two factors and an a from each of the remaining two factors. This can be done in $C(4,2)$ ways. Since $C(4,2) = 6$, a^2x^2 occurs six times in expansion.
For a^1x^3, you select an x from each of three factors and an a from the remaining one factor. This can be done in $C(4,3)$ ways. Since $C(4,3) = 4$, a^1x^3 occurs four times in the expansion.
For a^0x^4, you select an x and no a's from each of the four factors. This can be done in $C(4,4)$ ways. Since $C(4,4) = 1$, x^4 occurs only once in the expansion.

3. The expansion consists of the sum of all these terms.
Thus,
$$(a + x)^4 = C(4,0)a^4x^0 + C(4,1)a^3x^1 + C(4,2)a^2x^2 + C(4,3)a^1x^3 + C(4,4)a^0x^4$$
$$= 1a^4 + 4a^3x + 6a^2x^2 + 4ax^3 + 1x^4.$$
This result is the same as obtained previously. Note that the row $n = 4$ of Pascal's triangle consists of the five combinations:
$$C(4,0), C(4,1), C(4,2), C(4,3), C(4,4).$$

Study the above explanation thoughtfully. It is the basis for the proof of the binomial theorem that follows.

THEOREM

$$(a + x)^n = C(n,0)a^nx^0 + C(n,1)a^{n-1}x^1 + C(n,2)a^{n-2}x^2 + C(n,3)a^{n-3}x^3$$
$$+ \ldots + C(n,k)a^{n-k}x^k + \ldots + C(n,n)a^0x^n, \text{ where } n \in W.$$

Proof: For the expansion of $(a + x)^n$, consider
$$(a_1 + x_1)(a_2 + x_2)(a_3 + x_3) \ldots (a_n + x_n).$$
Since there are n factors, the terms are of degree n. Without coefficients, the $n + 1$ terms are
$$a^nx^0, a^{n-1}x^1, a^{n-2}x^2 \ldots, a^{n-k}x^k, \ldots, a^1x^{n-1}, a^0x^n$$
Each term is obtained by selecting one, and only one letter from each of the n factors, then multiplying these letters together.
For a^nx^0 you select n a's and no x's from the n factors. This can be done in $C(n,0)$ ways. The coefficient of a^nx^0 is $C(n,0)$.

For $a^{n-1}x^1$ you select an x from one factor and an a from each of the remaining $n - 1$ factors. This can be done in $C(n,1)$ ways. The coefficient of $a^{n-1}x^1$ is $C(n,1)$.

For $a^{n-2}x^2$, you select an x from each of two factors and an a from each of the remaining $n - 2$ factors. This can be done in $C(n,2)$ ways. The coefficient of $a^{n-2}x^k$ is $C(n,2)$.

For $a^{n-k}x^k$ you select k x's from each of k factors and an a from each of the remaining $n - k$ factors. This can be done in $C(n,k)$ ways. Thus, the coefficient of $a^{n-k}x^k$ is $C(n,k)$.

Therefore, the terms of the expansion have the form $C(n,k)a^{n-k}x^k$ where $k = 0, 1, 2, 3, \ldots, n.$

The binomial expansion consists of the sum of all of these terms:

$$(a + x)^n = C(n,0)a^nx^0 + C(n,1)a^{n-1}x^1 + C(n,2)a^{n-2}x^2 + C(n,3)a^{n-3}x^3$$
$$+ \ldots + C(n,k)a^{n-k}x^k + \ldots + C(n,n)a^0x^n$$

Note: • The term $C(n,k)a^{n-k}x^k$ is called the **general term**.

• The proof of the binomial theorem implies that in Pascal's triangle, the $(n + 1)$st row is

$C(n,0), C(n,1), C(n,2), \ldots, C(n,k), \ldots, C(n,n-2), C(n,n-1), C(n,n)$

For example, the sixth row, $n = 5$, is

$C(5,0), C(5,1), C(5,2), C(5,3), C(5,4), C(5,5)$.

• In chapter 1, you learned that $C(n,t) = C(n,r)$ if $t + r = n$. Thus, the coefficients of the terms of the expansion that are the same 'distance' from the beginning and end are equal. For example, in row $n = 5$, the second number $C(5,1)$ equals the second last number $C(5,4)$. Both equal 5.

• In chapter 1, you also found out that the following are true.

$$C(n,k) = \frac{n!}{(n-k)!k!}$$
$$= \frac{n(n-1)(n-2)\ldots(n-k+1)}{k!}$$

Thus,

$C(n,0) = 1$

$C(n,1) = n$

$$C(n,2) = \frac{n(n-1)}{2!}$$

$$C(n,3) = \frac{n(n-1)(n-2)}{3!}$$

And so on. Thus, an alternative form for the binomial expansion is as follows:

$$(a + x)^n = a^nx^0 + na^{n-1}x^1 + \frac{n(n-1)}{2!}a^{n-2}x^2 + \frac{n(n-1)(n-2)}{3!}a^{n-3}x^3$$
$$+ \ldots + \frac{n(n-1)(n-2)\ldots(n-k+1)}{k!}a^{n-k}x^k + \ldots + a^0x^n$$

Example 1

Expand $(2 + x)^8$.

Solution 1 You have the choice of two ways of expanding $(a + x)^n$ using either $C(n,k)$ or using the expression for $C(n,k)$. In this first solution, you will employ the former method.

$$(a + x)^n = C(n,0)a^nx^0 + C(n,1)a^{n-1}x^1 + C(n,2)a^{n-2}x^2 + C(n,3)a^{n-3}x^3$$
$$+ \ldots + C(n,k)a^{n-k}x^k + \ldots + C(n,n)a^0x^n.$$

Here $a = 2$, $x = x$ and $n = 8$.

Thus,

$$(2 + x)^8 = C(8,0)2^8x^0 + C(8,1)2^{8-1}x^1 + C(8,2)2^{8-2}x^2 + C(8,3)2^{8-3}x^3 + C(8,4)2^{8-4}x^4$$
$$+ C(8,5)2^{8-5}x^5 + C(8,6)2^{8-6}x^6 + C(8,7)2^{8-7}x^7 + C(8,8)2^{8-8}x^8$$
$$= 1(2^8)x^0 + 8(2^7)x^1 + 28(2^6)x^2 + 56(2^5)x^3 + 70(2^4)x^4$$
$$+ 56(2^3)x^5 + 28(2^2)x^6 + 8(2^1)x^7 + 1(2^0)x^8$$
$$= 256 + 1024x + 1792x^2 + 1792x^3 + 1120x^4$$
$$+ 448x^5 + 112x^6 + 16x^7 + x^8$$

Note: The values of the $C(n,k)$'s can be obtained using either row $n = 8$ in Pascal's triangle or the formula for $C(n,k)$ in terms of factorials.

Solution 2   You can also use the other expansion, namely

$$(a + x)^n = a^nx^0 + na^{n-1}x^1 + \frac{n(n-1)}{2!}a^{n-2}x^2 + \frac{n(n-1)(n-2)}{3!}a^{n-3}x^3$$
$$+ \ldots + \frac{n(n-1)(n-2)\ldots(n-k+1)}{k!}a^{n-k}x^k + \ldots + a^0x^n$$

Here $a = 2$, $x = x$ and $n = 8$.

$$(a + x)^8 = 2^8x^0 + 8(2^{8-1})x^1 + \frac{8(8-1)}{2!}2^{8-2}x^2 + \frac{8(8-1)(8-2)}{3!}2^{8-3}x^3$$
$$+ \frac{8(8-1)(8-2)(8-3)}{4!}2^{8-4}x^4$$
$$+ \frac{8(8-1)(8-2)(8-3)(8-4)}{5!}2^{8-5}x^5$$
$$+ \frac{8(8-1)(8-2)(8-3)(8-4)(8-5)}{6!}2^{8-6}x^6$$
$$+ \frac{8(8-1)(8-2)(8-3)(8-4)(8-5)(8-6)}{7!}2^{8-7}x^7$$
$$+ \frac{8(8-1)(8-2)(8-3)(8-4)(8-5)(8-6)(8-7)}{8!}2^{8-8}x^8$$
$$= 256 + 1024x + 1792x^2 + 1792x^3 + 1120x^4$$
$$+ 448x^5 + 112x^6 + 16x^7 + x^8. \quad \blacksquare$$

Example 2   Expand $(3m - 2y)^4$.

Solution   Since $n = 4$, the expansion needed is
$$(a + x)^4 = C(4,0)a^4x^0 + C(4,1)a^3x^1 + C(4,2)a^2x^2 + C(4,3)a^1x^3 + C(4,4)a^0x^4$$
where $a = 3m$ and $x = -2y$.

Thus,
$$(3m - 2y)^4 = C(4,0)(3m)^4(-2y)^0 + C(4,1)(3m)^3(-2y)^1 + C(4,2)(3m)^2(-2y)^2$$
$$+ C(4,3)(3m)^1(-2y)^3 + C(4,4)(3m)^0(-2y)^4$$
$$= 1(81m^4)(1) + 4(27m^3)(-2y) + 6(9m^2)(4y^2) + 4(3m)(-8y^3) +$$
$$1(1)(16y^4)$$
$$= 81m^4 - 216m^3y + 216m^2y^2 - 96my^3 + 16y^4. \quad \blacksquare$$

5.3 Exercises

1. Evaluate the following:
   a) $C(7,2)$ b) $C(5,3)$ c) $C(8,3)$ d) $C(20,12)$

2. a) Expand $(a + x)^6$ using
   $$(a + x)^n = C(n,0)a^n x^0 + C(n,1)a^{n-2}x^1$$
   $$+ C(n,2)a^{n-2}x^2 + \ldots$$
   $$+ C(n,n)a^0 x^n$$
   b) Expand $(a + x)^6$ using
   $$(a + x)^n = a^n x^0 + na^{n-1}x^1$$
   $$+ \frac{n(n - 1)}{2!}a^{n-2}x^2 + \ldots$$
   $$+ a^0 x^n$$

3. Expand the following using the binomial theorem.
   a) $(a + x)^7$
   b) $(b - c)^5$
   c) $(m + z)^5$
   d) $(2 + x)^5$
   e) $(a + 1)^8$
   f) $(3 - b)^4$

4. Expand.
   a) $(a + 2b)^4$
   b) $(3a + 4b)^4$
   c) $(3 - 2m)^3$
   d) $(4a - 5)^3$
   e) $(2x + 3a)^5$
   f) $(1 - m^2)^5$
   g) $(3 + x)^6$
   h) $(H + T)^7$

5. Expand.
   a) $(2 - 3x)^5$
   b) $(1 + x^2)^5$
   c) $(2k + 4b)^3$
   d) $(r - 2s)^4$
   e) $(5 - 2k)^3$
   f) $(m^2 - 1)^5$

6. Expand.
   a) $\left(\dfrac{1}{2} + x\right)^3$
   b) $(0.1 + 0.5x)^4$
   c) $\left(\dfrac{3}{5} + \dfrac{x}{4}\right)^3$
   d) $(2.1 + 3.2x)^5$

7. Find the first three terms of the expansion of each of the following. Do not simplify.
   a) $(H + T)^{50}$
   b) $(a - b)^{30}$
   c) $(2k + 4b)^8$
   d) $(r - 2s)^4$
   e) $(1 + x)^{50}$
   f) $(b - 3)^{90}$

8. Write the last three terms in the following expansions. Do not simplify.
   a) $(H + T)^{50}$ b) $(a - b)^{30}$ c) $(2k + 4b)^8$

9. Prove the binomial theorem in the form $(m + k)^y$, $y \in W$.

10. Expand each of the following using the binomial theorem. Simplify each term but do not add terms.
    a) $\left(\dfrac{1}{2} + \dfrac{1}{2}\right)^3$
    b) $\left(\dfrac{1}{2} + \dfrac{1}{2}\right)^4$
    c) $\left(\dfrac{1}{4} + \dfrac{3}{4}\right)^3$
    d) $(0.1 + 0.9)^3$

11. Use the binomial theorem to show the following are true.
    a) $(1 + 1)^2 = C(2,0) + C(2,1) + C(2,2)$
    b) $(1 + 1)^3 = C(3,0) + C(3,1) + C(3,2) + C(3,3)$
    c) Guess what the expansion of $(1 + 1)^4$ will be. Verify your guess.
    d) Compare your results of a) and b) with those of section 1.7.

12. a) Use the binomial theorem to show the following is true.
    $$(1 - 1)^4 = C(4,0) - C(4,1) + C(4,2)$$
    $$- C(4,3) + C(4,4)$$
    b) Show that $C(4,0) + C(4,2) + C(4,4)$
    $$= C(4,1) + C(4,3)$$

13. Expand.
    a) $\left(x + \dfrac{2}{x}\right)^4$ b) $\left(x - \dfrac{1}{x}\right)^3$ c) $\left(x - \dfrac{2}{x^2}\right)^5$

14. a) Find the seventh term in the expansion of $(a + x)^{20}$. Do not simplify your answer.
    b) Find the 30th term in the expansion of $(a + x)^{50}$. Do not simplify your answer.

15. a) Find the term containing a^3 in the expansion of $(a + 3x)^4$.
    b) Find the term containing x^3 in the expansion of $(a + 3x)^4$.

16. The first two terms in the expansion of $(2 + kx)^8$ are $256 + 6144x$. Find the value of k.

17. The first three terms in the expansion of $(1 + bx)^n$ are $1 + 7.5x + 22.5x^2$. Find b and n.

18. a) Expand $(1 + x)^3$.
    b) Expand $(1 + 2m - m^2)$ by replacing x in part a) by $(2m - m^2)$.

In Search of the Expansion of $(a + x)^n$ for $n \in R$

In section 5.3 you found that for $n \in W$, the expansion of $(a + x)^n$ could be written as follows:

$$(a + x)^n = a^n x^0 + na^{n-1}x^1 + \frac{n(n-1)}{2!}a^{n-2}x^2 + \frac{n(n-1)(n-2)}{3!}a^{n-3}x^3$$
$$+ \ldots + \frac{n(n-1)(n-2) \ldots (n-k+1)}{k!}a^{n-k}x^k + \ldots a^0x^n.$$

A similar result is true when n is *not* a whole number. In this case, however, there are two important differences. Instead of a series with a finite number of terms, you will have an *infinite number* of terms. In addition, the expansion is true only for certain values of a and x. Indeed, the expansion is true only for values of a and x such that $-1 < \frac{x}{a} < 1$.

The result (which will not be proved) is the following.

$$(a + x)^n = a^n x^0 + na^{n-1}x^1 + \frac{n(n-1)}{2!}a^{n-2}x^2 + \frac{n(n-1)(n-2)}{3!}a^{n-3}x^3 \quad \textcircled{1}$$
$$+ \ldots + \frac{n(n-1)(n-2) \ldots (n-k+1)}{k!}a^{n-k}x^k + \ldots$$

Historically, before the advent of the calculator, this form of the binomial theorem was used to calculate roots of numbers as in the following example.

Example Use the binomial expansion for $n \in R$ to obtain a value for $\sqrt[3]{66}$, correct to 4 decimal places.

Solution First you must observe that $\sqrt[3]{66} = 66^{\frac{1}{3}}$.   66 must be written $a + x$.
In order to do the subsequent calculations, it is necessary to select a perfect cube for a. Hence, you should choose $a = 64$ and $x = 2$. Note that
$$-1 < \frac{2}{64} < 1, \text{ and } 64^{\frac{1}{3}} = 4. \text{ Let } 66^{\frac{1}{3}} = (a + x)^n, n \in R$$

Substituting $a = 64$, $x = 2$ and $n = \frac{1}{3}$ in $\textcircled{1}$ gives

$$66^{\frac{1}{3}} = (64^{\frac{1}{3}})(2^0) + \left(\frac{1}{3}\right)(64^{\frac{1}{3}-1})(2^1) + \frac{\left(\frac{1}{3}\right)\left(\frac{1}{3}-1\right)}{2!}(64^{\frac{1}{3}-2})(2^2) + \frac{\frac{1}{3}\left(\frac{1}{3}-1\right)\left(\frac{1}{3}-2\right)}{3!}(64^{\frac{1}{3}-3})(2^3) \ldots$$

$$= 4 \qquad + \left(\frac{1}{3}\right)\left(\frac{1}{4}\right)^2(2) \quad + \frac{\left(\frac{1}{3}\right)\left(-\frac{2}{3}\right)}{2}\left(\frac{1}{4}\right)^5(4) \quad + \frac{\left(\frac{1}{3}\right)\left(-\frac{2}{3}\right)\left(-\frac{5}{3}\right)}{6}\left(\frac{1}{4}\right)^8(8) \ldots$$

$$\doteq 4 + 0.041\ 666\ 667 - 0.000\ 434\ 028 + 0.000\ 007\ 536 \ldots$$
$$\doteq 4.0412 \quad \blacksquare$$

Use the method of the Example to find the following, correct to 3 decimal places.

a) $\sqrt{27}$ 　　　　b) $\sqrt[3]{126}$ 　　c) $\sqrt[5]{1028}$

MAKING

Food Needs and World Resources

Mathematics is used by economists and social scientists to model the food needs and resources of the entire world. Different people can come to different conclusions using the same information. Thus, it is important for you to understand the statistically based mathematics behind the conclusions you may read. The following questions will help you understand what your ideas and beliefs about the food resources and food needs of the world are. Then you can use the statistical information provided to check the validity of your ideas.

1. You are informed almost daily that the world is becoming over populated. How much space do all of the people of the world actually occupy?

   a) Suppose that each person in the world is enclosed in a thinly walled box so that a person could stand comfortably. Then suppose that all of these boxes were placed in a large cube, completely filling it. Which of the following would be closest to the length of the side of this large cube?
   A) 1 km   B) 10 km   C) 100 km   D) 1000 km   E) 10 000 km

   b) Suppose now that each person in the world was given enough space on the ground to stand comfortably as close together as possible but without touching anyone else. If everyone stood inside a square, which of the following numbers would be closest to the length of each side of this square?
   A) 10 km   B) 20 km   C) 100 km   D) 1000 km   E) 10 000 km

2. Suppose that all of the people of the earth were moved to Canada and placed in a strip 300 km wide immediately north of the United States border. Which one of the following numbers multiplied by the population density of Toronto gives a number closest to the population density of this strip across Canada?
   A) 0.1   B) 1   C) 10   D) 100   E) 1000

3. You hear about people who are starving not only in third world countries but even here in Canada. Imagine that you must feed all of the people of the world using only the food that is produced each year in Canada and the United States. Suppose also, that you could use only grain and other edible field crops. You are commissioned to divide this food among the whole population of the world so that each person receives the same mass of food daily. Which of the following would be closest to that mass of food?
   A) 0.0002 kg   B) 0.002 kg   C) 0.02 kg   D) 0.2 kg   E) 2 kg

Examine the following answers to see how your ideas compare with the facts. The statistics used to obtain the answers are found in the 1987 *World Almanac* and the 1985 *Canada Yearbook*.

1. **a)** Assume that a typical person needs a box about
   2 m $\times$ 0.5 m $\times$ 0.4 m. The volume of such a box is 0.4 m^3. The
   population of the world (1985) is 4.8×10^9. Thus the total volume
   that all of these boxes would occupy is
   $(4.8 \times 10^9) \times 0.4$ m$^3 = 1.92 \times 10^9$ m$^3 = 1.92$ km^3. The side of the
   large box needed to hold this volume would be $\sqrt[3]{1.92} \doteq 1.24$ km.
   Thus the correct answer is A.

   b) Assume that each person in the world is standing on the ground
   on a rectangle that is 0.5 m = 0.0005 km wide by
   0.4 m = 0.0004 km deep. Thus, each person occupies an area of
   0.0005×0.0004 km$^2 = 2 \times 10^{-7}$ km^2. The 4.8 billion people of the
   earth would take up an area of
   $(2 \times 10^{-7}) \times (4.8 \times 10^9) = 9.6 \times 10^2$ km^2. If this area formed a
   square the side of the square would be $\sqrt{9.6 \times 10^2} \doteq 31$ km.
   The correct answer is B.

2. The population of metropolitan Toronto (1984) is 2 124 291. The area
   of metropolitan Toronto is 624 km^2. Thus, the population density of
   Toronto is 2 124 291 ÷ 624 = 3404 people per km^2. The distance
   across Canada from coast to coast is 5187 km. Thus the area of Canada
   within 300 km of the border of the United States is
   $5187 \times 300 = 1\ 566\ 100$ km^2. Therefore, if the whole world lived in
   Canada within 300 km of the United States border the population
   density of Canada would be $(4.8 \times 10^9) \div 1\ 566\ 100 = 3150$ people per
   km^2. Thus, the correct answer is B.

3. The figures in the following table are for 1980 to 1984 and give the
   yield by crop in kilograms.

Crop	Canada	United States
grain	591×10^8	2945×10^8
potatoes	28×10^8	184×10^8
soybeans, peas, beans	12×10^8	134×10^8
other edible field crops	31×10^8	400×10^8
totals	662×10^8	3663×10^8

The total food available each year from Canada and the United States
is 4325×10^8 kg.

If all of this food were divided among the 4.8 billion inhabitants of
the earth, each would receive $(4325 \times 10^8) \div (4.8 \times 10^9) \doteq 90$ kg per
year or 90 ÷ 365 $\doteq$ 0.25 kg per day. The correct answer is D.

The answers to these questions lead to other questions. Is there any
necessity for countries to be overcrowded? Do the people of the world
really need to worry about the world being too small? With so much food
in Canada and the United States why are there people starving throughout
the world? Mathematics can not answer questions such as these, for they
are political and moral questions. But mathematics can help you determine
the truth about some of the beliefs you hold and the information you are
given.

5.4 The General Term of $(a + x)^n$

The expansion of $(a + x)^n$ has $n + 1$ terms. In certain situations, especially those in problems on probability in chapter 7, you need only a few of these $n + 1$ terms. Suppose, for example, you are driving on a street that has three traffic lights and the probability that you will be stopped by any one light is 0.4. You wonder what the chance (or probability) is that you will get through the three lights without stopping. In chapter 7 you will learn that the required probability is the first term $C(3,0)a^3x^0$ in the expansion of $(a + x)^3$, where $a = 0.6$ and $x = 0.4$.

In order to be able to select any term you wish of a binomial expansion, you must be familiar with the general term.
In the expansion of $(a + x)^n$ the terms are:

$C(n,0)a^nx^0 \rightarrow$ 1st term, t_1

$C(n,1)a^{n-1}x^1 \rightarrow$ 2nd term, t_2

$C(n,2)a^{n-2}x^2 \rightarrow$ 3rd term, t_3

$C(n,3)a^{n-3}x^3 \rightarrow$ 4th term, t_4

$C(n,4)a^{n-4}x^4 \rightarrow$ 5th term, t_5

$\vdots \qquad\qquad \vdots$

$C(n,k)a^{n-k}x^k \rightarrow (k + 1)$st term, t_{k+1}

$\vdots \qquad\qquad \vdots$

$C(n,n)a^0x^n \rightarrow (n + 1)$st term, t_{n+1}

Notice the pattern relating the exponent of x to the numbering of terms.

Thus, in this expansion, t_{20} would contain x^{19}.

PROPERTY

The general term of $(a + x)^n$ is the term $t_{k+1} = C(n,k)a^{n-k}x^k$.

Example 1

a) Write the general term of $(p + q)^8$.
b) Evaluate the term containing q^5.
c) Evaluate the term containing p^2.
d) Evaluate the fourth term.

Solution

a) The general term of $(a + x)^n$ is $C(n,k)a^{n-k}x^k$.
Here $a = p$, $x = q$, $n = 8$. Therefore $t_{k+1} = C(8,k)p^{8-k}q^k$.

b) For the term containing q^5, $k = 5$. $C(8,5)p^{8-5}q^5 = \dfrac{8!}{5!3!}p^3q^5 = 56p^3q^5$

c) For the term containing p^2, the exponent of q must be $8 - 2 = 6$ because (the exponent of p) + (the exponent of q) = 8. So $k = 6$.

Thus, the term containing p^2 is $C(8,6)p^2q^6 = \dfrac{8!}{6!2!}p^2q^6 = 28p^2q^6$.

d) Let the general term be the fourth term, $t_4 = t_{k+1}$. Therefore, $k + 1 = 4$ or $k = 3$. Thus, the fourth term is $C(8,3)p^{8-3}q^3 = \dfrac{8!}{5!3!}p^5q^3 = 56p^5q^3$. ∎

Example 2

a) Find the general term of $\left(x^2 + \dfrac{2}{x^2}\right)^6$.

b) Find the term containing x^4.

Solution

a) For $(a + x)^n$, the general term is $C(n,k)a^{n-k}x^k$.

Here, $a = x^2$, $x = \dfrac{2}{x^2}$ and $n = 6$.

Thus, the general term is $C(6,k)(x^2)^{6-k}\left(\dfrac{2}{x^2}\right)^k$

$$= C(6,k)\ x^{12-2k}\ 2^k\ x^{-2k}$$
$$= C(6,k)\ 2^k x^{12-4k}$$

b) For the term with x^4 you must have
$$x^{12-4k} = x^4$$

Thus, $12 - 4k = 4$ or $k = 2$

Therefore, the term containing x^4 is $C(6,2)2^2x^4 = 60x^4$. ■

Example 3

Suppose you toss fifty pennies at the same time. This is the situation posed in the introduction to this chapter. The probability that a head will occur thirty times and a tail the remaining twenty times is given by the term containing H^{30} in the expansion of $(H + T)^{50}$, where $H = T = 0.5$. Find this probability, correct to 4 decimal places.

Solution

The general term of $(H + T)^{50}$ is $C(50,k)H^{50-k}T^k$.

Here, $50 - k = 30$

$k = 20$

Thus, the required probability is $C(50,20)H^{30}T^{20}$

$$= C(50,20)(0.5)^{30}(0.5)^{20}$$
$$= \frac{50!}{30!\ 20!}(0.5)^{50}$$
$$\doteq 0.0419$$

Therefore, the probability of thirty heads occurring when tossing fifty pennies is 0.0419. ■

5.4 Exercises

1. **a)** Write the general term of $(p + q)^5$.
   b) Evaluate the term containing q^2.
   c) Evaluate the term containing p^2.
   d) Evaluate the fourth term.

2. **a)** Write the general term of $(a + b)^{12}$.
   b) Evaluate the term containing a^5.
   c) Evaluate the term containing b^5.
   d) Evaluate the seventh term.

3. **a)** Write the general term of $(m + t)^{20}$.
   b) Evaluate the term containing m^{15}.
   c) Evaluate the term containing t^7.
   d) Evaluate the fourteenth term.

4. Find the term with the indicated power in the expansion of the given binomial.
   a) $(H + T)^5$, T^4
   b) $(m + t)^{20}$, m^{14}
   c) $(3y + 2a)^{12}$, y^7

5. **a)** Write the general term of $(0.9 + 0.1)^5$.
   b) Evaluate the term containing $(0.1)^3$, correct to 5 decimal places.
   c) Evaluate the term containing $(0.9)^4$, correct to 5 decimal places.

6. **a)** Write the general term of $(0.4 + 0.6)^8$.
   b) Evaluate the term containing $(0.4)^2$, correct to 5 decimal places.
   c) Evaluate the term containing $(0.6)^5$, correct to 5 decimal places.

7. **a)** Write the first three terms of $(p + q)^5$.
   b) Evaluate your answers in part a) for $p = \dfrac{5}{6}$ and $q = \dfrac{1}{6}$, correct to 5 decimal places.

8. For each of the following, find the general term, and, if it exists, the term containing x^5.
   a) $\left(x + \dfrac{1}{x}\right)^9$
   c) $\left(x^2 + \dfrac{1}{x}\right)^5$
   b) $\left(x^2 + \dfrac{3}{x^2}\right)^9$

9. Suppose you toss twenty pennies at the same time. The probability that a head will occur twelve times and a tail the remaining eight times is given by the term containing H^{12} in the expansion of $(H + T)^{20}$ where $H = T = 0.5$. Find this probability, correct to 4 decimal places.

10. In the introduction to this section, you were presented with a traffic light problem. The probability that you will get through three lights without stopping is the first term of the expansion of $(0.6 + 0.4)^3$. Calculate this probability, correct to 4 decimal places.

11. You are writing a multiple choice test. Every question has five choices, only one of which is correct. You have no idea how to answer eight of the questions. The probability that you will get two questions correct out of the eight you cannot do is the third term in the expansion of $(0.8 + 0.2)^8$. Calculate this probability, correct to 4 decimal places.

12. Show that the general term of $\left(\dfrac{2}{3} + \dfrac{1}{3}\right)^5$ is $C(5,k)2^{5-k}3^{-5}$.

13. Show that the general term of $\left(\dfrac{p}{r} + \dfrac{q}{r}\right)^n$ is $C(n,k)p^{n-k}q^k r^{-n}$.

14. Find the coefficient of x^5 in the expansion of $(1 - x)^7 (1 + 2x)^{15}$.

15. Prove that the kth term of the expansion of $(1 + 0.03)^{22}$ is less than 0.1 of the $(k - 1)$st term, provided k is greater than four.

16. Find the term independent of x in the expansion of $\left(4x - \dfrac{1}{2\sqrt{x}}\right)^{12}$.

17. If x^m occurs in the expansion of $\left(x + \dfrac{1}{x}\right)^n$, show that $n - m$ must be an even number.

5.5 Pascal's Triangle

In section 5.1 you discovered Pascal's triangle. The triangle was known long before the time of Pascal. In 1303 the Chinese mathematician Chu-Shih-Chieh listed the first eight rows in a book that he wrote. Indeed, the triangle was known to Indian mathematicians around 200 BC. The triangle is attributed to Pascal because he prepared an interesting book on it called *Treatise on the Arithmetical Triangle*. This book was published in 1665, three years after his death.

The first five rows of Pascal's triangle are repeated below.

$$
\begin{array}{ccccccccc}
 & & & & 1 & & & & \\
 & & & 1 & & 1 & & & \\
 & & 1 & & 2 & & 1 & & \\
 & 1 & & 3 & & 3 & & 1 & \\
1 & & 4 & & 6 & & 4 & & 1 \\
\end{array}
$$

Notice again that each number is the sum of the adjacent numbers on either side of it in the row above.

Recall also that,

$C(1,0) = 1$ and $C(1,1) = 1$
$C(2,0) = 1, C(2,1) = 2, C(2,2) = 1$
$C(3,0) = 1, C(3,1) = 3, C(3,2) = 3, C(3,3) = 1$
$C(4,0) = 1, C(4,1) = 4, C(4,2) = 6, C(4,3) = 4, C(4,4) = 1$

Thus, if $C(0,0)$ is defined as 1, you can write the first five rows of Pascal's triangle as follows:

$$
\begin{array}{ccccccccc}
 & & & & C(0,0) & & & & \\
 & & & C(1,0) & & C(1,1) & & & \\
 & & C(2,0) & & C(2,1) & & C(2,2) & & \\
 & C(3,0) & & C(3,1) & & C(3,2) & & C(3,3) & \\
C(4,0) & & C(4,1) & & C(4,2) & & C(4,3) & & C(4,4) \\
\end{array}
$$

If you use the method for forming numbers from the preceding row, you can see that the following must be true.

$C(2,1) = C(1,0) + C(1,1)$
$C(3,1) = C(2,0) + C(2,1)$
$C(3,2) = C(2,1) + C(2,2)$
$C(4,3) = C(3,2) + C(3,3)$ and so on.

Hence, you would expect that a number in the row $n = 8$ would be related to numbers in the row $n = 7$ as in the example that follows.

It should also be clear that in Pascal's triangle for any row, terms the same distance from either side are equal. For example, in row $n = 4$, 1 and 4 appear on the left and on the right. For row n, the term $C(n,k)$ which is k numbers from the left should equal the term k numbers from the right, namely $C(n, n - k)$. This is certainly true because each equals $\dfrac{n!}{(n - k)! \, k!}$.

Example 1   Prove that $C(8,5) = C(7,4) + C(7,5)$.

Solution   **Proof:**

$L.S. = C(8,5) \qquad R.S. = C(7,4) + C(7,5)$

$\qquad = \dfrac{8!}{5!\,3!} \qquad\qquad = \dfrac{7!}{3!\,4!} + \dfrac{7!}{2!\,5!}$

$\qquad\qquad\qquad\qquad = \dfrac{5(7!)}{5(4!)(3!)} + \dfrac{3(7!)}{5!\,3(2!)}$ common denominator on *R.S.* is 5! 3!

$\qquad\qquad\qquad\qquad = \dfrac{(5+3)(7!)}{5!\,3!}$

$\qquad\qquad\qquad\qquad = \dfrac{8!}{5!\,3!} = L.S.$ ■

Note: Example 1 could also have been done by calculating the actual values of *L.S.* and *R.S.*

L.S. = 56 and R.S. = 35 + 21 or 56

The method used in Example 1 can be used to prove the general result. The general result linking row n with row $n - 1$ is proved in Example 2.

Example 2   Prove that $C(n,k) = C(n - 1, k - 1) + C(n - 1, k)$.

Solution   **Proof:**

$L.S. = C(n,k) \qquad R.S. = C(n - 1, k - 1) + C(n - 1, k)$

$\qquad = \dfrac{n!}{(n - k)!\,k!} \qquad = \dfrac{(n - 1)!}{(n - 1 - (k - 1))!\,(k - 1)!} + \dfrac{(n - 1)!}{(n - 1 - k)!\,k!}$

$\qquad\qquad\qquad\qquad = \dfrac{k(n - 1)!}{(n - k)!\,(k)(k - 1)!} + \dfrac{(n - k)(n - 1)!}{(n - k)(n - k - 1)!\,k!}$

$\qquad\qquad\qquad\qquad = \dfrac{(k + n - k)(n - 1)!}{(n - k)!\,k!}$

$\qquad\qquad\qquad\qquad = \dfrac{n(n - 1)!}{(n - k)!\,k!}$ common denominator on *R.S.* is $(n - k)!\,k!$

$\qquad\qquad\qquad\qquad = \dfrac{n!}{(n - k)!\,k!} = L.S.$ ■

5.5 Exercises

1. a) Write the first twelve rows of Pascal's triangle starting with $n = 0$, (namely 1) up to the row $n = 11$, (namely $1, 11, \ldots$).
   b) Write the first twelve rows of Pascal's triangle in terms of combinations $C(n,k)$.

2. Use your answers to question 1 a) and 1 b) to evaluate the following:
   a) $C(8,3)$ **c)** $C(7,4)$
   b) $C(11,5)$ **d)** $C(9,5)$

3. a) $C(10,5)$ is in the eleventh row $(n = 10)$ of Pascal's triangle. Express $C(10,5)$ in terms of numbers from the tenth row $(n = 9)$.
   b) $C(32,8)$ is in the thirty-third row $(n = 32)$ of Pascal's triangle. Express $C(32,8)$ in terms of numbers from the thirty-second row $(n = 31)$.
   c) What number in row $n = 35$ equals $C(34,14) + C(34,15)$?

4. a) In Pascal's triangle, what other number in row $n = 46$ has the same value as $C(46,13)$?
   b) Under what conditions will $C(12,m) = C(12,t)$?

5. a) Prove that $C(n,k) = C(n,n - k)$.
   b) Explain the significance of the result in part a) to Pascal's triangle.

6. a) Prove that $C(40,18) = C(39,17) + C(39,18)$.
   b) Prove that $C(n + 1,k) = C(n,k - 1) + C(n,k)$.
   c) Explain the significance of the result in part b) to Pascal's triangle.

7. a) Expand $(1 - x)^n$ using the binomial theorem.
   b) By setting $x = 1$ in your answer to part a) show the following is true.
   $C(n,0) - C(n,1) + C(n,2) - C(n,3) + \ldots + (-1)^n C(n,n) = 0$.

8. a) Use the binomial theorem to evaluate $(1 + 1)^n$ in terms of combinations, $C(n,k)$
   Hence, show that
   $C(n,0) + C(n,1) + C(n,2) + C(n,3) + \ldots + C(n,n - 3) + C(n,n - 2) + C(n,n - 1) + C(n,n) = 2^n$.
   b) Use part a) to prove that the sum of the binomial coefficients in row $n = t$ of Pascal's triangle is 2^t.

9. a) By examining the numbers in row $n = 6$ of Pascal's triangle show that
   $C(6,0) + 2C(6,1) + 3C(6,2) + 4C(6,3) + 5C(6,4) + 6C(6,5) + 7C(6,6) = 2^5 (2 + 6)$.
   b) State a result similar to that of a) for the numbers in the row $n = 7$ in Pascal's triangle.

10. By considering the expansions of $(1 + 1)^{n-1}$ and $(1 + 1)^n$ show that
   $C(n,0) + 2C(n,1) + 3C(n,2) + 4C(n,3) + \ldots + (n + 1)C(n,n) = 2^{n-1}(2 + n)$.

11. a) In Pascal's triangle, row $n = 2$ is 1 2 1. Observe that the number $121 = 11^2$. Row $n = 3$ is 1 3 3 1. Is the number $1331 = 11^3$?
   b) Show that for rows $n = 4$ and $n = 5$ the numbers obtained by grouping the elements of the rows as in part a) are 11^4 and 11^5, respectively.
   c) Use the fact that $11 = (10 + 1)$ to explain your observations of parts a) and b).

12. a) By direct substitution of values from Pascal's triangle, prove that
   $$\frac{C(5,1)}{C(5,0)} + \frac{2C(5,2)}{C(5,1)} + \frac{3C(5,3)}{C(5,2)} + \frac{4C(5,4)}{C(5,3)} + \frac{5C(5,5)}{C(5,4)} = 15$$
   b) Prove that
   $$\frac{C(n,1)}{C(n,0)} + \frac{2C(n,2)}{C(n,1)} + \frac{3C(n,3)}{C(n,2)} + \frac{4C(n,4)}{C(n,3)} + \ldots \frac{nC(n,n)}{C(n,n - 1)} = \frac{n(n + 1)}{2}$$

In Search of Patterns in Pascal's Triangle

If you write Pascal's triangle in the following manner, many different patterns become more apparent:

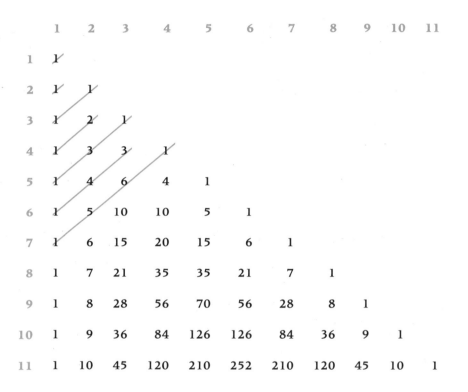

	1	2	3	4	5	6	7	8	9	10	11
1	1										
2	1	1									
3	1	2	1								
4	1	3	3	1							
5	1	4	6	4	1						
6	1	5	10	10	5	1					
7	1	6	15	20	15	6	1				
8	1	7	21	35	35	21	7	1			
9	1	8	28	56	70	56	28	8	1		
10	1	9	36	84	126	126	84	36	9	1	
11	1	10	45	120	210	252	210	120	45	10	1

Pattern 1

If you add the numbers in each row you obtain the following sequence
1, 2, 4, 8, 16, 32, 64...
which is the sequence of the powers of 2. Explain why this is equivalent to saying that
$C(n,0) + C(n,1) + C(n,2) + C(n,3) + \ldots + C(n,n-3) + C(n,n-2) + C(n,n-1) + C(n,n) = 2^n$.
Prove this fact is true using the expansion of $(a + x)^n$ with $a = x = 1$.

Pattern 2

Look at the sequence formed by the different columns.

a) How would you describe the sequence in the first column?

b) How would you describe the sequence in the second column? What would be the number in this column in the twelfth row from the top? In what row would you find the number k?

c) The numbers in the third column are called the triangular numbers. Examine the following diagrams, so that you will understand why these numbers are called triangular numbers.

1 •   3   6

Use the relationship between Pascal's triangle and the numbers $C(n,k)$ to determine the triangular numbers in the row beginning 1 n.

d) Examine the other columns in Pascal's triangle to see if you can determine any patterns in the corresponding sequences.

Pattern 3

If you add the numbers along each of the diagonals drawn in Pascal's triangle you will obtain the following sequence.
1, 1, 2, 3, 5, 8, 13, 21, 34, 55,...
This sequence of numbers is called the Fibonacci sequence and the numbers in the sequence are called Fibonacci numbers. This sequence was discovered at the start at the thirteenth century by an Italian mathematician, Leonardo of Pisa, who was also called Fibonacci.

a) Find the next five numbers in the above sequence.

b) Check that
$t_1 = 1$, $t_2 = 1$, $t_3 = t_2 + t_1$, $t_4 = t_3 + t_2$ and $t_n = t_{n-1} + t_{n-2}$, $n > 2$.
($t_1 = 1$, $t_2 = 1$, $t_n = t_{n-1} + t_{n-2}$, $n > 2$ is a recursion formula for the Fibonacci sequence.)

c) Calculate the value of $t_n^2 - t_{n-1} \times t_{n+1}$ for $n = 3, 4, 5$ and 6.
Guess the formula that will give the value of $t_n^2 - t_{n-1} \times t_{n+1}$ for $n > 2$.

d) Find the sum $t_1^2 + t_2^2 + t_3^2 + \ldots + t_{k-1}^2 + t_k^2$ for $k = 3, 4, 5 \ldots$.
Hence, guess the formula for $t_1^2 + t_2^2 + t_3^2 + \ldots + t_{k-1}^2 + t_k^2$, $k > 2$, in terms of other terms of the sequence.

The numbers 1, 3, 1 and 1, 4, 3 and 1, 5, 6, 1 are said to lie on the "rising diagonals" of Pascal's triangle.

e) Show that the sum of the numbers in the fourth diagonal (1,2) plus the sum of the numbers in the fifth diagonal (1,3,1) is equal to the sum of the numbers in the sixth diagonal (1,4,3).

f) Find a relationship that appears to be true among the numbers in any three consecutive diagonals.

Summary

- There are two equivalent expressions for the expansion of $(a + x)^n$, $n \in W$.

  I. $(a + n)^n = C(n,0)a^n x^0 + C(n,1)a^{n-1}x^1 + C(n,2)a^{n-2}x^2 + C(n,3)a^{n-3}x^3$
  $$+ \ldots + C(n,k)a^{n-k}x^k + \ldots + C(n,n)a^{n-n}x^n.$$

  II. $(a + x)^n = a^n x^0 + na^{n-1}x^1 + \dfrac{n(n-1)}{2!}a^{n-2}x^2 + \dfrac{n(n-1)(n-2)}{3!}a^{n-3}x^3$
  $$+ \ldots + \dfrac{n(n-1)(n-2)\ldots(n-k+1)}{k!}a^{n-k}x^k + \ldots + a^0 x^n.$$

- The coefficients of $(a + x)^t$ are the numbers in the $(t + 1)$st row in Pascal's triangle.
- Pascal's triangle up to row $n = 4$ is as follows:

			1				
		1		1			
	1		2		1		
1		3		3		1	
1	4		6		4		1

  $C(0,0)$
  $C(1,0)\quad C(1,1)$
  $C(2,0)\quad C(2,1)\quad C(2,2)$
  $C(3,0)\quad C(3,1)\quad C(3,2)\quad C(3,3)$
  $C(4,0)\quad C(4,1)\quad C(4,2)\quad C(4,3)\quad C(4,4)$

  where $C(n,k) = C(n-1, k-1) + C(n-1, k)$.
- The general term of $(a + x)^n$ is the term $C(n,k)a^{n-k}x^k$ and is the $(k + 1)$st term, that is t_{k+1}.
- The sum of the binomial coefficients in row $n = t$ is 2^t.

Inventory

Answer the following by filling in the blanks.
1. For $(a + x)^{15}$
   a) There are _____ terms.
   b) The term with x^5 has a with exponent _____.
   c) The term with a^6 has x with exponent _____.
   d) The coefficient of the term containing x^3 is _____.
   e) The coefficient of the term containing a^9 is _____.
   f) The eight term is _____.
2. a) The row $n = 8$ in Pascal's triangle is 1, 8, 28, 56, 70, 56, 28, 8, 1.
      The row $n = 9$ is _____.
   b) The first four numbers in row $n = 10$ of Pascal's triangle are 1, 10, 45, 120. These same numbers appear in row $n =$ _____ in the _____ positions.
3. a) The general term for $(a + x)^7$ is _____.
   b) $C(12,k)m^{12-k}b^k$ is the general term for _____.
4. For the expansion with general term $C(10,k)3^k x^{10-3k}$, the term containing x^7 occurs for $k =$ _____. The term containing x^{-8} occurs for $k =$ _____.

Review Exercises

1. **a)** Write the first fourteen rows of Pascal's triangle, as numbers.
   b) Write row $n = 15$ of Pascal's triangle, using combinations $C(n,k)$.

2. Expand the following using the binomial theorem.
   a) $(a + x)^5$ **c)** $(m + b)^6$ **e)** $(a + 2)^7$
   b) $(a - c)^5$ **d)** $(3 + x)^4$ **f)** $(4 - b)^3$

3. Expand.
   a) $(a + 2b)^3$ **c)** $(2 - 2a)^7$ **e)** $(2x + 3a)^5$
   b) $(3a + 2b)^4$ **d)** $(2t - 7)^4$ **f)** $(1 - b^2)^4$

4. Expand.
   a) $(2 - 3x)^6$ **c)** $(2t + 4b)^3$ **e)** $(5 - 2s)^3$
   b) $(1 + x^2)^5$ **d)** $(r - 2s)^4$ **f)** $(m^2 - 1)^5$

5. Find the first three terms of the expansion of each of the following. Do not simplify.
   a) $(a + x)^{200}$ **c)** $(2 + 4b)^5$ **e)** $(1 + x^2)^{50}$
   b) $(w - 2)^{40}$ **d)** $(s - 2r)^{30}$ **f)** $(f - 3)^{95}$

6. Expand each of the following using the binomial theorem. Simplify each term but do not add terms.
   a) $\left(\dfrac{1}{2} + \dfrac{1}{2}\right)^4$ **b)** $\left(\dfrac{1}{3} + \dfrac{2}{3}\right)^3$ **c)** $(0.3 + 0.7)^2$

7. Expand.
   a) $\left(x + \dfrac{2}{x}\right)^3$ **b)** $\left(x - \dfrac{1}{x}\right)^4$ **c)** $\left(x^2 + \dfrac{3}{x^2}\right)^5$

8. Write the general term of each of the following. Leave your answer in terms of $C(n,k)$.
   a) $(a + x)^7$ **b)** $(2 + m)^{24}$ **c)** $(H + T)^{50}$

9. **a)** Write the general term of $(p + q)^{11}$.
   b) Evaluate the term containing q^2.
   c) Evaluate the term containing p^5.
   d) Evaluate the seventh term.

10. For each of the following, find the general term, and, if possible, the term containing x^3.
    a) $\left(x + \dfrac{1}{x}\right)^7$ **b)** $\left(x^2 + \dfrac{2}{x}\right)^3$ **c)** $\left(x^2 + \dfrac{1}{x^3}\right)^9$

11. Find the indicated term in the expansion in each of the following:
    a) $(m + 5)^{12}$; tenth term
    b) $\left(2x + \dfrac{3}{b}\right)^{72}$; thirtieth term
    c) $\left(x^2 + \dfrac{1}{x^2}\right)^8$; the middle term
    d) $\left(x + \dfrac{1}{x}\right)^6$; the term that does not contain an x

12. Prove that $C(n + 1,k) = C(n,k - 1) + C(n,k)$

13. Prove that the sum of the binomial coefficients in row $n = t$ of Pascal's triangle is 2^t.

14. A die is tossed thirty times in a row. The probability that an even face will turn up exactly twelve times is given by the term containing q^{12} in the expansion of $(p + q)^{30}$, where $p = \dfrac{1}{2}$ and $q = \dfrac{1}{2}$. Find this probability, correct to 4 decimal places.

15. Use the expansion of $(1 - 1)^n$, where n is an even number, to prove that
    $C(n,0) + C(n,2) + C(n,4) + \ldots + C(n,n) = C(n,1) + C(n,3) + C(n,5) + \ldots + C(n,n - 1).$

16. **a)** Expand $(1 - x)^4$.
    b) Expand $(1 + 2x)^3$.
    c) Find the coefficient of x^2 in $(1 - x)^4(1 + 2x)^3$.

17. Find the first three terms in the expansion of $(1 + x)^n + (1 - x)^n$.

18. Show that the coefficient of x^n in $(1 + x)^{2n}$ is twice the coefficient of x^n in $(1 + x)^{2n-1}$.

19. In the expansion of $(1 + x)^{43}$, the coefficients of the $(2m + 1)$st term and the $(m + 2)$st term are equal. Find the value of m.

20. The coefficient of the $(3r)$th term equals the coefficient of the $(r + 2)$th term in the expansion of $(1 + x)^{2n}$. Find the relationship between r and n.

CHAPTER SIX

Finite and Infinite Series

Did you know that some Greek philosophers taught that objects do not actually move, that you only imagine movement?

One Greek, Zeno, who lived in the 5th century B.C. from 495–435, argued something like the following.

Suppose that you are able to move from point A to point Z.

A ————————————————— B ———— C — D — Z

To travel from point A to point Z you must first arrive at the midpoint B, of AZ. After reaching B you must then get to C, the midpoint of BZ; before going all of the way to Z you must be at D, the midpoint of CZ, and so on. No matter what point you reach there is always a midpoint in front of you at which you must arrive before getting to Z. In other words, there is always an infinite number of points that must be attained before you can get to Z. This means you must make an infinite number of moves. But it is impossible to make an infinite number of moves in a finite length of time, so you will never reach Z. But the same argument can be used for the first segment AB, so you can never reach B. The conclusion, according to Zeno, is that you really cannot move at all!

This argument is called Zeno's paradox: a paradox because the statement seems absurd. Most people are convinced that they are able to move.

Zeno's paradox can be explained mathematically by considering the successive distances you must travel to get to the midpoints $B, C, D, \ldots$

If $AZ = 1$, then $AB = \dfrac{1}{2}$, $BC = \dfrac{1}{4}$, $CD = \dfrac{1}{8}, \ldots$.

Thus, the total distance you travel equals

$$\frac{1}{2} + \frac{1}{4} + \frac{1}{8} + \frac{1}{16} + \frac{1}{32} + \frac{1}{64} + \ldots.$$

Zeno argued that there is no last term in the series, so that you would have to go on forever to reach Z. Mathematicians agree that there is no last term. But they point out that no matter how many terms you do add, as long as the number of terms is *finite*, the sum will be less than 1. (You will have arrived at some midpoint before Z.) And mathematicians also argue that the sum of the *infinite* number of terms of this series *will* equal 1, the distance from A to Z. In this chapter, you will see why mathematicians say the sum of $\frac{1}{2} + \frac{1}{4} + \frac{1}{8} + \frac{1}{16} + \frac{1}{32} + \frac{1}{64} + \ldots$ is 1.

Another of Zeno's paradoxes concerned the Greek legend about the warrior Achilles and a tortoise. Achilles and the tortoise ran a race in which Achilles ran ten times faster than the tortoise. To make the race appear fair, the tortoise was given 100 metres head start. Zeno said that it would be impossible for Achilles to catch up to the tortoise. While Achilles was running the 100 metres to reach the place from which the tortoise started, the tortoise had travelled 10 metres; then while Achilles ran these 10 metres, the tortoise would go 1 metre; in the time it took Achilles to make up this 1 metre, the tortoise would crawl another 0.1 metres, and so on forever. Each of Achilles' trips of 100 m, 10 m, 1 m, 0.1 m, 0.01 m,... took a finite length of time. Since an infinite number of trips was needed, Zeno said that Achilles would never catch up to the tortoise.

Activities

1. The distance travelled, in metres, by Achilles is the sum of the infinite series $100 + 10 + 1 + 0.1 + 0.01 + 0.001 + \ldots$. Show this distance equals the infinite decimal $111.1111\ldots$.

2. By dividing 1 by 9 show that the distance in 1 equals $111\frac{1}{9}$ m.

3. Suppose that Achilles ran at 10 m/s and the tortoise at 1 m/s. Complete the following table of distances travelled by each in the first 12 seconds.

Time from start (s)		0	1	2	3	4	5	6	7	8	9	10	11	12
Distance from start	Achilles	0	10	20	30									
	Tortoise	100	101	102	103									

4. Use the chart to find the time it takes for Achilles to be at the same place as the tortoise.

5. What do you thing of Zeno's arguments that there can be no motion?

6. Argue in the fashion of Zeno that a bowman cannot hit the bull's-eye of a target with an arrow.

7. Look up the definition of the term ''paradox''. Why is Zeno's argument called a paradox?

6.1 Series, Sequences and Sigma Notation

In the introduction you met the following **infinite series**.

$$\frac{1}{2} + \frac{1}{4} + \frac{1}{8} + \dots$$

This series is obtained by placing + signs between consecutive terms of the corresponding **sequence**

$$\frac{1}{2}, \frac{1}{4}, \frac{1}{8}, \dots$$

This sequence can also be written

$$\frac{1}{2^1}, \frac{1}{2^2}, \frac{1}{2^3}, \dots$$

Each term in a series or sequence has both a *term number* and a *term value* as the following table indicates.

term number	1	2	3	4	5	...	n	...
term value	$\frac{1}{2^1}$	$\frac{1}{2^2}$	$\frac{1}{2^3}$	$\frac{1}{2^4}$	$\frac{1}{2^5}$	...	$\frac{1}{2^n}$	...

The term value corresponding to the term number n is abbreviated t_n, and is called the *general term*. Thus, $t_n = \frac{1}{2^n}$.

Example 1   Find the first four terms of the sequence and series defined by the following general terms.

a) $t_n = 3n + 1$

b) $t_n = \dfrac{1}{4n - 3}$

Solution   a) Let $n = 1, t_1 = 3(1) + 1 = 4$
$\phantom{\text{Let}} n = 2, t_2 = 3(2) + 1 = 7$
$\phantom{\text{Let}} n = 3, t_3 = 3(3) + 1 = 10$
$\phantom{\text{Let}} n = 4, t_4 = 3(4) + 1 = 13$

The first four terms of the sequence are 4, 7, 10, 13.
The first four terms of the series are $4 + 7 + 10 + 13$.

b) Let $n = 1, t_1 = \dfrac{1}{4(1) - 3} = 1$

$\phantom{\text{b) Let}} n = 2, t_2 = \dfrac{1}{4(2) - 3} = \dfrac{1}{5}$

$$n = 3, t_3 = \frac{1}{4(3) - 3} = \frac{1}{9}$$

$$n = 4, t_4 = \frac{1}{4(4) - 3} = \frac{1}{13}$$

The first four terms of the sequence are $1, \frac{1}{5}, \frac{1}{9}, \frac{1}{13}$.

The first four terms of the series are $1 + \frac{1}{5} + \frac{1}{9} + \frac{1}{13}$. ■

For the series of Example 1 a) the first n terms are as follows.
$4 + 7 + 11 + 13 + \ldots + (3n + 1)$.
A notation has been developed to enable such a series to be written in more compact form. The abbreviation for this series is

$$4 + 7 + 11 + 13 + \ldots + (3n + 1) = \sum_{k=1}^{n} (3k + 1).$$

$\sum_{k=1}^{n} (3k + 1)$ is read "the sum of $3k + 1$ for $k = 1$ to $k = n$".

Similarly the series

$1^2 + 2^2 + 3^2 + 4^2 + 5^2$ can be abbreviated $\sum_{k=1}^{5} k^2$

$\sum_{k=1}^{5} k^2$ is read "the sum of k^2 for $k = 1$ to $k = 5$".

This notation is called the *sigma notation* because the notation uses the Greek letter sigma, Σ, which corresponds to the English letter S, for "sum".

The variable k is called the **index of summation**. The number 1 is called the **lower limit** (or **initial value**) and the number 5 is called the **upper limit** (or **final value**).

Example 2 Write each series in expanded form and find its sum.

a. $\sum_{k=1}^{6} k^2$ **b.** $\sum_{n=1}^{5} (2n + 1)$

Solution **a)** To obtain the series in expanded form you must substitute, in turn, the integers 1, 2, 3, 4, 5 and 6 for k into k^2. Thus

$$\sum_{k=1}^{6} k^2 = 1^2 + 2^2 + 3^2 + 4^2 + 5^2 + 6^2$$

$$= 1 + 4 + 9 + 16 + 25 + 36$$

The sum is 91.

b) Substitute the integers 1, 2, 3, 4 and 5 for n into $2n + 1$.

$$\sum_{n=1}^{5} (2n + 1) = [2(1) + 1] + [2(2) + 1] + [2(3) + 1] + [2(4) + 1] + [2(5) + 1]$$

$$= 3 + 5 + 7 + 9 + 11$$

The sum is 35. ■

You should realize that it is not necessary to use any special letter as the index of summation. Each of the following, for example, represent the same series, namely $1^2 + 2^2 + 3^2 + 4^2 + 5^2 + 6^2$

$$\sum_{a=1}^{6} a^2, \quad \sum_{n=1}^{6} n^2, \quad \sum_{i=1}^{6} i^2, \quad \sum_{x=1}^{6} x^2$$

The letters k, a, n, i, and x, are called *dummy variables*. The sum 91 does not depend on the variable used with the Σ symbol. Also, when the series is written out using plus signs (+) instead of the Σ sign, the dummy variable does not appear.

Example 3

Write each series in expanded form.

a) $\displaystyle\sum_{k=1}^{4} 2 \times 3^k$ b) $\displaystyle\sum_{j=1}^{6} (ja + 1)$ c) $\displaystyle\sum_{a=3}^{8} 5a$

Solution

a) $\displaystyle\sum_{k=1}^{4} 2 \times 3^k = 2 \times 3^1 + 2 \times 3^2 + 2 \times 3^3 + 2 \times 3^4$

b) $\displaystyle\sum_{j=1}^{6} (ja + 1) = 1a + 1 + 2a + 1 + 3a + 1 + 4a + 1 + 5a + 1 + 6a + 1$

c) $\displaystyle\sum_{a=3}^{7} 5a = 5(3) + 5(4) + 5(5) + 5(6) + 5(7) + 5(8)$ ∎

Example 4

Write each of the following series using Σ notation.

a) $3 + \dfrac{3}{2} + \dfrac{3}{4} + \dfrac{3}{8}$ b) $3 + \dfrac{3}{2} + \dfrac{3}{4} + \dfrac{3}{8} + \ldots$ to n terms.

Solution

a) You should observe any pattern, and rewrite the series.

$3 + \dfrac{3}{2^1} + \dfrac{3}{2^2} + \dfrac{3}{2^3}$ The first term may be written as $\dfrac{3}{2^0}$.

Thus $3 + \dfrac{3}{2} + \dfrac{3}{4} + \dfrac{3}{8} = \displaystyle\sum_{k=1}^{4} \dfrac{3}{2^{k-1}}$

b) In this case the number of terms is n.

$3 + \dfrac{3}{2^1} + \dfrac{3}{2^2} + \dfrac{3}{2^3} + \ldots + \dfrac{3}{2^{n-1}} = \displaystyle\sum_{k=1}^{n} \dfrac{3}{2^{k-1}}$ ∎

6.1 Exercises

1. For the sequence 8, 13, 18, 23, 28, 33 complete the following.
   a) The sequence has _____ terms.
   b) The term value for the 5th term is _____.
   c) The term number for the term 33 is

      _____.
   d) For the term 23, the term number is _____, and the term value is _____.
   e) The corresponding series is _____.

2. Find the first four terms of the sequence and series defined by the following general terms.

   a) $t_k = 2 + 4k$ b) $t_n = 3 \times 2^n$ c) $t_a = \dfrac{1}{2a + 5}$

3. Write each series in question 2 in sigma notation.

4. Which of the following is a compact form for $1^n + 2^n + 3^n + 4^n$?

   a) $\displaystyle\sum_{n=1}^{4} n^k$ b) $\displaystyle\sum_{k=1}^{4} k^n$ c) $\displaystyle\sum_{k=1}^{4} n^k$ d) $\displaystyle\sum_{n=1}^{4} k^n$

5. For each of the following series written in abbreviated form, state the value of $t_1, t_4,$ and t_n.

   a) $\displaystyle\sum_{k=1}^{n} (3k \times 2)$ b) $\displaystyle\sum_{j=1}^{n} (j^3 + 1)$ c) $\displaystyle\sum_{a=1}^{n} \dfrac{1}{(3a - 1)}$

6. Write each series in expanded form.

   a) $\displaystyle\sum_{m=1}^{4} m$ d) $\displaystyle\sum_{n=1}^{6} 3n$

   b) $\displaystyle\sum_{m=1}^{5} 4 \times 2^m$ e) $\displaystyle\sum_{i=1}^{5} (2i + 3)$

   c) $\displaystyle\sum_{n=1}^{5} n^2$ f) $\displaystyle\sum_{k=1}^{4} (-1)^k 5$

7. Write each of the following series using Σ notation.
   a) $1 + 2 + 3 + 4 + 5$
   b) $1^3 + 2^3 + 3^3 + 4^3 + 5^3$
   c) $4^2 + 5^2 + 6^2 + 7^2 + 8^2$
   d) $c + c^2 + c^3 + c^4 + c^5$
   e) $2(3^4) + 2(3^5) + 2(3^6) + 2(3^7)$
   f) $t_1 + t_2 + t_3 + t_4 + t_5 + t_6$

8. Write each of the following series in expanded form. Do the three series have the same number of terms? equal sums?

   a) $\displaystyle\sum_{k=1}^{4} 3k$ b) $\displaystyle\sum_{k=2}^{5} 3(k - 1)$ c) $\displaystyle\sum_{k=6}^{9} 3(k - 5)$

9. Write each of the following series in expanded form. Do the two series have the same number of terms? equal sums?

   a) $\displaystyle\sum_{k=1}^{4} 3k$ b) $\displaystyle\sum_{k=2}^{5} 3k$

10. Use Σ notation to represent each of the following series, each of which has n terms.

    a) $\dfrac{1}{1} + \dfrac{1}{2} + \dfrac{1}{3} + \dfrac{1}{4} + \dfrac{1}{5} + \ldots + \dfrac{1}{n}$
    b) $2 + 7 + 12 + \ldots + (5n - 3)$
    c) $-2 + 2 - 2 + \ldots + (-1)^n 2$
    d) $1 + 2k + 3k^2 + \ldots + nk^{n-1}$

11. Prove each of the following by writing each series in expanded form.

    a) $\displaystyle\sum_{k=1}^{4} m = 4m$

    b) $\displaystyle\sum_{i=1}^{5} 3t_i = 3 \sum_{i=1}^{5} t_i$

    c) $\displaystyle\sum_{k=1}^{5} (x_k + y_k) = \sum_{k=1}^{5} x_k + \sum_{k=1}^{5} y_k$

    d) $\displaystyle\sum_{k=5}^{15} a_k = \sum_{k=7}^{17} a_{k-2}$

12. Show, by writing each series in expanded form, that

    $$\sum_{i=1}^{3} a_i b_i \neq \sum_{i=1}^{3} a_i \times \sum_{i=1}^{3} b_i$$

13. Prove each of the following.

    a) $\displaystyle\sum_{k=1}^{n} m = nm$

    b) $\displaystyle\sum_{i=1}^{n} ax_i = a \sum_{i=1}^{n} x_i$

    c) $\displaystyle\sum_{k=1}^{n} (x_k + y_k) = \sum_{k=1}^{n} x_k + \sum_{k=1}^{n} y_k$

    d) $\displaystyle\sum_{k=p}^{t} a_k = \sum_{k=p+m}^{t+m} a_{k-m}$

M A K I N G

Mathematics Contests

Mathematics and sports are very similar in their competitiveness. And nowhere is that competition more vividly seen than in math contests like the Putnam.

William Lowell Putnam was a great believer in intercollegiate intellectual competition, and in 1882, while at Harvard, he wrote an article extolling its virtues. It was an interest he held throughout his life. In 1927 his widow created a trust called the William Lowell Putnam Intercollegiate Memorial Fund to finance an annual competition. At first, the subject was English, but after Mrs. Putnam's death in 1935, it was changed to mathematics. The goal was "to stimulate healthful rivalry in mathematical studies in the colleges and universities of the United States and Canada."

The University of Toronto won the first Putnam, in 1938, and managed to win three more times during the next five years. Since then, the competition has been dominated by Harvard, and the California Institute of Technology. The University of Waterloo, in Ontario, is always near the top and easily has the best record of the Canadian entries over the last 12 years.

The Putnam is to undergraduate mathematics what the Rose Bowl is to U.S. college football. In 1983, 2055 students at 345 universities and colleges in North America participated in the competition. The University of Waterloo placed third, behind first place California Institute of Technology, and Washington University, St. Louis, Missouri. Princeton came fourth, Harvard seventh and Yale tenth.

The 1983 results were not a fluke. The University of Waterloo has placed among the top 10 competing universities on the continent five times since 1978, including a second place finish in 1982. And in 1974, Waterloo came first—tops in North America.

David Ash, an undergraduate at Waterloo in 1983, finished in the top five in North America with a score of 88 out of 120.

Ten points are awarded for each perfect solution, and there are 12 questions. The top individual score was 98—a phenomenal result, for no one ever solves every problem. Most earn part-marks for getting close to a solution.

Dr. Bruno Forte, one of the trainers of the Waterloo team, says the best math students enjoy games, physical and cerebral. "One of the appeals of math," he says, "is a feeling of power, the power of the brain." Forte likes to talk of 'mathematical intuition,' the ability some students have to grasp a solution immediately, to see a 'vision' of it before they try to work it out on paper. It is most common in young mathematicians, before their heads are filled with memorized solutions. "It is like the piano, like poetry—the more you know, the less intuitive you become. You start to rely on what you've memorized."

Dr. Ron Dunkley, assistant dean of mathematics at Waterloo University and executive director of the Canadian Mathematics Competition, says there are two ways to solve a mathematics problem. One is the 'brute force' method, a battle of attrition, grinding down a problem until it collapses in a heap; the other is the 'elegant' method, the sparse, clean attack. "It really is something to see," Dunkley says. "It can bring tears to your eyes."

This year, many students across Canada will enter the American High School Mathematics Examination, while thousands of others will participate in their local district competitions. Mathematics competitions are now part of the fabric of the math community. From William Lowell Putnam's belief in intercollegiate competition, important, exciting, and grand contests have grown on every level of mathematics education.

6.2 Arithmetic and Geometric Series

You have been hired to work for ten weeks during the summer. Your employer is a person who wants her employees to think, so she gives you the choice of two salaries.

Salary 1: $200 the first week, $210 the second week, $220 the third week and so on, with your salary increasing by $10 each week.
Salary 2: $1 the first week, $3 the second week, $9 the third week and so on, with your salary of each week, after the first week, being three times the salary of the previous week.

Which salary should you choose?

Salary 1 can be represented by the series $200 + 210 + 220 + \ldots$ to 10 terms.
Salary 2 can be expressed by the series $1 + 3 + 9 + \ldots$ to 10 terms.

D E F I N I T I O N

In the series for salary 1, there is a **common difference** of 10 between successive terms since $10 = 210 - 200 = 220 - 210 = \ldots$.
Such a series is called an **arithmetic series**.

To determine if a series is an arithmetic series, check that the difference between successive terms is the same number.

Thus the finite series $8 + 13 + 18 + 23 + 28$ is arithmetic,
                                                +5   +5   +5   +5

whereas the finite series $8 + 10 + 13 + 17 + 22$ is not.
                                        +2   +3   +4   +5

The common difference is usually represented by the variable d. Hence any term of an arithmetic series is obtained by adding the common difference to the preceding term.
Thus $t_k = t_{k-1} + d, k > 1$ is a formula for an arithmetic series.

D E F I N I T I O N

In the series for salary 2, there is a **common ratio** of 3 between successive terms, since $3 = 3 \div 1 = 9 \div 3 = \ldots$.
Such a series is called a **geometric series**.

To determine if a series is a geometric series, check that the ratio of any term to the preceding term is the same number.

Thus the finite series $2 + 10 + 50 + 250 + 1250$ is geometric,
                                                ×5   ×5   ×5   ×5

whereas the finite series $2 + 4 + 12 + 48 + 240$ is not.
                                        ×2   ×3   ×4   ×5

The common ratio is usually represented by the variable r. Hence any term of a geometric series is obtained by multiplying the preceding term by the common ratio.
Thus $t_k = t_{k-1} \times r, k > 1$ is a formula for a geometric series.

Recall that in grade 11 you learned the following formulas for arithmetic and geometric series.

Arithmetic series: $t_n = a + (n - 1)d$

$\quad$ where $\quad a =$ the first term
$\quad\quad\quad\quad\quad d =$ the common difference
$\quad\quad\quad\quad\quad n =$ the term number
$\quad\quad\quad\quad\quad t_n =$ the term value

Geometric series: $t_n = a \times r^{n-1}$

$\quad$ where $\quad a =$ the first term
$\quad\quad\quad\quad\quad r =$ the common ratio
$\quad\quad\quad\quad\quad n =$ the term number
$\quad\quad\quad\quad\quad t_n =$ the term value

Example 1 Each of the following is either a geometric or an arithmetic series. For each, indicate which type of series it is, state the value of d or r, and give the value of t_8.

a) $16 + 11 + 6 + \ldots$ $\qquad\qquad$ b) $3 + 6 + 12 + \ldots$

Solution a) There is a common difference of $d = -5$ ($= 11 - 16 = 6 - 11$).
$\quad\quad$ Thus, the series is arithmetic.
$\quad\quad$ Here $\quad a = 16, d = -5, n = 8$ and $t_n = ?$
$\quad\quad$ but $\quad t_n = a + (n - 1)d$
$\quad\quad$ thus, $t_8 = a + 7d = 16 + 7(-5) = -19$.

b) There is a common ratio of $r = 2$ ($= 6 \div 3 = 12 \div 6$).
$\quad\quad$ Thus, the series is geometric.
$\quad\quad$ Here $\quad a = 3, r = 2, n = 8$ and $t_n = ?$
$\quad\quad$ but $\quad t_n = a \times r^{n-1}$
$\quad\quad$ thus, $t_8 = 3 \times 2^7 = 384$. ■

Example 2   Find the salary you would receive during the tenth week for each of the two choices.

  a) Salary 1: $200 the first week, with the salary increasing each week by $10

  b) Salary 2: $1 the first week, with the salary of any week, after the first, being three times the salary of the previous week

Solution   a) The series for Salary 1 is $200 + 210 + 220 + \ldots$
    This series is arithmetic with
$$a = 200, d = 210 - 200 = 10, n = 10, t_n = ?$$
    but, $t_n = a + (n - 1)d$
    thus, $t_{10} = a + 9d = 200 + 9(10) = \$290.$
    You would receive $290 during the 10th week.

  b) The series for Salary 2 is $1 + 3 + 9 + 27 + \ldots$
    This series is geometric with
$$a = 1, r = 3 \div 1 = 3, n = 10, t_n = ?$$
    but, $t_n = a \times r^{n-1}$
    thus, $t_{10} = a \times r^9 = 1 \times 3^9 = 19\ 693.$
    You would receive $19 683 during the tenth week.   ■

Which of the two salaries would you choose? Why?

Example 2 indicates why geometric series and sequences are sometimes called *series and sequences of rapid growth*.

Example 3   Suppose that the two salary schedules of Example 2 were to continue indefinitely. Determine in what week the salaries would be as follows.

  a) $630 for Salary 1   b) $177 147 for Salary 2

Solution   a) For Salary 1, the series is arithmetic with
$$a = 200, d = 10, n = ?, t_n = 630$$
    but, $t_n = a + (n - 1)d$
    thus, $630 = 200 + (n - 1)10$
    $630 = 200 + 10n - 10$
    $n = 44$
    Thus, the salary would be $630 in the 44th week.

b) For Salary 2, the series is geometric with
$$a = 1, r = 3, n = ?, t_n = 177\ 147$$
but, $t_n = a \times r^{n-1}$
thus, $177\ 147 = 1 \times 3^{n-1}$

$$3^{11} = 3^{n-1}$$ $3^{11} = 177\ 147$
$$11 = n - 1$$
$$n = 12$$

Thus, the salary would be \$177 147 in the 12th week.   ■

Example 4   The 3rd term of a series has a term value of 64 while the 7th term is 4. Determine the first three terms of the series given that the series is
a) arithmetic   **b)** geometric

Solution   **a)** For an arithmetic series $t_n = a + (n - 1)d$
since $t_3 = 64$, then $64 = a + 2d$ ①
since $t_7 = 4$, then $4 = a + 6d$ ②
subtract ① − ② to eliminate a $60 = -4d$
thus $d = -15$
substituting in ① $64 = a + 2(-15)$
thus $a = 94$
Therefore, the first 3 terms are 94, 79, 64.

b) For a geometric series $t_n = a \times r^{n-1}$
since $t_3 = 64$, then $64 = a \times r^2$ ①
since $t_7 = 4$, then $4 = a \times r^6$ ②
divide ② ÷ ① to eliminate a

thus $\dfrac{4}{64} = \dfrac{a \times r^6}{a \times r^2}$

$$\dfrac{1}{16} = r^4$$

thus $r = \dfrac{1}{2}$ or $r = -\dfrac{1}{2}$

substituting in ① $64 = a\left(\dfrac{1}{2}\right)^2$ or $64 = a\left(-\dfrac{1}{2}\right)^2$

in both cases, $a = 256$

Therefore, there are two geometric series, the first 3 terms of which are 256, 128, 64, or 256, −128, 64.   ■

You should note in Example 4 that the first term, a, is eliminated *by subtraction for an arithmetic series* but *by division for a geometric series*.

6.2 Exercises

Unless otherwise indicated each series or sequence is either arithmetic or geometric.

1. Each of the following is either a geometric or an arithmetic series. For each, indicate which type of series it is, state the value of d or r, and give the next two terms.
   a) $3 + 6 + 9 + \ldots$
   b) $1 + 5 + 9 + \ldots$
   c) $27 + 9 + 3 + \ldots$
   d) $(k + 3) + (k + 6) + (k + 9) + \ldots$
   e) $2c^2 + 4c^3 + 8c^4 + \ldots$
   f) $4 + 1 - 2 - \ldots$
   g) $\dfrac{1}{8} + \dfrac{1}{4} + \dfrac{1}{2} + \ldots$
   h) $1.3 + 0.13 + 0.013 + \ldots$

2. Find the 8th and 10th term of each of the following series.
   a) $7 + 14 + 28 + \ldots$
   b) $15 + 45 + 135 + \ldots$
   c) $1.5 + 0.15 + 0.015 + \ldots$
   d) $-8 + 4 - 2 + \ldots$
   e) $37 + 31 + 25 + \ldots$
   f) $12 + 11.7 + 11.4 + \ldots$

3. For each of the following series find the general term, then write the series for n terms in compact form using sigma notation.
   a) $3 + 7 + 11 + \ldots$
   b) $8 + \dfrac{8}{3} + \dfrac{8}{9} + \ldots$
   c) $5 + 15 + 45 + \ldots$
   d) $25 + 12 - 1 - \ldots$

4. How many terms are there in each of the following series?
   a) $7 + 13 + 19 + \ldots + 217$
   b) $1.5 + 3 + 6 + \ldots + 3072$

5. Find the first term and the common difference for each of the arithmetic sequences for which two terms are as indicated.
   a) $t_4 = 5,\quad t_8 = 21$
   b) $t_6 = 10,\ t_{13} = -46$

6. Determine a and r for the geometric sequences of real numbers two of whose terms are as indicated.
   a) $t_2 = 12,\quad t_6 = 972$
   b) $t_7 = -200,\ t_{12} = \dfrac{8}{125}$

7. Assume that whenever you wash a pair of blue jeans, the jeans lose 5% of their color.
   a) How much of the original color would remain in the jeans after four washes?
   b) To be in style you must wash your jeans until at most 30% of the original color remains. What is the minimum number of times you must wash your jeans?

8. The fifth term of a geometric series of real numbers is 5 and the eighth term is -40. Find the third term.

9. From 11:00 to 11:05 the number of cells in a bacteria sample doubled every 30 s. At 11:05 the number of cells counted was 5120. Assuming the same rate of increase each 30 seconds find the number of cells that could be counted at the following times.
   a) 11:00
   b) 11:03
   c) 11:06
   d) 11:21

10. You are hired at a job that pays a starting salary of \$350/week. If you do satisfactory work you will be given a \$75/week increase in salary every three weeks. Assuming that you will get these raises, what would you expect your weekly salary to be 12 weeks after you are hired? 36 weeks after you are hired?

11. The cost for maintenance and repairs for your car increases as the age of your car increases. For your 1987 Squarerooter the cost of maintenance and repairs increases \$105 each year. In 1987, maintenance and repairs cost you \$235. How much will you spend for maintenance and repair during 1991?

6.3 The Sum of an Arithmetic Series

In section 6.2 you were given the choice of two salaries over a period of ten weeks. The first salary for the ten weeks was given by the arithmetic series, $200 + 210 + 220 + 230 + 240 + 250 + 260 + 270 + 280 + 290$.

If you wish to calculate your salary over this time you will need to add the 10 terms. The sum of 10 terms of a series or sequence is abbreviated S_{10}. Thus $S_{10} = 200 + 210 + 220 + 230 + 240 + 250 + 260 + 270 + 280 + 290$.

If you reverse the order of the terms you obtain
$$S_{10} = 290 + 280 + 270 + 260 + 250 + 240 + 230 + 220 + 210 + 200.$$

Adding these two values for S_{10} vertically, you find
$$S_{10} + S_{10} = 490 + 490 + 490 + 490 + 490 + 490 + 490 + 490 + 490 + 490.$$
$$\xleftarrow{\hspace{2cm}} \text{10 terms} \xrightarrow{\hspace{2cm}}$$

Thus, $2(S_{10}) = 10 \times 490$

or $S_{10} = \dfrac{4900}{2} = 2450$.

The same method can be used to find the sum of n terms of the arithmetic series $a + (a + d) + (a + 2d) + \ldots$.

Example 1   Find a formula for the sum of n terms of the arithmetic sequence with first term a, common difference d, and term value of the nth term, t_n.

Solution   After the first term, each term is found by adding d to the previous term. But working *backwards* from t_n each term is found by subtracting d from the term after it. Hence, the term immediately before t_n is $t_n - d$.
Thus, the terms of the sequence are
$a, a + d, a + 2d, a + 3d, \ldots, t_n - 2d, t_n - d, t_n$.
Thus,
$$S_n = a + (a + d) + (a + 2d) + \ldots + (t_n - 2d) + (t_n - d) + t_n$$

Reversing the order you obtain,
$$S_n = t_n + (t_n - d) + (t_n - 2d) + \ldots + (a + 2d) + (a + d) + a$$

Adding vertically,
$$2(S_n) = (a + t_n) + (a + t_n) + (a + t_n) + \ldots + (a + t_n) + (a + t_n) + (a + t_n)$$
$$\xleftarrow{\hspace{2cm}} n \text{ terms} \xrightarrow{\hspace{2cm}}$$

Thus, $2(S_n) = n \times (a + t_n)$

$$S_n = \frac{n(a + t_n)}{2}.$$

This formula is usually written
$$S_n = \frac{n}{2}(a + t_n). \quad \blacksquare$$

Example 2   Find the sum of the arithmetic series
$12 + 17 + \ldots + 257$.

Solution   Here $a = 12$, $d = 17 - 12 = 5$, $n = ?$, $t_n = 257$, $S_n = ?$.
To find S_n, you must first find n using
$$t_n = a + (n - 1)d$$
Thus, $257 = 12 + (n - 1)5$
$$n = 50.$$
Since you now know the series has 50 terms, you can find S_{50}.

But $S_n = \dfrac{n}{2}(a + t_n)$

$$S_{50} = \frac{50}{2}(12 + 257)$$
$$= 25(269)$$
thus $S_{50} = 6725.$
The sum of the series is 6725.   ■

A second formula may be obtained for S_n using the fact that
$t_n = a + (n - 1)d$.

$$S_n = \frac{n}{2}(a + t_n)$$

$$= \frac{n}{2}(a + a + (n - 1)d)$$

$$= \frac{n}{2}(2a + (n - 1)d)$$

For an arithmetic series,

FORMULA $S_n = \dfrac{n}{2}(a + t_n)$ or $S_n = \dfrac{n}{2}(2a + (n - 1)d)$
where a = the first term
d = the common difference
n = the number of terms to be added
t_n = the value of the nth term
S_n = the sum of the n terms

Example 3   A pile driver begins to drive a piling into the ground. On the first impact, the piling moves 90 cm into the ground. On the second, the piling moves an additional 87 cm. Assuming the distances the piling moves on successive impacts form an arithmetic series, find the total distance the piling has moved after 15 impacts.

Solution   Here $a = 90$
$$d = 87 - 90 = -3$$
$$n = 15$$
$$t_n = ?$$
$$S_n = ?$$

You can solve this problem using either of the two formulas for S_n.

To use the first formula you must find the value of t_n. The second formula can be used directly.

Using the second formula $S_n = \dfrac{n}{2}(2a + (n - 1)d)$

$$S_{15} = \frac{15}{2}(2(90) + 14(-3))$$
$$= 7.5(180 - 42) = 1035$$

Thus, after 15 impacts the piling has travelled 1035 cm into the ground. ■

Example 4   Evaluate $\displaystyle\sum_{k=1}^{20}(4k - 6)$.

Solution $\displaystyle\sum_{k=1}^{20}(4k - 6) = (4(1) - 6) + (4(2) - 6) + (4(3) - 6) + \ldots + (4(20) - 6)$

$$= \qquad -2 \quad + \quad 2 \quad + \quad 6 \quad + \ldots + \quad 74$$

This is an arithmetic series with
$a = -2, d = 2 - (-2) = 4, t_n = 74,$ and $n = 20$.

But $\qquad S_n = \dfrac{n}{2}(a + t_n)$

$$= \frac{20}{2}(-2 + 74)$$
$$= 720$$

Thus,
$$\sum_{k=1}^{20}(4k - 6) = 720. \quad ■$$

6.3 Exercises

1. Find the sum of each of the following series using the method of Example 1, but not the formula.
   a) $11 + 16 + 21 + 26 + 31 + 36 + 41 + 46 + 51 + 56$
   b) $23 + 74 + 125 + 176 + 227 + 278 + 329$

2. Find the sum of each of the following arithmetic series, to the number of terms indicated.
   a) $4 + 6 + 8 + \ldots$, to 20 terms
   b) $5 + 3 + 1 + \ldots$, to 30 terms
   c) $8 + 16 + 24 + \ldots$, to 19 terms
   d) $14 + 21 + 28 + \ldots$, to 10 terms

3. Find the sum of each of the following arithmetic series.
   a) $4 + 7 + 10 + \ldots + 76$
   b) $9 + 15 + 21 + \ldots + 189$
   c) $208 + 201 + 194 + \ldots + (-9)$
   d) $1.2 + 1.5 + 1.8 + \ldots + 4.5$

4. Evaluate the sum of each of the following arithmetic series.
   a) $\sum\limits_{k=1}^{10} (3k + 1)$
   b) $\sum\limits_{k=1}^{20} (5k + 2)$
   c) $\sum\limits_{k=1}^{100} (8 - 2k)$

5. Find the number of terms of the arithmetic series $33 + 27 + 21 + \ldots$ whose sum is 33.

6. Your rock group has been approached by a record company. The company offers you a fee of $20 000 for recording and a royalty for each record sold. At the end of one year, you receive $230 000 for the sale of 500 000 records. What royalty are you paid for each record?

7. Find a formula for the sum of the first n natural numbers, namely,
   $$\sum\limits_{k=1}^{n} k = 1 + 2 + 3 + \ldots + n.$$

8. As an expert in parachute jumping you know that in a free fall you fall 4.9 m in the first second, 14.7 m in the second second, 24.5 m in the third second, and so on in an arithmetic sequence.
   a) How far do you fall in the first 5 s of free fall?
   b) You jump from a height of 2822 m. You wish to open your chute when you are 1000 m above the ground. How many seconds after you have left the plane should you wait to pull the rip cord?

9. In a triangular shaped theatre with 14 rows there are 40 seats in the first row. The next eight rows decrease by two seats each so that the second row has 38 seats, the third row 36 seats and so on. The remaining rows decrease by four seats each. How many seats are there in the theatre?

10. Michel Handel obtains a winter job piling logs. She is paid $0.30 for every log she puts in a pile. Her employer insists that each pile be trapezoidal in shape with 15 logs on the bottom row, 14 logs on the row second from the bottom and so on in arithmetic sequence. The top row must contain 3 logs.
    a) How many logs are in each complete pile Michel makes?
    b) How many piles must Michel complete in a day if she wishes to earn at least $110 a day?

11. Suppose that you work for a construction company preparing bids for new buildings the company would like to construct. For a certain building you calculate that the cost per square metre for the ground floor is $560, and the cost per square metre for the 4th floor is $650. You know that the costs per square metre for successive floors form an arithmetic sequence.
    a) Find the cost of building the top floor of a building with 75 floors.
    b) What is the cost per square metre of building all 75 floors?

6.4 The Sum of a Geometric Series

In section 6.2 you were given the choice of two salaries over a period of ten weeks. The second salary total for the ten weeks was given by the geometric series

$$1 + 3 + 9 + 27 + 81 + 243 + 729 + 2187+ +6561 + 19\ 689.$$

If you wish to calculate your salary over this time you will need to add the 10 terms, obtaining S_{10}.

Thus,

$$S_{10} = 1 + 3 + 9 + 27 + 81 + 243 + 729 + 2187 + 6561 + 19\ 689. \qquad ①$$

Multiply each term on both sides of this equation by the common ratio $r = 3$.

$$3(S_{10}) =\ \ 3 + 9 + 27 + 81 + 243 + 729 + 2187 + 6561 + 19\ 689 + 59\ 049. \quad ②$$

Subtracting, ② − ①, you obtain

$$3(S_{10}) - S_{10} = -1 + 59\ 049$$
$$2(S_{10}) = 59\ 048$$

Thus, $S_{10} = 59\ 048 \div 2 = 29\ 024.$

The same method can be used to find the sum of n terms of the geometric series $a + ar + ar^2 + ar^3 +\ldots +ar^{n-1}$

Example 1   Find the sum of n terms of the geometric series with first term a and common ratio r, namely $a + ar + ar^2 + ar^3 +\ldots + ar^{n-1}$

Solution
$$S_n = a + ar + ar^2 + ar^3 +\ldots +ar^{n-1} \qquad ①$$
$$r(S_n) =\ \ \ \ \ ar + ar^2 + ar^3 +\ldots +ar^{n-1} + ar^n \qquad ②$$

Subtract ① − ②
$$S_n - r(S_n) = a - ar^n$$

Thus, $S_n(1 - r) = a(1 - r^n)$

$$S_n = \frac{a(1 - r^n)}{1 - r}, \text{ provided } r \neq 1. \quad ∎$$

Example 2   Find S_9 for the geometric series
$$6 + 18 + 54 +\ldots$$

Solution   Here $a = 6$, $r = \dfrac{18}{6} = 3$, $n = 9$, $S_n = ?$

$$S_n = \frac{a(1 - r^n)}{1 - r}$$

$$S_9 = \frac{6(1 - 3^9)}{1 - 3} = \frac{6(1 - 19\ 683)}{-2} \text{ or } 59\ 046. \quad ∎$$

Observe that in Example 2 the denominator of S_n is *negative*. This negative number occurs because $r > 1$. To avoid negative denominators, S_n can be written differently by multiplying numerator and denominator by -1.

$$S_n = \left(\frac{-1}{-1}\right)\frac{a(1-r^n)}{1-r} \text{ thus, } S_n = \frac{a(r^n-1)}{r-1}.$$

FORMULA

For a geometric series

$$S_n = \frac{a(1-r^n)}{1-r}, r \neq 1 \quad \text{or} \quad S_n = \frac{a(r^n-1)}{r-1}, r \neq 1$$

where a is the first term n is the number of terms
       r is the common ratio S_n is the sum of the n terms

To simplify your calculations you should use the formula that makes the denominator a positive number.

Example 3 Find, correct to 4 decimal places, $\sum\limits_{k=1}^{8} 3(-0.4)^{k-1}$

Solution $\sum\limits_{k=1}^{8} 3(-0.4)^{k-1} = 3(-0.4)^0 + 3(-0.4)^1 + 3(-0.4)^2 + 3(-0.4)^3$

$$+ 3(-0.4)^4 + 3(-0.4)^5 + 3(-0.4)^6 + 3(-0.4)^7$$

This is a geometric series with $a = 3$, $r = -0.4$, and $n = 8$.
Since $1 - r = 1 - (-0.4) = 1.4 > 0$, you should use the formula

$$S_n = \frac{a(1-r^n)}{1-r}$$

$$= \frac{3(1-(-0.4)^8)}{1-(-0.4)} \doteq \frac{3(1-0.000\ 655\ 36)}{1.04}$$

$$\doteq 2.882\ 724\ 9 \text{ or } 2.8827, \text{ correct to 4 decimal places. } \blacksquare$$

Example 4 Your ancestors in the first, second and third generations back are your natural parents, grandparents and great-grandparents respectively. What total number of ancestors do you have in the first 15 generations back?

Solution The first generation back you have two ancestors. Each of these has two ancestors so that the second generation back you have $2 \times 2 = 2^2$ ancestors. The third generation back you have $2 \times 2 \times 2 = 2^3$ ancestors. Thus, the number of ancestors are the terms of a geometric series
with $a = 2$, and $r = 2$. Here you wish to find S_n for $n = 15$.

$$S_n = \frac{a(r^n-1)}{r-1} = \frac{2(2^{15}-1)}{2-1} \text{ or } 65\ 534$$

You have a total of 65 534 ancestors in the first 15 generations back (provided, of course, none of your ancestors overlap). $\blacksquare$

6.4 Exercises

Where feasible, round off the series sums correct to 6 decimal places.

1. Use the method of Example 1, page 235 to find the sum of following geometric series.
   a) $5 + 15 + 45 + 135 + 405 + 1215 + 3645$
   b) $0.8 + 0.4 + 0.2 + 0.1 + 0.05 + 0.025 + 0.0125 + 0.00625$

2. Find the sum of each of the following geometric series to the indicated number of terms.
   a) $3.5 + 7 + 14 + \ldots$ to 10 terms
   b) $9 + 3 + 1 + \ldots$ to 8 terms
   c) $6 - 24 + 96 - \ldots$ to 7 terms
   d) $0.03 + 0.003 + 0.0003 + \ldots$ to 6 terms
   e) $64 - 16 + 4 - \ldots$ to 12 terms
   f) $\dfrac{1}{6} + \dfrac{1}{12} + \dfrac{1}{24} + \ldots$ to 13 terms

3. Find the sum of the following geometric series.
   a) $\displaystyle\sum_{k=1}^{9} 3(2^k)$ b) $\displaystyle\sum_{n=1}^{40} 64\left(\dfrac{1}{2}\right)^n$

4. Find the sum of the given geometric series.
   a) $4 + 8 + 16 + \ldots + 1024$
   b) $1 + \dfrac{1}{3} + \dfrac{1}{9} + \ldots + \dfrac{1}{3^9}$

5. A geometric series of 9 terms has a common ratio of 3 and a sum of 757. Find the value of the first term.

6. You put $200 in a credit union each month at the first of the month from May 1 to October 1 inclusive. The trust company puts 2% interest into your account at the end of every month.
   a) Show that the amount of money you have in your account on October 1 is the sum of the geometric series
   $200(1.02)^5 + 200(1.02)^4 + 200(1.02)^3 + 200(1.02)^2 + 200(1.02) + 200.$
   b) Find the sum of the series in a).

7. Given the geometric series $\dfrac{1}{2} + \dfrac{1}{4} + \dfrac{1}{8} + \ldots$
   a) find the partial sums S_1, S_2, S_3, S_4.
   b) Can any partial sum S_n be equal to 1?
   c) Can any partial sum be greater than 1?

8. How many ancestors do you have in the first 20 generations back, counting only parents, grandparents, and the like?

9. You have just been notified that you have won the provincial lottery that gives you the choice of one of the following for your prize.
   a) a one-time prize of $6 000 000
   b) 40 different prizes for 40 consecutive days consisting of 1¢ on the first day, 2¢ on the second day, and so on, with the prize doubling each day
   Which prize should you select to obtain the larger amount of money?
   Justify your answer.

10. Under certain conditions favorable to the growth of bacteria, one cell divides into two cells every 10 minutes. A certain bacteria culture begins with 7 cells. How many cells will be present at the end of the 6th hour?

11. The square has a side of length 8 cm. The midpoints of consecutive sides are joined to form a second square. This process is continued to form a total of 5 squares. Find the sum of the perimeters of these 5 squares.

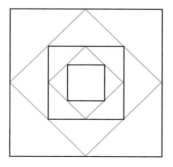

6.5 The Infinite Geometric Series

In the introduction to this chapter you learned about Zeno's paradox through which Zeno tried to explain that motion cannot exist. To travel from point A to point Z, a distance of 1 metre, you must reach the midpoint B of AZ, then you must arrive at the midpoint C of BZ, and so on. Since you contact an infinite number of midpoints before you can reach Z, Zeno argued that it would take you an infinite length of time.

What Zeno failed to point out was that you do not stop at midpoints but 'flow' through each one. A mathematical examination of the successive distances travelled from midpoint to midpoint should help you in the understanding of the solution to the paradox.

These successive distances are $\dfrac{1}{2}, \dfrac{1}{2^2}, \dfrac{1}{2^3}, \dfrac{1}{2^4}, \dfrac{1}{2^5}, \ldots, \dfrac{1}{2^n}$ (metres)

which correspond to the series $\dfrac{1}{2} + \dfrac{1}{2^2} + \dfrac{1}{2^3} + \dfrac{1}{2^4} + \dfrac{1}{2^5} + \ldots + \dfrac{1}{2^n}$, where $t_n = \dfrac{1}{2^n}$.

Consider the following partial sums of the series.

$$S_1 = \frac{1}{2} = \frac{1}{2}$$

$$S_2 = \frac{1}{2} + \frac{1}{4} = \frac{3}{4}$$

$$S_3 = \frac{1}{2} + \frac{1}{4} + \frac{1}{8} = \frac{7}{8}$$

$$S_4 = \frac{1}{2} + \frac{1}{4} + \frac{1}{8} + \frac{1}{16} = \frac{15}{16}$$

$$S_5 = \frac{1}{2} + \frac{1}{4} + \frac{1}{8} + \frac{1}{16} + \frac{1}{32} = \frac{31}{32}$$

The partial sums S_n are getting larger, but each sum is smaller than 1. To see what happens when n is larger, you can use the formula

$$S_n = \frac{a(1 - r^n)}{1 - r}$$

Thus, for example, $\quad S_{20} = \dfrac{\dfrac{1}{2}\left(1 - \left(\dfrac{1}{2}\right)^{20}\right)}{1 - \dfrac{1}{2}} = 1 - \dfrac{1}{2^{20}}$

Using your calculator you will find $\dfrac{1}{2^{20}} = 0.000\,000\,9537$.

Thus $\quad S_{20} = 0.999\,999\,0463$

Similarly $S_{30} = 1 - \dfrac{1}{2^{30}}$

$$S_{50} = 1 - \dfrac{1}{2^{50}}$$

Indeed $\quad S_n = \dfrac{\dfrac{1}{2}\left(1 - \left(\dfrac{1}{2}\right)^n\right)}{1 - \dfrac{1}{2}} = \dfrac{\dfrac{1}{2}\left(1 - \dfrac{1}{2^n}\right)}{\dfrac{1}{2}}$

Therefore, $S_n = 1 - \dfrac{1}{2^n}$

It is clear that S_n can never be larger than 1 because you are always subtracting the positive number $\dfrac{1}{2^n}$ from 1.

Also, $\dfrac{1}{2^n}$ gets smaller and smaller as n increases so that $1 - \dfrac{1}{2^n}$ gets closer and closer to the value of 1.

A look at the graph of $y = S_n$ shows that the line $y = 1$ is an asymptote.

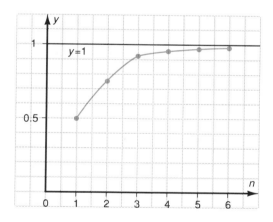

The value 1 is called the **limit** of the partial sums S_n as n increases indefinitely beyond all bounds. The phrase "as n increases indefinitely beyond all bounds" is also stated "as n approaches infinity" and is abbreviated "$n \to \infty$".

The limit as n approaches infinity is abbreviated S_∞.

Thus, $S_\infty = \lim\limits_{n \to \infty} S_n$.

It is customary to call this limit of partial sums, namely 1, the sum of the infinite series

$$\frac{1}{2} + \frac{1}{4} + \frac{1}{8} + \frac{1}{16} + \dots + \frac{1}{2^n} + \dots$$

P R O P E R T Y	In general, the sum of the infinite series $t_1 + t_2 + t_3 + \ldots$, is denoted S_∞, if such a finite value exists. When a finite value does exist for the sum S_∞, the series is said to *converge* to this value of S_∞. A series that does *not* converge is said to *diverge*.

A *series converges* to a number S_∞ if the partial sums S_n get closer and closer to S_∞ as n gets very large.

Thus, the series $\dfrac{1}{2} + \dfrac{1}{4} + \dfrac{1}{8} + \dfrac{1}{16} + \ldots + \dfrac{1}{2^n} + \ldots$ converges to the value 1.

Some people use this fact as the basis of their argument to show that Zeno was incorrect.

Now that you have seen that at least one infinite geometric series converges, you might well ask whether or not all infinite geometric series converge. Consider the series $2 + 4 + 8 + 16 + \ldots + 2^n + \ldots$

The partial sums are

$$
\begin{aligned}
S_1 &= 2 & &= 2 \\
S_2 &= 2 + 4 & &= 6 \\
S_3 &= 2 + 4 + 8 & &= 14 \\
S_4 &= 2 + 4 + 8 + 16 & &= 30 \\
S_5 &= 2 + 4 + 8 + 16 + 32 & &= 62
\end{aligned}
$$

The partial sums are getting larger and larger. Do the sums get closer and closer to any finite number?

The nth partial sum can be obtained using the formula

$$S_n = \frac{a(r^n - 1)}{r - 1}, \text{ where } a = 2, \text{ and } r = 2.$$

Thus, $S_n = \dfrac{2(2^n - 1)}{2 - 1} = 2^{n+1} - 2.$

For $n = 20$, $S_{20} = 2^{21} - 2 = 2\,097\,150 - 2 = 2\,097\,148$, which is rather large. As n increases, 2^{n+1} gets larger and larger. Indeed, there is no number S_∞ that S_n approaches as n gets larger and larger.
The series does *not* converge.
You should now wonder, under what conditions will a geometric series converge?

The series $\dfrac{1}{2} + \dfrac{1}{4} + \dfrac{1}{8} + \dfrac{1}{16} + \ldots + \dfrac{1}{2^n}, \ldots$ converges because the number

$\left(\dfrac{1}{2}\right)^n$ in the value $\dfrac{\dfrac{1}{2}\left(1 - \left(\dfrac{1}{2}\right)^n\right)}{1 - \dfrac{1}{2}}$ of S_n is *very close to zero* when n is very large.

But for any geometric series $S_n = \dfrac{a(1 - r^n)}{1 - r}$.

Therefore, S_n will converge if r^n is close to 0 when n is very large.
This will occur provided $-1 < r < 1$, or $|r| < 1$.

Example 1   Find the value of S_∞ for the infinite geometric series
$a + ar + ar^2 + ar^3 + \ldots + ar^{n-1} + \ldots$ where $|r| < 1$.

Solution $S_\infty = \lim\limits_{n \to \infty} S_n$ where $S_n = \dfrac{a(1 - r^n)}{1 - r}$

Since $|r| < 1$, r^n gets closer and closer to 0 as n gets larger and larger.

Thus, $S_n = \dfrac{a(1 - r^n)}{1 - r}$ gets closer and closer to $\dfrac{a(1 - 0)}{1 - r}$.

Thus, $S_\infty = \dfrac{a}{1 - r}$.   ■

FORMULA

For the geometric series $a + ar + ar^2 + ar^3 + \ldots + ar^{n-1} + \ldots$

$S_\infty = \dfrac{a}{1 - r}$, provided $|r| < 1$.

Example 2   For each of the following geometric series, determine whether or not the series converges. If the series does converge, then find the value of S_∞.
a) $6 + 2.4 + 0.96 + \ldots$ **b)** $6 - 15 + 37.5 + \ldots$

Solution   **a)** Here $a = 6$, $r = 2.4 \div 6 = 0.4$
$|r| = |0.4| < 1$. Thus, the series does converge.

Therefore, $S_\infty = \dfrac{a}{1 - r} = \dfrac{6}{1 - 0.4} = 10$.

b) Here $a = 6$, $r = -15 \div 6 = -2.5$
But $|r| = |-2.5| = 2.5 > 1$.
Therefore, the series does not converge.   ■

Example 3   **a)** Express the repeating decimal 0.321 321 321 ... as an infinite series.
b) Show that the series in a) converges and find S_∞.

c) Express 0.321 321 321 ... as a rational number $\dfrac{a}{b}$, where $a, b \in I$, $b \neq 0$.

Solution   **a)** 0.321 321 321 ...
= 0.321 +
   0.000 321 +
   0.000 000 321 +
   0.000 000 000 321 + ...

b) This series is a geometric series with $a = 0.321$ and
$r = 0.000\ 321 \div 0.321 = 0.001$.
Since $|r| = |0.001| < 1$, the series converges.

$S_\infty = \dfrac{a}{1 - r} = \dfrac{0.321}{1 - 0.001}$

$= \dfrac{0.321}{0.999} = \dfrac{107}{333}$

c) Thus, 0.321 321 321 ... $= \dfrac{107}{333}$.   ■

Example 4 A patient is given an injection of 8 units of a certain drug every 24 h. The drug is eliminated gradually from the patient's body so that t days after an injection the amount remaining from that injection is $8e^{-0.25t}$

If the treatment is continued indefinitely, how many units (correct to 2 decimal places) of the drug will eventually be in the patient's body immediately before an injection? ($e \doteq 2.718\ 281\ 828$)

Solution The first day after the first injection the amount of medication remaining is that due to one injection, namely $8e^{-0.25(1)}$

The second day after the first injection the amount of medication remaining is that due to two injections, namely $8e^{-0.25(1)} + 8e^{-0.25(2)}$

The third day after the first injection the amount of medication remaining is that due to three injections, namely $8e^{-0.25(1)} + 8e^{-0.25(2)} + 8e^{-0.25(3)}$

The nth day after the first injection the amount of medication remaining is that due to n injections, namely $8e^{-0.25(1)} + 8e^{-0.25(2)} + 8e^{-0.25-(3)} + \ldots + 8e^{-0.25(n)}$

This is a geometric series with $a = 8e^{-0.25}$ and $r = e^{-0.25}$, and $|e^{-0.25}| \doteq 0.778\ 8007 < 1$

The amount of medication in a patient's body is eventually the limit S_n of this geometric series as S_n approaches infinity, that is,

$$S_{\infty} = \frac{a}{1-r}$$

Thus, $S_{\infty} = \dfrac{8e^{-0.25}}{1 - e^{-0.25}}$

$$= \frac{8(2.718\ 281\ 2828^{-0.25})}{1 - 2.718\ 281\ 828^{-0.25}}$$

$$\doteq 28.166\ 293$$

$$\doteq 28.17, \text{ correct to 2 decimal places}$$

If the treatment is continued indefinitely, there will be 28.17 units of the drug in the patient's body immediately before each injection. ■

6.5 Exercises

1. For each of the following infinite geometric series determine whether or not the series converges. If the series does converge find the value of S_∞.

   a) $3 + \dfrac{3}{5} + \dfrac{3}{25} + \ldots$

   b) $16 - 12 + 9 \ldots$

   c) $36 + 42 + 49 + \ldots$

   d) $8 + 1.6 + 0.32$

   e) $0.31 + 0.62 + 1.24 + \ldots$

   f) $15 - \dfrac{75}{7} + \dfrac{375}{49}$

2. Write each of the following repeating decimal numbers using an infinite geometric series; then express each as a rational number $\dfrac{a}{b}$ where $a, b \in I$, and $b \neq 0$. (Non-standard notation is used to clarify the period of each decimal.)

   a) 0.67 67 67 ...   d) 2.365 365 365 ...

   b) 0.5431 5431 5431   e) 0.001 001 001 ...

   c) 0.1243 43 43 ...   f) 0.999999999 ...

3. In the introduction you met another of Zeno's paradoxes about Achilles and the tortoise. Find the sum of the infinite series of successive distances travelled by Achilles, namely the series
   $100 + 10 + 1 + 0.1 + 0.01 + 0.001 + \ldots$

4. A ball is dropped from a height of 20 metres and continuously bounces up then falls down. After each bounce the ball rises to a height that is 0.3 of the maximum height it reached on its previous bounce. Find the total distance, both up and down, that the ball has travelled by summing an infinite geometric series.

5. Show by example that two infinite geometric series that have the same sum S_∞ do not have to be the same series.

6. For a certain infinite geometric series, $a = 3$ and $S_\infty = 7.5$. Find the value of r.

7. A pile driver begins to drive a piling into the ground. On the first impact, the piling moves 80 cm into the ground. On the second the piling moves an additional 72 cm. Assuming the distances the piling moves on successive impacts form a geometric series, find the total distance the piling will move if the pile driver continues her work indefinitely.

8. A patient is given an injection of 15 units of a certain drug every 24 h. The drug is eliminated gradually from the patient's body so that t days after an injection the amount remaining from that injection is $15e^{-0.5t}$. If the treatment is continued indefinitely, how many units, correct to 2 decimal places, of the drug will eventually be in the patient's body immediately before an injection? ($e \doteq 2.718\ 281\ 828$)

9. You have just won a lottery! You and your heirs will be paid forever according to the following schedule. The first year you will receive $50 000. The second year you will receive $47 500. The third year you will receive $45 125. If the amounts you receive in successive years are the terms of a geometric series, calculate the total money you and your heirs will receive.

10. a) Show by example that the sum of a convergent infinite series can be less than the first term.

    b) Determine the conditions on a and r so that the sum of a convergent infinite series will be less than the first term.

11. Write a program to calculate and print the partial sum of a geometric series. The program should allow you to input the values of a, r and n. Then the program might enter a loop in which the term value is calculated and added to the sum of the previous terms. At each pass through the loop the computer would print the term number, the term value, and the partial sum.

In Search of the Sum of Other Infinite Series

1. The infinite series $\dfrac{1}{2} + \dfrac{1}{3} + \dfrac{1}{4} + \dfrac{1}{5} + \ldots$ is called a *harmonic series*.

   The general term $t_n = \dfrac{1}{n+1}$ gets closer and closer to 0 as n gets larger and larger. You might expect this series to converge, but it does not. Use the following to convince yourself.

   a) Show that $t_2 + t_3 > \dfrac{1}{2}$.

   b) Show that $t_4 + t_5 + t_6 > \dfrac{1}{2}$.

   c) Show that $t_7 + t_8 + t_9 + t_{10} > \dfrac{1}{2}$.

   d) Show, using a), b) and c), that $\dfrac{1}{2} + \dfrac{1}{3} + \dfrac{1}{4} + \dfrac{1}{5} + \ldots > \dfrac{1}{2} + \dfrac{1}{2} + \dfrac{1}{2} + \ldots$

   e) Prove that the harmonic series diverges, by showing the series

   $\dfrac{1}{2} + \dfrac{1}{2} + \dfrac{1}{2} + \dfrac{1}{2} + \ldots$ diverges.

2. During the 18th century the concept of the convergence of an infinite series had not been formulated with precision. Mathematicians of that day often spoke of the 'sum' of a series that is now classified as divergent.

   Giving a divergent series a 'sum' led to many contradictions, as the following will show. Comment on each of the following explanations, each of which gives a different sum for the infinite series $1 - 1 + 1 - \ldots$

   a) $1 - 1 + 1 - 1 + 1 - 1 + \ldots = (1 - 1) + (1 - 1) + (1 - 1) + \ldots$
   $$= \quad 0 \quad + \quad 0 \quad + \quad 0 \quad + \ldots$$
   $$= 0$$

   b) $1 - 1 + 1 - 1 + 1 - 1 + \ldots = 1 - (1 - 1) - (1 - 1) - \ldots$
   $$= 1 - \quad 0 \quad - \quad 0 \quad - \ldots$$
   $$= 1$$

   c) Let $\quad S = 1 - 1 + 1 - 1 + 1 - 1 + \ldots$
   $$= 1 - (1 - 1 + 1 - 1 + 1 - 1 + \ldots)$$
   $$= 1 - S$$
   Thus, $S = 1 - S$, that is, $2S = 1$.

   Thus, $S = \dfrac{1}{2}$

   d) By long division you can show
   $$\frac{1}{1 + x} = 1 - x + x^2 - x^3 + x^4 - x^5 + \ldots.$$
   Substituting $x = 1$ in this equation you obtain
   $$\frac{1}{2} = 1 - 1 + 1 - 1 + 1 - 1 + \ldots$$

Reference: *Infinite Series* A. I. Markushevich, D.C. Heath, 1976.

6.6 Other Series

You are the business manager for the Jen-Eri-Nei Company. You need to hire students for the 8 weeks of summer vacation. You begin with 1 student the first week and hire an extra student each week. Thus, the number of students that you hire in successive weeks over the summer forms an arithmetic series $1 + 2 + 3 + 4 + 5 + 6 + 7 + 8$.

You decide on an interesting way of paying the students. The pay per student for week 1 will be \$3, for week 2 the pay per student will be \$9, in week 3 you will pay each student \$27, and so on, in a geometric sequence. Thus, the salaries you pay each successive week form a geometric series $3 + 9 + 27 + 81 + 243 + 729 + 2187 + 6561$. How much money will you need for salaries during the 8 weeks?

During week 1 you pay 1 student   \$3 each for a total of 1×3 dollars
During week 2 you pay 2 students   \$9 each for a total of 2×9 dollars
During week 3 you pay 3 students   \$27 each for a total of 3×27 dollars
During week 4 you pay 4 students   \$81 each for a total of 4×81 dollars
During week 5 you pay 5 students   \$243 each for a total of 5×243 dollars
During week 6 you pay 6 students   \$729 each for a total of 6×729 dollars
During week 7 you pay 7 students   \$2187 each for a total of 7×2187 dollars
During week 8 you pay 8 students   \$6561 each for a total of 8×6561 dollars
The total you will need is the sum of the series
$1 \times 3 + 2 \times 9 + 3 \times 27 + 4 \times 81 + 5 \times 243 + 6 \times 729 + 7 \times 2187 + 8 \times 6561$.

DEFINITION

Such a series is called an **arithmetic-geometric series** because each term consists of the product of one term from the arithmetic series $1 + 2 + 3 + 4 + 5 + 6 + 7 + 8$ and the corresponding term from the geometric series $3 + 9 + 27 + 81 + 243 + 729 + 2187 + 6561$.

Let this sum be S. Thus,
$S = 1 \times 3 + 2 \times 9 + 3 \times 27 + 4 \times 81 + 5 \times 243 + 6 \times 729 + 7 \times 2187 + 8 \times 6561$
Multiply each term by the common ratio 3 of the geometric series, and write corresponding terms of the geometric series one above the other.
$3S = \qquad 1 \times 9 + 2 \times 27 + 3 \times 81 + 4 \times 243 + 5 \times 729 + 6 \times 2187 + 7 \times 6561$
$\qquad\qquad\qquad\qquad\qquad\qquad\qquad\qquad\qquad\qquad + 8 \times 19\,683$

Subtracting you will obtain
$S - 3S = 3 + 9 + 27 + 81 + 243 + 729 + 2187 + 6561 - 8 \times 19\,683$
All but the last term on the right side is a geometric series with $a = 3$, $r = 3$, and $n = 8$, so the sum of these terms can be found using the formula

$$S_n = \frac{a(r^n - 1)}{r - 1}$$

Thus, $-2S = \dfrac{3(3^8 - 1)}{3 - 1} - 157\,464$

$\qquad\qquad 8 \times 19\,683 = 157\,464$

$\qquad S = 73\,812.$

You would need to pay out \$73 812 in salaries over the eight weeks.

The arithmetic-geometric series for these salaries is a special case of the arithmetic-geometric series which combines
the arithmetic series $1 + 2 + 3 + 4 + \ldots + n$ and
the geometric series $x + x^2 + x^3 + x^4 + \ldots + x^n$
that is,

$$1x + 2x^2 + 3x^3 + 4x^4 + \ldots + nx^n = \sum_{k=1}^{n} kx^k$$

Example 1

Find a formula for the sum of the arithmetic-geometric series

$$1x + 2x^2 + 3x^3 + 4x^4 + \ldots + nx^n = \sum_{k=1}^{n} kx^k$$

Solution

Let the sum be S_n.
Thus, $\quad S_n = 1x + 2x^2 + 3x^3 + 4x^4 + \ldots + (n-1)x^{n-1} + nx^n$

Multiply each term by the common ratio x of the geometric series and write corresponding terms of the geometric series one above the other.

$$xS_n = \qquad 1x^2 + 2x^3 + 3x^4 + \quad \ldots \quad + (n-1)x^n + nx^{n+1}$$

Subtracting, you will obtain

$$S_n - xS_n = x + x^2 + x^3 \ldots + x^n - nx^{n+1}$$

Now all but the last term on the right side is a geometric series with $a = x$, $r = x$ and $n = n$, so the sum of these terms can be found using the formula

$$S_n = \frac{a(r^n - 1)}{r - 1}.$$

Thus, $(1 - x)S_n = \dfrac{x(x^n - 1)}{x - 1} - nx^{n+1}$

Multiplying each side by -1 and using the fact that
$-1(1 - x) = x - 1$, you obtain

$$(x - 1)S_n = -\frac{x(x^n - 1)}{x - 1} + nx^{n+1}$$

$$\text{Thus, } S_n = \frac{nx^{n+1}}{x - 1} - \frac{x(x^n - 1)}{(x - 1)^2}. \quad \blacksquare$$

FORMULA

For the arithmetic-geometric series

$$1x + 2x^2 + 3x^3 + 4x^4 + \ldots + nx^n = \sum_{k=1}^{n} kx^k$$

$$S_n = \frac{nx^{n+1}}{x - 1} - \frac{x(x^n - 1)}{(x - 1)^2}$$

Example 2   Assuming that the series $3 + 18 + 81 + \ldots$ is arithmetic-geometric, find x and, correct to 5 significant figures, S_{20}.

Solution   The series $3 + 18 + 81 + \ldots = 1 \times 3 + 2 \times 9 + 3 \times 27 + \ldots$
Since this series is arithmetic-geometric, $x = 3$.
Substituting $x = 3$ and $n = 20$ into

$$S_n = \frac{nx^{n+1}}{x - 1} - \frac{x(x^n - 1)}{(x - 1)^2}$$

you obtain

$$S_{20} = \frac{20(3)^{21}}{3 - 1} - \frac{3(3^{20} - 1)}{(3 - 1)^2}$$
$$= 10(3^{21}) - 0.75(3^{20} - 1) = 3^{20}(30 - 0.75) + 0.75$$
$$= 29.25(3^{20}) + 0.75 \doteq 1.0199 \times 10^{11}, \text{ correct to 5 significant figures.} \quad \blacksquare$$

Example 3   Use the fact that $\dfrac{1}{k(k + 1)} = \dfrac{1}{k} - \dfrac{1}{k + 1}$ to find the sum of 20 terms of the

series $\dfrac{1}{1(2)} + \dfrac{1}{2(3)} + \dfrac{1}{3(4)} + \dfrac{1}{4(5)} + \ldots + \dfrac{1}{n(n + 1)}$

Solution   Let the sum of the 20 terms of the series be

$$S_{20} = \frac{1}{1(2)} + \frac{1}{2(3)} + \frac{1}{3(4)} + \frac{1}{4(5)} + \ldots + \frac{1}{20(21)}$$

Use $\dfrac{1}{k(k + 1)} = \dfrac{1}{k} - \dfrac{1}{k + 1}$ to express each term of the series as a difference of two fractions.

Thus,

$$\begin{aligned}
\frac{1}{1(2)} &= \frac{1}{1} - \frac{1}{2} \\
\frac{1}{2(3)} &= \frac{1}{2} - \frac{1}{3} \\
\frac{1}{3(4)} &= \frac{1}{3} - \frac{1}{4} \\
\frac{1}{4(5)} &= \frac{1}{4} - \frac{1}{5} \\
\vdots\quad &\quad \vdots \quad \vdots \\
\frac{1}{19(20)} &= \frac{1}{19} - \frac{1}{20} \\
\frac{1}{20(21)} &= \frac{1}{20} - \frac{1}{21}
\end{aligned}$$

Observe carefully that

$-\dfrac{1}{2}$ occurs on the *R.S.* in line 1, while

its opposite, $\dfrac{1}{2}$, is in line 2. Also,

$-\dfrac{1}{3}$ occurs on the *R.S.* in line 2, while

its opposite, $\dfrac{1}{3}$, is in line 3.

Similarly occurring are $-\dfrac{1}{4}, \dfrac{1}{4}$ and so on,

to $-\dfrac{1}{20}$ and $\dfrac{1}{20}$.

Thus when the *R.S.* is added vertically, each of these fractions with its opposite will give 0. But adding vertically on the *L.S.* you obtain S_{20}.

Thus, $S_{20} = \dfrac{1}{1} - \dfrac{1}{21} = \dfrac{20}{21} \quad \blacksquare$

The method of Example 3 can be used whenever the terms of a series can be broken up into *partial fractions* in which the same fraction appears with the opposite sign in adjacent terms.

Three series derived from the natural numbers are useful in doing certain types of problems. The series, together with their sums to n terms, are as follows.

$$\sum_{k=1}^{n} k = 1 + 2 + 3 + \ldots + n = \frac{n(n+1)}{2}$$

$$\sum_{k=1}^{n} k^2 = 1^2 + 2^2 + 3^2 + \ldots + n^2 = \frac{n(n+1)(2n+1)}{6}$$

$$\sum_{k=1}^{n} k^3 = 1^3 + 2^3 + 3^3 + \ldots + n^3 = \left(\frac{n(n+1)}{2}\right)^2$$

The second formula will be proven in Example 4. You will be asked to prove the other two in the exercises.

Example 4   Use the identity $x^3 - (x-1)^3 = 3x^2 - 3x + 1$ to prove that
$$\sum_{k=1}^{n} k^2 = 1^2 + 2^2 + 3^2 + \ldots + n^2 = \frac{n(n+1)(2n+1)}{6}$$

Solution   The method you will use will be to substitute $n = 1, 2, 3, \ldots, n-1, n$ into the given identity, writing each on a separate line.
You will then add vertically.

Substitute into	$x^3 - (x-1)^3 = 3x^2$	$-3x$	$+1$
Let $x = 1$,	$1^3 - (1-1)^3 = 3(1)^2$	$-3(1)$	$+1$
Let $x = 2$,	$2^3 - (2-1)^3 = 3(2)^2$	$-3(2)$	$+1$
Let $x = 3$,	$3^3 - (3-1)^3 = 3(3)^2$	$-3(3)$	$+1$
Let $x = 4$,	$4^3 - (4-1)^3 = 3(4)^2$	$-3(4)$	$+1$

$\vdots$

Let $x = n-1$,	$(n-1)^3 - (n-2)^3 = 3(n-1)^2$	$-3(n-1)$	$+1$
Let $x = n$,	$n^3 - (n-1)^3 = 3(n)^2$	$-3(n)$	$+1$

Adding vertically, observing on the *L.S.* that opposites on adjacent lines add to give 0, you obtain

$$n^3 - 0^3 = 3(1^2 + 2^2 + 3^2 + \ldots + n^2) - 3(1 + 2 + 3 + \ldots + n) + (1 + 1 + 1 + \ldots + 1).$$

$$n^3 = 3\sum_{k=1}^{n} k^2 \qquad\qquad - 3\frac{n(n+1)}{2} \qquad\qquad + n$$

$$n^3 + \frac{3n(n+1)}{2} - n = 3\sum_{k=1}^{n} k^2$$

$$3\sum_{k=1}^{n} k^2 = \frac{2n^3 + 3n^2 + 3n - 2n}{2} = \frac{n(2n^2 + 3n - 1)}{2} \text{ or } \frac{n(n+1)(2n+1)}{2}$$

Thus, $\sum_{k=1}^{n} k^2 = \frac{n(n+1)(2n+1)}{6}$ ∎

The result of Example 5 will be needed in chapter 7 on probability in section 7.7 on hypergeometric distribution.

Example 5

Use the identity $(1 + x)^5 (1 + x)^8 = (1 + x)^{13}$ to prove that

$$\sum_{j=0}^{7} C(5,j) \, C(8,7 - j) = C(13,7).$$

Solution

The method you will use will be to expand each binomial in the identity then to compare certain coefficients of x on both sides.

$$(1 + x)^5 (1 + x)^8 = (1 + x)^{13}$$

or $\displaystyle\sum_{i=0}^{5} C(5,i)x^i \times \sum_{k=1}^{8} C(8,k)x^k = \sum_{m=0}^{13} C(13,m)x^m$

On the R.S., $C(13,7)$ is the coefficient of x^7. But the coefficients of x^7 on the L.S. must equal the coefficient of x^7 on the R.S.

On the L.S., x^7 is obtained by multiplying x^i, $0 \leqslant i \leqslant 5$, from the first summation by x^k, $0 \leqslant k \leqslant 8$, from the second summation where $i + k = 7$.

But on the L.S. the term with x^{i+k} is $C(5,i)x^i \times C(8,k)x^k$ which has $C(5,i)C(8,k)$ as coefficient.

Since $x^7 = x^0 x^7 = x^1 x^6 = x^2 x^5 = x^3 x^4 = x^4 x^3 = x^5 x^2$, the coefficient of x^7 on the L.S. must be

$C(5,0)C(8,7) + C(5,1)C(8,6) + C(5,2)C(8,5)$
$+ C(5,3)C(8,4) + C(5,4)C(8,3) + C(5,5)C(8,2).$

Thus,

$$C(13,7) = C(5,0)C(8,7) + C(5,1)C(8,6) + C(5,2)C(8,5)$$
$$+ C(5,3)C(8,4) + C(5,4)C(8,3) + C(5,5)C(8,2)$$
$$= \sum_{j=0}^{7} C(5,j)C(8,7 - j) \quad \blacksquare$$

In general, you may use the identity $(1 + x)^n \times (1 + x)^t = (1 + x)^{n+t}$ to prove that $\displaystyle\sum_{j=0}^{k} C(n,j)C(t,k - j) = C(n + t,k).$

6.6 Exercises

1. Use the method of Example 1 to find the sum of the arithmetic-geometric series
$1(5) + 2(5^2) + 3(5^3) + \ldots + n(5^n)$.

2. Find the sum of the n terms of each of the following arithmetic-geometric series.
   a) $8 + 128 + 1536 + \ldots$
   b) $5 + 50 + 375 + \ldots$
   c) $1 + \dfrac{2}{5} + \dfrac{3}{25} + \ldots$
   d) $0.2 + 0.08 + 0.024 + \ldots$

3. Find the sum of 30 terms, correct to 5 significant figures, of the arithmetic-geometric series $\sum\limits_{k=1}^{n} k(0.6)^k$

4. a) Use the method of Example 1 to show that the arithmetic-geometric series $1x + 2x^2 + 3x^3 + \ldots$ converges to
   $$S_\infty = \frac{x}{(1-x)^2}, \text{ provided } |x| < 1.$$
   Assume $\lim\limits_{n \to \infty} nx^{n+1} = 0$.
   b) Find the S_∞ of the arithmetic-geometric series $1 + \dfrac{2}{5} + \dfrac{3}{25} + \ldots$
   c) Find S_∞ for the arithmetic-geometric series in question 3.

5. a) Prove that
   $$\frac{3}{(3k-2)(3k+1)} = \frac{1}{3k-2} - \frac{1}{3k+1}$$
   b) Use the result of a) and the method of Example 3 to evaluate
   $$\sum_{k=1}^{n} \frac{3}{(3k-2)(3k+1)}$$

6. Find the sum of n terms of the series
$$\frac{1}{1(3)} + \frac{1}{3(5)} + \frac{1}{5(7)} + \ldots + \frac{1}{(2n-1)(2n+1)}$$

7. Use the identity $x^2 - (x-1)^2 = 2x - 1$ to prove that
$$\sum_{k=1}^{n} k = 1 + 2 + 3 + \ldots + n = \frac{n(n+1)}{2}.$$

8. Use the identity
$x^4 - (x-1)^4 = 4x^3 - 6x^2 + 4x - 1$ to prove that
$$\sum_{k=1}^{n} k^3 = 1^3 + 2^3 + 3^3 + n^3 = \left(\frac{n(n+1)}{2}\right)^2$$

9. a) What identity would you use to find a formula for $\sum\limits_{k=1}^{n} k^4$?
   b) Find a formula for the sum in a).

10. a) Use the identity
    $(1+x)^9 \times (1+x)^{12} = (1+x)^{21}$ to prove that
    $$\sum_{j=0}^{4} C(9,j)C(12,4-j) = C(21,4).$$
    b) Prove that
    $$\sum_{j=0}^{8} C(9,j)C(12,8-j) = C(21,8).$$

11. Use the identity
    $(1+x)^n \times (1+x)^t = (1+x)^{n+t}$ to prove that
    $$\sum_{j=0}^{k} C(n,j)C(t,k-j) = C(n+t,k).$$

12. Complete the following.
    a) $C(25,6) = \sum\limits_{j=0}^{\blacksquare} C(15,j)C(\underline{},\underline{})$
    b) $C(30,\underline{}) = \sum\limits_{j=0}^{10} C(18,\underline{})C(\underline{},\underline{} - j)$
    c) $C(\underline{},\underline{}) = \sum\limits_{j=0}^{\blacksquare} C(12,\underline{})C(5,3-j)$

13. Use the method of Example 1 to find the sum of n terms of the more general arithmetic-geometric series
$2(3) + 7(9) + 12(27) + \ldots + (5n-3)(3^n)$.

14. The value of π can be calculated using the following infinite series.
$$\pi^2 = 6 + \frac{6}{1^2} + \frac{6}{2^2} + \frac{6}{3^2} + \frac{6}{4^2} + \ldots$$
Write a computer program to use this series to determine a value for π.

In Search of Proof Without Words

Sum of Integers $1 + 2 + 3 + \ldots + n = \dfrac{n^2}{2} + \dfrac{n}{2} = \dfrac{n(n+1)}{2}$

Sum of squares $1^2 + 2^2 + 3^2 + \ldots + n^2 = \dfrac{1}{3}n(n+1)\left(n + \dfrac{1}{2}\right) = \dfrac{n(n+1)(2n+1)}{6}$

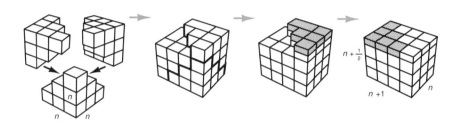

Sum of cubes $1^3 + 2^3 + 3^3 + \ldots + n^3 = (1 + 2 + 3 + \ldots + n)^2 = \left(\dfrac{n(n+1)}{2}\right)^2$

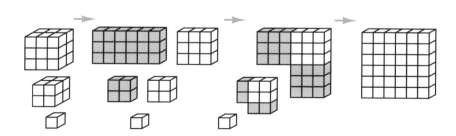

6.7 Mathematical Induction

Guessing is an important part of mathematical thinking. Guessing is sometimes called **induction**. Mathematicians frequently try to guess the answer to a problem, then attempt to prove or disprove that guess. Consider the series

$$\frac{1}{1 \times 2} + \frac{1}{2 \times 3} + \frac{1}{3 \times 4} + \frac{1}{4 \times 5} + \ldots + \frac{1}{n(n+1)}$$

What is the sum of this series?

To try to guess this sum, you might list the partial sums as follows.

$$S_1 = \frac{1}{1 \times 2} = \frac{1}{2}$$

$$S_2 = \frac{1}{1 \times 2} + \frac{1}{2 \times 3} = \frac{2}{3}$$

$$S_3 = \frac{1}{1 \times 2} + \frac{1}{2 \times 3} + \frac{1}{3 \times 4} = \frac{3}{4}$$

$$S_4 = \frac{1}{1 \times 2} + \frac{1}{2 \times 3} + \frac{1}{3 \times 4} + \frac{1}{4 \times 5} = \frac{4}{5}$$

These values for S_n suggest the formula $S_n = \dfrac{n}{n+1}$

In order to prove this formula you will need to learn a method of deduction called **proof by mathematical induction.** Read the following carefully to understand what such a proof is.

Proof by mathematical induction follows from a special property of the set of natural numbers N. Originally, the natural numbers were used for counting, which is simply a process that leads from one number n to its successor $n + 1$. This is the basis of the special property of N called *the inductive property* of N. Stated simply, this property is the following. Any subset M of natural numbers that has the following two properties must be the entire set N.

PROPERTY

Property 1: $1 \in M$ Property 2: If $k \in M$, then $k + 1 \in M$

The inductive property of N is the foundation of the method of proof called mathematical induction. If a mathematical statement or formula contains the natural number n, mathematical induction can sometimes be used to prove that the statement or formula is true for all $n \in N$. Such a proof is based on the following *principle of mathematical induction*.

A statement involving the natural number n is true for every $n \in N$ provided the following are true.

a) The statement is true for $n = 1$.

b) The truth of the statement for $n = k$ implies the statement is true for $n = k + 1$.

The principle of mathematical induction can be derived from the inductive property of N. Suppose M is the set of natural numbers for which a statement is true. Then a) implies that $1 \in M$. But b) shows that k belonging to M implies that $k + 1 \in M$. The inductive property of N allows the conclusion that $M = N$.

In practice, you should use *three steps in a proof by mathematical induction*.

Step 1: Show the statement is true for $n = 1$.
Step 2: Assume that the statement is true for $n = k$.
Step 3: Prove the statement is true for $n = k + 1$, using the result of step 2.

Example 1 Use mathematical induction to prove the following formula for $n \in N$.
$1 + 3 + 5 + \ldots + (2n - 1) = n^2$.

Solution *Step 1:* Prove the statement is true for $n = 1$.
For $n = 1$, $L.S. = 1$, $R.S. = 1^2 = 1$.
Since $L.S. = R.S.$, the statement is true for $n = 1$.

Step 2: Assume the formula is true for $n = k$. That is, assume
$1 + 3 + 5 + \ldots + (2k - 1) = k^2$. ①

Step 3: Prove the formula is true for $n = k + 1$. That is, prove
$1 + 3 + 5 + \ldots + (2k + 1) = (k + 1)^2$.
$L.S. = 1 + 3 + 5 + \ldots + (2k - 1) + (2k + 1)$
$\qquad = [1 + 3 + 5 + \ldots + (2k - 1)] + (2k + 1)$ the same as ①,
$\qquad = [k^2] + (2k + 1)$ [by step 2] with $(2k + 1)$ added
$\qquad = (k + 1)^2 = R.S.$

Thus, by the principle of mathematical induction,
$1 + 3 + 5 + \ldots + (2n - 1) = n$, for all $n \in N$. ■

The principle of mathematical induction can only be used to prove a given formula is true. The principle does not help you to obtain such a formula.

Sometimes a formula can be guessed for summing a series, as you did for the series $\dfrac{1}{1 \times 2} + \dfrac{1}{2 \times 3} + \dfrac{1}{3 \times 4} + \dfrac{1}{4 \times 5} + \ldots + \dfrac{1}{n(n + 1)}$.
The formula you guessed for the sum of this series is proven in Example 2.

Example 2 Prove, by mathematical induction

$$\frac{1}{1 \times 2} + \frac{1}{2 \times 3} + \frac{1}{3 \times 4} + \frac{1}{4 \times 5} + \ldots + \frac{1}{n(n+1)} = \frac{n}{n+1}$$

Solution   *Step 1* For $n = 1$, $L.S. = \dfrac{1}{1 \times 2} = \dfrac{1}{2}$, $R.S. = \dfrac{1}{1+1} = \dfrac{1}{2} = L.S.$

Step 2 Assume $\dfrac{1}{1 \times 2} + \dfrac{1}{2 \times 3} + \dfrac{1}{3 \times 4} + \ldots + \dfrac{1}{k(k+1)} = \dfrac{k}{k+1}$

Step 3 Prove $\dfrac{1}{1 \times 2} + \dfrac{1}{2 \times 3} + \dfrac{1}{3 \times 4} + \dfrac{1}{4 \times 5} + \ldots + \dfrac{1}{(k+1)(k+2)} = \dfrac{k+1}{k+2}$

$$L.S. = \frac{1}{1 \times 2} + \frac{1}{2 \times 3} + \frac{1}{3 \times 4} + \frac{1}{4 \times 5} + \ldots + \frac{1}{(k+1)(k+2)}$$

$$= \frac{1}{1 \times 2} + \frac{1}{2 \times 3} + \frac{1}{3 \times 4} + \frac{1}{4 \times 5} + \ldots + \frac{1}{k(k+1)} + \frac{1}{(k+1)(k+2)}$$

$$\left(\text{This is the } L.S. \text{ of step 2 with } \frac{1}{(k+1)(k+2)} \text{ added.} \right)$$

$$= \left[\frac{1}{1 \times 2} + \frac{1}{2 \times 3} + \frac{1}{3 \times 4} + \frac{1}{4 \times 5} + \ldots + \frac{1}{k(k+1)} \right] + \frac{1}{(k+1)(k+2)}$$

$$= \left[\frac{k}{k+1} \right] + \frac{1}{(k+1)(k+2)} \qquad \text{using step 2}$$

$$= \frac{k(k+2) + 1}{(k+1)(k+2)}$$

$$= \frac{k^2 + 2k + 1}{(k+1)(k+2)}$$

$$= \frac{(k+1)(k+1)}{(k+1)(k+2)}$$

$$= \frac{k+1}{k+2} = R.S.$$

Thus, by the principle of mathematical induction, the formula is true. ∎

6.7 Exercises

1. State the three steps in a proof using mathematical induction.

2. State the $(k + 1)$st term for each of the following series.
   a) $6 + 12 + 18 + \ldots + 6k$
   b) $3 + 5 + 7 + \ldots + (2k + 1)$
   c) $1 + 4 + 7 + \ldots + (3k - 2)$
   d) $2 + 4 + 8 + \ldots + 2k$

3. Prove the following statements using mathematical induction, where $n \in \mathbb{N}$.
   a) $6 + 12 + 18 + \ldots + 6n$
      $= n(3n + 3)$
   b) $3 + 5 + 7 + \ldots + (2n + 1)$
      $= n(2 + n)$
   c) $1 + 4 + 7 + \ldots + (3n - 2)$
      $= \dfrac{n(3n - 1)}{2}$
   d) $2 + 4 + 8 + \ldots + 2^n = 2^{n+1} - 2$
   e) $\sum\limits_{j=1}^{n}(5j + 1) = \dfrac{n(5n + 7)}{2}$
   f) $\sum\limits_{j=1}^{n}(2j - 1) = n^2$

4. Guess and prove, by mathematical induction, the formula for the sum S_n of the following series.
   a) $\dfrac{1}{1 \times 3} + \dfrac{1}{3 \times 5} + \dfrac{1}{5 \times 7}$
      $+ \dfrac{1}{7 \times 9} + \ldots + \dfrac{1}{(2n - 1)(2n + 1)}$
   b) $2 + 7 + 12 + \ldots + (5n - 3)$
   c) $\sum\limits_{s=1}^{11}\dfrac{1}{(3s - 2)(3s + 1)}$

5. Prove the following formulas by mathematical induction.
   a) $\sum\limits_{s=1}^{n} s = \dfrac{n(n + 1)}{2}$
   b) $\sum\limits_{s=1}^{n} s^2 = \dfrac{n(n + 1)(2n + 1)}{6}$
   c) $\sum\limits_{s=1}^{n} s^3 = \left(\dfrac{n(n + 1)}{2}\right)^2$

6. Use mathematical induction to prove that the sum of n terms of an arithmetic series with first term a and common difference d is $S_n = \dfrac{n}{2}(2a + (n - 1)d)$.

7. Use mathematical induction to prove that the sum of n terms of a geometric series with first term a and common ratio r is $S_n = \dfrac{a(r^n - 1)}{r - 1}$.

8. Prove using mathematical induction.
   a) $1^2 + 3^2 + 5^2 + \ldots + (2n - 1)^2$
      $= \dfrac{n(2n - 1)(2n + 1)}{3}$
   b) $\sum\limits_{i=1}^{n}(4i^2 - 3i + 2) = \dfrac{n(8n^2 + 3n + 7)}{6}$
   c) $\dfrac{1}{2} + \dfrac{1}{4} + \dfrac{1}{8} + \ldots + \dfrac{1}{2^n} = 1 - \dfrac{1}{2^n}$

9. The principle of mathematical induction can be used to prove the truth of certain inequalities. Examine the following proof that $2^n < n!$ for $n \in \mathbb{N}$, $n \geqslant 4$.

   Answer the questions.

   Step 1 Prove the statement is true for $n = 4$. Why is $2^4 < 4!$?
   Step 2 Assume that $2^k < k!$
   Step 3 Prove $2^{k+1} < (k + 1)!$

   Proof:

$2^k < k!$	why?
$2 \times 2^k < 2 \times k!$	why?
$2^{k+1} < 2 \times k!$	why? ①
$2 < k + 1$	why?
$2 \times k! < (k + 1)k!$	why?
$2 \times k! < (k + 1)!$	why? ②

   ① and ② prove that
   $2^{k+1} < (k + 1)!$ why?

10. Use mathematical induction to prove the following for $n \geqslant 2$.
    $\left(1 - \dfrac{1}{4}\right)\left(1 - \dfrac{1}{9}\right)\left(1 - \dfrac{1}{16}\right) \ldots \left(1 - \dfrac{1}{n^2}\right)$
    $= \dfrac{n + 1}{2n}$

In Search of a Proof of the Binomial Theorem

The principle of mathematical induction provides another proof for the binomial theorem, $(a + x)^n = \sum_{k=0}^{n} C(n,k)a^{n-k}x^k$, for $n \in W$.

In the proof you must use the result $C(n,k) = C(n - 1, k - 1) + C(n - 1, k)$ proved on page 212 and $\sum_{k=p}^{t} a_k = \sum_{k=p+m}^{t+m} a_{k-m}$ proved in 6.1 Exercises, 13d).

Proof: For $n = 0$, the formula is true because $L.S. = (a + x)^0 = 1$,
$$R.S. = C(0,0)a^0x^0 = 1.$$

Step 1 Let $n = 1$.

$L.S. = (a + x)^1 \qquad R.S. = \sum_{k=0}^{1} C(1,k)a^{n-k}x^k$
$$= C(1,0)a^1x^0 + C(1,1)a^0x^1 = 1a + 1x = a + x = L.S.$$

Step 2 Assume the formula is true for $n = s$. (s is used rather than k, since k is already used as a dummy variable in the summation.)

Assume $(a + x)^s = \sum_{k=0}^{s} C(s,k)a^{s-k}x^k$.

Step 3 Prove the formula is true for $n = s + 1$, that is, prove

$(a + x)^{s+1} = \sum_{k=0}^{s+1} C(s + 1,k)a^{s+1-k}x^k$.

$(a + x)^{s+1} = (a + x)(a + x)^s \qquad$ [L.S. of step 2 multiplied by $(a + x)$].

$$= (a + x)\sum_{k=0}^{s} C(s,k)a^{s-k}x^k$$

$$= a\sum_{k=0}^{s} C(s,k)a^{s-k}x^k + x\sum_{k=0}^{s} C(s,k)a^{s-k}x^k$$

$$= \sum_{k=0}^{s} C(s,k)a^{s-k+1}x^k + \sum_{k=0}^{s} C(s,k)a^{s-k}x^{k+1}$$

Now by changing the limits of the summation, you obtain

$(a + x)^{s+1} = \sum_{k=0}^{s} C(s,k)a^{s-k+1}x^k + \sum_{k=1}^{s+1} C(s,k - 1)a^{s-k+1}x^k$.

$(a + x)^{s+1} = C(s,0)a^{s+1}x^0 + \sum_{k=1}^{s} C(s,k)a^{s-k+1}x^k + \sum_{k=1}^{s} C(s,k - 1)a^{s-k+1}x^k + C(s,s)a^0x^{s+1}$

$$= C(s,0)a^{s+1}x^0 + \sum_{k=1}^{s} [C(s,k) + C(s,k - 1)]a^{s-k+1}x^k + C(s,s)a^0x^{s+1}$$

But, 1. $C(s,0) = 1 = C(s + 1,0)$
2. $C(s,s) = 1 = C(s + 1,s + 1)$
3. $C(s,k) + C(s,k - 1) = C(s + 1,k)$

Thus, $(a + x)^{s+1} = C(s + 1,0)a^{s+1}x^0 + \sum_{k=1}^{s} C(s + 1,k)a^{s-k+1}x^k + C(s + 1,s + 1)a^0x^{s+1}$.

This may be combined under one summation giving

$(a + x)^{s+1} = \sum_{k=0}^{s+1} C(s + 1,k)a^{s-k+1}x^k$, which is what needed to be proven.

Summary

To each sequence $t_1, t_2, t_3, \ldots, t_n$ there corresponds the series

$$t_1 + t_2 + t_3 + \ldots + t_n = \sum_{k=1}^{n} t_k.$$

In the following formulas

a represents the value of the first term

n represents the *term number*, that is, the position of the t_n in the sequence

t_n represents the *term value*, that is, the value of the term in the nth position

S_n represents the *sum* of the n terms

d represents the *common difference* r represents the *common ratio*

d = any term − the preceding term r = any term ÷ the preceding term

Arithmetic Series

$$t_n = a + (n - 1)d \qquad\qquad S_n = \frac{n}{2}(a + t_n) \text{ or } S_n = \frac{n}{2}(2a + (n - 1)d)$$

Geometric Series

$$t_n = a \times r^{n-1} \qquad\qquad S_n = \frac{a(r^n - 1)}{r - 1} \text{ or } S_n = \frac{a(1 - r^n)}{1 - r}$$

If $|r| < 1$, then S_n converges to the sum $S_\infty = \dfrac{a}{1 - r}$.

Arithmetic-Geometric Series

$$1x + 2x^2 + 3x^3 + 4x^4 + \ldots + nx^n = \sum_{k=1}^{n} kx^k \qquad\qquad S_n = \frac{nx^{n+1}}{x - 1} - \frac{x(x^n - 1)}{(x - 1)^2}$$

Other Series

• Whenever the terms of a series can be broken up into *partial fractions* in which the same fraction appears with the opposite sign in adjacent terms, the sum of the series can be found by writing each term on a separate line and adding vertically.

• series associated with the natural numbers

$$\sum_{k=1}^{n} k = 1 + 2 + 3 + \ldots + n \qquad = \frac{n(n + 1)}{2}$$

$$\sum_{k=1}^{n} k^2 = 1^2 + 2^2 + 3^2 + \ldots + n^2 \qquad = \frac{n(n + 1)(2n + 1)}{6}$$

$$\sum_{k=1}^{n} k^3 = 1^3 + 2^3 + 3^3 + \ldots + n^3 \qquad = \left(\frac{n(n + 1)}{2}\right)^2$$

• $\displaystyle\sum_{k=1}^{n} (t_k - t_{k-1}) = t_n - t_0$

• $C(n + t, k) = \displaystyle\sum_{j=0}^{k} C(n, j)C(t, k - j)$

Mathematical Induction

There are three steps in a proof by mathematical induction.

Step 1: Show the statement is true for $n = 1$.

Step 2: Assume that the statement is true for $n = k$.

Step 3: Prove the statement is true for $n = k + 1$, using the result of step 2.

Inventory

Complete each of the following.

1. For an arithmetic series, in terms of a and d, $t_8 = $ ___ and $S_8 = $ ___.

2. For a geometric series, in terms of a and r, $t_6 = $ ___ and $S_{13} = $ ___.

3. For the arithmetic series $3 + 8 + 13 + \ldots + 68$, $a = $ ___, d ___, ___ $= 68$.

4. The finite geometric series $6 + 24 + 96 + \ldots$ has 14 terms. Hence, $a = $ ___, $r = $ ___, $t_{14} = $ ___.

5. The geometric series $a + ar + ar^2 + \ldots$ converges to $S_\infty = $ ___ provided ___.

6. For the geometric series with $a = 3$ and $r = 0.9$, the value of S_∞ is ___.

7. A geometric series with $a = 0.5$ does not converge. Which of the following cannot be a value for r? a) 2   b) −2   c) 0.2   d) −0.2

8. For the series $x + 2x^2 + 3x^3 + \ldots,$ $t_n = $ ___ and $S_n = $ ___.

9. $\displaystyle\sum_{k=1}^{100} (t_k - t_{k-1}) = t$ ___ $- t$ ___

10. a) $\displaystyle\sum_{j=0}^{k} C(n,j)C(t,k-j) = C(\underline{\quad},\underline{\quad})$

    b) $\displaystyle\sum_{j=0}^{8} C(7,j)C(9,8-j) = C(\underline{\quad},\underline{\quad})$

    c) $\displaystyle\sum_{j=0}^{\blacksquare} C(5,j)C(\underline{\quad},9-j) = C(43,\underline{\quad}).$

    d) $\displaystyle\sum_{j=0}^{\blacksquare} C(\underline{\quad},j)C(8,\underline{\quad}-j) = C(20,14)$

Review Exercises

1. Write each series in expanded form.

   a) $\sum_{m=1}^{4} m^2$

   b) $\sum_{n=1}^{5} n^4$

   c) $\sum_{m=1}^{5} 3(5^m)$

   d) $\sum_{n=1}^{6} \frac{1}{n}$

   e) $\sum_{j=1}^{4} (3j + 5)$

   f) $\sum_{k=1}^{4} (-1)^k 5$

2. Write each of the following series using Σ notation.

   a) $1 + 2 + 3 + 4 + 5 + 6$
   b) $1^3 + 2^3 + 3^3 + 4^3$
   c) $3^2 + 4^2 + 5^2 + 6^2 + 7^2$
   d) $y + y^2 + y^3 + y^4$
   e) $5(3^4) + 5(3^5) + 5(3^6) + 5(3^7)$
   f) $t_3 + t_4 + t_5 + t_6 + t_7$

3. Each of the following is either a geometric or an arithmetic series. For each, indicate which type of series it is, state the value of d or r, and give the next two terms.

   a) $2 + 6 + 18 + \ldots$
   b) $9 + 5 + 1 + \ldots$
   c) $28 + 4 + \frac{4}{7} + \ldots$
   d) $(m - 3) + (m - 6) + (m - 9) + \ldots$
   e) $3a^2 + 6a^3 + 12a^4 + \ldots$
   f) $8 + 4 - 0 - \ldots$
   g) $\frac{7}{8} + \frac{5}{8} + \frac{3}{8} + \ldots$
   h) $2.4 + 0.24 + 0.024 + \ldots$

4. Find the 7th and 12th term of each of the following arithmetic or geometric series.

   a) $14 + 28 + 42 + \ldots$
   b) $135 + 45 + 15 + \ldots$
   c) $1.9 + 0.19 + 0.019 + \ldots$
   d) $-6 + 3 - 1.5 + \ldots$
   e) $47 + 41 + 35 + \ldots$
   f) $14 + 13.6 + 13.2 + \ldots$

5. An infinite geometric series has a sum $S_\infty = 16$. The sum of the first two terms is 4. Find a and r.

6. For each of the following arithmetic or geometric series find the general term then write the series in compact form using sigma notation.

   a) $4 + 8 + 12 + \ldots$
   b) $7 + \frac{7}{5} + \frac{7}{25} + \ldots$
   c) $4 + 12 + 36 + \ldots$
   d) $15 + 2 - 11 + \ldots$

7. How many terms are there in each of the following arithmetic or geometric series?

   a) $24 + 29 + 34 + \ldots + 349$
   b) $12 + 36 + 108 + \ldots 8748$

8. Find the first term and the common difference for each of the arithmetic sequences for which two terms are as indicated.

   a) $t_3 = 7, t_7 = 23$
   b) $t_9 = 37, t_{16} = -12$

9. Determine a and r for the geometric sequences of real numbers, two of whose terms are as indicated.

   a) $t_3 = 4, t_7 = 324$
   b) $t_6 = 320, t_{11} = \frac{-5}{16}$

10. A series has a 3rd term with term value 18 and a 6th term equal to 486. Find the first 3 terms of the series of the following kind.

    a) arithmetic   b) geometric

11. Find the sum of each of the following arithmetic series to the number of terms indicated.

    a) $3 + 5 + 7 + \ldots$, to 18 terms
    b) $4 + 2 + 0 + \ldots$, to 36 terms
    c) $24 + 16 + 8 + \ldots$, to 10 terms
    d) $11 + 17 + 23 + \ldots$, to 28 terms

12. Find the sum of each of the following arithmetic series.

    a) $4 + 10 + \ldots + 82$
    b) $321 + 314 + \ldots + (-99)$

13. Evaluate.

    a) $\sum_{k=1}^{15} (4k - 2)$

    b) $\sum_{k=1}^{99} (5 - 2k)$

14. Find the sum of each of the following geometric series to the indicated number of terms.
   a) $4.5 - 9 + 18 - \ldots$, to 10 terms
   b) $54 + 18 + 6 + \ldots$, to 7 terms

15. Evaluate.
   a) $\sum_{k=1}^{5} 2(3^k)$ **b)** $\sum_{j=1}^{20} 32\left(\frac{1}{2}\right)^j$

16. Find the sum of the given geometric series
   a) $7 + 14 + 28 + \ldots + 3584$
   b) $\frac{1}{5^2} + \frac{1}{5^3} + \frac{1}{5^4} + \ldots + \frac{1}{5^{10}}$

17. A geometric series of five terms has a common ratio of 6 and a sum of 4665. Find the value of the first term.

18. For each of the following infinite geometric series determine whether or not the series converges. If the series does converge, find the value of S_∞.
   a) $8 + \frac{8}{7} + \frac{8}{49} + \ldots$
   b) $6 + 18 + 54 + \ldots$
   c) $1 - 31 + 961 - \ldots$
   d) $81 + 40.5 + 20.25 + \ldots$

19. Write each of the following repeating decimal numbers using an infinite geometric series; then express each as a rational number $\frac{a}{b}$ where $a, b \in I$, and $b \neq 0$.
   a) $0.51\ 51\ 51\ \ldots$
   b) $0.631\ 631\ 631\ \ldots$
   c) $5.34\ 17\ 17\ 17\ \ldots$

20. For a certain infinite geometric series, $a = 13$, and $S_\infty = 9.75$. Find the value of r.

21. Find the sum of n terms of each of the following arithmetic-geometric series.
   a) $5 + 50 + 375 + \ldots$
   b) $2c^2 + 8c^3 + 24c^4 + \ldots$
   c) $\frac{1}{3} + \frac{2}{9} + \frac{1}{9} + \ldots$
   d) $1.3 + 3.38 + 6.591 + \ldots$

22. Find the sum of 20 terms, correct to 5 significant figures, of the arithmetic-geometric series $\sum_{k=1}^{n} k(0.2)^k$.

23. a) Find S_∞ for the arithmetic-geometric series in question 22.
   b) For what values of c will the series in 21b) converge?

24. Use the fact that
$$\frac{3}{(3n-1)(3n+2)} = \frac{1}{3n-1} - \frac{1}{3n+2}$$
to find the sum of n terms of the series
$$\frac{1}{2(5)} + \frac{1}{5(8)} + \frac{1}{8(11)} + \ldots + \frac{1}{(3n-1)(3n+2)}$$

25. a) Given that $t_k = k^2 + k$, show that $t_k - t_{k-1} = 2k$.
   b) Use the fact that $\sum_{k=1}^{n}(t_k - t_{k-1}) = t_n - t_0$
   to evaluate $\sum_{k=1}^{100} 2k$.

26. a) Prove that $C(15,7) = \sum_{j=0}^{7} C(9,j)C(6,7-j)$.
   b) Write two summations for $C(15,7)$ different from the summation in part a).

27. Prove the following statements using mathematical induction, where $n \in N$.
   a) $4 + 11 + 18 + \ldots + (7n - 3)$
   $= \frac{n(7n+1)}{2}$
   b) $1 + 3 + 5 + \ldots + (2n - 1) = n^2$
   c) $1 + 2 + 4 + \ldots + 2^{n-1} = 2^n - 1$
   d) $1(2) + 2(4) + 3(8) + \ldots + n(2^n)$
   $= 2 + (n - 1)2^{n+1}$
   e) $\sum_{s=1}^{n}(4s + 1) = n(2n + 3)$

28. Find the sum of 10 terms of the arithmetic-geometric series
$$1 + 3\left(\frac{1}{4}\right) + 5\left(\frac{1}{16}\right) + \ldots$$

29. A square has sides of 30 cm. The midpoints of the sides are joined to form an inscribed square. The midpoints of this second square are joined to form a third square. The process is continued indefinitely. Find the following.
   a) the sum of the perimeters of the infinite sequence of squares
   b) the sum of the areas of the infinite sequence of squares

30. A jogger discovers that running every day builds up his leg muscles. In the first week, his muscles increase by 3 mm. The amount of increase each week is 0.85 of the increase the week before. By how much do his leg muscles increase the seventh week?

31. A series has a 4th term with term value 155 and a 9th term equal to 4960. Find the first 3 terms of the series given the following.
   a) The series is arithmetic.
   b) The series is geometric.

32. A ball is dropped from a height of 20 metres and continuously bounces up then falls down. After each bounce the ball rises to a height that is 0.3 of the maximum height it reached on its previous bounce. Find the total distance, both up and down, that the ball has travelled after reaching the top of its tenth bounce.

33. Given the series $3 + 5 + 10 + 18 + 29 + \ldots$,
   a) Show that the differences between successive terms form the arithmetic series $2 + 5 + 8 + 11 + \ldots$.
   b) Use a) to show that, for the original series, $t_n - t_{n-1} = 3n - 4$, $n \geqslant 2$.
   c) Find the sum of $n - 1$ terms of the arithmetic series in a).
   d) Use your result of c) and the fact that
   $$\sum_{k=2}^{n} (t_k - t_{k-1}) = t_n - t_1$$ to prove that, for the original series, $t_n = \dfrac{3n^2 - 5n + 8}{2}$.

34. A circular saw will continue to turn after the power is shut off. After this, the speed of turning of the saw each second is $\dfrac{4}{5}$ of the speed the previous second. During the first 6 s after the power is turned off the saw turns 295 times. Find the approximate speed of the saw when the power was turned off.

35. You are pounding a nail into a board and notice the nail moves 15 mm with the first impact and an additional 12 mm with the second impact. Predict the total distance the nail will have moved into the board after the fifth impact in the following situations.
   a) The successive distances the nail moves form arithmetic series.
   b) The successive distances the nail moves form a geometric series.

36. You buy a used car for $5000. Once driven off the lot your car depreciates by 25%. Each year that follows your car depreciates an additional $600. What is the depreciated value of your car after you have owned it for five years?

37. You are hired as a computer specialist with a starting salary of $2400 a month. Each month your salary will increase by $80.
   a) Write a series showing your salary each month for the first nine months.
   b) What total amount will you earn in the first nine months?

38. a) Write a computer program to show that the harmonic series
   $$1 + \frac{1}{2} + \frac{1}{3} + \frac{1}{4} + \frac{1}{5} + \ldots \text{ diverges.}$$
   b) Write a computer program to show that the alternating series
   $$1 - \frac{1}{2} + \frac{1}{3} - \frac{1}{4} + \frac{1}{5} - \ldots \text{ converges to}$$
   $0.693\ 147\ 180 \ldots$

CHAPTER SEVEN

Applications of Probability

In 1654 a French gambler, Chevalier de Mere, asked the French mathematician Blaise Pascal to consider why betting even money on a particular dice game was a losing proposition. The work that Pascal did is considered to be the formal beginning of the mathematical study of probability.

The game in question was to roll a pair of dice 24 times. The game was won if at least one double six was rolled. In this chapter you will learn techniques to calculate the probability of winning this game (just slightly less than 50%).

Probability theory is still applied to the practice of gambling, but the applications of probability have extended to many other more worthwhile endeavors.

In 1866, the Austrian monk Gregor Mendel used probability theory to establish the modern theory of genetics.

Probability theory is now an integral part of economics, biology, the health sciences and telecommunications, and has become one of the corner stones of the physical sciences.

Consider the following game. A person stands at a street corner. A coin is flipped. If the coin lands *heads* the person goes one block east. If the coin lands *tails* the person goes one block west.

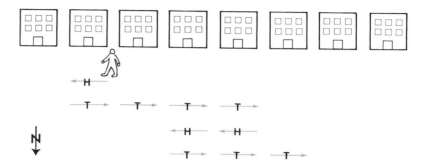

After ten flips of the coin, what is the probability that the person had returned to the starting point?

After ten flips of the coin what is the most likely distance to be from the starting point?

How would these probabilities be affected if the coin were not 'fair' and landed *heads* with a probability of $\frac{2}{3}$?

This simple game is an example of a Random Walk problem. More complicated Random Walk problems and their solutions are very important in a field of the physical sciences known as *statistical mechanics*.

In statistical mechanics, the scientist uses probability theory to predict the most likely behaviour of individual atoms and molecules. The behaviour of these individual particles is then used to describe the behaviour of the object they form.

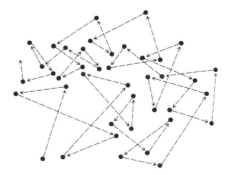

In this chapter, you will continue the study of probability that you began in chapter 2. If you choose a career involving the physical sciences this study of probability will continue.

7.1 Random Variables

In a group of 100 students, 60 students prefer cola A over cola B and 40 prefer cola B over cola A. Ten students are chosen at random. What is the probability that exactly three will prefer cola B over cola A?

Five cards are dealt from a shuffled standard 52-card deck. What is the probability that all five cards will be spades?

In a manufacturing process for a stereo component, it is known that 1% of the components produced will be defective. Ten components are shipped, without being checked for defects, to a retailer. What is the probability that none of the ten components is defective?

The preceding problems are very similar to the type of problem that you were solving in chapter 2. Although they seem to be very different situations, all three of the problems can be solved using the same type of probability model. In this chapter you will study the theory which allows you to use similar probability models for many seemingly different situations. You will then have the opportunity to use this theory in a variety of applications.

Begin by reviewing the vocabulary of probability. Consider the following **experiment**. A card is drawn from a standard 52-card deck and the suit of the card is noted. Each time the experiment is performed is a **trial**. There are four possible **outcomes** for this experiment. The set of all possible outcomes, {club, diamond, heart, spade}, is a **sample space** of the experiment. Any subset of a sample space is an **event**.

For example, there is the event that a red card is drawn. This is the subset {diamond, heart} of the sample space. Each outcome, regarded as a singleton subset of a sample space, is also an event. Thus, the event of drawing a heart is the subset {heart}.

Now look at a new idea. Let each outcome in a sample space be associated with a single number. For example, you could use the following pairings: (heart, 0), (club, 1), (spade, 2), (diamond, 3). This pairing of each outcome with a single number is an instance of that extremely important concept in mathematics, *function*. The domain of this function is a sample space of an experiment. The range of the function is a set of numbers, {0, 1, 2, 3}.

For any trial the function has a value. If, on a given trial, a spade is drawn from the deck, then the function has the value 2. For any trial there is no guarantee as to what value the function will have, because the outcomes vary randomly from one trial to the next. Because of this, the function is known as a **random variable**.

DEFINITION

Let S be a (discrete) sample space for an experiment. Let X be a function mapping each outcome in S to a real number.
Then X is a **random variable**. It is usual to speak of X as a random variable *on S*.

All of the sample spaces in this chapter are discrete. Typically, random variables are named using capital letters from the latter part of the alphabet.

Example 1 a) An experiment consists of flipping a coin three times and noting the outcome. Describe a random variable Y which maps each outcome to the number of heads which occurs in a trial.

  b) List the range of Y.

Solution a) Let H represent a coin landing heads up and T represent a coin landing tails up. Then a sample space for the experiment can be written {HHH, HHT, HTH, HTT, THH, THT, TTH, TTT}. HTH is the outcome where heads turned up on the first and third flip and tails turned up on the second flip. $Y(\text{HHH}) = 3$, $Y(\text{HHT}) = 2$, $Y(\text{HTH}) = 2$, $Y(\text{HTT}) = 1$, $Y(\text{THH}) = 2$, $Y(\text{THT}) = 1$, $Y(\text{TTH}) = 1$ and $Y(\text{TTT}) = 0$.

  b) The values taken by Y are 0, 1, 2 and 3.
  Therefore, the range of Y is {0, 1, 2, 3}. ■

The experiment and random variable in Example 1 can be used to link the concepts of a random variable and the probability of an event. What is the probability that there will be exactly two heads in three flips of the coin? If E is the event of exactly two heads occurring in three flips, then E is the subset {HHT, HTH, THH} of the sample space. From chapter 2, $P(E)$ is the probability that the event E occurs. $P(E) = \dfrac{n(E)}{n(S)} = \dfrac{3}{8}$.

What is the probability that for any trial, the random variable Y will have the value 2? Y has the value 2, only when there are exactly two heads in three flips. Therefore, the probability of Y having the value 2 on any trial is the same as $P(E)$, that is, $\dfrac{3}{8}$.

A common notation for "the probability that Y has the value 2 on any given trial" is $P(Y = 2)$.

The notation can be extended. $P(Y < 2)$ is the probability that Y has a value less than two on any given trial. This probability is the same as the probability of having less than two heads in three flips.

This is equal to $P(Y = 0) + P(Y = 1) = \dfrac{1}{8} + \dfrac{3}{8} = \dfrac{1}{2}$.

In many cases, a sample space associated with an experiment is itself a set of numbers. A natural function to use as a random variable in such a case is the function which maps each outcome to itself.

Example 2   A single cubic die is rolled and the number of dots on the up face is noted.
A sample space for this experiment is $S = \{1, 2, 3, 4, 5, 6\}$.
A random variable for this sample space is $X(s) = s$ for each $s \in S$.
That is, $X(5) = 5$ and so on. Find

a) $P(X = 3)$

b) $P(X \geqslant 5)$

c) $P(1 < X \leqslant 4)$

d) $P(X > 6)$.

Solution   a) $P(X = 3)$ is the same as the probability of rolling a 3.

Assuming a fair die, $P(X = 3) = \dfrac{1}{6}$.

b) $P(X \geqslant 5)$ is the same as the probability of rolling a 5 or a 6.

$P(X \geqslant 5) = \dfrac{1}{6} + \dfrac{1}{6} = \dfrac{1}{3}$.

c) $P(1 < X \leqslant 4)$ is the same as the probability of rolling a 2, 3 or 4.

$P(1 < X \leqslant 4) = \dfrac{1}{6} + \dfrac{1}{6} + \dfrac{1}{6} = \dfrac{1}{2}$.

d) $P(X > 6)$ is the same as the probability of more than 6 dots showing on
the up face. This is impossible. Therefore, $P(X > 6) = 0$.   ■

Example 3   A pair of cubic dice is rolled and the number of dots showing on the up
face of each die is noted.

List two different sample spaces associated with the experiment and
describe two random variable functions for each sample space.

Solution   Some possibilities are:
1. A sample space S is the set of 36 ordered pairs
$\{(1,1),\ (1,2),\ (1,3),\ldots,\ (2,1),\ (2,2),\ (2,3),\ldots,\ (6,4),\ (6,5),\ (6,6)\}$.

Each ordered pair represents a particular outcome. For example, $(3,4)$
represents the outcome of three dots showing on the first die and
four dots showing on the second.

Let X be the function which maps each ordered pair in S to the sum of
the two numbers in the ordered pair.

For example, $X(3,4) = 3 + 4 = 7$.

The value of the random variable X for any roll of dice is simply the total number of dots showing on the two up faces. The range of X is the set $\{2, 3, 4, 5, 6, 7, 8, 9, 10, 11, 12\}$.

Let Y be the function which maps each ordered pair (a, b) in S to the quotient $\frac{a}{b}$. Then $Y\,((2,3)) = \frac{2}{3}$.

Notice that $Y((4,6)) = \frac{4}{6} = \frac{2}{3} = Y((2,3))$.

The range of Y is

$$\left\{ 1, 2, 3, 4, 5, 6, \frac{1}{2}, \frac{1}{3}, \frac{1}{4}, \frac{1}{5}, \frac{1}{6}, \frac{2}{3}, \frac{2}{5}, \frac{3}{2}, \frac{3}{4}, \frac{3}{5}, \frac{4}{3}, \frac{4}{5}, \frac{5}{2}, \frac{5}{3}, \frac{5}{4}, \frac{5}{6}, \frac{6}{5} \right\}$$

2. A sample space R consists of two outcomes:
the two up faces show the same number of dots, and,
the two up faces show different numbers of dots.
Let U be the function that maps to 1 the outcome that both dice show the same number of dots, and maps to 0 the outcome that both dice show different numbers of dots.
The random variable U could be used to model a game in which a player won if he rolled doubles, and lost otherwise.
A value of 1 for U indicates a win, and a value of 0 indicates a loss.

Let V be the function that maps to 5 the outcome that both dice show the same number of dots, and maps to -5 the outcome that both dice show different numbers of dots.

The random variable V could be used to model a game in which a player won \$5 if he rolled doubles and lost \$5 otherwise. Over several trials (plays of the game) the sum of the values of V would indicate a player's winnings or losses over those games. ■

Example 3 illustrates the great generality of the use of random variables when applied to a particular experiment. You cannot speak of *the* sample space associated with an experiment. Nor can you speak of *the* random variable defined on a sample space. It is always *a* random variable defined on *a* sample space associated with an experiment.

Quite often random variables are described informally, without explicitly indicating either the experiment or the sample space associated with the experiment on which the random variable is defined. Following are several pairs of informal, and complete, descriptions of random variables.

Example 4 Give a formal description of each of the following informally described random variables.

   a) The number of hearts in a 13-card bridge hand is the random variable U.

   b) A group of students is polled as to whether or not they like cola A. The students are asked one after another until a student is found who likes cola A, or 100 students have been polled. The random variable V is the number of students polled.

   c) The Hamilton Tiger Cats play the Toronto Argonauts in a Canadian Football League match. The random variable W is the number of points scored by the Tiger Cats minus the points scored by the Argonauts.

Solution **a)** The experiment is to deal 13 cards from a shuffled standard 52-card deck and observe which of the cards are hearts. A sample space S consists of the $C(52,13) \doteq 6.35 \times 10^{11}$ possible hands that could be dealt. U maps each outcome in S to the number of hearts in that outcome (13-card hand).
The range of U is $\{0, 1, 2, 3, 4, 5, 6, 7, 8, 9, 10, 11, 12, 13\}$.

   b) The experiment is to ask the students until one student has replied "yes", or 100 students have been polled. If y represents a student saying "yes" and n represents a student saying "no", then a sample space S for the experiment could be represented by strings of n's ending with a single y, or a string of 100 n's, or a single y. The string '$nnnnny$' is the outcome that 5 students said "no", and the sixth student said "yes". V maps each outcome in S to the length of the string. Therefore, $V(nnnnny) = 6$.
The range of V is $\{1, 2, \ldots, 100\}$.

   c) The experiment consists of holding the football game and noting the number of points scored by each team. A sample space S could be represented by the ordered pairs (H,T) of natural numbers where H is the number of points scored by the Hamilton team and T is the number of points scored by Toronto. W maps each ordered pair (H,T) to the integer H minus T. Notice that although there are practical limits to the domain and range of W, there are no theoretical limits. For example, it is unlikely that Hamilton will score 5 points and Toronto 100 points, giving W a value of -95 for that outcome, but it is not theoretically impossible. ■

As Example 4 illustrates, the use of random variables in many situations is implicit rather than explicit. In order for you to successfully use random variables in solving problems, you must learn to identify occasions when the concepts of random variables are being used informally.

7.1 Exercises

1. A game is played where one card is dealt from a shuffled standard 52-card deck and the value of the card is observed. Aces have a value of 11 and the face cards (jacks, queens and kings) have a value of 10. Let S be the sample space consisting of 52 outcomes, one for each card in the deck. X is the random variable which maps each card to the value of the card.
   a) List the range of X.
   b) What is the value of X if the king of diamonds is dealt?
   c) Find $P(X = 5)$, $P(2 \leqslant X < 5)$ and $P(X \geqslant 10)$.

2. A game is played where two cards are dealt from a shuffled standard 52-card deck and the value of each card is observed. Aces have a value of 11 and the face cards (jacks, queens and kings) have a value of 10. Let S be the sample space consisting of all possible two-card hands. X is the random variable which maps each two-card hand to the sum of the values of the cards.
   a) List the range of X.
   b) What is the value of X for the hand (jack of spades, two of hearts)?
   c) Find the number of outcomes in S.
   d) For how many hands will X have the value 4?
   e) Find $P(X = 4)$, $P(X \leqslant 5)$ and $P(X > 21)$.

3. Three cubic dice are rolled and the number of dots shown by each die is noted. The random variable X maps each roll to the sum of the number of dots showing on each die. The triple (a,b,c) represents the outcome that a dots show on one die, b dots on a second die and c dots on the third die.
   a) What is the range of X?
   b) What is the value of $X(3,2,5)$?
   c) For what triples of numbers (a,b,c) does $X(a,b,c) = 12$?
   d) How many outcomes are in the sample space?

e) Find $P(X = 12)$.

4. A tetrahedral die has four faces numbered 1, 2, 3 and 4. The die is rolled three times and the number on the down face (which is not visible) is noted each time. A sample space S consists of the outcomes which can be represented as ordered triples of numbers, each number being the number on the down face for a particular roll. A random variable Y is the function which maps each possible outcome in S to the number of times in three rolls the number 4 is not visible. If the number 4 is visible on all three rolls then the value of Y is 0.
   a) How many outcomes are there in the sample space?
   b) What is the range of Y?
   c) Find $P(Y = 2)$.

5. The experiment in question 4 is changed from rolling the die three times to rolling the die until the 4 is not visible. Let 0 represent the case that a 4 is visible on a particular roll and let 1 represent the case that the 4 is face down on a particular roll. A string of 0's and 1's could be used to represent an outcome in a sample space S. For example, 0001 indicates that the 4 was not on the down face for the first three rolls, but was on the down face on the fourth roll. Z is the random variable that maps each outcome to the number of rolls before the 4 is on the down face.
   a) Describe a function rule for Z. That is, describe a rule determining to which number Z would map a particular outcome in S.
   b) How many outcomes are in S?
   c) List the range of Z.

6. An ecologist studies the life expectancies of wolves in a certain territory. The ages in years of 100 wolves when they die are noted. Use the observed ages as a sample space to define three different random variables on the data.

7. A student is selected randomly from a class of twenty. It is then noted whether or not the student is left-handed. A sample space S consists of the twenty possible choices of students.
   a) Define a random variable L on S with $\{0,1\}$ as range. L is to model the situation where success is designated as choosing a left-handed student and failure is choosing a right-handed student.
   b) Exactly eight of the students are left handed. Use your definition of L in a) to find $P(L = 1)$ and $P(L = 0)$.

8. A coin is flipped and a cubic die rolled. It is noted whether the coin lands heads or tails. The number of dots showing on the up face of the die is also noted.
   a) List a sample space S for this experiment, using ordered pairs.
   b) Define a random variable on S which has a range of $\{-6, -5, -4, -3, -2, -1, 1, 2, 3, 4, 5, 6\}$.
   c) Define a random variable on S which has a range of $\{0, 1\}$.

9. Give a complete description of the following informally described random variables.
   a) The random variable X is the number of heads when three coins are tossed.
   b) The random variable Y is 1 if doubles are rolled with a pair of dice, and 0 otherwise.
   c) The random variable Z is the age in years of a student selected from a class of 25 students.
   d) The random variable W is the number of people who are color-blind in a randomly selected group of ten.
   e) Case lots of 144 widgets are shipped from the manufacturer without being tested for defects.
   The random variable U is the number of defective widgets in a case lot.

10. A bag contains five red marbles and five black marbles.
    a) A single marble is taken from the bag and its color noted. Describe a sample space and define a random variable on the sample space.
    b) Three marbles are taken from the bag and the color of each marble noted. Describe, in words, a sample space of 120 equally likely outcomes for this experiment. Define two different random variables on this sample space.
    c) A marble is taken from the bag, its color is noted, and then it is returned to the bag. This is done three times. Describe how a sample space for this experiment differs from that of b).
    d) Describe how a sample space would differ from that in b), if six marbles were taken from the bag instead of three.
    e) Describe how a sample space would differ from that in c) if a marble were selected and then replaced six times.

11. The use of random variables allows for the algebraic expression of compound experiments. For example, a pair of cubic dice is rolled. The random variable X maps a roll to the number of dots showing on the first die. The random variable Y maps a roll to the number of dots showing on the second die. Then $X + Y$ is the random variable which maps a roll to the total number of dots showing on the pair of dice.
    a) Find the range of $X - Y$.
    b) Find the range of $|X - Y|$.
    c) Evaluate $(X - Y)(2,5)$, $|X - Y|(2,5)$, $X^2(2,5)$, $(2X^2 - Y)(2,5)$.

7.2 Probability Distributions and Expected Value

In section 7.1 you looked at an experiment where a pair of cubic dice were rolled and the number of dots on the up face of each die was noted. A sample space S for this experiment consisted of 36 equally likely outcomes which could be represented by the ordered pairs

{(1,1), (1,2), (1,3), (1,4), (1,5), (1,6), (2,1), (2,2), (2,3), (2,4), (2,5), (2,6), (3,1), (3,2), (3,3), (3,4), (3,5), (3,6), (4,1), (4,2), (4,3), (4,4), (4,5), (4,6) (5,1), (5,2), (5,3), (5,4), (5,5), (5,6), (6,1), (6,2), (6,3), (6,4), (6,5), (6,6)}.

The random variable X is defined on S so that X maps each outcome in S to the sum of the number of dots on the up faces. The range of X is {2, 3, 4, 5, 6, 7, 8, 9, 10, 11, 12}.

$P(X = k)$ denotes the probability that X has a certain value k on any particular roll. Using the definition in chapter 2, $P(X = k) = \dfrac{n(E_k)}{n(S)}$ where E_k is the event (set of outcomes) that X maps to k.

For example, for $k = 8$,

$E_k = \{(2,6),\ (3,5),\ (4,4),\ (5,3),\ (6,2)\}. \quad P(X = 8) = \dfrac{n(E_k)}{n(S)} = \dfrac{5}{36}.$

When $P(X = k)$ has been tabulated for each value k in the range of X, a function called the **probability distribution** of X is established.

Sample Space $\xrightarrow{\ \ X\ \ }$	Range of $X \xrightarrow{\ \ f\ \ }$	$P(X = k) = \dfrac{n(E_k)}{n(S)}$
(1,1)	2	$\dfrac{1}{36}$
(1,2),(2,1)	3	$\dfrac{2}{36}$
(1,3),(2,2),(3,1)	4	$\dfrac{3}{36}$
(1,4),(2,3),(3,2),(4,1)	5	$\dfrac{4}{36}$
(1,5),(2,4),(3,3),(4,2),(5,1)	6	$\dfrac{5}{36}$
(1,6),(2,5),(3,4),(4,3),(5,2),(6,1)	7	$\dfrac{6}{36}$
(2,6),(3,5),(4,4),(5,3),(6,2)	8	$\dfrac{5}{36}$
(3,6),(4,5),(5,4),(6,3)	9	$\dfrac{4}{36}$
(4,6),(5,5),(6,4)	10	$\dfrac{3}{36}$
(5,6),(6,5)	11	$\dfrac{2}{36}$
(6,6)	12	$\dfrac{1}{36}$

f is the probability distribution function of the random variable X.

DEFINITION

If X is a random variable, then the probability distribution of X is the function f which maps each value k in the range of X to the probability $P(X = k)$. That is, for each k in the range of X, $f(k) = P(X = k)$.

Since X is a function, each outcome in S is mapped by X to a *single* value. This implies that the E_k are mutually exclusive. Also, X maps every outcome in S to some value. Therefore, every outcome in S belongs to exactly one subset E_k of S. Therefore, the E_k are disjoint subsets of S whose union is the whole set S. Also, if f is a probability distribution function of the random variable X and k is in the range of X, then $f(k)$ is a probability. These considerations lead to the following properties.

PROPERTIES

If f is a probability distribution function of the random variable X and the range of X is $\{k_1, k_2, \ldots, k_n\}$, then

1. $0 \leq f(k_i) \leq 1$ for $i = 1, \ldots, n$. That is, all probabilities have values between 0 and 1, inclusive.

2. $\sum\limits_{i=1}^{n} f(k_i) = 1$. That is, the sum of all probability values in a distribution is 1.

It is common to refer to the *probability distribution of an experiment* rather than the *probability distribution function of a random variable associated with the experiment*.

Example 1

A fair coin is tossed three times and it is noted each time whether the coin falls heads or tails. Y is the random variable which maps each possible outcome to the number of heads which occur in a particular trial.
Use a table to define the probability distribution of Y.

Solution

A sample space with eight equally likely outcomes for the experiment is
$S = \{HHH, HHT, HTH, HTT, THH, THT, TTH, TTT\}$.
The range of Y is $\{0, 1, 2, 3\}$. The events E_i, where i represents the number of heads occurring, are
$E_0 = \{TTT\}$, $E_1 = \{HTT, THT, TTH\}$, $E_2 = \{HHT, HTH, THH\}$ and $E_3 = \{HHH\}$.
The probability distribution of Y is given by

k_i	0	1	2	3
$P(Y = k_i)$	$\dfrac{1}{8}$	$\dfrac{3}{8}$	$\dfrac{3}{8}$	$\dfrac{1}{8}$

■

Closely related to the probability distribution is the concept of the **expected value** or mean value of a random variable. Suppose the experiment in Example 1 is repeated for many trials. The value Y for each trial is noted and the arithmetic average of these values is calculated. As more and more trials are performed, this average would tend towards a number known as the expected value of Y.

F O R M U L A	If the random variable Y has $\{k_1, k_2, \ldots, k_n\}$ as a range and f is the probability distribution function of Y, then the expected value of Y, written as $E(Y)$, is $$\sum_{i=1}^{n} k_i \times f(k_i)$$

Example 2 Calculate the expected value of the random variable Y described in Example 1.

Solution
$$E(Y) = 0 \times \frac{1}{8} + 1 \times \frac{3}{8} + 2 \times \frac{3}{8} + 3 \times \frac{1}{8} = \frac{3}{2}$$

The expected value of Y is $\frac{3}{2}$. That is, if you performed the experiment many times and averaged the number of heads occurring in each experiment, the average would be close to $1\frac{1}{2}$. ■

Example 3 The random variable Z has $\{0, 1, 2, 3, 4, 5, 6, 7, 8, 9\}$ as a range. Following is the probability distribution function f of Z.

x	0	1	2	3	4	5	6	7	8	9
f(x)	0.05	0.05	0.05	0.10	0.15	0.15	0.10	0.20	0.05	0.10

a) Find $P(Z = 4)$, $P(Z \leqslant 3)$ and $P(Z > 7)$.

b) Calculate $E(Z)$.

Solution **a)** Recall that $f(x) = P(Z = x)$.
$P(Z = 4) = f(4) = 0.15$
$P(Z \leqslant 3) = f(0) + f(1) + f(2) + f(3) = 0.05 + 0.05 + 0.05 + 0.10 = 0.25$
$P(Z > 7) = f(8) + f(9) = 0.05 + 0.10 = 0.15$

b) $E(Z) = 0.05 \times 0 + 0.05 \times 1 + 0.05 \times 2 + 0.10 \times 3 + 0.15 \times 4 +$
$\qquad 0.15 \times 5 + 0.10 \times 6 + 0.20 \times 7 + 0.05 \times 8 + 0.10 \times 9$
$\qquad = 5.1$ ■

Example 4 illustrates another, but similar, meaning of expected value.

Example 4   You roll a die and observe the number of dots on the up face. If you roll a 1 or a 6 you win $5. If you roll a 2, 3, 4, or 5 you lose $2. If you play this game many times what would you expect your average gain or loss per game to be?

Solution   The situation can be modelled by the random variable W. A sample space consists of the six equally likely outcomes $\{1, 2, 3, 4, 5, 6\}$ where each number represents the number of dots on the up face.
$W(1) = W(6) = 5$. $W(2) = W(3) = W(4) = W(5) = -2$.

$P(W = 5) = \dfrac{2}{6}$ or $\dfrac{1}{3}$ and $P(W = -2) = \dfrac{4}{6}$ or $\dfrac{2}{3}$.

Therefore, $E(W) = 5 \times \dfrac{1}{3} + (-2) \times \dfrac{2}{3} = \dfrac{1}{3}$.

In the long run, you can expect to average a gain of $\$\dfrac{1}{3}$ per game. ■

Experimental probabilities, based on relative frequencies over a number of observations, can also be the basis for probability distributions.

Example 5   Groups of three students were selected at random from a school and the number of female students in each group was noted. Thirty groups had no females, 105 groups had exactly one female, 120 groups had exactly two females and 45 groups were all female.
a) Define a random variable to model this situation and list the probability distribution for the random variable.
b) Find the expected value of this random variable. Give an interpretation for this number.

Solution   a) A trial of the experiment is to select three students at random from the school population and note the gender of each student.
A sample space for this experiment is all possible groups of three students. Let the random variable X map each possible group of three students to the number of females in the group. The range of X is $\{0, 1, 2, 3\}$.
Use the relative frequencies from the observed groups to list the probability distribution of X.
$30 + 105 + 120 + 45 = 300$ groups were observed. Using the relative frequencies as probabilities, the following distribution results.

k	0	1	2	3
$P(X = k)$	$\dfrac{30}{300}$	$\dfrac{105}{300}$	$\dfrac{120}{300}$	$\dfrac{45}{300}$

Therefore, the probability distribution function f for X is
$f(0) = 0.10$, $f(1) = 0.35$, $f(2) = 0.40$, $f(3) = 0.15$
b) $E(X) = 0 \times 0.10 + 1 \times 0.35 + 2 \times 0.40 + 3 \times 0.15 = 1.6$
Over a large number of observations, the average of the number of females in each group will be about 1.6. ■

7.2 Exercises

1. Two letters are chosen at random from the set of letters {A, B, C, D, E}. X is the random variable which maps each possible pair of letters to the number of vowels occurring in the pair.
   a) What is the range of X?
   b) For each value k in the range of X, calculate $P(X = k)$.
   c) Use a table and the results from b) to list the probability distribution of X.

2. The number of children in each of two hundred families is noted. The results are tabulated.

Number of children	0	1	2	3	4	5
Number of families	20	40	40	20	60	20

   a) If a family is chosen at random from the 200 families, what is the experimental probability that the family selected will have exactly 3 children?
   b) Y is the random variable which maps each family to the number of children in the family. List the probability distribution for Y.
   c) Use the probability distribution from b) to find $P(Y \leqslant 3)$ and $P(Y > 3)$.

3. A particular bridge has the following probability distribution for the number of accidents occuring on the bridge, on any day.

Number of accidents	0	1	2	3	4	5
Probability	0.15	0.20	0.15	0.35	0.10	0.05

   a) Calculate the expected value for a random variable with this distribution.
   b) How many accidents would you expect to occur on the bridge over a year?

4. Calculate the expected values for the random variables described in questions 1 and 2.

5. A sales manager knows from past experience the probabilities that salesperson A will sell a given number of automobiles in a week. The table lists the distribution of these probabilities.

Number of cars sold	0	1	2	3	4
Probability	0.10	0.15	0.35	0.25	0.15

   a) Find the probability that salesperson A sells more than two cars in any given week.
   b) Find the probability that A sells less than two cars in any given week.
   c) If the probability distribution is that of the random variable X which maps each week to the number of cars sold by A, calculate $E(X)$, the expected value of X.
   d) Interpret the meaning of $E(X)$ in terms of observing the number of cars sold by A each week over many weeks.

6. A game is played where a cubic die is rolled and the number of dots on the up face is noted. If the number of dots is an even number n, then you win n^2 dollars. If the number of dots is an odd number n, you lose n^2 dollars.
   a) Define a random variable W which maps each possible roll of the die to the number of dollars you win on that roll. Use negative numbers to indicate losses.
   b) List the probability distribution for W.
   c) Calculate the expected value for W, that is, $E(W)$.
   d) Interpret $E(W)$ as the average amount you would win or lose per game if you played the game many times.
   e) If it cost you $3 each time to play the game, would you make a profit in the long run?

7.3 Uniform Probability Distributions

A card is chosen at random from a standard 52-card deck. The suit and face value of the card is noted. A sample space S for this experiment consists of 52 equally likely outcomes. Each outcome corresponds to a particular card.

What is the probability that the card chosen on a particular draw is the king of hearts? The event {king of hearts} corresponds to a single outcome and is therefore a simple event. The probability is $\frac{1}{52}$.

Let X be a random variable which maps each outcome in S to a different number in the set {1, 2, ..., 52}. For example, the clubs could be mapped, from ace to king, to the numbers 1, 2, ..., 13; diamonds mapped to 14, 15, ..., 26; hearts mapped to 27, 28, ..., 39; and spades mapped to 40, 41, ..., 52. Then X(king of hearts) = 39 and $P(X = 39) = \frac{1}{52}$.

What is the probability distribution of X? The range of X is {1, 2, ... 52}.

It is clear that for any $k \in$ {1, 2, ..., 52}, $P(X = k) = \frac{1}{52}$. The probabilities in this distribution are the same for each value in the range of X.
A probability distribution in which each probability has the same value is called a **uniform distribution**.

DEFINITION

Let X be a random variable with range {$x_1, x_2, ..., x_n$}.
The probability distribution function f is a **uniform (probability) distribution** if $f(x_1) = f(x_2) = ... = f(x_n)$.

The following examples illustrate situations which can be modelled using random variables with uniform distributions.

Example 1

A card is chosen at random from a standard 52-card deck. The suit and face value of the card is noted. A sample space S for this experiment consists of 52 equally likely outcomes. Each outcome corresponds to a particular card. Define two different random variables on S that have uniform distributions.

Solution

Two possibilities follow.
Let Y be the random variable with range {1, 2, 3, 4}. If the card chosen is a club, Y maps that outcome to 1. If the card is a diamond, Y maps the outcome to 2. If the card is a heart, Y maps the outcome to 3. If the card is a spade, Y maps the outcome to 4.
There are 13 cards in each suit.

$$P(Y = 1) = P(Y = 2) = P(Y = 3) = P(Y = 4) = \frac{13}{52} = \frac{1}{4}.$$

Therefore, Y has a uniform distribution.

Let Z be the random variable with range $\{1, 2 \ldots, 13\}$. Z maps each card to its face value with $Z(\text{ace}) = 1$; $Z(\text{jack}) = 11$; $Z(\text{queen}) = 12$; and $Z(\text{king}) = 13$. There are 4 cards of each face value.

$P(Z = k) = \dfrac{4}{52} = \dfrac{1}{13}$ for $k = 1, 2, \ldots, 13$.

Therefore, Z has a uniform distribution. ■

Example 2
A perfect icosahedral die has 20 faces. Each face is an equilateral triangle congruent to each of the other faces. The number 0 is on two of the faces, the number 1 on another two faces and so on up to the number 9. The die is rolled and the number on the up face is noted.
Show that this experiment can be modelled by a random variable with a uniform distribution.

Solution
Let U be the random variable which maps each roll to the number observed on the up face. The range of U is $\{0, 1, \ldots, 9\}$. There are 20 equally likely outcomes in the sample space and U takes a particular value for exactly two of those outcomes.

Therefore, $P(U = k) = \dfrac{2}{20} = \dfrac{1}{10}$ for $k = 0, 1, \ldots, 9$. ■

Example 3
Twenty raffle tickets numbered 1 through 20 are placed in a hat. The winning ticket is drawn from the hat.
What is the probability that a ticket with a particular number from 1 to 20 on it will win?

Solution
This is a situation which could be modelled by a uniform distribution. There are 20 equally likely outcomes for the experiment. The probability of each simple event is $\dfrac{1}{20}$. The random variable V simply maps each possible draw of a ticket to the number on the ticket. ■

Notice that it is *not* essential that the tickets be numbered *consecutively* from 1. It *is* essential, in order to have a uniform distribution, that each ticket have a different number on it.

Example 4   A school has 90 students enrolled in a grade 12 mathematics course. There are five sections of the course. The following table shows the enrollment for each section.

Section	A	B	C	D	E
Number of students	18	18	18	18	18

A Math 12 student is selected at random and her section is noted. Show that this situation can be modelled by a uniform distribution.

Solution   Let W be the random variable which maps
A to 1; B to 2; C to 3; D to 4 and E to 5.
The probability of a randomly selected student belonging to a particular section is the relative frequency of students occurring in that section. Because the classes are all of the same size, the probability of a randomly selected student belonging to a particular section is $\dfrac{18}{90} = \dfrac{1}{5}$.

Then $P(W = 1) = P(W = 2) = P(W = 3) = P(W = 4) = P(W = 5) = \dfrac{1}{5}$. ■

Example 5   A cubic die is rolled and the number of dots on the up face is noted. A coin is flipped and it is noted whether it lands heads or tails. If the coin lands heads, you win a number of dollars equal to the number of dots showing on the die. If the coin lands tails, you lose a number of dollars equal to the dots showing on the die.
Model this game with the product of two random variables X and Y such that $X \times Y$ has a uniform distribution.

Solution X maps each roll of the die to the number of dots showing.
Y maps heads to 1 and tails to -1.
Then $X \times Y$ maps each compound experiment (play of the game) to your winnings for the game. For example, if a four is rolled and the coin lands tails, then $(X \times Y) = (4,\text{tails}) = 4 \times -1 = -4$.
Your winnings for that game is a loss of \$4.
The range of X is $\{-6, -5, -4, -3, -2, -1, 1, 2, 3, 4, 5, 6\}$ and

$P(X = k) = \dfrac{1}{12}$ for each value k in the range of X. ■

From the preceding examples you can find some general conditions for situations which can be modelled by uniform distributions.

- If S is a sample space on an experiment with n equally likely outcomes $\{x_1, x_2, \ldots, x_n\}$ then define the random variable U on S by $U(x_i) = i$ for $i = 1, \ldots, n$. Then U has the uniform probability distribution

$$f(i) = P(U = i) = \frac{1}{n} \text{ for } i = 1, \ldots, n.$$

- If S is divided into k events $E_1, E_2, \ldots, E_k$ such that the events are mutually exclusive and S equals the union of the events, and $n(E_1) = n(E_2) = \ldots n(E_k)$, then define the random variable V on S by $V(x_i) = j$ if the outcome x_i is in the event E_j.

Then V has a uniform distribution $f(j) = P(V = j) = \frac{1}{k}$ for $j = 1, \ldots, k$.

- If a probability distribution is based on relative frequencies and the relative frequencies for all the possible observations are the same, then the distribution is uniform.

- If two experiments A and B are independent and have uniform distributions such that each outcome in A has probability $\frac{1}{n}$ and each outcome in B has probability $\frac{1}{m}$, then there is a distribution for the compound experiment, A and B, such that each outcome has a probability of $\frac{1}{(n \times m)}$.

PROPERTY

If X is a random variable with range $\{x_1, x_2, \ldots, x_n\}$ and X has a uniform probability distribution f, then $f(x_i) = \frac{1}{n}$ for $i = 1, 2, \ldots, n$ and the expected value of X is $E(X) = \frac{1}{n}(x_1 + x_2 + \ldots + x_n)$.

Example 6

Use the uniform distribution in Example 3 to determine the probability that the ticket drawn will have a single digit number.

Solution

The probability of choosing any particular number is $\frac{1}{20}$.

Nine of these numbers are single digit numbers.

Therefore, the probability of drawing a ticket with a single digit number is

$$9 \times \left(\frac{1}{20}\right) = \frac{9}{20}. \quad \blacksquare$$

Example 7   Use the uniform distribution in Example 2 for rolling a number with an icosahedral die.

a) Calculate the probability that a prime number will be rolled.

b) Find the expected value of the random variable U. Give an interpretation to this value.

Solution   a) Each number $\{0, 1, 2, \ldots, 9\}$ has the probability of $\frac{1}{10}$ of appearing on any roll. There are four single digit primes, $\{2, 3, 5, 7\}$.

Therefore, there is a probability of $4 \times \left(\frac{1}{10}\right) = \frac{2}{5}$

of rolling a prime number.

b) The range of U is $\{0, 1, 2, \ldots, 9\}$.

Therefore, $E(U) = \frac{1}{10}(0 + 1 + \ldots + 9) = 4.5$.

If the die were rolled a great many times and the arithmetic average of the numbers showing on each roll were calculated, the average would be very close to 4.5. ■

Example 8   a) Use the uniform distribution for the game described in Example 5, to calculate the probability of winning more than \$3 in any play of the game.

b) Use the expected value of $X \times Y$ to predict the average amount you would win or lose per game if you played the game many times.

Solution   a) The range of $X \times Y$ has 12 elements.

$P((X \times Y) > 3) = P((X \times Y) = 4) + P((X \times Y) = 5) + P((X \times Y) = 6)$

$$= 3 \times \frac{1}{12}$$

$$= \frac{1}{4}.$$

There is a 25% chance of winning more than \$3 on any particular play of the game.

b) $E(X \times Y) = \frac{1}{12}(-6 + -5 + \ldots + -1 + 1 + \ldots + 6) = 0.$

Over many games, your winnings per game would average \$0. That is, in the long run you would break even. ■

7.3 Exercises

1. The aces and face cards are removed from a standard 52-card deck. Then a card is randomly selected from the remaining cards. The random variable X maps each possible draw of a card to its face value.
   a) What is the range of X?
   b) Find $P(X = 6)$.
   c) Use a table to list the probability distribution of X to show that the distribution is uniform.
   d) Calculate $E(X)$.

2. U is a random variable with a uniform probability distribution. The range of U is $\{2, 3, 5, 7, 9, 11, 13\}$. Find the values of the following.
   a) $P(U = 11)$ c) $P(U > 9)$
   b) $P(U \leqslant 7)$ d) $E(U)$

3. There are twenty colored balls in a box. The colors are green, white, red and yellow. A ball is selected at random from the box. The random variable Y maps a green ball to 10, a white ball to 20, a red ball to 30 and a yellow ball to 40.
   Y has a uniform probability distribution.
   a) How many balls of each color are there?
   b) Find $P(Y = 20)$ and $P(Y \geqslant 20)$.

4. Suppose that the box in question 3 contains n balls and k colors $C_1, C_2, \ldots, C_k$ and the random variable T maps each possible selection of a ball from its color C_i to i. Specify the number of balls of each color in order to ensure that T has a uniform probability distribution.

5. A roulette wheel has 36 numbers (1 through 36) on which the ball can land. On any spin what is the probability that the ball will land on
   a) an even number?
   b) a prime number?
   c) a perfect square?
   d) a multiple of 3?

6. One million people were asked to name their favorite one-digit number. Let X be the random variable which maps each person asked to the number that the person chose.
   a) List the range of X.
   b) Assuming that X has a uniform probability distribution, list the distribution.
   c) Use the uniform distribution in b) to calculate $E(X)$.
   d) The average of all the numbers chosen was 6.4. Use this fact and the value $E(X)$ to show that the distribution of numbers chosen was not uniform.

7. A computer generates a three-digit number using a random number generator. That is, each three-digit number has the same likelihood of being generated as any other.
   a) Find the probability that the number generated is 235.
   b) Find the probability that the number generated consists of three identical digits.

8. A telephone number consists of a three-digit exchange number followed by four digits. A telephone advertising service has a computer programmed to telephone a particular exchange followed by four randomly selected digits.
   a) If your telephone number is in that exchange, what is the probability that a particular call will be made to your telephone number?
   b) If there are 3 500 telephones in service in the exchange, what is the probability that the computer will generate an in-service number?

9. An experiment has 10 equally likely outcomes represented by the sample space $S = \{a, b, c, d, e, f, g, h, i, j\}$. Define three different random variables on S such that each random variable has a uniform distribution.

10. A person is selected at random from a large population. The random variable S maps the person to the day of the year (numbered 1 through 365) on which the person was born.

a) If S has a uniform distribution, then what is the probability that a randomly chosen person will have a birthday in September? after December 25?

b) Do you think that, in fact, S does have a uniform distribution? Use the birth dates of your classmates to see if a uniform probability model is appropriate for this situation.

11. A pizza shop sells pizza with 30 different combinations of toppings. The combinations of toppings are numbered 1 through 30. A pizza is ordered using a randomly selected number. Only pizzas with order numbers 25 and greater have anchovies. All even numbered pizzas have pepperoni. Find the probability that the pizza ordered has

a) anchovies

b) anchovies and pepperoni

c) neither anchovies nor pepperoni

d) pepperoni, but no anchovies.

12. A coin is flipped. X is a random variable which maps heads to 1 and tails to 2. Z is a random variable which maps heads to 7 and tails to 11.
A die is rolled. The random variable Y maps each roll to the number of dots showing on the up face.

a) Show that the random variable $X \times Y$ does not have a uniform distribution.

b) Show that $Z \times Y$ does have a uniform distribution.

c) Does $Z + Y$ have a uniform distribution? Justify your answer.

d) Define a random variable T on the sample space {heads, tails} for the coin flip such that both $T \times Y$ and $T + Y$ have uniform distribution.

13. The random variable W has a uniform probability distribution function f. The range of W is $\{x_1, x_2, \ldots, x_n\}$. Use the definition of mathematical expectation,
$$E(W) = f(x_1) \times x_1 + \ldots + f(x_n) \times x_n$$
to prove that
$$E(W) = \frac{1}{n}(x_1 + x_2 + \ldots + x_n).$$

14. The random variable U has the range $\{1, 2, \ldots, n\}$ and has a uniform probability distribution. Prove that $E(U) = \dfrac{(n+1)}{2}$.
$$\left(\text{Use the fact that } 1 + 2 + \ldots + n = \frac{n(n+1)}{2}. \right)$$

15. During rush hours, from 07:00 to 09:30, the number of vehicles passing a particular intersection every half-hour was counted. 2600 vehicles went through the intersection during the $2\frac{1}{2}$ hours.
The results were tabulated.

Time	07:00 –07:30	07:30 –08:00	08:00 –08:30	08:30 –09:00	09:00 –09:30
Number of vehicles	n_1	n_2	n_3	n_4	n_5

The random variable T maps each vehicle to the half-hour $\{1, 2, 3, 4, 5\}$ during which it crossed the intersection. T has a uniform probability distribution.

a) Find the value of each of the n_i, $i = 1, \ldots, 5$.

b) Find the probability that a randomly selected vehicle passed through the intersection before 09:00.

c) Find the average time which the vehicles pass through the intersection.

d) Discuss why the probability distribution for T is uniform during rush hours. Would the distribution likely be uniform if the vehicles were counted during half-hour intervals throughout the day?

7.4 Binomial Experiments

A coin is flipped to see whether it lands heads or tails.

A multiple-choice question has five possible answers. The answer chosen is either correct or incorrect.

A widget is chosen from a bin of recently manufactured widgets. It is tested to see if it works. The widget is either defective or working.

A bag contains 10 red marbles and 20 black marbles. A single marble is chosen at random from the bag and its color is noted. The marble selected is either red or black.

Each of the preceding situations has exactly two possible outcomes. One outcome might be called "success" and the other outcome "failure". An experiment can be defined for each situation by repeating the action. Each repetition is called a trial of the experiment.

Example 1 shows how different experiments can be defined by repeated trials.

Example 1 A trial consists of flipping a fair coin. A success occurs when the coin lands heads. A failure occurs when the coin lands tails. The coin is flipped three times.

a) What is the probability of a success on the third flip?

b) What is the probability of successes on the first two flips?

c) What is the probability that there will be exactly two successes in the experiment?

Solution a) The probability of a fair coin landing heads on any flip of the coin is $\frac{1}{2}$. Therefore the probability of a "success" on the third flip is also $\frac{1}{2}$.

b) The trials are independent. Therefore, the probability of success on the first and second flips is the product of the probability of success on the first flip and the probability of success on the second flip.

Probability of success on the first two flips is $\frac{1}{2} \times \frac{1}{2} = \frac{1}{4}$.

c) There are eight possible outcomes for this experiment, {(HHH), (HHT), (HTH), (HTT), (THH), (THT), (TTH), (TTT)}. Three of the outcomes belong to the event "exactly two of the three flips were successful".

Therefore the probability of exactly two successes in three flips is $\frac{3}{8}$. ∎

Each of the three experiments described in Example 1 has the following characteristics.

1. Each trial has exactly two outcomes, "success" and "failure".

2. Each trial is independent of any other trial of the experiment, that is, the probabilities of "success" and "failure" in any trial are unaffected by the results of any other trial.

3. The number of trials (three in this case) is specified.

4. The probability of a "success" in each trial and a "failure" in each trial remains the same for each trial.

Any experiment which has these four characteristics is called a **Bernoulli experiment** or a **binomial experiment**. The Swiss mathematician Jakob Bernoulli (1654—1705) was one of the first to work on probability. The calculation of probabilities in such experiments is closely linked to the binomial theorem which you studied in chapter 5.
This relationship will be explored in the next section.

Example 2   Model each of the following situations using a binomial experiment. Specify an individual trial of the experiment, the number of trials n, the probability of success p, and of failure $q = 1 - p$, in any trial.

a) A game consists of rolling a cubic die ten times and noting the number of dots of the up face each time. You win on a roll if you roll a 1 or a 6. Otherwise you lose. The number of times that you win in a single game is noted.

b) A stand of 300 trees is infested by a type of insect. There is a 75% chance that an infested tree will die. The number of trees that survive the infestation is noted.

c) In a coin laundry a machine dryer will completely dry its load of clothes 95% of the time. On a particular day, the dryer is used for 16 loads of clothing. The number of loads that are completely dried is noted.

Solution   a) Each roll of the die is a trial. There are 10 rolls, so that $n = 10$. On each roll the probability of success (a win) is $p = \dfrac{2}{6} = \dfrac{1}{3}$.
Therefore the probability of failure on any roll is $q = 1 - \dfrac{1}{3} = \dfrac{2}{3}$.

b) Each tree's success in surviving the insects is a trial. There are 300 trees so that $n = 300$. If success is defined as surviving, then the probability of not surviving is $q = 0.75$.
Therefore, the probability of success is $p = 1 - 0.75 = 0.25$.

c) Each load of wash is a trial. Therefore, $n = 16$. If success is defined as a load of wash being completely dried, then $p = 0.95$. Therefore the probability of a load being not completely dried is $q = 1 - 0.95 = 0.05$. ∎

The following examples look at situations which can be modelled by experiments that are similar to binomial experiments, but fail to meet all four of the requirements.

Example 3 A multiple-choice question has five possible answers. The answer chosen is either correct or incorrect. A student answers four questions. On three of the questions the student guesses the answer randomly among the five possible responses. On the fourth question, the student knows that two of the responses are incorrect. The student guesses an answer from among the remaining three responses.

a) Explain why this situation is modelled by an experiment which is not a binomial experiment.

b) Modify the situation so that it can be modelled by a binomial experiment.

Solution a) The probability of the student randomly guessing the correct answer for the first three questions is $\frac{1}{5}$. However, by eliminating two of the responses from question 4, the student has increased the probability of guessing the right answer to $\frac{1}{3}$. If each question is considered a trial in an experiment, then the experiment is not a binomial experiment because the probability of success in each trial is not identical to those in the other trials.

b) The multiple choice test becomes a binomial experiment if each answer is chosen completely randomly. ■

Example 4 A widget is chosen from a bin of recently manufactured widgets. The widget is tested to see if it works. The widget is either defective or working. Widgets are selected from the bin and tested until a defective widget is found, or ten widgets have been tested.

a) Explain why this situation is modelled by an experiment which is not a binomial experiment.

b) Modify the situation so that it can be modelled by a binomial experiment.

Solution a) The experiment with the widgets does not have a specified number of trials. The experiment has a maximum of 10 trials, but may well end with fewer trials if a defective widget is found.

b) The widget experiment will be binomial if the probability of choosing a defective widget remains constant throughout the testing, *and* if it is specified that exactly ten widgets are tested. ■

Example 5   A bag contains 10 red marbles and 20 black marbles. A single marble is chosen at random from the bag and its color is noted. Without replacing the marble, another one is chosen. Six marbles are chosen in this manner.

a) Explain why this situation is modelled by an experiment which is not a binomial experiment.

b) Modify the situation so that it can be modelled by a binomial experiment.

Solution   a) By not replacing the marble, the probability of success (red marble chosen) in any given trial is affected by the results of the preceding trials. For example, if a red marble was chosen on the first selection, then only nine red marbles remain in a bag of nineteen marbles. The probability of choosing a red marble on the second selection is $\frac{9}{19}$ rather than the probability of choosing a red marble on the first selection, which is $\frac{10}{30} = \frac{1}{3}$. The trials are not independent. Therefore, the experiment is not a binomial experiment.

b) The marble experiment will be binomial if the marble chosen at each selection is put back in the bag before the next selection.   ■

Example 6   A bag contains 10 red marbles, 10 black marbles and 10 white marbles. A single marble is chosen at random from the bag and its color is noted. The marble is replaced and another selection is made. Six marbles are chosen in this manner and the number of each color chosen is noted.

a) Explain why this situation is modelled by an experiment which is not a binomial experiment.

b) Modify the situation so that it can be modelled by a binomial experiment.

Solution   a) Because the marble is replaced after each selection, the trials are independent. The probability of choosing a particular color on any given selection is always $\frac{10}{30} = \frac{1}{3}$. Each trial has *three* possible outcomes, however, rather than the *two* specified in the characteristics of a binomial experiment.

b) The marble experiment will be binomial if selecting a white marble is defined as success for each trial, and failure is the selection of a red or black marble.   ■

7.4 Exercises

1. Model each of the following situations using a binomial experiment.
For each experiment, specify
an individual trial;
the number of trials n;
the probability of success p, and of failure q, for any given trial.

   a) Livestock recover from a particular disease 40% of the time. A herd of 50 animals contract the disease. The number of animals which recover is noted.

   b) A basketball player makes 82% of her free throws. In a game, she has 12 free throws. The number of points she scored is noted.

   c) There are 35 defective computer chips for every 1000 made in a factory. A batch of 200 contains a number of defective chips, which is recorded.

   d) A salesperson notes that he is able to make sales to 20 out of every 100 potential customers with whom he speaks. The number of sales he makes, in talking with 10 potential customers, is noted.

   e) A pair of cubic dice is rolled and the total number of dots shown on the two up faces is noted. You win if 10 dots are showing. The number of wins in 100 rolls is recorded.

   f) A test consists of 20 TRUE-FALSE items. The response for each question is guessed. The number of correct responses is tallied.

   g) A poll indicates that at a particular time, 38% of Canada's voters preferred the NDP, 32% preferred the Liberals and 30% preferred the Conservatives. Eighty voters chosen at random are polled. The number of voters who prefer the NDP is recorded.

2. Explain why each of the following situations described below is modelled by an experiment which is not a binomial experiment.

   a) A cubic die is rolled. If the number of dots showing on the up face is even, you win $1 for each dot. If the number of dots is odd, you lose $1 for each dot. The amount of money won (or lost) after five rolls is recorded.

   b) Five cards are dealt from a well shuffled deck. The number of spades occurring in the five cards is noted.

   c) A tennis player in a tournament plays five matches. The probability of winning the first match is 0.5. If the player wins, the probability of his winning the next match increases by 0.05. If the player loses, the probability of his winning the next match decreases by 0.05. The number of matches the player wins at the tournament is noted.

   d) A brown-eyed father and a green-eyed mother have a 25% chance of having a green-eyed child. The parents have children until one is green-eyed. The number of children that the parents have is noted.

   e) A stretch of road has four traffic lights. The probability of encountering a red light at the first and third intersections is 0.6 and the probability of encountering a red light at the second and fourth intersections is 0.7. The road is driven and the number of red lights encountered is observed.

3. Modify each of the situations described in question 2 so that each one can be modelled by a binomial experiment.

MAKING

Probability in Insurance

Life is full of risks. People try to protect themselves and their families from situations involving risk, that is, situations in which losses can occur. One method of protection from financial losses that might result from accident, death, fire, or loss of a job is to buy insurance. For example, different types of coverage can insure an individual against the loss of a wage earner, additional medical expenses, the loss of a house due to fire, or damages arising from a car accident.

Insurance companies provide many types of protection. Individuals who want to be insured against particular kinds of losses make regular payments to an insurance company. In return the insurance company agrees to pay these people a sum of money if they suffer a loss. All people buying insurance share the costs of losses through their regular payments. Even if they never suffer a loss, and therefore do not receive any money from the insurance company, these people have been afforded a feeling of security.

In order for insurance companies to make a profit, after paying clients for losses and meeting administrative costs, they must be able to predict the likelihood that an insured person will suffer a loss. Probability plays an important role in the accuracy of this prediction.

AUTO INSURANCE

One common form of protection is automobile insurance. This table contains information about Canadian accident statistics compiled between 1981 and 1983.

Group (age in years)	Number of Claims per 100 Cars	Average Claim Cost (Property and Bodily Injury)
Males (unmarried)		
18 and under	22.49	$3249
19-20	15.47	$3533
21-22	11.61	$3625
23-24	9.52	$3454
Males (married)		
20 and under	14.97	$4035
21-24	8.80	$3009
Females		
20 and under	7.19	$2714
21-24	5.46	$2737
Male or Female		
25 and over	6.51	$2998

a) Which group of drivers is most likely to be involved in a car accident?

b) Which group is least likely to be involved in a car accident?

c) Why do you think married males are better insurance risks than unmarried males?

d) What might account for the smaller claims costs for unmarried males 18 and under as compared to unmarried males 21 to 22?

e) Does the fact that females have fewer claims mean that they are better drivers than males? Explain.

LIFE INSURANCE

Another common form of protection is life insurance. Life insurance companies must be able to predict how long a client might live before deciding the cost of his or her regular payments. Some of this information is found in mortality tables. This sample table for males is based on statistics gathered between 1958 and 1964 from American, British, and Canadian insurance company records.
(The table begins with 1 000 000 male births.)

Age Group (years)	Number Living through 10-year Period	Deaths in 10-year Period	Deaths per 1000 People
0-9	992 014	7 986	7.99
10-19	986 761	5 253	5.25
20-29	976 596	10 163	10.17
30-39	965 472	11 124	11.12
40-49	936 750	28 722	28.72
50-59	860 201	76 549	76.55
60-69	676 273	183 928	183.93
70-79	376 636	299 637	299.64
80-89	92 516	284 120	284.12
90-99	4 120	88 396	88.40
100-110	0	4 120	4.12

a) Calculate the probability that a male will live through his teens.

b) Calculate the probability of a male living to be 100.

c) What percentage of the male population live to be octogenarians?

d) What might account for a higher death rate in the first 10 years of life as compared to the second 10 years of life?

e) What do you think is the biggest cause of death for males in their twenties, sickness or accident?

7.5 Binomial Distributions

In the last section, properties of a binomial experiment were listed.
A binomial experiment consists of n independent trials.
Each trial has exactly two outcomes labelled "success" and "failure".
The probability of success p and the probability of failure $q = 1 - p$
remains the same for each trial.

Each binomial experiment has associated with it a very natural random
variable. This random variable maps each occurrence of the experiment to
the number of successes which occur. If a binomial experiment consists of
n trials, then the range of the random variable would be $\{0, 1, 2, \ldots, n\}$.

For example, consider the binomial experiment in which a fair coin was
flipped three times. For each flip, *heads* was designated to be a success and
tails a failure. The number of trials is three. Let S map each possible
outcome of the experiment to the number of successes (*heads*) which occur.
Then S is a random variable with a range of $\{0, 1, 2, 3\}$.

Associated with the random variable S is the following
probability distribution.

$x \in$ Range (S)	0	1	2	3
$P(S = x)$	$\dfrac{1}{8}$	$\dfrac{3}{8}$	$\dfrac{3}{8}$	$\dfrac{1}{8}$

S is a random variable defined on a binomial experiment. Because of this,
the probability distribution associated with S is known as a
binomial distribution.

DEFINITION

Given a binomial experiment which consist of n trials, let S be the random
variable which maps each possible outcome of the experiment to the
number of successes which occur. Then S is a binomial random variable
and the probability distribution associated with S is a binomial
distribution.

A notation commonly used with binomial distributions to indicate the
probability of exactly x successes in n trials where the probability of
success in each trial is p is $b(x;n,p)$.
If S is the binomial random variable for a binomial experiment
with n trials and probability of success p for each trial,
then $b(x;n,p) = P(S = x)$.

For the coin flipping experiment, $n = 3$, $p = \dfrac{1}{2}$ and $q = \dfrac{1}{2}$.

$P(S = 2)$ is the probability that exactly two heads will occur in three flips.

Then $b\left(2;3,\dfrac{1}{2}\right) = P(S = 2) = \dfrac{3}{8}$.

The $b(x;n,p)$ notation is useful because it identifies a probability calculation which is applicable to many seemingly different situations. For example, $b\left(2;3,\dfrac{1}{2}\right) = \dfrac{3}{8}$ is the probability of

- having exactly two heads in three flips of a fair coin
- exactly two of three children in a family being girls (assuming boys and girls occur with equal likelihood)
- answering two of three TRUE-FALSE questions correctly by guessing
- encountering two red traffic signals in a sequence of three traffic lights where there is a 50% chance of being stopped at any one signal.

As suggested in chapter 5 and again in the last section, the calculation of $b(x;n,p)$ is closely related to the binomial theorem.

Example 1

Calculate $b(3;5,0.6)$.

Solution

$b(3;5,0.6)$ is the probability of 3 successes in a binomial experiment consisting of 5 trials. The probability of success for each trial is 0.6, so that the probability of failure for any trial is $1 - 0.6 = 0.4$.

There are $2^5 = 32$ outcomes to the binomial experiment. Each outcome corresponds to a 5-tuple of the form, for example, (S,S,F,F,S), representing successes on the first, second and fifth trials and failures on the third and fourth trials.

Since the trials are independent, the probability of (S,S,F,F,S) occurring is $(0.6) \times (0.6) \times (0.4) \times (0.4) \times (0.6) = (0.6)^3 (0.4)^2$. Notice that this is the probability of any outcome of the experiment in which exactly three of the trials are successful (and consequently two of the trials are failures). (S,S,S,F,F) and (S,S,F,F,S) are different and hence, mutually exclusive events. The probability of (S,S,S,F,F) or (S,S,F,F,S) occurring is therefore the sum of these two probabilities, that is, $(0.6)^3(0.4)^2 + (0.6)^3(0.4)^2$.

The probability of three successes in five trials is going to be $k \times (0.6)^3(0.4)^2$ where k is the number of outcomes to the experiment in which exactly three successes occur. Each outcome which has exactly three successes can be represented by a string of three S's and two F's. From your work in chapter 1, you will recognize that the number of distinct ways of arranging three S's and two F's is $\dfrac{5!}{3!2!}$.

But $\dfrac{5!}{3!2!}$ is $C(5,3)$. Therefore, $k = C(5,3) = \dfrac{5!}{2!3!}$.

Therefore, $b(3;5,0.6) = C(5,3)(0.6)^3(0.4)^2 = 10 \times 0.216 \times 0.064 = 0.13824$. ∎

The method of Example 1 can be generalized to give the following result.

FORMULA

$b(x;n,p) = C(n,x) p^x q^{n-x}$, where $q = 1 - p$.

Example 2

A test consists of ten multiple choice questions each with five possible answers, of which only one is correct. If the response to each question is chosen by random guessing, then what is the probability that six of the answers chosen will be correct?

Solution

Model the situation by a binomial experiment. There are ten trials.

The probability of success on any trial is $\frac{1}{5} = 0.2$.

To find the probability of exactly six successes calculate $b(x;n,p)$ where $x = 6$, $n = 10$ and $p = 0.2$.

$b(6;10,0.2) = C(10,6)(0.2)^6(0.8)^4 = 210 \times 0.000064 \times 0.4096 \doteq 0.0055$.

There is a probability of less than 0.6% of guessing six questions correctly. ■

Example 3

A particular disease is fatal to sheep, 20% of the time. If a flock of 12 sheep all contract this disease, what is the probability that exactly four of the sheep will die from the disease?

Solution

Model the situation by a binomial experiment in which "success" is defined as a sheep dying from the disease and "failure" is a sheep surviving.

There are 12 trials. In each trial, the probability of success is 0.2.

The probability that four sheep will die from the disease is given by $b(x;n,p)$ where $x = 4$, $n = 12$ and $p = 0.2$.

$b(4;12,0.2) = C(12,4)(0.2)^4(0.8)^8 = 495 \times 0.0016 \times 0.1678 \doteq 0.1329$, accurate to 4 significant figures.

There is a 13.3% chance (approximately) that exactly four of the sheep will die. ■

A binomial distribution is related to the binomial theorem in the following way. A binomial distribution is a listing of the probabilities $b(x;n,p)$ for $x = 0, 1, \ldots n$, where $b(x;n,p) = C(n,x)\, p^x q^{n-x}$.
From the binomial theorem the expansion of $(q + p)^n$ is

$$C(n,0)q^n + C(n,1)q^{n-1}p + C(n,2)q^{n-2}p^2 + \ldots + C(n,n-1)qp^{n-1} + C(n,n)p^n$$
$$= b(0;n,p) + b(1;n,p) \quad + b(2;n,p) \quad + \ldots + b(n-1;n,p) \quad + b(n;n,p)$$

where $q = 1 - p$.

Therefore, $b(x;n,p)$ is the $x + 1$st term of the expansion of $(q + p)^n$ where $q = 1 - p$

Example 4   A binomial experiment consists of five trials where the probability of success in any one trial is $\dfrac{1}{3}$.
List the binomial distribution associated with this experiment.

Solution   The binomial distribution matches each $x \in \{0, 1, 2, \ldots n\}$ with $b(x;n,p)$ where $n = 5$ and $p = \dfrac{1}{3}$.

To find each $b(x;n,p)$ expand $(q + p)^n$ where $q = 1 - p = \dfrac{2}{3}$.

Using the binomial theorem,

$$\left(\frac{2}{3} + \frac{1}{3}\right)^5$$

$$= \left(\frac{2}{3}\right)^5 + 5\left(\frac{2}{3}\right)^4\left(\frac{1}{3}\right) + 10\left(\frac{2}{3}\right)^3\left(\frac{1}{3}\right)^2 + 10\left(\frac{2}{3}\right)^2\left(\frac{1}{3}\right)^3 + 5\left(\frac{2}{3}\right)\left(\frac{1}{3}\right)^4 + \left(\frac{1}{3}\right)^5$$

$$= \frac{32}{243} + \frac{80}{243} + \frac{80}{243} + \frac{40}{243} + \frac{10}{243} + \frac{1}{243}$$

The probability distribution is

x	0	1	2	3	4	5
$b\left(x;5,\dfrac{1}{3}\right)$	$\dfrac{32}{243}$	$\dfrac{80}{243}$	$\dfrac{80}{243}$	$\dfrac{40}{243}$	$\dfrac{10}{243}$	$\dfrac{1}{243}$

Example 5   A bag contains 10 red marbles and 20 black marbles. A marble is chosen at random from the bag, its color is noted and then it is returned to the bag. This process is repeated five times. Find the probability of each of the following. Make your answer accurate to 4 significant figures.

a) selecting a red marble exactly three of the five times

b) selecting a red marble less than three of the five times

c) selecting a red marble four or more times

d) selecting a red marble less than four times

Solution   The situation described can be modelled by a binomial experiment consisting of $n = 5$ trials. If selecting a red marble is designated a success, then $p = \dfrac{10}{30} = \dfrac{1}{3}$ and $q = 1 - p = \dfrac{2}{3}$. The binomial distribution for this experiment was tabulated in Example 4.

a) The probability of selecting a red marble exactly three times is
$$P(\text{red} = 3) = b\left(3;5,\frac{1}{3}\right) = \frac{40}{243} \doteq 0.1646.$$

b) The probability of selecting a red marble less than three times is the probability of selecting a red marble no times, once, or twice.
$$P(\text{red} < 3) = b\left(0;5,\frac{1}{3}\right) + b\left(1;5,\frac{1}{3}\right) + b\left(2;5,\frac{1}{3}\right)$$
$$= \frac{32}{243} + \frac{80}{243} + \frac{80}{243} = \frac{192}{243} \doteq 0.7901.$$

c) The probability of selecting a red marble four or more times is
$$P(\text{red} \geqslant 4) = b\left(4;5,\frac{1}{3}\right) + b\left(5;5,\frac{1}{3}\right)$$
$$= \frac{10}{243} + \frac{1}{243} = \frac{11}{243} \doteq 0.0453.$$

d) The probability of selecting a red marble less than four times is the complement of the probability of selecting a red marble four or more times, that is,
$$P(\text{red} < 4) = 1 - P(\text{red} \geqslant 4).$$
From part c), $P(\text{red} \geqslant 4) = \dfrac{11}{243}$ so that
$$P(\text{red} < 4) = 1 - \frac{11}{243} \doteq 0.9547. \quad \blacksquare$$

Example 6   In a computer chip factory, 35 out of every 1000 chips produced are defective. A batch of 20 chips is chosen at random. What is the probability that at most 10% of the chosen chips are defective?

Solution   Model the situation by a binomial experiment. There are 20 trials ($n = 20$). If choosing a defective chip is defined as success, $p = \dfrac{35}{1000} = 0.035$.

Therefore, $q = 1 - p = 0.965$.

10% of 20 is 2. The probability that at most two of the twenty chips are defective is

$b(0;20,0.035) + b(1;20,0.035) + b(2;20,0.035)$
$= C(20,0)(0.965)^{20} + C(20,1)(0.035)(0.965)^{19} + C(20,2)(0.035)^2(0.965)^{18}$
$\doteq 0.9687$.

There is about a 97% chance that a randomly selected batch of twenty chips will have two or fewer defective chips.   ■

Example 7   A salesperson estimated that she is able to make a sale to 40% of the people to whom she makes a presentation. She makes a presentation to eight people. Which is greater, the probability that she will sell to all of the people in the group or the probability that she will sell to none of the group?

Solution   Model the situation by a binomial experiment. Each person is a trial so that $n = 8$. The probability of success (making a sale) for each trial is $p = 0.4$.

Then the probability of selling to all the people is
$b(8;8,0.4) = C(8,8)(0.4)^8 \doteq 0.000\ 6554$.
The probability of selling to none of the group is
$b(0;8,0.4) = C(8,0)(0.6)^8 \doteq 0.016\ 7962$.
$0.016\ 7962 \div 0.000\ 6554 \doteq 25.63$.

The probability of selling to none of the group is about 26 times greater than the probability of selling to all of the group, but both probabilities are small.   ■

7.5 Exercises

1. Evaluate each of the following.

a) $b\left(3;5,\dfrac{1}{2}\right)$

c) $b\left(2;6,\dfrac{3}{5}\right)$

b) $b\left(9;10,\dfrac{1}{4}\right)$

d) $b(3;8,0.01)$

2. Each of the following probabilities can be calculated using $b(x;n,p)$. In each case, identify the value of x, n and p which is to be used.

a) What is the probability of exactly three heads occurring in four flips of a fair coin?

b) A card is drawn from a standard 52-card deck and its suit noted. The card is returned to the deck and the deck is reshuffled. This is done ten times. What is the probability that five of the cards will be hearts?

c) A bag contains 12 red marbles and 6 green marbles. A marble is drawn from the bag, its color noted and returned to the bag. What is the probability of the marble being red on six draws in a row?

d) A test consists of 20 multiple-choice questions, each with 5 responses. If you guess randomly on each question, what is the probability of guessing exactly four of the correct answers?

e) In a soft-drink bottling plant, 90% of the 250 ml bottles contain more than 240 ml of pop. Six bottles of pop are chosen at random to make up a case. What is the probability that none of the bottles will contain 240 ml or less?

f) An airplane has four jet turbine engines. In flight, the probability of any single engine failing is 0.0001. What is the probability of exactly three of the engines failing while the plane is in flight?

g) There is a 98% chance that any patient will recover from a certain disease if he is given a particular medical treatment. Otherwise, the patient will remain ill. Fifty patients undergo the treatment. What is the probability that exactly five of these patients will not recover?

3. Calculate each of the probabilities in question 2.

4. A binomial experiment consists of 12 trials with a probability of success of 0.2 for each trial. B is the random variable which maps each possible outcome of the experiment to the number of successes in the 12 trials. Calculate the following.

a) $P(B = 1)$

c) $P(B < 10)$

b) $P(B \leqslant 2)$

d) $P(0 \leqslant B < 3)$

5. A binomial experiment consists of seven trials. The probability of success on each trial is 0.2. B is the random variable which maps each possible outcome of the experiment to the number of successes in the seven trials. Use the expansion of $(0.8 + 0.2)^7$ to list the probability distribution of B.

6. A family with five children is selected at random. Assuming male children and female children occur with equal likelihood, find the probabilities of each of the following.

a) Four of the children are girls.

b) At least two of the children are boys.

c) Two or three of the children are girls.

7. There is a 10% chance of earning an A in a particular mathematics course. Seven students taking the course are randomly chosen. Find the probabilities of each of the following.

a) All seven students will earn grades lower than A.

b) At most two of the students will earn an A in the course.

c) Exactly one student will not earn an A in the course.

d) More than two students will earn an A in the course.

8. A deck of ESP cards is used by psychologists to test for extra-sensory perception. The deck consists of five cards, each with a different symbol. In a particular experiment, a person was asked to identify, without seeing it, the symbol on a card drawn from the deck. The card was then returned to the deck and the procedure was repeated 20 times. The person correctly identified the symbol on the dealt card 16 times out of 20.
   a) Calculate the probability of 16 or more correct identifications if the person guessed randomly.
   b) What does the probability calculated in part a) suggest?

9. A certain surgical operation on the knee is known to be successful 95% of the time. Twelve people have this operation.
   a) What is the probability that the operation will be successful in all twelve cases?
   b) What is the probability of at least one of the operations being unsuccessful?

10. At a roller skate factory it is known that 15 out of every 500 roller skates produced will have defective ball bearings. For every truckload of roller skates shipped from the factory, 20 randomly selected roller skates are tested for defective ball bearings. If none of the roller skates tested are found to be defective, the truckload is shipped. If any of the skates are found to be defective, all of the skates in the truckload are inspected.
    a) Find the probability that none of the roller skates in a random sample of 20 will be found defective.
    b) Find the probability that none of the roller skates will be found defective in a random sample of 50 skates.

11. A baseball player has a batting average of 0.300. Assume that this indicates that each time he comes to bat, there is a 30% chance that he will make a safe hit. In each game the player comes to bat six times.
    a) What are the possible number of safe hits that the player might have in this game?
    b) Let B be the binomial random variable which maps each possible game for the batter to the number of safe hits made in the game. List the probability distribution for the random variable B.
    c) Which value of B (number of safe hits) in the distribution has the greatest probability?

12. a) Calculate the expected value of B,
$$E(B) = \Sigma\ (x_i \times P(B = x_i))$$
$$= \Sigma\ (x_i \times b(x_i;6,0.3))$$
Compare this result with that of part c) in question 11.
    b) B is a binomial random variable with $n = 6$ trials and $p = 0.3$ probability of success on each trial. Compare $E(B)$ with the product np.
    c) B is a binomial random variable with n trials. Each trial has a probability p of success. Prove that the expected value of B, $E(B) = \Sigma\ x_i \times P(B = x_i)$
$$= \Sigma\ x_i \times b(x_i;n,p),$$
is equal to the product np.
(Hint: You may assume that $k \times C(n,k) = n \times C(n-1,k-1)$ for $k = 1, 2, 3, \ldots n$)

13. A poll indicated that 35% of the voters in Canada preferred the current party in office to the opposition party. Twenty Canadians are interviewed.
    a) What is the most likely number of the twenty to support the government? (Use the results of question 12).
    b) Calculate the probability that exactly half of the group support the government.

In Search of the Poisson Distribution

A binomial experiment is repeated 1000 times. There is a 1% chance of success in any one trial. Calculate the probability of exactly three successes in 1000 trials.

This is a straightforward problem which can be solved using a binomial distribution.

The probability of exactly three successes in the binomial experiment described is $b(3;1000,0.01) = C(1000,3) \times (0.01)^3 \times (0.99)^{997}$. It is possible to calculate the probability as approximately 0.00739.

In 1837 the French mathematician Simeon-Denis Poisson published a paper which introduced a probability distribution function now known as the **Poisson distribution**. This distribution has many uses, particularly in the statistical study of phenomena involving a large number of events such as traffic accidents, insurance mortality tables, radioactive decay and the number of telephone calls through a particular exchange.

The Poisson distribution can also be used to approximate binomial distributions where the value of n is large and the value of p is small.

PROPERTY

If np is of moderate size, then $b(x;n,p)$ can be approximated by the Poisson distribution $\dfrac{e^{-M}M^x}{x!}$ where M is the product np and e is the irrational number $e \doteq 2.71828$.

Example Use the Poisson distribution to approximate $b(3;1000,0.01)$.

Solution $M = np = 1000 \times 0.01 = 10$

$\therefore b(3;1000,0.01) = \dfrac{e^{-10} \times 10^3}{3!} \doteq 0.00757$.

This approximation is less than 0.0002 different from the value calculated above for $b(3;1000,0.01)$. ∎

Activities

1. Use the Poisson distribution to approximate the following.
   a) $b(6;5000,0.002)$ b) $b(5;200,0.03)$
2. Use the approximations from question 1 to answer the following.
   a) Insurance mortality tables indicate that there is a probability of 0.002 that a person at a particular age will die. If the company has 5000 policies issued to people of that age, what is the probability that exactly six claims will be made by that group in a year?
   b) 3% of all the canned goods on the shelves of a supermarket are spoiled. 200 cans are chosen at random and inspected for spoilage. What is the probability that five of the cans chosen will be spoiled?

7.6 Hypergeometric Variables

A class consists of 15 boys and 25 girls. A group of eight students is randomly selected from the class. What is the probability that five of the eight students will be girls?

The probability model used to determine the likelihood of five girls being chosen is similar to that of a binomial experiment. As the following shows, the model differs from that of a binomial experiment in one important respect.

Let a trial be the selection of a student from the class. Each such trial has two outcomes, "a girl is selected" and "a boy is selected".
The experiment consists of eight trials.
Success for an individual trial is defined as "a girl is selected".
The problem asks for the probability of five successes in eight trials.

The experiment is not binomial, however, because the trials are not independent. That is, the probability of selecting a girl in a trial is affected by the selections in previous trials. Such a model is called a **hypergeometric model.**

A hypergeometric model differs from a binomial model in that the probability of success differs from trial to trial. In a binomial model, the probability of success is the same for each trial.

The probability of selecting a girl on the first trial is $\frac{25}{40} = \frac{5}{8}$.

If a girl is chosen for the first selection, the probability of choosing a girl on the second selection is $\frac{24}{39}$. If a boy is chosen for the first selection,

the probability of choosing a girl on the second selection is $\frac{25}{39}$.

The probability of success in a trial depends on the results of the preceding trials.

The class is a set consisting of two different kinds of objects, boys and girls. Eight objects (students) are selected from this set randomly. This selection may be thought of as happening all at once or as eight selections of individuals from the class where the students, once chosen, are not returned to the class.
This is known as *random selection without replacement*.

A sample space S for the experiment is the set of all possible groups of eight which may be selected from the class. Let H be the random variable which maps each possible group of eight students to the number of girls in that group. The range of H is {0, 1, 2, 3, 4, 5, 6, 7, 8}.
H is an example of a **hypergeometric random variable.**

DEFINITION

Consider a set of objects in which each object is one of two types, say white or black. The set has $a + b$ objects where a is the number of white objects and b is the number of black objects. Let S be the sample space consisting all possible selections of n objects ($n < a + b$) from the set. Let H be the random variable which maps each n-tuple in S to the number of white objects in the n-tuple. Then H is a hypergeometric random variable.

Some care must be taken in establishing the range of a hypergeometric random variable.

Example 1   Six marbles are randomly selected, *without replacement*, from a bag containing eight white marbles and two black marbles.

a) What is the range of the hypergeometric random variable H_1 which maps each selection of six marbles to the number of black marbles in the selection?

b) What is the range of the hypergeometric random variable H_2 which maps each selection of six marbles to the number of white marbles in the selection?

Solution   a) Since each selection can have at most two black marbles, a selection may have 0, 1 or 2 black marbles.
Range $(H_1) = \{0, 1, 2\}$

b) Since any selection of six marbles can have at most two black marbles, each selection must have at least four white marbles.
Range $(H_2) = \{4, 5, 6\}$ ■

Example 2   In a widget plant, 5% of the widgets made are defective. In a production run of 1000 widgets, 100 widgets are randomly selected and tested.

a) Describe a random variable H which would answer the question "How many of the widgets tested were defective?".

b) List the range of the random variable described in part a).

Solution   a) Let H be the hypergeometric random variable which maps each possible selection of 100 widgets to the number of defective widgets in that selection.

b) Of the 1000 widgets, 5% × 1000 = 50 widgets are defective. Therefore, in a sample of 100 widgets you can have at most 50 defective widgets. Therefore, range $(H) = \{0, 1, \ldots, 50\}$.   ■
The following examples further illustrate the characteristics of situations which can be modelled by a hypergeometric random variable.

Example 3   Five cards are dealt from a shuffled deck. The number of cards of each suit is noted.

a) Explain why this situation can not be modelled by a hypergeometric random variable.

b) Modify the situation so that a hypergeometric random variable would be an appropriate model.

Solution   **a)** The collection from which the objects are selected (the deck of cards) consists of four kinds of objects (hearts, spades, diamonds, clubs) rather than the two kinds specified for a hypergeometric random variable.

b) Specify two kinds of objects for the original set of objects. For example, the deck of cards consists of hearts and non-hearts. Note the number of hearts in a five-card hand.   ■

Example 4   One hundred people are telephoned and asked whether they like or dislike a particular television show. There is no provision to ensure that the same person is not phoned twice. The number of people polled who answer that they like the show is noted.

a) Explain why this situation can not be modelled by a hypergeometric random variable.

b) Modify the situation so that a hypergeometric random variable would be an appropriate model.

Solution   **a)** Because there is the possibility that a person might be asked her/his opinion more than once, the random selection of opinions is not without replacement.

b) Ensure that each person is telephoned at most once. The selection of opinions is then without replacement, since once an opinion is taken out of the 'pool of opinions', it is not returned to be chosen again.   ■

Example 5   People are telephoned and asked whether they like or dislike a television show. No person is telephoned twice. The number of people who must be polled until 100 people indicate that they like the show is noted.

a) Explain why this situation can not be modelled by a hypergeometric random variable.

b) Modify the situation so that a hypergeometric random variable would be an appropriate model.

Solution   **a)** A hypergeometric random variable is based on random selections of a specified number of objects. The number of people who must be telephoned is at least 100, but the maximum number of telephone calls to be made is indefinite.

b) Specify the number of telephone calls to be made. The observation must be altered to note the number of people polled who like the show.   ■

7.6 Exercises

1. Describe a hypergeometric random variable which models each of the following situations.
   Identify the two kinds of objects being selected and the numbers *a* and *b* of each type.
   The choice of one kind of object is designated as success.
   Specify the range of the random variable.
   a) A bin of fruit contains four apples and eight oranges. Five pieces of fruit are randomly chosen from the bin. The number of apples in the selection is noted.
   b) A thirteen-card bridge hand is dealt from a shuffled 52-card deck. The number of spades in the hand is noted.
   c) A bag contains three red marbles, four blue marbles and five green marbles. Six marbles are randomly selected from the bag. The number of blue marbles selected is noted.
   d) A production run of 100 videotapes is known to have five defective tapes. Twenty of the 100 tapes are tested. The number of defective tapes is noted.
   e) In a box of 12 dozen heads of lettuce, eight of the heads are spoiled. A person randomly selects a dozen heads of lettuce from the box. The number of spoiled heads in the selection is noted.
   f) On a school basketball team of 11 women, four of the women measure over 1.7 m in height. Five of the players are chosen at random as a starting line-up. The number of women over 1.7 m tall in the line-up is noted.
   g) In a class of 50 students, 42 of them have driver's licences. Ten students are selected at random from the class. The number of those selected who have a driver's licence is noted.

2. Explain why it is not appropriate to model each of the following situations by a hypergeometric random variable.
   a) In a recent election there were two candidates for mayor. A village had 3000 registered voters. One hundred telephone calls were made, asking voters which candidate they preferred. No effort was made to ensure that a person was not polled more than once. The number of voters preferring candidate A was noted.
   b) In a high school timetable, at a particular time, the senior students had a choice of Mathematics, English, or Music. Of the 150 seniors, 25 were randomly selected. The number of students taking each subject was noted.
   c) Following the maxim "If at first you don't succeed, try, try again", Oscar reached into a drawer containing twenty different colored socks and randomly withdrew socks until he had a match for the single purple sock he had withdrawn on the first try. The number of socks he had to take out before getting another purple sock was counted.
   d) A bag contains six blue marbles and three yellow marbles. A marble is taken out, its color noted and it is returned to the bag. This is done four times. The number of yellow marbles selected is recorded.
   e) A class consists of 15 boys and 25 girls. Students are selected one at a time, at random, to form a committee. The selection continues until three girls have been chosen for the committee.

3. Modify each of the situations described in question 2 so that it would be appropriate to model the situation with a hypergeometric random variable.

7.7 Hypergeometric Distributions

The preceding section began with a probability problem in which a group of eight students was randomly selected from a class consisting of 15 boys and 25 girls. The question asked was "What is the probability that five of the eight students will be girls?"

If H is the hypergeometric random variable which maps each possible group of eight students to the number of girls in the group, then range $(H) = \{0, 1, 2, 3, 4, 5, 6, 7, 8\}$. Associated with each $x \in$ range (H) there is a probability $P(H = x)$.

The function that maps each $x \in$ range (H) to $P(H = x)$ is a hypergeometric probability distribution, or more simply, a **hypergeometric distribution**.

$P(H = 5)$ can be calculated by using the methods of chapter 1.
The number of possible groups of eight which can be chosen from the class of $15 + 25 = 40$ students is $C(40,8)$.
If a group of eight has five girls, then it must have three boys. There are $C(25,5)$ ways of choosing five girls from 25 and $C(15,3)$ ways of choosing three boys from 15. Therefore, there are $C(25,5) \times C(15,3)$ ways of choosing a group consisting of five girls and three boys.

The probability of having a group of five girls and three boys is the number such groups which can be chosen, divided by the total number of possible groups of eight.

Therefore, $P(H = 5) = \dfrac{C(25,5) \times C(15,3)}{C(40,8)} \doteq 0.3143$, to 4 significant figures.

This calculation can be generalized.

FORMULA

Let a set consist of a objects of type A and b objects of type B. Consider the random selection of n objects from this set.
If H is the hypergeometric random variable mapping each n-tuple to the number of type A objects in that n-tuple, then

$$P(H = x) = \dfrac{C(a,x) \times C(b,n - x)}{C(a + b,n)} \quad \text{for each } x \in \text{ range } (H).$$

Example 1
Five cards are dealt from a shuffled deck of 52 cards.
a) Calculate the probability that exactly three of the cards are aces.
b) Calculate the probability that all five cards are of the same suit.
c) Compare the probabilities found in parts a) and b).

Solution
a) The deck of cards consists of 4 aces and 48 non-aces. Let H be the random variable which 'counts' the number of aces in any selection of five cards. Then $a = 4$, $b = 48$, $n = 5$ and $x = 3$.

$$P(H = 3) = \frac{C(4,3) \times C(48,2)}{C(52,5)} = \frac{4512}{2598960} = 0.001\ 736.$$

The probability of exactly three of the five cards dealt being aces is about 0.0017.

b) The deck of cards consists of 13 spades and 39 non-spades. Let H be the random variable which 'counts' the number of spades in a five-card selection. Then $a = 13$, $b = 39$, $n = 5$, and $x = 5$.

$$P(H = 5) = \frac{C(13,5) \times C(39,0)}{C(52,5)} = \frac{1287}{2598960} = 0.000\ 4952.$$

This probability calculation can be repeated for the mutually exclusive events of having five hearts, diamonds or clubs.
Therefore, the probability of having five cards of the same suit is

$$\frac{1287}{2598960} + \frac{1287}{2598960} + \frac{1287}{2598960} + \frac{1287}{2598960} = \frac{5148}{2598960} = 0.001\ 981.$$

c) The probability of being dealt five cards of the same suit is greater than the probability of being dealt three aces. ∎

Example 2
A drawer contains five red socks and ten blue socks.
If three socks are randomly selected, what is the probability of each of the following?
a) choosing a pair of red socks
b) choosing a pair of blue socks
c) choosing a matched pair of socks

Solution
a) Use a hypergeometric random variable H to find the number of red socks in the three chosen. Then $a = 5$, $b = 10$, and $n = 3$.
For a pair to be chosen, $x = 2$ or $x = 3$.

$$P(H = 2) + P(H = 3) = \frac{C(5,2) \times C(10,1)}{C(15,3)} + \frac{C(5,3) \times C(10,0)}{C(15,3)}$$

$$= \frac{100}{455} + \frac{10}{455} = \frac{110}{455} = 0.2418.$$

There is about a 24.2% chance of choosing a pair of red socks.

b) Let H be used to find the number of blue socks in this instance. Then $a = 10$, $b = 5$, $n = 3$, $x = 2$ or 3.

$$P(H = 2) + P(H = 3) = \frac{C(10,2) \times C(5,1)}{C(15,3)} + \frac{C(10,3) \times C(5,0)}{C(15,3)}$$

$$= \frac{225}{455} + \frac{120}{455} = \frac{345}{455} = 0.7582.$$

There is about a 75.8% chance of choosing a blue pair.

c) The probability of choosing a matched pair of socks is equal to the sum of the probabilities of choosing *either* a pair of red, *or* a pair of blue socks, since these are mutually exclusive events.

$$P(\text{matched pair}) = \frac{110}{455} + \frac{345}{455} = 1$$

This means you are certain to have a matched pair of socks if you select any three from the drawer. (Obviously, you could have obtained this result through another line of reasoning.) ■

Example 3   Of 100 widgets produced in a production run, 5% are known to be defective. Eight widgets are randomly selected and tested. What is the probability that none of the widgets tested is defective?

Solution   There are 5 defective and 95 working widgets.
$a = 5$, $b = 95$, $n = 80$, and $x = 0$.
The probability that none of the widgets tested is defective is given by

$$\frac{C(5,0) \times C(95,8)}{C(100,8)} = 0.6532. \quad ■$$

The expression arrived at in Example 3 is very tedious to evaluate with the typical hand-held calculator.
The probability can be approximated, however, by assuming a binomial distribution rather than a hypergeometric distribution.

The difference between the hypergeometric and binomial models for the widget testing is that, for the hypergeometric model, the eight widgets were chosen without replacement. In a binomial model the widget would have to be returned to the original group after it had been tested, so that there is a chance that the widget could be tested a second time. Notice however, that the number of widgets chosen (8) is small compared to the total number of widgets (100). The probability of a widget being chosen for testing a second time is slim.

Example 4 Approximate the probability asked for in Example 3, using a binomial random variable rather than a hypergeometric random variable. Compare this probability with that calculated in Example 3.

Solution For the binomial distribution, define success to be choosing a defective widget for testing.
Then $p = 0.05$ and $q = 0.95$. $n = 8$ and $x = 0$.
$b(0;8,0.05) = C(8,0)(0.05)^0(0.95)^8 = 0.6634$.
The difference in probabilities is just over 1%, which is reasonably close agreement for such high probabilities. ■

PROPERTY

In general, the binomial distribution can be used to approximate a probability in a hypergeometric distribution if
• the number of objects is greater than 50 ($a + b > 50$)
• the size of the selection n is less than 10% of the total number of objects.

$$\left(\frac{n}{a + b} < 0.1\right)$$

• the probability of success p in the binomial distribution

is $\dfrac{a}{a + b}$ in the hypergeometric distribution.

7.7 Exercises

1. A set consists of five objects of type A and 15 of type B. Eight objects are selected randomly without replacement. H is the random variable which maps each possible selection to the number of objects of type A.
   a) What is the range of H?
   b) Calculate $P(H = 5)$.
   c) Calculate $P(H < 4)$.

2. A bin of fruit contains four apples and eight oranges. Five pieces of fruit are randomly chosen from the bin.
   a) What is the probability that exactly three apples are chosen?
   b) What is the probability that all of the pieces of fruit chosen are oranges?
   c) What is the probability that all of the pieces of fruit chosen are apples?

3. A 13-card bridge hand is dealt from a shuffled 52-card deck.
   a) What is the probability that the hand will have a void in spades, that is, contain no spades?
   b) What is the probability that the hand will be all spades?
   c) What is the probability that the hand will contain more than 10 spades?

4. A five card hand is dealt from a shuffled 52-card deck.
   a) What is the probability of having exactly two aces in the hand?
   b) What is the probability of having four aces in the hand?
   c) How many times greater is the likelihood of being dealt a pair of aces than that of being dealt four aces in a hand?

5. A box contains five dozen heads of lettuce. There are eight spoiled heads in the box. A person chooses a dozen heads at random. What is the probability that he did not choose any of the spoiled heads?

6. A box contains three red marbles, four blue marbles and five green marbles. Six marbles are randomly selected from the bag.
   a) What is the probability of all three red marbles being chosen?
   b) What is the probability of none of the red marbles being chosen?
   c) Which is more likely, that all of the red marbles are chosen or that none of the red marbles are chosen? How many times more likely?

7. In a class of 50 students, 42 have driver's licences. Ten students are selected at random from the class.
   a) What is the probability that all of the students selected have driver's licences?
   b) What is the probability that all of the students who do not have their licences are selected?

8. A production run of 45 videotapes is known to have three defective tapes. Nine of the tapes are randomly selected and shipped to a store.
   a) What is the probability of at least one of the defective tapes being shipped?
   b) What is the probability that the store will receive more than two defective tapes?

9. There are three sheep ill in a flock of 20. Six sheep are randomly chosen to be tested for illness. If none of the sheep tested is found to be ill, the flock is sent to market. What is the probability that the sheep will be sent to market?

10. A class has 35 women and 20 men. Five people are randomly selected from the class.
   a) What is the probability that all five selected will be male?
   b) What is the probability that there will be more women than men selected?

11. a) Show how the hypergeometric distribution used to calculate the probabilities in question 10 may be appropriately approximated by a binomial distribution.
   b) What is the value of p, the probability of success in a single trial, for the approximating binomial distribution?
   c) Approximate the probabilities requested in 10 a) and 10 b). Using the binomial distribution, compare these approximations to the exact probabilities.

12. A village has 3000 registered voters. In a recent election there were two candidates for mayor. Candidate A was supported by 1200 of the voters, and the rest supported candidate B. Twenty different voters were polled about the candidate they preferred for mayor.
   a) Write the calculation needed to find the probability that exactly five of the people polled preferred candidate A.
   b) Show that it is appropriate to approximate the calculation in a) with a binomial distribution. Specify the value of p for the approximating distribution.
   c) Calculate the approximate probability that exactly five of the people polled preferred candidate A.

13. a) Three cards are dealt from a shuffled standard 52-card deck. What is the probability that all three will be hearts?
   b) A card is dealt from a deck. The card's suit is noted and then the card is returned to the deck. This is done three times. What is the probability that all three times a heart will be dealt?
   c) What type of random variable can be used to model the situation in a)? in b)?
   d) Is it appropriate to approximate the probability in a) using the probability in b)? Why, or why not?
   e) How would the answer to d) be affected if eight cards were dealt in a) and b), and the probabilities that all eight cards were hearts in both cases were calculated?
   f) Modify the situation in a) and b) to having eight cards dealt. Calculate the probabilities that all eight cards will be hearts, for both situations. Compare these probabilities.

14. Three friendly jet fighters and eight enemy planes are engaged in combat in close proximity to each other. Four SAM's (surface-to-air missiles) are launched. Each missile seeks and destroys at random one of the planes overhead. What is the probability that the SAM's do not destroy any of the friendly aircraft?

15. Let a set consist of a objects of type A and b objects of type B. Let H be the hypergeometric random variable which maps each possible selection of n objects from the set to the number of type A in the selection. Show that all the probabilities in the hypergeometric probability distribution sum to 1. That is, show that

$$\sum_{x=0}^{n} P(H = x) = 1. \qquad \text{Hint: Use the identity}$$

$$C(n + t, k) = \sum_{n=0}^{k} C(n, j) \times C(t, k - j)$$

from chapter 6, and the fact that if $x \notin$ range (H), then $p(H = x) = 0$.

Summary

- A **random variable** is a function from a sample space of an experiment into a set of numbers. Any activity which has a numerical outcome can be modelled by a random variable.

- A **probability distribution** of a random variable is the function which maps each number in the range of the random variable, to the probability of that number being the outcome of an experiment.

- If X is a random variable, $k \in$ range (X), and f is the probability distribution function for X, then $f(k) = P(X = k)$.

- A probability distribution function of a random variable which maps each member of the range of the random variable to the same probability is a **uniform distribution**.

- A random variable which has an associated uniform distribution is a uniform random variable.
  If U is a uniform random variable and range $(U) = \{1, 2, \ldots, n\}$
  then $P(U = k) = \dfrac{1}{n}$ and $P(U \leqslant k) = \dfrac{k}{n}$ for $k = 1, 2, \ldots, n$

- A **binomial experiment** consists of a specified number of independent trials n where each trial has exactly two outcomes. One of the outcomes is designated "success", the other, "failure". For each trial the probability of success p is the same, and $q = 1 - p$ is the probability of failure.

- S is a **binomial random variable** if S maps each possible outcome of a binomial experiment to the number of successes occurring in that outcome.

- $b(x;n,p) = C(n,x)p^x q^{n-x}$ is the probability of x successes in a binomial experiment of n trials with a probability p of success on each trial.
  If S is the binomial random variable for the experiment, then $P(S = x) = b(x;n,p)$.

- $b(x;n,p)$ is the $x + 1$st term of the expansion of $(q + p)^n$.

- The list of all the probabilities $b(x;n,p)$ for $x = 0, 1, \ldots, n$ is a **binomial distribution**.

- An experiment consists of randomly selecting without replacement n objects from a set consisting of a objects of type A and b objects of type B. The random variable H which maps each possible n-tuple to the number of objects of type A in the n-tuple is a **hypergeometric random variable**.

- $P(H = x) = \dfrac{C(a,x) \times C(b,n - x)}{C(a + b,n)}$

- If $a + b > 50$ and $\dfrac{n}{a + b} < 0.1$, then $P(H = x)$ may be approximated by the binomial distribution $b(x;n,p)$ where $p = \dfrac{a}{a + b}$.

Inventory

Complete the following statements by filling in the blanks.

1. Two cubic dice are rolled and the product of the number of dots on both up faces is calculated. A function which maps each possible outcome of this experiment to the product calculated is **a)** _____ . The range of the function is **b)** _____ .

2. A card is taken from a standard 52-card deck. The suit of the card is observed.
   The number of possible outcomes for this experiment is **a)** _____ .
   The probability for each outcome is **b)** _____ .
   The probability distribution for this experiment is **c)** _____ .

3. In a binomial experiment the probability of success on the first trial is $\frac{2}{3}$. The probability of success on the second trial is _____ .

4. On a book shelf there are three mathematics books and four physics books. Five books are selected at random. The random variable which maps each possible selection to the number of mathematics books selected is **a)** _____ random variable.
   The range of this random variable is **b)** _____ .

In questions 5-8, identify which type of random variable, uniform, binomial or hypergeometric, is most the appropriate to use to answer the question posed.

5. Six marbles are taken from a bag containing 10 white marbles and 12 black marbles. What is the probability that four white marbles are chosen?

6. A single cubic die is rolled five times. What is the probability that six dots will appear on the up face, in exactly three of the five rolls?

7. Five students in a class of 25 are asked whether they intend to take mathematics in university or not. 15 of the students do plan to take mathematics in university. What is the probability that none of the five asked plans to take mathematics?

8. Twenty tickets numbered from 1 to 20 are placed in a hat. A ticket is randomly selected. What is the probability that the ticket numbered 7 will be selected?

In questions 9-11, write expressions which can be used to calculate the following.

9. $P(U \leqslant 5)$ where U is the uniform random variable which maps a randomly selected letter to its position in the alphabet.

10. $b(3;5,0.2)$

11. $P(H = 3)$ where H is a hypergeometric random variable with $a = 3$, $b = 12$ and $n = 5$.

Review Exercises

1. Eight cards are numbered 1 through 8 and shuffled. Two cards are drawn from the deck and the numbers on the cards are noted. Let S be the sample space of all possible pairs of cards which could be dealt. X is the random variable which maps each possible pair to the sum of the numbers on the card. Y is the random variable which maps each possible pair to the product of the numbers on the cards.
   a) How many outcomes are in S?
   b) List the range of X and of Y.
   c) Find $P(X = 3)$, $P(Y = 8)$, and $P(X = 8)$.
   d) Find $P(X \leqslant 8)$ and $P(2 \leqslant Y \leqslant 5)$.
   e) List the probability distribution for X.
   f) Calculate the expected value of X.
   g) Show that $(X - Y)^2$ and $(X^2 - 2XY + Y^2)$ are the same random variable.

2. Give a complete description of the following informally described random variables.
   a) The random variable X is the number of people who have blue eyes in a randomly selected group of 15.
   b) Two socks are chosen at random from a set of 5 blue socks and 3 red socks. A random variable W is 2 if a pair of blue socks is chosen, 1 if a pair of red socks is chosen and 0 if an unmatched pair is chosen.
   c) Two dice are rolled and the number of dots on the up faces noted. You win, on each roll, the number of dollars equal to the product of the dots minus the sum of the dots. G is the random variable which maps each roll to your winnings.

3. A pair of cubic dice is rolled and the number of dots on the up faces noted. You win if you roll a 7, an 11 or doubles. If you play the game six times, what is the probability that you win more than half of the games?

4. One card is selected at random from a deck of thirty cards numbered from 1 to 30. X is the random variable which maps the card selected to the number on the card.
   a) What type of random variable is X?
   b) Find $P(X = 21)$, $(P(X < 18)$ and $P(5 \leqslant X \leqslant 14)$.
   c) Find $E(X)$ and $E(3X - 5)$.
   d) Define a random variable U on the sample space $\{1, 2, \ldots, 30\}$ which has range $\{1, 2, 3\}$ and is uniform.
   e) Define a random variable U on the sample space $\{1, 2, \ldots, 30\}$ which has range $\{1, 2, 3\}$ and is not uniform.

5. A particular mathematics contest consists of fifteen questions. The answer to each question is a non-negative integer from 0 to 999.
   a) An answer to a question on the contest is randomly guessed. What is the probability of guessing the correct answer?
   b) If the only thing you can determine is that the answer is a two-digit number, what is the probability that you will guess the correct answer?
   c) Assume that each number from 0 to 999 is as likely to be an answer as any other. How many of the answers in a fifteen question contest will be three-digit numbers? How many of the answers will be prime numbers?

6. S is the set of perfect squares less than 100. A number is chosen at random from S. X is the random variable mapping the number chosen to itself.
   a) What is the probability that on any given selection the value of X is a single digit number?
   b) If the selections are done 1 000 000 times and the arithmetic average of the numbers selected is calculated, what is a likely value for the average?
   c) Show that $\sqrt{X}$ is a uniform random variable. Is $\sqrt{E(X)} = E(\sqrt{X})$?

7. The number of people who hold valid driver's licences in each of sixty families is noted. The results are tabulated.

Number of licences	0	1	2	3	4
Number of families	3	12	24	15	6

   a) If a family is chosen at random from the 60 families, what is the experimental probability that at least one member of the family has a licence?
   b) Let V be the random variable which maps each family to the number of members in the family with licences. List the probability distribution for V.
   c) Find the expected value of V.
      Ten thousand families are assumed to have the same distribution as the sixty families. Give an interpretation of the meaning of $E(V)$ if the number of family members with licences is noted for each of the ten thousand families.

8. Evaluate each of the following.
   a) $b(5;8,0.6)$
   b) $b\left(20;21,\dfrac{3}{4}\right)$
   c) $b(12;15,0.9)$
   d) $b(12;15,0.1)$

9. A game consists of 24 rolls of a pair of dice. The game is won if at least one double six is rolled. Calculate the probability of winning.

10. Quality control testing indicates that three out of every 20 bags of Munch Crunch Junk Food contains less than 300 g of Munch Crunch. Twelve bags are chosen at random.
    a) What is the probability that all of the bags contain 300 g or more of Munch Crunch?
    b) What is the probability that more than two of the bags will have less than 300 g of Munch Crunch?

11. A person stands at a street corner and flips a fair coin. If the coin lands heads, then the person travels one block east. If the coin lands tails, the person travels one block west. The coin is flipped ten times.
    a) What is the probability that the person has returned to the starting point after ten flips?
    b) After ten flips of the coin, what is the most likely distance for the person to be from the starting point?
    c) How would the results in a) and b) change if the coin is not fair and the probability of landing heads is $\dfrac{2}{3}$?

12. An airline calculates that 12% of the people who reserve a flight will fail to show up. Eight flight reservations are chosen at random.
    a) Find the probability that all eight people will show up for their flights.
    b) Find the probability that at least two of the people will fail to show.
    c) What is the most likely number of people to show up?

13. A committee consists of twelve women and eight men. A sub-committee of five people is selected at random from the committee. X is the random variable which maps each possible sub-committee to the number of women on the committee.
    a) What type of random variable is X? What is the range of X?
    b) Find $P(X = 0)$.
    c) What is the probability that there will be at most one man on the sub-committee?
    d) What is the size of the smallest sub-committee that must have at least one female member? What is the probability that this sub-committee will contain exactly one woman?

14. In a bag there are 20 white marbles and 30 black marbles. Four marbles are randomly selected.
    a) Find the probability that exactly three of the marbles selected are black.
    b) Show that it is appropriate to approximate the probability in a) using a binomial distribution. Calculate this approximation and compare with a).

15. Going into a football game, a field goal kicker had been successful on 28 of 35 field goal attempts. During the game, the player successfully kicked five field goals in five attempts.
    a) Based on his performance before the game, what was the probability of his being successful on all five kicks in this game?
    b) What was the most likely number of successes for the kicker, based on his previous performance?

16. Livestock recover from a particular disease 60% of the time. A herd of 10 animals contract the disease.
    a) How many times more likely is it for all of the animals to recover than for none of the animals to recover?
    b) How would your answer to part a) change if there were 8 animals in the herd? 12 animals?
    c) How would your answer change in part a) if the recovery rate were 40%? 80%?

17. A candy store operator finds that $\frac{5}{8}$ of the number of people who come into his store make a purchase. In a particular hour, 48 people came into the store. Find each of the following probabilities.
    a) Exactly half of the number of people made a purchase.
    b) Thirty of the people made a purchase.
    c) All of the people made a purchase.

18. A roulette wheel consists of 36 compartments numbered 1 to 36. The wheel is spun. The ball is equally likely to stop at any of the compartments. A person bets on three compartments on each of five spins.
    a) What is the probability that the person will win at least once?
    b) What is the probability that the person will win more often than not?

19. An archer has a 12% chance of hitting the centre of a target on any given shot. In a tournament she fires 25 arrows.
    a) Calculate and list the probabilities that she will hit the target's centre exactly x times, $x = 1, 2, \ldots, 6$, in the 25 shots.
    b) Which value of x in part a) has the greatest probability?
    c) Let B be the binomial random variable which maps each possible tournament to the number of times she hits the target centre. Use the results of question 12 of 7.5 Exercises, page 297, to calculate the expected value B. Compare this with your result in part b).
    d) The range of B is $\{0, 1, 2, \ldots, 25\}$. Which value of B will have the greatest probability?
    e) What conclusion can you infer about the expected value of a binomial random variable, and the value of the random variable which has the greatest probability?

CHAPTER EIGHT

Statistics

In the early eighteenth century a French mathematician working in Britain, Abraham DeMoivre, invented an equation and curve. These described extremely well many situations where a distribution of a set of measures is clustered around one central value and spread out in an even fashion to both sides of this centre. Further work investigating the properties and uses of this curve was done by the German mathematician Karl Friedrich Gauss and the French scientist Pierre Simon Laplace, during the first half of the nineteenth century.

It was the Belgian statistician and sociologist, Adolphe Quetelet, who applied this curve in 1835 to the concept of the 'average person', and argued that many measurable human traits resulted in distributions with this bell-shaped curve, which consequently became known as the 'normal' distribution curve.

You will encounter the normal distribution curve in the study of just about every situation that involves sets of measures. In this chapter you will begin an investigation of normally distributed sets of measures. Following are situations involving normal distributions.

- A group of students is writing a college admissions examination which has a maximum score of 800. The mean score for the examination was 420, with a standard deviation of 110. Susan scored 695. What percent of the population writing the examination scored the same, or less, than she did?

- On a stretch of highway, vehicle speeds are observed to be normally distributed. The mean speed is 75 km/h with a standard deviation of 4 km/h. If 500 vehicles pass by in an hour, about how many of them would be travelling in excess of 80 km/h?

- The times that people wait in a grocery checkout line are normally distributed. The mean waiting time is 10 minutes with a 2.5 minute standard deviation. What is the probability that Jack will be through the checkout line in less than five minutes?
- The number of candies put in each package is normally distributed. The mean number of candies per package is 200 with a standard deviation of 10. A package of candies will be accepted only if there are between 175 and 220 candies in the package. Out of 5000 packages, about how many will have to be rejected?
- In a mature stand of trees, the tree heights are normally distributed with a mean height of 8.5 m and a standard deviation of 0.6 m. If a tree is randomly selected from the stand, what is the probability that it will be over 7 m in height?
- A laboratory technician is required to make a number of precise measurements. The random errors associated with the measuring process result in a normally distributed set of measures with a mean of 0.55 mg and a standard deviation of 0.05 mg. What is the probability that a measurement will be 0.58 mg or greater?

8.1 Frequency Distributions

Forty students each took ten shots with a basketball from the free throw line. The number of successful shots (baskets) made by each student was recorded. The results were as follows.

6, 3, 9, 4, 6, 6, 4, 5, 3, 4, 8, 5, 4, 6, 3, 4, 6, 8, 6, 5,
5, 6, 4, 5, 3, 5, 9, 4, 8, 6, 6, 4, 8, 5, 6, 4, 5, 6, 4, 6.

This collection of numbers is know as a **data set**. By itself, the data set does not give us much information about the students' performance as a group. In this section and the next you will look at techniques for organizing, summarizing and analysing data. Such techniques belong to the study of **descriptive statistics**.

The data can be organized into a table using a **tally count** to indicate how many of the forty students had made a particular number of baskets.

Number of Baskets	0	1	2	3	4	5	6	7	8	9	10
				IIII	⊬⊬ ⊬⊬	⊬⊬ III	⊬⊬ ⊬⊬ II		IIII	II	

This tally count can be used to make a **frequency distribution table**. The frequency distribution indicates how often a particular number of baskets occurred. For example, eight students made five baskets. The frequency of making five baskets is eight.

Baskets	0	1	2	3	4	5	6	7	8	9	10
Frequency	0	0	0	4	10	8	12	0	4	2	0

The frequency distribution can be graphed. The horizontal scale is used to indicate the number of baskets made in ten free throws. The vertical scale is used to indicate the frequency. Rectangular blocks of width 1 are centred on the number of baskets made. The height of each block represents the frequency. The resulting graph is known as a **histogram** or a **frequency distribution diagram**.

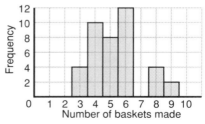

Associated with each frequency in the distribution is a **relative frequency**. Eight of the forty students made exactly five baskets.

The relative frequency of five baskets being made is $\frac{8}{40} = 0.2$. Expressing 0.2 as a percent, you can say 20% of the students made exactly five baskets.

Example 1

a) Use the frequency distribution table for the basketball free throws to make a relative frequency distribution table.

b) Use the relative frequency distribution table to make a relative frequency distribution diagram.

Solution

a) The frequencies have a sum of 40 (the number of students making the free throws). Calculate the relative frequency for the number of baskets made by dividing each frequency in the table by 40.

Baskets	0	1	2	3	4	5	6	7	8	9	10
Frequency	0	0	0	4	10	8	12	0	4	2	0
Relative Frequency	0.0	0.0	0.0	0.1	0.25	0.2	0.3	0.0	0.1	0.05	0.0

b) The relative frequency distribution diagram is identical to the frequency distribution diagram except that the vertical scale of frequencies is replaced by the corresponding relative frequencies.

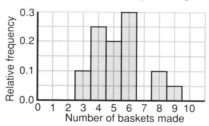

Frequencies and relative frequencies can be used to answer questions such as "How many students made exactly eight baskets?" (four students) and "What percent of the students made exactly four baskets?" (25% of the students).

In order to answer a question such as "How many students made at most five baskets?" you need to find the **cumulative frequencies**. The cumulative frequency of getting five baskets is the sum of the frequencies of getting five, four, three, two, one or no baskets. This is $8 + 10 + 4 + 0 + 0 + 0 = 22$.

22 of the 40 students got five baskets or less.

The **cumulative relative frequency** can be calculated by adding the appropriate relative frequencies. Hence, the cumulative relative frequency for getting five baskets or less is the sum of the relative frequencies of getting five, four, three, two, one or no baskets. This is $0.2 + 0.25 + 0.1 + 0.0 + 0.0 + 0.0 = 0.55$.

Another way of calculating this cumulative relative frequency is to divide the cumulative frequency by 40. $\frac{22}{40} = 0.55$.

Cumulative frequency distribution tables and diagrams can be made in the same way as frequency distribution tables and diagrams. The same is true for cumulative relative frequency distribution tables and cumulative relative frequency distribution diagrams.

Example 2   **a)** Use the free throw frequency distribution to make a table indicating cumulative and cumulative relative frequencies.

b) Use the table from part a) to make a single diagram indicating both cumulative and cumulative relative frequencies.

Solution   **a)** Use the frequency distribution to find cumulative frequencies for a given number of baskets by adding the frequency of that number of baskets with the frequencies of all numbers of baskets less than that one.
Find each cumulative relative frequency by dividing each cumulative frequency by 40.

Baskets	0	1	2	3	4	5	6	7	8	9	10
Frequency	0	0	0	4	10	8	12	0	4	2	0
Cum. freq.	0	0	0	4	14	22	34	34	38	40	40
Cum. rel. freq.	0.0	0.0	0.0	0.1	0.35	0.55	0.85	0.85	0.95	1	1

b) Make the cumulative frequency distribution diagram in the same way as the frequency distribution diagram, but use cumulative frequencies for the vertical scale. Place corresponding cumulative relative frequencies beside the cumulative frequencies on the scale or (as shown) on the other side.

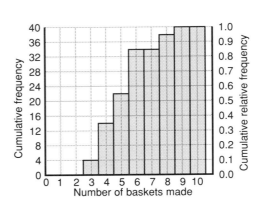

8.1 Exercises

Use the following information for
questions 1 and 2.
Three hundred rats run a maze. The time in
seconds required by each rat is recorded and the
following frequency distribution results.

Time (s)	8	9	10	11	12	13	14	15
Number of rats	15	24	48	54	72	42	33	12

1. a) Construct a frequency diagram.
      Use the right hand vertical scale
      to indicate relative frequency.
   b) What percent of the rats finish the maze
      in 11, 12 or 13 seconds?
   c) What percent of the rats finished the
      maze in ten seconds or less?

2. a) Construct a cumulative frequency
      diagram.
      Use the right hand vertical scale
      to indicate cumulative relative
      frequency.
   b) What percent of the rats completed the
      maze in 13 seconds or less?
   c) Find the time in seconds so that 50% of
      the rats completed the maze in that or a
      faster time.
   d) The rats that completed the maze in
      eight seconds were faster than what
      percent of the rats?

The following relative frequency diagram
displays the fraction of a group of high school
students which watches television for a
specified number of hours each day.
Use this diagram for questions 3, 4 and 5.

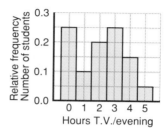

3. a) Use the relative frequency diagram to
      make a frequency distribution table.
      Assume that the total number of
      students represented is 80.
   b) What percent of the students watch
      television for one hour or less?
      How many students is this,
      if there are 80 students?
   c) What percent of the students watch
      television for two or three hours?
   d) If 120 students watched exactly four
      hours, how many students are
      represented in the diagram?

4. a) Use the diagram to make a cumulative
      relative frequency diagram.
   b) Find the number of hours such that
      50% of the students watch television
      this number of hours or less.
   c) What percent of the students watch
      more than three hours of television?

5. In the relative frequency diagram the width
   of each rectangle is 1 and the height of each
   rectangle is the relative frequency as a
   decimal. What is the sum of the areas of all
   of the rectangles? Why is this so?

A number of students were asked how much money they had spent in the last week. These amounts, rounded to the nearest $5, are listed below. Use this data for questions 6, 7 and 8.

30, 20, 5, 40, 20, 25, 35, 30, 25, 20, 30, 15, 20, 20, 25, 10, 20, 25, 15, 10, 20, 30, 30, 20, 40, 10, 15, 25, 25, 15, 30, 5, 20, 30, 15, 25, 20, 25, 5, 20, 30, 5, 10, 40, 20, 15, 30, 20, 5, 35

6. **a)** Make a tally count of the data and use the tally count to make a frequency and a relative frequency diagram.

   b) Of the amounts of money spent, which amount was the most common?
   What percent of the students spent that amount?

   c) What percent of the students spent less than $10?
   $10 or more, but less than $20?
   $20 or more, but less than $30?
   $30 or more?

   d) Use the results of c) to make a frequency distribution based on money spent, rounded to the nearest $10. Which distribution, rounded to the nearest $5, or rounded to the nearest $10, gives more information?

7. **a)** Use the data to make a cumulative frequency and cumulative relative frequency diagram for the distribution.

   b) Find a value m such that 25% of the students spend $$m$ or less.
   Find a value M such that 75% of the students spend $$M$ or less.
   What percent of the students spend an amount greater than or equal to $$m$ but less than or equal to $$M$?

8. If a student is chosen randomly from the group, what is the probability that the student chosen spent
   a) $30 that week?
   b) $30 or more that week?
   c) $15 or more but less than $30 that week?

Following is a cumulative frequency diagram for the distribution of the number of days in June receiving specific numbers of hours of sunlight.
Use this diagram to answer questions 9 and 10.

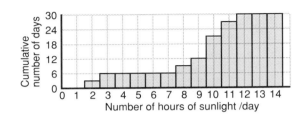

9. **a)** What percent of the days received nine hours of sunlight or less?

   b) What percent of the days received more than nine hours of sunlight?

   c) What is the relationship between the answers to a) and b)?

   d) The rectangles centred on 3 h, 4 h, 5 h, 6 h and 7 h all have the same height. What does this indicate about the distribution?

   e) What is the maximum number of hours of sunlight received on any day in June? the minimum number of hours?

10. **a)** What is the change in the number of days having two hours of sunlight to the number of days having three hours? the number of days having nine hours of sunlight to the number of days having ten hours?

    b) Use the cumulative frequency diagram to make a frequency diagram.

    c) According to the distribution, how many days in June had exactly eight hours of sunlight?

    d) What is the most common number of hours of sunlight for the month?

    e) What on the cumulative frequency diagram represents the greatest frequency in the distribution?

8.2 Summary Statistics

In the previous section you learned how to organize and display a collection of numbers or data. A second step after organizing and illustrating these sets of data is to summarize certain characteristics about the distribution of the data, or about how a particular datum fits into the distribution. Numbers which are used to describe characteristics of data sets and their distributions are called **statistics**.

One statistic which is closely related to the cumulative relative frequencies of a distribution is the **percentile** statistic. The 70th *percentile* of a distribution is that number in the data set such that 70% *of the numbers in the set are less than or equal to that number*. A percentile is most easily found from a cumulative relative frequency diagram.

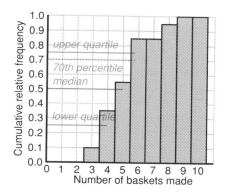

Above is the cumulative relative frequency diagram for the data set of the number of baskets made in ten attempts by each of 40 students, from the last section. The cumulative relative frequency of 0.7 corresponds to 70%. A horizontal line is drawn from the cumulative relative frequency of 0.7 on the vertical scale until it intersects one of the blocks of the diagram. The block which this horizontal line intersects is centred on the number 6. Therefore the 70th percentile of this distribution is 6.

DEFINITIONS

Several percentiles have special names.
The 50th percentile is known as the **median** of the distribution.
From the figure you can see that the median of this distribution is 5.
The **upper quartile** is the 75th percentile and
the **lower quartile** is the 25th percentile.
The upper and lower quartiles of this distribution are 6 and 4 respectively.
Continue the investigation of the data distribution of the number of baskets made in ten attempts by 40 students.

Following is a table indicating frequency (f), relative frequency (r.f.), cumulative frequency (c.f.) and cumulative relative frequency (c.r.f.) for each possible number of baskets made.

Baskets	0	1	2	3	4	5	6	7	8	9	10
Frequency (f)	0	0	0	4	10	8	12	0	4	2	0
Rel. freq. (r.f.)	0	0	0	0.1	0.25	0.2	0.3	0	0.1	0.05	0
Cum. freq. (c.f.)	0	0	0	4	14	22	34	34	38	40	40
Cum. rel. freq. (c.r.f.)	0.0	0	0	0.1	0.35	0.55	0.85	0.85	0.95	1.00	1.00

DEFINITION

The **range** of a distribution is the difference between the largest number occurring in the data set and the least number.

For this distribution the least number of baskets made by any students is 3 and the greatest number is 9. The range of this distribution is $9 - 3 = 6$.

DEFINITION

The **mean** of a distribution is the arithmetic average of all the numbers in the data set.

For the basketball free throw distribution, the mean could be calculated by summing the number of baskets made by each student and dividing by 40.

(Note that if you are using a scientific calculator with statistical functions, the mean of a data set may be represented by $\bar{x}$ or μ. You will need to find out how to place your calculator in statistical mode and how to enter the 40 numbers from the data set.)

Because the data has been organized into frequency and relative frequency distributions there are possible shortcuts in the calculation of the mean. One short cut is to multiply each number of baskets made by the corresponding frequency, sum these products and divide by 40. This is the calculation.

$$\frac{1}{40}[(3)(4) + (4)(10) + (5)(8) + (6)(12) + (7)(0) + (8)(4) + (9)(2)] = 5.35$$

An equivalent way of calculating the mean is to multiply each number of baskets made by its relative frequency and then sum the products. With this method it is unnecessary to divide by 40. (The division was done already when the relative frequencies were calculated). This is the calculation.

$$(3)(0.1) + (4)(0.25) + (5)(0.2) + (6)(0.3) + (7)(0) + (8)(0.1) + (9)(0.05) = 5.35$$

DEFINITION   The **deviation** of a number in a data set is the difference between the number and the mean of the distribution. In the free throw distribution, since the mean is 5.35, the deviation of 8 is $8 - 5.35 = 2.65$. The deviation of 5 is $5 - 5.35 = -0.35$.

In order to see how closely the numbers of a data set cluster around the mean of the data, a statistic known as the **mean deviation** is sometimes calculated.

DEFINITION   The mean deviation of a data set is the mean of the absolute values of the deviation of each number in the data set.

Example 1   Calculate the mean deviation of the free throw distribution.

Solution   Use the frequency distribution table to make a list of the absolute values of the deviations for the numbers of baskets made.

Baskets	3	4	5	6	7	8	9
Absolute value of deviation	2.35	1.35	0.35	0.65	1.65	2.65	3.65
Frequency	4	10	8	12	0	4	2

Add the products of the absolute values of the deviations and the corresponding frequencies. Divide this sum by 40.
$(2.35)(4) + (1.35)(10) + (0.35)(8) + (0.65)(12) + (1.65)(0) + (2.65)(4) + (3.65)(2)$
$= 51.4$

The mean deviation is $\dfrac{51.4}{40} = 1.285$.   ■

Note that the entries for 0, 1, 2, 10 baskets were omitted from the calculation, since each had a frequency of zero. The entry for 7 baskets could have been omitted also.

Another statistic similar to the mean deviation is the **standard deviation**. The standard deviation is more complicated to calculate than the mean deviation. As you will see later in this chapter, it is extremely useful in many applications of statistics.

FORMULA   The standard deviation for a distribution can be calculated in the following manner.

1. Calculate the square of the deviation for each number in the data set.

2. Sum these squares and divide by the number of data.

3. Find the square root of the result from step *2*.

Example 2   Calculate the standard deviation, correct to 2 decimal places, of the free throw distribution.

Solution   Use the frequency distribution table to produce a table of squares of deviations.

Baskets	3	4	5	6	7	8	9
(Deviation)^2	5.5225	1.8225	0.1225	0.4225	2.7225	7.0225	13.3225
Frequency	4	10	8	12	0	4	2

Calculate the mean of the (deviation)^2 using the corresponding frequencies.

$\frac{1}{40}[(4)(5.5225) + (10)(1.8225) + (8)(0.1225) + (12)(0.4225) + (0)(2.7225) +$

$(4)(7.0225) + (2)(13.3225)] = 2.5275$

The standard deviation of the distribution is $\sqrt{2.5275} \doteq 1.59$. ∎

(Note that if you are using a scientific calculator in statistical mode the above calculation is equivalent to entering the forty numbers in the data set and pressing the $\boxed{\sigma_N}$ key.)

The statistics in this section fall into roughly three categories.

Statistics such as percentile and deviation measure the relation of a particular datum to the complete data set.

The mean and median statistics are often called *measures of central tendency* because they tend to identify the 'centre' of a distribution.

The range, mean deviation and standard deviation are called *measures of dispersion*. These statistics tend to indicate whether a distribution is closely clustered around its centre, or spread out.

Summary statistics can be used to compare groups of measurements as well as describe individual groups. All of the following sequence of examples are based on two data sets.

Example 3   At the Arts, Sciences and Technology Centre in Vancouver there is a device which measures how good a person's balance is. The person balances on a board centred over a fulcrum for 30 seconds. The device measures how many seconds out of 30 the person was in balance.
David tried the experiment ten times and recorded times of
18 s, 12 s, 20 s, l6 s, 15 s, 17 s, 22 s, 15 s, 18 s, and 17 s.
Lorene tried the device seven times and recorded times of
28 s, 22 s, 16 s, 13 s, 12 s, 15 s, and 27 s.
Using David's times as data, calculate the
a) range, b) median, c) mean, d) mean deviation, e) standard deviation.

Solution   **a)** Range = 22 − 12 = 10.

b) To find the median, rank the times:
22, 20, 18, 18, 17, 17, 16, 15, 15, 12.
There are ten times. The 'middle time' (50th percentile of the distribution) is the arithmetic average of the 5th and 6th times.
Median is $\dfrac{(17 + 17)}{2} = 17$.

c) Mean is $\dfrac{1}{10}$ (22 + 20 + 18 + 18 + 17 + 17 + 16 + 15 + 15 + 12) = 17

d) Mean deviation is $\dfrac{1}{10}$ (5 + 3 + 1 + 1 + 0 + 0 + 1 + 2 + 2 + 5) = 2

e) Standard deviation is $\sqrt{\dfrac{1}{10}(25 + 9 + 1 + 1 + 0 + 0 + 1 + 4 + 4 + 25)}$
$\doteq 2.646$ ∎

Example 4   Using Lorene's times as data, calculate the
a) range, **b)** median, **c)** mean, **d)** mean deviation, **e)** standard deviation.

Solution   **a)** Range = 28 − 12 = 16.

b) Rank Lorene's times: 28, 27, 22, 16, 15, 13, 12. There are seven times.
The median is the 4th time.
Median is 16 s.

c) Mean is $\dfrac{1}{7}$ (28 + 27 + 22 + 16 + 15 + 13 + 12) = 19

d) Mean deviation is $\dfrac{1}{7}$ (9 + 8 + 3 + 3 + 4 + 6 + 7) $\doteq$ 5.71

e) Standard deviation is $\sqrt{\dfrac{1}{7}[(81 + 64 + 9 + 9 + 16 + 36 + 49)]}$
$\doteq 6.141.$ ∎

Example 5   Use the summary statistics calculated in Examples 3 and 4 to describe and compare the balances of David and Lorene as indicated by this test.

Solution   David balances for a mean of 17 s. The median is also 17 s. The mean deviation and standard deviation indicate little variability in his results.

Lorene had a mean of 19 s and a median time of 16 s. The mean deviation and standard deviation are large in comparison to the mean and median. This indicates a lot of variability in the results.

Lorene 'averaged' (using the mean) a longer time balancing than David. Also, her best result of 28 s was considerably better than David's best result.

However, David's results were much more consistent than Lorene's. The range, mean deviation, and standard deviation for David's times were all substantially lower than the corresponding statistics for Lorene's times.

Because of the greater dispersion in Lorene's times, the median of 16 s might be a truer 'average' than the mean of 19 s. ∎

8.2 Exercises

Below is a cumulative frequency diagram for the distribution of annual incomes for 50 families. Use the diagram to answer questions 1-3.

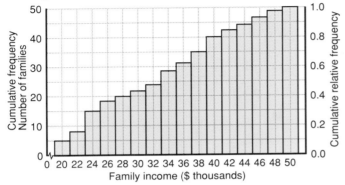

1. a) What is the median income?
   b) Find the upper quartile and the lower quartile for the distribution.
   c) What income is at the 90th percentile?
   d) What is the percentile rank of an annual income of $28 000?

2. The interquartile range of a distribution is the difference between the upper quartile measure and the lower quartile measure.
   a) Find the interquartile range for this distribution.
   b) What percent of the 50 families have incomes within the interquartile range?

3. Another representation of a distribution is a **box and whisker plot**.
   Below is a typical plot.

   a is the least measure in the distribution, b is the greatest measure, l is the lower quartile measure, m is the median, and u is the upper quartile measure. Make a box and whisker plot of the distribution.

Below are the team standings for the American and National Baseball Leagues early in June in one year.
Use these figures to answer questions 4-6.

American League East Division				National League East Division			
	W	L	Pct.	GBL		W	L	Pct.	GBL

American League East Division				
	W	L	Pct.	GBL
New York	35	21	.625	—
Toronto	33	20	.623	$\frac{1}{2}$
Milwaukee	29	23	.558	4
Detroit	28	25	.528	$5\frac{1}{2}$
Baltimore	27	28	.491	$7\frac{1}{2}$
Boston	25	31	.446	10
Cleveland	19	36	.345	$15\frac{1}{2}$

National League East Division				
	W	L	Pct.	GBL
St. Louis	33	20	.623	—
Chicago	31	24	.564	3
Montreal	28	26	.519	$5\frac{1}{2}$
New York	28	26	.519	$5\frac{1}{2}$
Philadelphia	26	26	.500	$6\frac{1}{2}$
Pittsburgh	24	29	.453	9

American League West Division				
	W	L	Pct.	GBL
Kansas City	30	23	.566	—
Minnesota	29	26	.527	2
Seattle	28	28	.500	$3\frac{1}{2}$
Oakland	27	27	.500	$3\frac{1}{2}$
California	25	31	.446	$6\frac{1}{2}$
Chicago	22	30	.423	$7\frac{1}{2}$
Texas	22	30	.423	$7\frac{1}{2}$

National League West Division				
	W	L	Pct.	GBL
Cincinnati	32	23	.582	—
San Francisco	30	25	.525	2
Houston	27	27	.500	$4\frac{1}{2}$
Atlanta	27	28	.491	5
Los Angeles	26	29	.473	6
San Diego	14	43	.246	19

4. a) Using only the American League standings calculate the mean and standard deviation for the win-loss percentages for the East Division and then for the West Division.
   b) Which division has a better mean win-loss percentage?
   c) Which division shows the greatest variability?
   d) The GBL column indicates the number of "games behind the leader". Find the mean of the GBL's for the East Division then for the West Division. How do these means relate to your answer to c)?

5. Which team in the American League East has the greatest deviation score for win-loss percentages? In the American League West?

6. a) Without calculating, state which division in the National League has the greater mean win-loss percentage? the greater standard deviation?
   b) Verify your answer to a) by calculating the mean and standard deviation of the win-loss percentages for each division.
   c) If the first and last place team were dropped from each division, which division would experience the greatest change in mean and standard deviation for win-loss percentages?

Below is a table of maximum and minimum temperatures recorded in 14 locations in British Columbia one day in June. Use the information in the table to answer questions 7-13.

	Max	Min
Comox	18	10
Cranbrook	31	13
Fort Nelson	13	9
Fort St. John	17	10
Kamloops	26	15
Mackenzie	22	10
Penticton.................	27	13
Prince George.............	23	9
Prince Rupert	11	8
Revelstoke	25	11
Stewart	13	10
Terrace...................	13	9
Victoria	19	12
Williams Lake	22	6

7. a) Calculate the mean of the maximum temperatures.
   b) List the maximum temperatures in order and find the median of the maximum temperatures.
   c) The mode of a distribution is the measure which occurs most frequently. Find the mode of the maximum temperatures.

8. Repeat question 7 using the minimum temperatures.

9. a) Using the maximum temperatures, calculate the range, mean deviation, and standard deviation.
   b) What percent of the temperatures are less than one mean deviation away from the mean?
   c) What percent of the temperatures are less than one standard deviation away from the mean?

10. Repeat question 9 using the minimum temperatures.

11. Which group of temperatures, the maximums or minimums, show the greatest variability? Justify your answer.

12. Find the deviation of each of the following.
    a) the highest and lowest maximum temperatures
    b) the highest and lowest minimum temperatures
    c) the median and mode of the maximum temperatures
    d) the median and mode of the minimum temperatures

13. a) Calculate the difference between the maximum and minimum temperatures for each location. Calculate the mean and standard deviation for these differences.
    b) Compare the mean of the differences calculated in a) to the difference between the mean maximum temperature and the mean minimum temperature.
    c) Does a relation similar to that found in b) exist between the standard deviation of the differences and the difference of the standard deviations for the maximum and minimum temperatures?

14. Two golfers both scored 76 on an 18-hole round of golf, strokes per hole as follows.
    Golfer A: 3, 5, 5, 3, 4, 2, 5, 5, 4,
       5, 5, 3, 6, 4, 5, 5, 3, 4

    Golfer B: 4, 3, 5, 5, 3, 4, 5, 3, 5,
       4, 3, 5, 5, 5, 4, 5, 4, 4
    a) Make a frequency distribution table for each golfer.
    b) Calculate the mean number of strokes for each hole for each golfer.
    c) Find the median and mode for the stroke distribution for each golfer.
    d) Which golfer showed the greater consistency in this round?
    e) Calculate the standard deviation for the stroke distribution for each golfer to verify your answer to d).

In Search of the Tchebychev Inequality

In section 8.2, three statistics measuring the dispersion, or the amount of spread, of a distribution were discussed. These statistics were the range, mean deviation and standard deviation. Of the three, the standard deviation was the most difficult to calculate and the least easy to relate directly to the measures in the distribution. It is, however, in many situations the preferred measure of dispersion in a distribution.

In the nineteenth century a Russian mathematician, Pafnuti Lvovich Tchebychev, rediscovered and published a result now known as the Tchebychev inequality. The Tchebychev inequality shows how deeply linked the standard deviation of a distribution is with the distribution.

Tchebychev inequality: For any collection of numbers with mean M and standard deviation s, let k be a number greater than s. Then the fraction of the numbers in the collection which are between $M - k$ and $M + k$ is *at least* $1 - \left(\dfrac{s^2}{k^2}\right)$.

Another way of viewing the situation is to let k be a multiple of the standard deviation s. If $k = 2 \times s$ then $1 - \left(\dfrac{s^2}{k^2}\right) = 1 - \left(\dfrac{s^2}{4s^2}\right)$ or $\dfrac{3}{4}$.

Therefore, for any distribution of numbers *at least* $\dfrac{3}{4}$ of the numbers lie between $M - 2 \times s$ and $M + 2 \times s$. In other words *at least* $\dfrac{3}{4}$ of any set of numbers lies within two standard deviations of the mean.

For an example, use the frequency distribution of the forty students taking ten basketball shots each (page 316). For this collection of numbers the mean was $M = 5.35$ and the standard deviation was $s = 1.59$. The frequency distribution table shows 38 of the numbers between 2.17 and 8.53.

Activities
1. Verify that Tchebychev's inequality holds for $k = 1.5 \times s$, $2.5 \times s$ and $3 \times s$.
2. Choose data sets from 8.2 Exercises for which you have calculated the mean and standard deviation. Choose values of k greater than the standard deviation and verify Tchebychev's inequality.
3. Collect an arbitrary set of numbers from the class. Calculate the mean and standard deviation. Make a frequency distribution of the numbers. Use this distribution to verify Tchebychev's inequality.
4. Calculate the least fraction of a set of numbers which must lie within 1.5, 3, and 4 standard deviations of the mean.
5. Why must the value of k in Tchebychev's inequality be greater than the standard deviation?

8.3 Probability and Statistics

At this stage you have some knowledge of how to determine the likelihood of an event occurring (probability) and how to organize and summarize a set of observations (statistics). You are now ready to forge links between the two fields of study.

Recall the example from section 8.1.
Forty students each took ten shots with a basketball.
The number of successful shots for each student was recorded.

Number	0	1	2	3	4	5	6	7	8	9	10
of Baskets				IIII	++++ ++++	++++ III	++++ ++++ II		IIII	II	

This data was organized and displayed as a frequency distribution diagram. In the diagram below, both the actual and the relative frequencies are displayed.

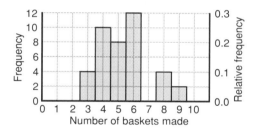

Now consider a simple problem from probability. Forty cards are each marked and placed in a bag. Four of the cards are marked with the number 3; ten cards are marked with the number 4; eight cards with the number 5; twelve cards with the number 6; four cards with the number 8 and two cards are marked with the number 9.

A card is selected at random from the bag. What is the probability that the card drawn has the number 5 on it? The sample space consists of 40 outcomes, one outcome for every card chosen. The event of having a 5 on the card consists of eight outcomes. The probability is $\frac{8}{40} = 0.2$.

Change the probability problem just slightly to relate it to the students shooting baskets. A student is selected at random from the group of 40. What is the probability that this student made exactly five baskets in ten attempts? Eight of the students did just that. Again, the probability is $\frac{8}{40} = 0.2$. But 0.2 is also the relative frequency of students making five baskets in the frequency distribution diagram!

The linking of relative frequencies and probabilities allows you to make probability statements about a population whose characteristics have been observed.

Example 1   A student is selected at random from the 40 students taking the ten basketball shots. Find the probability the student scored on more than five shots.

Solution   The notation $P(X = k)$ means the probability that the student selected scored on exactly k shots.
Using the relative frequencies as probabilities,
$P(X > 5) = P(X = 6) + P(X = 7) + P(X = 8) + P(X = 9) + P(X = 10)$
$= 0.3 + 0 + 0.1 + 0.05 + 0$
$= 0.45$
There is a 45% chance that the student selected from the group will score more than five shots.   ∎

When all of the relative frequencies are listed as probabilities, the result is a **probability distribution.**
The probability distribution for the 40 students can be represented in the following table.

k	0	1	2	3	4	5	6	7	8	9	10
$P(X = k)$	0	0	0	0.1	0.25	0.2	0.3	0	0.1	0.05	0

The relative frequency diagram for the data is known in this context as a **probability distribution graph.**

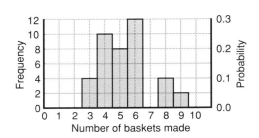

Example 2   A die is rolled 120 times. Each time the number of dots showing on the top face was recorded. The results were tabulated in the following frequency distribution.

Number of dots	1	2	3	4	5	6
Frequency	15	24	18	24	18	21

a) Make a probability distribution and graph from the frequency distribution.

b) Find the probability that if one of the 120 rolls were randomly selected there would be four dots showing.

c) Find the probability that if one of the rolls were chosen at random there would be more than three dots showing.

Solution   a) Find the relative frequency by dividing each frequency by 120. Let each relative frequency be the probability that any roll will have the associated number of dots showing.

Number of dots	1	2	3	4	5	6
Probability	0.125	0.2	0.15	0.2	0.15	0.175

Use the probability distribution to make a graph.

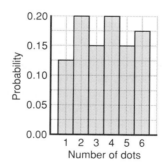

b) $P(X = 4) = 0.2$
There is a 20% chance that a randomly selected roll will have four dots showing.

c) $P(X > 3) = P(X = 4) + P(X = 5) + P(X = 6)$
$$= 0.2 + 0.15 + 0.175$$
$$= 0.525$$
There is a 52.5% chance that a randomly selected roll will have more than three dots showing. ■

The probability distribution investigated in Example 2 is based on observation and is an instance of an **experimental probability distribution**.

Compare the situation in Example 2 to the idea of a uniform random variable discussed in chapter 7. Rolling a die and observing the number of dots showing could be modelled by a uniform random variable in which the probability on any roll of a particular number of dots showing was $\frac{1}{6}$.

Number of dots	1	2	3	4	5	6
Probability	0.167	0.167	0.167	0.167	0.167	0.167

The probability distribution graph would be as follows.

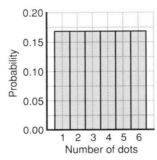

The probability distribution just described is an example of a **theoretical probability distribution.**

Example 3   A fair coin is flipped ten times. Make a probability distribution that lists the theoretical probability that exactly k heads occur in ten flips, where $k = 0, 1, \ldots, 10$. Make a graph of this distribution.

Solution   To make the theoretical probability distribution, use a binomial random variable B (chapter 7). B maps each experiment of ten coin flips to the number of heads occurring. The number of binomial trials is $n = 10$. The probability of success is $p = 0.5$. The range of B is $0, 1, \ldots, 10$. Calculate $P(B = k) = b(k;10,0.5)$ for $k = 0, 1, \ldots, 10$.

Heads	0	1	2	3	4	5	6	7	8	9	10
Probability	0.001	0.010	0.044	0.117	0.205	0.246	0.205	0.117	0.044	0.010	0.001

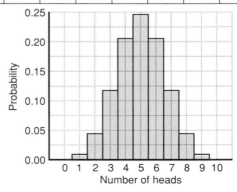

Example 4   Use the results of Example 3 to answer the following.
  a) What is the probability that exactly two heads will occur when a coin is flipped ten times?
  b) What is the probability that more than two but less than seven heads will occur in ten flips?
  c) Ten coins are flipped and the number of heads is recorded. If this experiment is repeated 1000 times, in how many of the experiments will eight or more heads occur?

Solution   **a)** Using the theoretical probability distribution, $P(B = 2) = 0.044$.
      Therefore, there is a 4.4% chance that exactly two heads will occur.
  b) The probability that more than two but less than seven heads will occur in ten flips may be expressed as
$$P(2 < B < 7) = P(B = 3) + P(B = 4) + P(B = 5) + P(B = 6)$$
$$= 0.117 + 0.205 + 0.246 + 0.205 = 0.773$$
      There is a 77.3% chance of between two and seven heads occurring.
  c) $P(B \geqslant 8) = P(B = 8) + P(B = 9) + P(B = 10)$
$$= 0.044 + 0.010 + 0.001 = 0.055$$
      In 1000 experiments, eight or more heads will occur
      $(1000) \times (0.055) = 55$ times. ■

Example 4 brings out three important aspects of theoretical probability distributions.

PROPERTIES
  • The probability of a single outcome is the *height* of the rectangle centred on that outcome in the distribution graph.

  • The probability of a range of outcomes is equal to the *area* of all the rectangles centred on the outcomes in the given range. (Since each rectangle has width 1 and height equal to the probability of the outcome on which the rectangle is centred.)

  • A probability distribution can be made into a frequency distribution by specifying a population size, N, and multiplying each probability in the distribution by the population size.

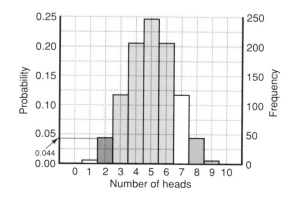

8.3 Exercises

A pair of fair dice is rolled 180 times.
For each roll, the number of dots showing
is recorded. The resulting frequency distribution
is shown below. Use this distribution in
answering questions 1-3.

Dots	2	3	4	5	6	7	8	9	10	11	12
Freq.	4	12	16	19	27	33	22	18	13	9	7

1. Use the frequency distribution to make an
   experimental probability distribution and
   graph.

2. Find the following experimental
   probabilities.
   For any roll the number of dots
   showing is as follows.
   a) exactly nine
   b) less than five
   c) greater than or equal to ten
   d) greater than four, but less than nine

3. Use the experimental probabilities to
   predict how many times in 1000 rolls
   exactly six dots would show.

4. Two fair dice are rolled and the total
   number of dots showing is observed.
   a) Establish a theoretical probability
      distribution and graph to model the
      situation.
   b) Use the theoretical distribution to make
      a frequency distribution for 36 rolls of
      the dice.
   c) Calculate the mean and standard
      deviation of the distribution in b).
   d) Use the theoretical distribution to make
      a frequency distribution for 1800 rolls
      of the dice.
   e) Calculate the mean and standard
      deviation of the distribution in d).
   f) How are the statistics in c) and e)
      related?

5. Make a theoretical probability distribution
   and graph for 120 rolls of a pair of dice.

6. Repeat question 2 using the theoretical
   probabilities from question 5.

7. Repeat question 3 using the theoretical
   probabilities from question 5.

Following is a relative frequency diagram of
grain heights (in cm) 30 days after sowing.
Use this diagram to answer questions 8-11.

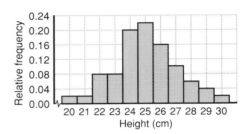

8. a) What is the height of the rectangle
      centred on 26 cm?
   b) What is the probability of a randomly
      chosen grain measuring 26 cm?
   c) How many of a sample of 1500 grain
      heights would you expect to measure
      26 cm?

9. a) What is the area under the graph of all
      of the rectangles centred on
      23 cm or less?
   b) Describe the probability associated
      with this area.

10. a) Convert the relative frequency
       distribution into a frequency
       distribution for 1500 grain heights.
    b) Calculate the mean and standard
       deviation of the distribution from
       part a).
    c) Find the probability that a grain chosen
       randomly from the 1500 will be taller
       than the height given by
       mean plus standard deviation.
       Find the probability that it will be
       shorter.

11. What is the sum of the areas of all of the
    rectangles in the diagram of grain heights?
    Why is this necessarily so?

8.4 Normal Distributions

In the last section you saw how a random variable had a theoretical probability distribution and graph associated with it. You also saw how a frequency distribution could be linked to an experimental probability distribution and graph.

The random variables you have looked at so far all have finite ranges. That is, there has been only a finite number of outcomes considered for each of the probability problems. Similarly, when you dealt with frequency distributions, each member of the population being studied fit into one of a finite number of classes. The probability distributions resulting from these situations are known as **discrete distributions**. The graphs of these distributions consist of a finite number of rectangles.

In this section we will consider the idea of a **continuous probability distribution** and will investigate what is most likely the most important class of such distributions, the **normal distributions**. The graph of a continuous distribution is a continuous curve.

To begin, consider this sequence of binomial distribution graphs. Each distribution is based on a binomial random variable in which the probability of success in any trial is $p = 0.5$. The first graph is based on a binomial random variable with 5 trials, the second graph with 10 trials and the third graph with 20 trials. If the same length is used for the horizontal axis on each graph, the rectangles which characterize the graph of a discrete distribution become narrower and narrower. If the midpoints of consecutive rectangle tops are joined, the resulting 'curve' becomes 'smoother' as the number of trials increases.

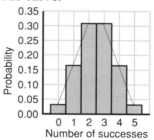

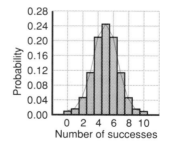

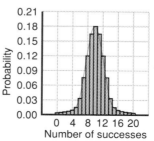

The next distribution graph is based on the binomial random variable with probability of success $p = 0.5$ and number of trials $N = 100$. The rectangles are so narrow that the graph is best represented by a continuous curve.

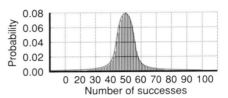

Now consider a frequency distribution diagram where the weights of 10 000 women athletes have been recorded.

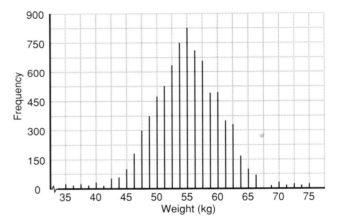

The women have been grouped by weight to the nearest 1.25 kg for the purposes of this graph. The graph again suggests a smooth continuous curve through the tops of the (very thin) rectangles. The continuous curve would have been less strongly suggested if the grouping had been to the nearest 5 kg and more strongly suggested if the grouping had been to the nearest 0.5 kg.

Practically, the weights had to be grouped into a finite number of cells (to the nearest 0.5 kg. or 0.1 kg). But theoretically, there is no limit to the number of groupings that could be used to classify the women by weight. The greater the number of groupings, the greater the sense of a continuous distribution graph.

Neither the binomial random variables nor the frequency distribution result in truly continuous distributions. However, both situations can be very effectively modelled by one particular class of continuous probability distributions, the normal distributions.

Below is the graph of the **standard normal distribution**. By understanding the properties of the standard normal distribution you will be able to work with other normal distributions.

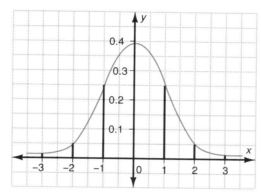

The graph of the standard normal distribution is a bell-shaped curve.

The bell is centred on the y-axis and is symmetric with respect to the y-axis.

The cap of the bell occurs in the interval $-1 \leqslant x \leqslant 1$.

The curve is completely above the x-axis.

It extends indefinitely in either direction away from the y-axis. As $|x|$ becomes increasingly large the curve comes closer to the x-axis.

The standard normal distribution is a model of a population with measures which have a mean of 0 and a standard deviation of 1.

For a point (x,y) on the curve, y is the probability of randomly selecting the measure x from the population.

To interpret the graph in terms of probabilities, remember (section 8.3) that the probability of a range of outcomes equals the area under the distribution graph for the corresponding segment of the horizontal axis. The area of the region bounded by the curve, the x-axis and the lines $x = 1$ and $x = 2$ is the probability that a measure chosen from the population will have a value of from 1 to 2 inclusive.

PROPERTIES

For a population modelled by the standard normal distribution:
• approximately **68%** of the population lies between -1 and 1
• approximately **95%** of the population lies between -2 and 2
• approximately **99%** of the population lies between -2.5 and 2.5

Another way of stating these properties is to say that, in a population modelled by a normal distribution, *68%* of the population has measures less than *one* standard deviation from the mean. Similarly, *95%* of the measures in the population are within *two* standard deviations from the mean, and *99%* are within *two and a half* standard deviations.

Example 1   A population is modelled by the standard normal distribution. Find the approximate percent of the population which have measures as follows
a) less than 1   **b)** less than −2   **c)** between 1 and 2

Solution   **a)** Use the symmetry of the graph.
68% of the population lie between −1 and 1.
This implies 34% of the population lie between 0 and 1.
50% of the population have measures less than 0.
Therefore, 50% + 34% = 84% of the population have measures less than 1.

b) 95% of the population have measures between −2 and 2.
Therefore, 5% have measures greater than 2, or less than −2.

By symmetry, $\frac{1}{2}$ (5%) = 2.5% have measures less than −2.

c) 47.5% of the population have measures between 0 and 2.
34% of the population have measures between 0 and 1.
Therefore 47.5% − 34% = 13.5% of the population have measures between 1 and 2. ∎

Not many populations of measures have 0 as a mean and 1 as a standard deviation. But if the measures are normally distributed and the mean and standard deviation are known, then the situation is very similar to the standard normal distribution.

Example 2   The weights of 10 000 women athletes are normally distributed. The mean of the weights is 55 kg and the standard deviation is 5 kg.
a) Find the number of women weighing between 50 and 60 kg.
b) Find the number of women weighing less than 45 kg.
c) Find a range of weights that would include 99% of the measures.

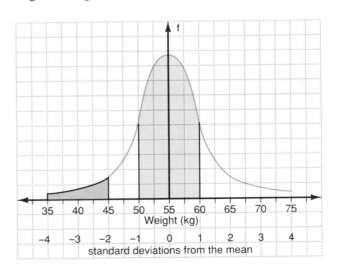

Solution The horizontal scale below the weight scale matches each weight with the weight's **standard score**, which is the number of standard deviations (multiples of 5 kg) that that weight is from the mean (55 kg).
The horizontal scale is now that of a standard normal distribution.

a) 50 kg has a standard score of −1 and 60 kg has a standard score of 1. Therefore, 68% of the women have weights between 60 kg and 50 kg. 68% × 10 000 = 6 800 of the women have weights in this range.

b) 45 kg has a standard score of −2,
since 45 is $\dfrac{45 - 55}{5} = -2$ standard deviations less than the mean.
2.5% × 10 000 = 250 of the women weigh less than 45 kg.

c) 99% of the area under a standard normal curve is bounded by $x = -2.5$ and $x = 2.5$. The weights corresponding to standard scores of −2.5 and 2.5 are 55 ± (−2.5)(5) = 42.5 and 67.5. Therefore, 99% of the women weigh between 42.5 and 67.5 kg. ■

Example 3 Explain why it would not be appropriate to model each of the following situations with a normal distribution.

a) A spinner is laid on the ground and spun 1000 times. After each spin the compass bearing of the tip of the spinner is noted.

b) In a factory, the mean salary is $20 000 with a standard deviation of $1000. 1% of the workers earn over $25 000.

c) In a given city the median age is 45 a and the mean age is 50 a.

Solution a) Each bearing from 0° to 359° is equally likely. The situation is better modelled by a uniform random variable. The associated distribution graph is a horizontal line with no 'clustering' about a single mean.

b) The standard score for $25 000 is 5. A normally distributed population cannot have 1% of its measures so far from its mean.

c) The distribution is not symmetric about the mean of 50 a. 45 a splits the population in half. ■

PROPERTIES In general, if a population is normally distributed and has mean M, standard deviation s, and x is a measure from the population, then

• the standard score of x is $\dfrac{(x - M)}{s}$

• approximately 68% of the measures lie between $M - s$ and $M + s$

• approximately 95% of the measures lie between $M - 2s$ and $M + 2s$

• approximately 99% of the measures lie between $M - (2.5)s$ and $M + (2.5)s$

8.4 Exercises

1. A population is modelled by a standard normal distribution. Find the approximate percent of the population which has the following measures.
   a) between 0 and 1
   b) less than −2.5 or greater than 2.5
   c) between 0 and −2
   d) between −1 and 2
   e) less than 0 or greater than 2

2. A population has a mean of 18 and a standard deviation of 3. Find the standard scores for the following values of x.
   a) $x = 15$ d) $x = 12$
   b) $x = 22.5$ e) $x = 20$
   c) $x = 16.5$ f) $x = 13$

3. The mean of a population is 42 and the standard deviation is 12. Find the measures in the population which have the following standard scores.
   a) 1   c) 1.5
   b) −2.5   d) −0.75

4. A normally distributed population has a mean of 45 and a standard deviation of 5. Find the approximate percent of the population which have a measure x in the following ranges.
   a) $40 \leqslant x \leqslant 50$ d) $35 \leqslant x \leqslant 50$
   b) $x \geqslant 55$ e) $50 \leqslant x \leqslant 55$
   c) $x \leqslant 32.5$

5. The life span of a particular species of turtle in captivity is normally distributed with a mean life span of 180 a and a standard deviation of 40 a.
   a) Of 1000 turtles in captivity, approximately how many will live more than 220 a? more than 260 a?
   b) Specify a range of lifespans centred on 180 a, such that 99% of the turtles will have lifespans in this range.
   c) What is the probability of a turtle in captivity living more than a century?

6. Intelligence Quotient (IQ) scores for a particular test are normally distributed with a mean score of 100 and a standard deviation of 16.
   a) What is the percentile rank of someone with an IQ or 116? 132? 140? That is, what percent of the population will have scores less than or equal to the given score?
   b) Specify a range of IQ scores centred on 100 such that $\frac{2}{3}$ of the population will have scores in that range.
   c) Find an IQ score such that 84% of the population has a higher IQ score.

7. The weights of the apples in a crop being sent to market are normally distributed with a mean weight of 200 g and a standard deviation of 30 g.
   a) If there are 120 apples in a basket, how many apples will weigh more than 230 g?
   b) An apple is rejected by the market if it weighs less than 140 g. How many apples will be rejected in a shipment of 80 baskets of 120 apples?
   c) Find two weights such that a total of 1% of the apples will weigh less than the lesser weight and more than the greater weight.

8. Explain why it is *not* appropriate to use a normal distribution to model each of the distributions described below.

a) The distribution has the following histogram.

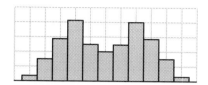

b) The distribution has the following histogram.

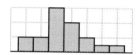

c) The distribution has the following box and whisker plot.

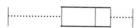

d) A game is played where a number is randomly chosen from the integers from 0 to 49. The distribution of the numbers chosen is noted.

e) In the distribution, $\frac{2}{3}$ of the population lies between 8 and 12, and 90% of the population lies between 6 and 14.

f) The median height of a group of basketball players is 205 cm and the mean height is 200 cm.

g) The grades of 75 students have a mean of 80% and a standard deviation of 6%. Six students have grades of over 92%.

h) The number of years a car is owned by its original purchaser has the following relative frequency distribution.

Time	1	2	3	4	5	6	7	8	9
R.f.	0.1	0.12	0.15	0.25	0.15	0.12	0.06	0.04	0.01

9. Describe five distributions which might be appropriately modelled by normal distributions.

10. Below is a frequency distribution of 500 measures, x.

x	8	10	12	14	16	18	20	22	24	26	28	30	32
f(x)	1	4	14	32	61	88	100	88	61	32	14	4	1

a) Draw a frequency diagram. Justify the use of a normal distribution to model this distribution.

b) Use the histogram from a) to estimate the mean and standard deviation.

c) Specify a range of measures, centred on the mean, which contains 68%, 95% and 99% of the population.

11. A pair of fair dice is rolled and the number of dots showing is observed.

a) Make a theoretical probability distribution for the above situation.

b) Calculate the mean and standard deviation of the frequency distribution based on 36 rolls and the theoretical probabilities.

c) Is it appropriate to model the distribution using a normal distribution? Justify your answer.

12. A fair coin is flipped ten times and the number of 'heads' occurring in the ten flips is noted. The theoretical probability distribution for this situation was developed on page 332. Use this distribution to decide whether or not it is appropriate to model this distribution using a normal distribution.

MAKING

May I Have Your Opinion?

It is arguable that mathematics has no greater direct impact on our lives than it does through the use of statistics in opinion polls.

Politicians use the results of polls to help themselves understand what is wanted and valued by their constituents.

Market researchers use surveys to determine which products will sell successfully, and to whom.

Network television programs are cancelled or renewed on the basis of their Nielsen ratings, the product of surveys.

The outcomes of elections are predicted with some accuracy, well before the first vote is cast.

The mathematical basis for using surveys is **statistical inference**. A pollster uses the methods of statistical inference to infer the opinions of a large population from a relatively small **sample**. As well as predicting the opinions of a large group from a smaller subgroup's opinions, the pollster can also use statistical techniques to determine the probability that his predictions are correct.

Informal opinion polls have been around for a long time. Early surveys about which candidate was favored in a political election were known as *straw polls*.

The modern history of opinion polls begins in 1935. In the early twentieth century an American magazine, *The Literary Digest*, would send out, before each presidential election, as many as 18 million cards to its readers, soliciting the readers' preference of candidate. As many as 2 million readers responded. On the basis of this sampling, the *Digest* was able to accurately predict the outcome of each presidential election (of 1932 and earlier). *The Literary Digest* ran its poll again in 1936 when the Republican, Alf Landon, ran against the Democrat candidate, Franklin D. Roosevelt. The prediction, based on the poll results, was that Landon would win the election.

In 1935, a group of statisticians and pollsters, George Gallup, Roger Crossley and Elmo Archibald, formed the American Institute of Public Opinion. The Institute favored a more scientific approach to sampling data and interpreting the results. Using a far smaller sample of opinions than the *The Literary Digest*, the Institute was able to accurately predict that Roosevelt would defeat Landon in the election.

One result of this success by the Institute was that *The Literary Digest* soon ceased publication. Another result was that the methods promoted by Gallup and his colleagues became so ubiquitous in society that the term *Gallup poll* is almost synonymous with opinion poll.

Here are some of the problems a pollster must address.

How large (or small) a sample will allow an accurate prediction?

How do you ensure a true opinion from the person being surveyed?

How do you ensure that the sample is unbiased, that is, truly representative of the population about which you are drawing inferences?

8.5 Applications of Normal Distributions

Normal distributions successfully model many populations that arise from both theory and observation. In this section you will investigate a number of these situations.

The critical characteristic of a normal distribution at this stage is the area under the distribution curve bounded by the curve, the x-axis and the lines $x = a$ and $x = b$. This area represents the probability that a randomly selected measure from the normally distributed population will have a value between a and b.

A table of values of areas, $A(z)$, for areas under the standard normal distribution curve from $x = 0$ to $x = z$ follows.

Areas Under the Standard Normal Distribution Curve

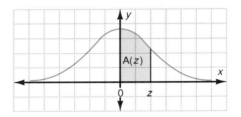

z	A(z)	z	A(z)	z	A(z)	z	A(z)
0.0	.0000	0.05	.0199	0.1	.0398	0.15	.0596
0.2	.0793	0.25	.0987	0.3	.1179	0.35	.1368
0.4	.1554	0.45	.1736	0.5	.1915	0.55	.2088
0.6	.2258	0.65	.2422	0.7	.2580	0.75	.2734
0.8	.2881	0.85	.3023	0.9	.3159	0.95	.3289
1.0	.3413	1.05	.3531	1.1	.3643	1.15	.3749
1.2	.3849	1.25	.3944	1.3	.4032	1.35	.4115
1.4	.4192	1.45	.4265	1.5	.4332	1.55	.4394
1.6	.4452	1.65	.4505	1.7	.4554	1.75	.4599
1.8	.4641	1.85	.4678	1.9	.4713	1.95	.4744
2.0	.4772	2.05	.4798	2.1	.4821	2.15	.4842
2.2	.4861	2.25	.4878	2.3	.4893	2.35	.4906
2.4	.4918	2.45	.4929	2.5	.4938	2.55	.4946
2.6	.4953	2.65	.4960	2.7	.4965	2.75	.4970
2.8	.4974	2.85	.4978	2.9	.4981	2.95	.4984
3.0	.4987	3.05	.4989	3.1	.4990	3.15	.4992
3.2	.4993	3.25	.4994	3.3	.4995	3.35	.4996
3.4	.4997	3.45	.4997	3.5	.4998	3.55	.4998
3.6	.4998	3.65	.4999	3.7	.4999	3.75	.4999
3.8	.4999	3.85	.4999	3.9	.5000	3.95	.5000

Example 1 Find the areas of the shaded regions for each of the following standard normal distribution curves.

a)

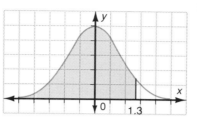

c)

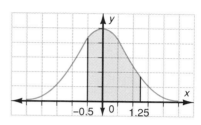

b)

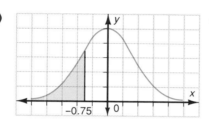

d)

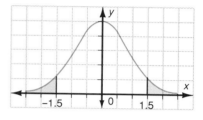

Solution a) $A(1.3) = 0.4032$ and the area to the left of the y-axis = 0.5000.
Therefore, the shaded area is 0.9032.

b) By symmetry, the area from $x = -0.75$ to $x = 0$ is $A(0.75) = 0.2734$.
Therefore, the shaded area is $0.5000 - 0.2734 = 0.2266$.

c) Shaded area equals $A(0.5) + A(1.25) = 0.1915 + 0.3944$.
Therefore, the shaded area is 0.5859.

d) The unshaded area equals $2 \times A(1.5) = 2 \times 0.4332$.
Therefore, the shaded area equals $1.0000 - 0.8664 = 0.1336$. ■

Example 2 For each of the following standard normal distribution curves, the area of the shaded region is given. In each case, find the value of z.

a)

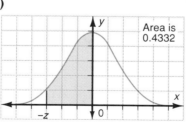

Area is 0.4332

b)

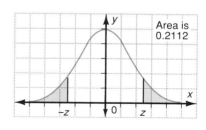

Area is 0.2112

Solution a) By symmetry, $A(-z) = 0.4332$. From the table, $-z = 1.5$.
Therefore, $z = -1.5$.

b)   Area under the curve from $-z$ to z is $1.0000 - 0.2112 = 0.7888$.
Then $A(z) = \left(\frac{1}{2}\right)(0.7888)$. $A(z) = 0.3944$. Therefore, $z = 1.25$. ■

Example 3   A population is modelled by the standard normal distribution. A measure is randomly selected from the population. Find the probability that the measure is between −0.5 and 0.65.

Solution $P(-0.5 < x < 0.65) = A(0.5) + A(0.65)$
$$= 0.1915 + 0.2422$$
$$= 0.4337 \quad\blacksquare$$

The areas under the curves of other normal distributions can also be calculated using the table of areas for the standard normal distribution. Each normal distribution can be specified by the mean M and standard deviation s of the distribution.

The notation $N(M,s)$ indicates the normal distribution with mean M and standard deviation s. Hence, $N(0,1)$ has mean 0 and standard deviation 1. That is, $N(0,1)$ denotes the standard normal distribution.

Below are the graphs of $N(0,1)$, $N(0,2)$ and $N\left(0,\frac{1}{2}\right)$.

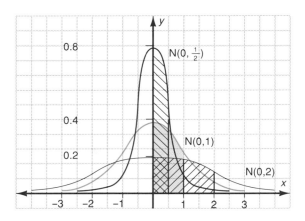

The graphs suggest that the greater the standard deviation, the greater the 'spread' of the curve. But also, the curve is compressed vertically. The vertical and horizontal compressions balance each other in the following manner.

The area under $N(0,1)$ from 0 to 1 equals the area under $N(0,2)$ from 0 to 2 equals the area under $N\left(0,\frac{1}{2}\right)$ from 0 to $\frac{1}{2}$.

In general, the area from 0 to z under N(0,1) will equal
the area from 0 to $2 \times z$ under N(0,2) or
the area from 0 to $\frac{1}{2} \times z$ under $N\left(0, \frac{1}{2}\right)$.

For the normal distribution N(0,s) the area under the curve from 0 to $s \times z$ equals the area under N(0,1) from 0 to z.

Example 4   Find the area under N(0,1.5) from $a = -0.6$ to $b = 1.8$.

Solution   Let $a = 1.5 \times a'$ and $b = 1.5 \times b'$. Then $a' = \frac{-0.6}{1.5}$ and $b' = \frac{1.8}{1.5}$
$a' = -0.4$ and $b' = 1.2$.
The area under N(0,1.5) from $a = -0.6$ to $b = 1.8$ equals the area under N(0,1) from $a' = -0.4$ and $b' = 1.2$.
This area equals $A(0.4) + A(1.2) = 0.1554 + 0.3849$. The area is 0.5403.   ■

Next let us consider the effect of changing the mean. Below are the graphs of N(0,1), N(2,1) and N(−3,1) on the same set of axes.

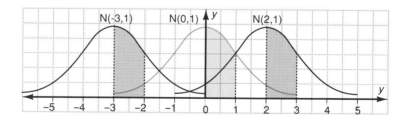

The graphs suggest the area under N(−3,1) from −3 to −2 equals the area under N(0,1) from 0 to 1 and equals the area under N(2,1) from 2 to 3.

In general, the area under N(M,1) from M to a equals the area under N(0,1) from 0 to $a - M$.

The results about standard deviations and means can be combined.

P R O P E R T I E S

The area under N(M,s) from a to b equals the area under N(0,1) from a' to b'
where $a' = \frac{(a - M)}{s}$ and $b' = \frac{(b - M)}{s}$.
a' and b' are called the **standard scores** for a and b respectively.

Example 5 A population is normally distributed with a mean of 6 and a standard deviation of 0.8. Find the probability that a randomly selected member of the population will have a measure greater than 7.

Solution $M = 6, s = 0.8, a = 7.$
$a' = \dfrac{(a - M)}{s} = \dfrac{(7 - 6)}{0.8} = 1.25.$
Find the area under N(0,1) for $z > 1.25$.
$A(1.25) = 0.3944.$
The area under N(0,1) for $z < 1.25$ is $0.5000 + 0.3944 = 0.8944$.
The area under N(0,1) for $z > 1.25$ is $1.000 - 0.8944 = 0.1056$.
The chance of randomly selecting a member of the population with measure greater than 7 is about 10.6%. ■

Example 6 For a particular production line in a widget factory it is known that the diameters of the widgets are normally distributed. The mean diameter is 10.35 cm and the standard deviation is 0.2 cm. To be useful, a widget must have a diameter between 10.25 cm and 10.65 cm. In a batch of 5000 widgets how many will have to be discarded because the diameter is too great or too small?

Solution Let $a = 10.25$ and $b = 10.65$. $M = 10.35$ and $s = 0.2$.
Then the standard scores for a and b are
$a' = \dfrac{(10.25 - 10.35)}{0.2}$ and $b' = \dfrac{(10.65 - 10.35)}{0.2}.$ $a' = -0.5$ and $b' = 1.5$.
The area under N(0,1) from -0.5 to 1.5 equals
$A(0.5) + A(1.5) = 0.1915 + 0.4332$. The area is 0.6247.
The probability that a widget's diameter is *un*acceptable is
$1.0000 - 0.6247 = 0.3753$.
$5000 \times 0.3753 = 1876.5$. Therefore, about 1877 of the widgets will have to be discarded. ■

Example 7 A particular species of housecat has a lifespan that is normally distributed, with a mean of 12 years and a standard deviation of 2.5 years. Find the probability of a kitten of this species living for 18 years or more.

Solution The standard score for 18 is $\dfrac{(18 - 12)}{2.5} = 2.4$.
The area under N(0,1) for $z \geqslant 2.4$ is $1.0000 - (A(2.4) + 0.5000) = 0.0082$.
The probability of the kitten living 18 or more years is about 0.8%. ■

8.5 Exercises

1. For each of the following standard normal curves use the table to find the area of the shaded regions.

a)

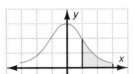

d)

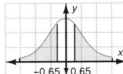

b)

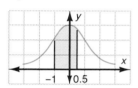

e)

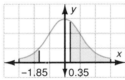

c)

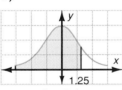

f)

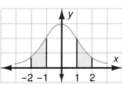

2. For each of the standard normal curves below find a value of z so that the shaded region has the specified area, A.

a)

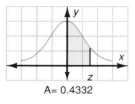

A= 0.4332

c)

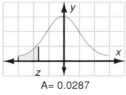

A= 0.0287

b)

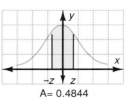

A= 0.4844

d)

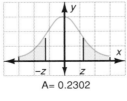

A= 0.2302

3. A population has a mean of 16 and a standard deviation of 1.2. Calculate the standard score for each of the following.
   a) 19   d) 14.98
   b) 14.2   e) 15.16
   c) 16.3   f) 18.58

4. For each of the following curves for the specified normal distributions N(M,s) find the area of the shaded regions.

a)

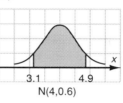

N(4,0.6)

d)

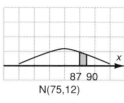

N(75,12)

b)

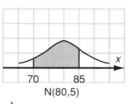

N(80,5)

e)

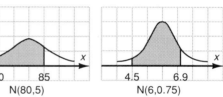

N(6,0.75)

c)

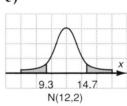

N(12,2)

f)

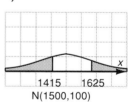

N(1500,100)

5. For each of the following curves for the specified normal distributions N(M,s) find values of a' and b' so that the shaded regions have the given area. a and b are equidistant from the mean in each case.

a)

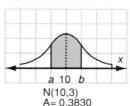

N(10,3)
A= 0.3830

b)

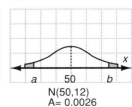

N(50,12)
A= 0.0026

6. A population is normally distributed with a mean of 170 and a standard deviation of 16. If a measure with value x is chosen at random from the population, find the probability that x is in the specified range.
   a) $x \geqslant 182$
   b) $x \leqslant 150$
   c) $146 \leqslant x \leqslant 194$
   d) $x \geqslant 198$ or $x \leqslant 142$
   e) $158 \leqslant x \leqslant 190$
   f) $154 \leqslant x \leqslant 166$

7. A laboratory technician is required to make a number of precise measurements. The random errors associated with the measuring process result in a normally distributed set of measures with a mean of 0.55 mg and a standard deviation of 0.05 mg. What is the probability that a measurement will be 0.58 mg or greater?

8. A group of students is writing a college admissions examination which has a maximum score of 800. The mean score for the examination was 420, with a standard deviation of 110. Susan scored 695. What percent of the population writing the examination scored 695 or less?

9. The times that people wait in a grocery checkout line is normally distributed. The mean waiting time is 10 minutes, with a 2.5 minute standard deviation. What is the probability that Jack will be through the checkout line in less than five minutes?

10. The number of candies put in each package is normally distributed. The mean number of candies per package is 200, with a standard deviation of 10. A package of candies will be accepted only if there are between 175 and 220 candies in the package. Out of 5000 packages, about how many will have to be rejected?

11. In a mature stand of trees, the tree heights are normally distributed, with a mean height of 8.5 m and a standard deviation of 0.6 m. If a tree is randomly selected from the stand, what is the probability that it will be over 7 m in height?

12. On a stretch of highway, vehicle speeds are observed to be normally distributed. The mean speed is 75 km/h, with a standard deviation of 4 km/h. If 500 vehicles pass by in an hour, about how many of them would be travelling in excess of 80 km/h?

13. A population is normally distributed with a mean of 10 and a standard deviation of 2. Find the percentile rank of the following measures.
    a) 12
    b) 6
    c) 9.5
    d) 11.5

14. A population is normally distributed with a mean of 50 and a standard deviation of 6. Find the least measure in the population having the following percentile ranks.
    a) 50th
    b) 90th
    c) 99th
    d) 20th

15. Infant weights are normally distributed with a mean weight of 3.4 kg and a standard deviation of 1 kg.
    a) In what percentile of the population of weights does a 4.5 kg infant rank?
    b) A set of triplets each weigh 1 kg. What is the percentile rank of the weight of each of the triplets?

16. A region receives an average 5100 mm of rain annually. If the annual rainfall is assumed to be normally distributed, with a standard deviation of 150 mm, find the probability of each of the following.
    a) More than 5500 mm of rain will fall in a year.
    b) Less than 5000 mm of rain will fall in a year.

17. Resting pulse rates of humans are normally distributed. The mean pulse rate is 72 beats per minute and the standard deviation is 10.
    a) What is the percentile rank of an athlete with a resting pulse rate of 48?
    b) How many of 5 billion people would have a rate less than 36 beats per minute?

In Search of the Mathematics of the Normal Distribution Curve

$$y = \left(\frac{1}{\sqrt{2\pi}}\right)e^{\left(\frac{-x^2}{2}\right)}$$

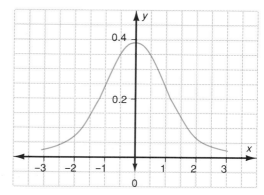

Above is the defining equation and graph of the standard normal distribution curve, N(0,1).

The equation and curve was invented by the French-born British mathematician, Abraham De Moivre (1667–1754). The French mathematician Pierre-Simon Laplace (1749–1827) and the German mathematician Karl Frederich Gauss (1777–1855) studied and further developed the properties of the curve. Indeed, the curve is sometimes called the Gaussian distribution curve.

The curve is of paramount importance in both probability and statistics. Its significance in these studies notwithstanding, the curve itself is so mathematically pleasing that it is worth the study of the pure mathematician. Look at the defining equation carefully and see how the equation results in the curve that you have been studying.

$y = f(x)$ where $f(x)$ is the function $\left(\frac{1}{\sqrt{2\pi}}\right)e^{\left(\frac{-x^2}{2}\right)}$

e is the base of the natural logarithms, an irrational number approximately equal to 2.72. You encountered e in your study of exponential and logarithmic functions. It is also a very important number in the study of calculus.

Because $e^{-a} = \frac{1}{e^a}$ and $\frac{x^2}{2}$ is always non-negative,

$f(x)$ will have its maximum value at $x = 0$.
$f(x)$ will be defined and positive for all numbers x, but as $|x|$ increases, $f(x)$ will become increasingly smaller.
$f(x)$ asymptotically approaches the x-axis as $|x|$ becomes increasingly large.
Since $\frac{x^2}{2}$ and $\frac{(-x)^2}{2}$ have the same value, $f(x) = f(-x)$ for every real number x.
Therefore, the graph of $y = f(x)$ is symmetric with respect to the y-axis.

If you study calculus, you will learn that points of inflection of a curve are points where the concavity of the curve changes. Points of inflection for the curve $y = f(x)$ occur for values of x such that $f''(x) = 0$. The points of inflection for the standard normal curve occur at $x = -1$ and $x = 1$.

For $-1 < x < 1$, the curve is concave down (the 'cap' of the characteristic bellshape). Elsewhere, the curve is concave up.

If the area under the curve of a probability distribution represents the probability of a range of outcomes happening, then all the area under any probability distribution curve must equal one. (All the probabilities in a distribution must sum to a probability of 1, certainly.) It is the factor $\dfrac{1}{\sqrt{2\pi}}$ which causes the area bounded by the curve and the x-axis to be 1.

Activities
1. Use a calculator to evaluate $f(x)$ for $x = 0, \pm1, \pm2$, and ±3. Compare these values with the graph of the curve.
2. The graph of the normal distribution $N(M,1)$ has the defining equation
$$y = \left(\frac{1}{\sqrt{2\pi}}\right)e^{\left(\frac{-(x-M)^2}{2}\right)}$$
   This is an equation of the form $y = f(x - M)$. Compare the graphs of $y = f(x)$ and $y = f(x - M)$ in the terms of translations.
3. Plot $y = f(x - M)$ for $M = 0, -1$, and 3 on the same set of axes.
4. The graph of the normal distribution $N(0,s)$ has the defining equation
$$y = \left(\frac{1}{s\sqrt{2\pi}}\right)e^{\left(\frac{\left(\frac{x}{s}\right)^2}{2}\right)}$$
   Show that this is of the form $y = \dfrac{1}{s} f\left(\dfrac{x}{s}\right)$.

   Compare the graphs of $y = f(x)$ and $y = \dfrac{1}{s} f\left(\dfrac{x}{s}\right)$

   in terms of vertical and horizontal compressions and stretches.
5. Plot $y = \dfrac{1}{s} f\left(\dfrac{x}{s}\right)$ for $s = 0, \dfrac{1}{2}$, and 2 on the same set of axes.
6. The graph of the normal distribution $N(M,s)$ has the defining equation
$$y = \left(\frac{1}{s\sqrt{2\pi}}\right)e^{\left(\frac{-(x-M)^2}{2s^2}\right)}$$
   Obtain access to a computer (or a calculator!) and software which will allow you to graph the curve of $N(M,s)$ for various values of M and s.

8.6 Normal Distribution Approximations of Binomial Distributions

A new medicine is being tested for its effectiveness against a particular disease. Untreated, a patient has a 50% chance of recovery.
16 patients were given the new medicine and of the 16, 11 recovered.
Was the new medicine effective in treating the disease
or did the 11 patients recover on their own?

One way to investigate the situation is to model it by a binomial random variable B. B maps from 16 patients to the number of recoveries.
Recovery is considered a success so that $p = 0.5$.
Each patient is a separate binomial trial so that $n = 16$.
The range of B is 0, 1, 2, ..., 15, 16.

The associated binomial probability distribution is graphed below.

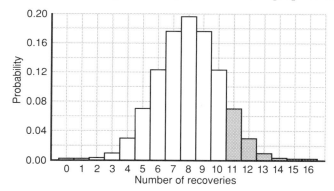

Consider the probability that 11 or more patients recover. This is represented on the graph by the combined areas of the rectangles centred on 11, 12, ..., 15, and 16.

In terms of the binomial random variable the probability is
$b(11;16,0.5) + b(12;16,0.5) + b(13;16,0.5) + b(14;16,0.5) + b(15;16,0.5) + b(16;16,0.5)$
$\doteq 0.0667 \quad + 0.0278 \quad + 0.0085 \quad + 0.0018 \quad + 0.0002 \quad + 0.00001$
$\doteq 0.1050$

There is a 10.5% chance that at least 11 recoveries would have happened if the medicine had not been used. This is a significantly large probability indicating that more testing is needed.

The above application required the calculation and summing of six terms of the binomial distribution. Without tables or a computer this is a tedious process. Think about how much worse the calculation would be if 2000 patients were treated and 720 recovered!

Recall that in section 8.4 there was a sequence of binomial distributions which suggested a normal distribution curve as a limit of the binomial distributions when the number of trials was very large. It is possible and, you shall see, very convenient to use normal distributions to approximate binomial distributions.

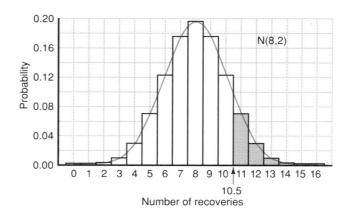

The normal distribution curve N(8,2) was 'fitted' over the binomial distribution. The choice of 8 as the mean and 2 as the standard deviation will be explained below.

Notice that the left-most edge of the rectangle centred on 11 in the binomial distribution is halfway between 10 and 11. That is, the edge is at 10.5. The probability of 11 or more recoveries is the area under the binomial distribution curve to the right of 10.5.

Find the area under N(8,2) for $a \geqslant 10.5$.

The standard score for a is $a' = \dfrac{(10.5 - 8)}{2}$ or 1.25.

$A(1.25) = 0.3944$.

Therefore, the area under N(8,2) for $a \geqslant 10.5$ is
$1.000 - (0.5000 + 0.3944) = 0.1056$.

The normal distribution N(8,2) gives us an approximation of 0.1056 as the probability of 11 or more recoveries. This is in excellent agreement with the calculated value of 0.1050.

It is important to understand why the value of 10.5 rather than 11 was used in the normal distribution approximation.

Go back to the original binomial distribution graph, repeated below,

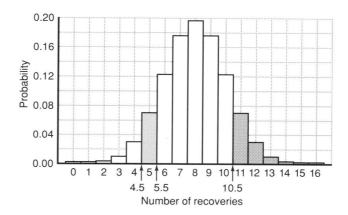

and look at the rectangle centred on 5.
The area of that rectangle represents the probability
that exactly 5 of the 16 patients will recover.
The area is equal to $b(5;16,0.5) = 0.0667$.
Now look at the normal curve fitted over the binomial distribution.
The rectangle centred on 5 corresponds to the region
under the normal curve from $a = 4.5$ to $b = 5.5$.
The area under $N(8,2)$ from $a = 4.5$ to $b = 5.5$ equals
the area under $N(0,1)$ from $a' = -1.75$ to $b' = -1.25$
$$= A(1.75) - A(1.25).$$
The normal approximation for the probability of exactly 5 recoveries is
$0.4599 - 0.3944 = 0.0655$.

Next comes the question of which normal distribution should be used to approximate a particular binomial distribution.
Let B be a binomial random variable.
Each experiment for B consists of n trials.
The probability of success for each trial is p, and $q = 1 - p$.
Therefore, if n is relatively large and the value of p is not close to either 0 or 1, the binomial distribution associated with B can be approximated by the normal distribution $N(M,s)$ where $M = np$ and $s = \sqrt{npq}$.

Example 1   A binomial random variable B consists of experiments with 20 trials. On each trial there is a 25% chance of success. Use a normal distribution to find the probability that for any particular experiment there will be 3 or more successes but less than 7 successes.

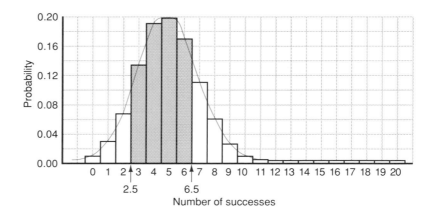

Solution   For B, $n = 20$, $p = 0.25$ and $q = 0.75$. The associated normal distribution is N(M,s) where

$M = np = (20) \times (0.25) = 5$ and $s = \sqrt{npq} = \sqrt{20 \times 0.25 \times 0.75} \doteq 1.94$

$P(3 \leqslant x < 7)$ is the area under N(5,1.94) from the left edge of the rectangle centred on 3 to the left edge of the rectangle centred on 7.

$P(3 \leqslant x < 7)$ is the area under N(5,1.94) from $a = 2.5$ to $b = 6.5$.

$a' = \dfrac{(2.5 - 5)}{1.94}$ $b' = \dfrac{(6.5 - 5)}{1.94}$

$\quad \doteq -1.3$ $\quad \doteq 0.75$

$P(3 \leqslant x < 7)$ equals, approximately,

$A(1.3) + A(0.75) = 0.4032 + 0.2734$ or 0.6766

The probability of 3 or more but less than 7 successes in a given experiment is about 68%.   ∎

Example 2   An examination consists of 36 multiple choice items, each with five different responses. What is the probability that a person could guess twelve or more correct answers?

Solution   Model the situation with a binomial random variable B with $n = 36$, $p = 0.2$ and $q = 0.8$.

Approximate the binomial distribution with the normal distribution N(M,s) where $M = 7.2$ and $s = 2.4$. Find the area under N(7.2,2.4) for $a \geqslant 11.5$.

$a' = \dfrac{(11.5 - 7.2)}{2.4} \doteq 1.8$. The area N(0,1) for $a' \geqslant 1.8$ is 0.0359.

The probability is about 3.6%.   ∎

8.6 Exercises

1. The binomial random variable, B, is such that the probability of success on each trial is $\frac{3}{5}$ and there are 24 trials.

   a) Find M and s so that the normal distribution $N(M,s)$ can be used to approximate probabilities in the distribution based on B.

   In b)-f) find the appropriate values of a' and b' to use with $N(M,s)$ for approximating the given probabilities. For example, to approximate $P(B \geqslant 16)$ using $N(M,s)$, use $a = 15.5$ and the standard score of a, $a' \doteq 0.46$ with $N(M,s)$.

   b) $P(B \leqslant 18)$ d) $P(12 < B < 16)$
   c) $P(B > 10)$ e) $P(12 \leqslant B \leqslant 16)$
   　　　　　　　　　 f) $P(B = 15)$

   (Hint: use the end points of the rectangle centred on 15.)

2. For the binomial random variable B, there is a 50% chance of success on each trial and there are 100 trials.

   a) Find values of M and s so that $N(M,s)$ can be used to approximate the binomial distribution.

   Use $N(M,s)$ to approximate the probability of each of the following.

   b) between 45 and 55 successes inclusive
   c) 40 or less successes
   d) more than 60 successes

3. Use the $N(M,s)$ found in 1 a) to approximate the probabilities given in 1 b)-f).

4. A fair coin is flipped 25 times and the number of heads occurring is observed.

   a) Find M and s so that $N(M,s)$ can be used to approximate the binomial distribution modelling the coin flip.

   Use $N(M,s)$ to approximate the probability of occurrence of each of the following.

   b) less than 8 heads occurred
   c) 16 or more heads occurred
   d) between 10 and 15 heads (inclusive)

5. A test for extra-sensory perception (ESP) involves cards with five different symbols. A card is randomly selected and the person tested must state which symbol is on the card. 100 cards are used in a test.

   a) Establish a binomial random variable B which maps each test to the number of cards on which the symbol was correctly stated. Base the probability of success on random guessing.

   b) Specify a normal distribution $N(M,s)$ which could be used to approximate the distribution of B.

   c) Leah has 30 correct calls in one test. Use $N(M,s)$ to approximate the probability of 30 or more correct calls if Leah were randomly guessing.

6. In a game, a card is drawn at random from a standard 52-card deck. The suit of the card is noted and the card is returned to the deck. You win if a heart is drawn. The game is played 27 times.

   a) Establish a binomial random variable B to model the probability distribution of the number of wins.

   b) Specify a normal distribution $N(M,s)$ which could be used to approximate the distribution of B.

   Use $N(M,s)$ to approximate the probability that you will win as follows.

   c) less than 5 times
   d) 10 times or more
   e) exactly 9 times

7. A new medicine is being tested for its effectiveness against a particular disease. Untreated, a patient has a 25% chance of recovery. 16 patients were given the new medicine and 11 of the sixteen recovered.

   a) Use a normal distribution to approximate the probability that eleven or more patients would recover if the medicine had not been administered.

   b) Compare the approximation in a) to the value for a 50% chance of recovery, calculated on page 353.

Summary

Descriptive Statistics

- The distribution of a set of numbers can be organized and displayed by
  a) making a tally count
  b) using the tally count to make a table of the frequency, relative frequency, cumulative frequency and cumulative relative frequency of each number
  c) using the table to make (relative) frequency diagrams and cumulative (relative) frequency diagrams.

- Numbers which describe characteristics of a distribution are called statistics.

- The mean (arithmetic average) of the numbers, and the median are statistics describing the 'centre' of the distribution.

- The percentile rank and deviation score of a number describe the position of the number relative to the distribution.

- The range, mean deviation and standard deviation are statistics which measure the amount of 'spread', or variability, there is in the distribution.

- Statistics of two different distributions can be used to compare the distributions.

Probability Distributions

- A frequency distribution can be used to find experimental probabilities.

- A theoretical probability distribution can be used to predict a frequency distribution for a population.

- If a number is selected at random from a distribution, then the probability of that number falling within a range of numbers from a to b is the area under the relative frequency distribution graph for $x = a$ to $x = b$.

- Distributions with a finite number of measures are called discrete distributions. Their graphs are characterized by rectangles centred on each measure.

- Distributions with an uncountable number of measures which form an unbroken spectrum are known as continuous distributions. Their graphs are characterized by an unbroken curve.

Normal Distributions

- The normal probability distribution is a continuous distribution which has a bell-shaped distribution curve.

- Many sets of observed measures are normally distributed. The normal distribution is also the limit of a sequence of binomial distributions where the number of trials is increasing.

- If a population has a set of measures which are normally distributed and the distribution has mean M and standard deviation s, then $N(M,s)$ represents the normal distribution of those measures.

- $N(0,1)$ is the standard normal distribution (mean of 0 and standard deviation of 1).

- The area under the curve of $N(M,s)$ from $x = a$ to $x = b$ equals the area under the curve of $N(0,1)$ from $x = a'$ to $x = b'$ where $a' = \dfrac{(a - M)}{s}$ and $b' = \dfrac{(b - M)}{s}$.
  a' and b' are the standard scores of a and b respectively.

- A table of pairs of values $(z,(A(z))$ gives the area under the curve of $N(0,1)$ from $x = 0$ to $x = z$.
  The symmetry of $N(0,1)$, and the fact that all the area under the curve $N(0,1)$ is 1, allows the area under $N(0,1)$ from $x = a$ to $x = b$ to be calculated using the table.

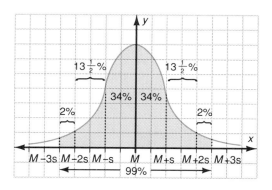

Inventory

Use the following frequency table and cumulative frequency diagram for questions 1-8. A die is rolled twenty times and the number of dots showing is observed each time.

Dots	1	2	3	4	5	6
Frequency	3	1	6	5	2	3

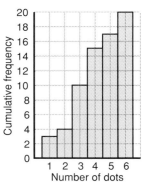

1. The range of the distribution is _____.
2. The upper quartile of the distribution is _____.
3. The observation of 5 dots is at the _____ percentile of this distribution.
4. The relative frequency of 3 dots is _____.
5. The mean of the distribution is _____.
6. The deviation score of 6 dots is _____.
7. The probability of a randomly selected observation being 1 or 2 dots is _____.
8. The theoretical probability of 1 or 2 dots showing when the die is rolled is _____.
9. A set of 5 measures has the deviation scores $-3, -2, -1, 1$ and 5. The standard deviation of the set is _____.

A set of measures is normally distributed with mean $M = 10$ and standard deviation $s = 2$. Use this set for questions 10 and 11.
10. _____ percent of the measures are between 8 and 12.
11. 99% of the measures lie between _____ and _____.
12. The area under the curve of $N(0,1)$ between $x = 0$ and $x = 1.5$ is _____.
13. If 5 is a number from a normally distributed set of numbers with mean 8 and standard deviation 1.5, then the standard score of 5 is ___.

B is a binomial random variable such that $P(B = x)$ is $b(x;24,0.6)$. Use this for questions 14 and 15.
14. If the binomial distribution based on B is to be approximated by the normal distribution $N(M,s)$ then $M =$ _____ and $s =$ _____.
15. If $N(M,s)$ is used to approximate the binomial distribution then $P(15 < B \leqslant 18)$ is approximated by the area under the curve of $N(M,s)$ from $x =$ _____ to $x =$ _____.

Review Exercises

1. Following is a frequency distribution of the age in years when the members of a given population first owned a car.

Age	16	17	18	19	20	21	22	23	24	25	26	27	28	29	30
Freq.	4	12	4	12	8	16	20	24	24	16	8	4	4	0	8

a) Use the distribution to make a frequency and relative frequency diagram.

b) Use the distribution to make a cumulative relative frequency diagram.

c) Find the median, lower quartile and upper quartile of the distribution.

d) What percent of the population owned their first car at age 26 years? less than 26 years?

e) What is the percentile rank of 26 years?

f) Find the interquartile range of the distribution.

g) Make a box and whisker plot of the distribution.

2. Below are the monthly sales (in $10 000) for a sporting goods store.

J	F	M	A	M	J	J	A	S	O	N	D
10	8	10	8	11	8	6	5	10	11	11	14

a) Find the median and the mean of the monthly sales.

b) Find the range and interquartile range of the sales.

c) Find the mean deviation and standard deviation of the sales.

d) What percent of the sales lie within one standard deviation of the mean?

3. A professional cola taster claims to be able to distinguish between the 'real thing' and the competitors. In 64 comparative tastings, the taster correctly identified the cola 41 times. Find the probability of 41 or more correct identifications, if the taster were merely guessing.

4. Below is a frequency diagram for the distribution of scores of a number of students on an examination

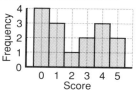

a) Make a cumulative relative frequency diagram of the distribution.

b) Find the median and mean scores.

c) Find the mean deviation and the standard deviation of the scores.

d) If a student's score is randomly selected, what is the probability that the score will be 3 or higher?

5. A group of 40 people was asked to give their favorite single digit number. The following frequency distribution resulted.

Num.	0	1	2	3	4	5	6	7	8	9
Freq.	0	5	2	1	4	5	8	12	2	1

a) List the experimental probability distribution associated with this frequency distribution.

b) Find the mean and standard deviation of the distribution.

c) If each digit was randomly chosen, then list the frequency distribution resulting from the theoretical probability distribution.

d) Find the mean and standard deviation of the distribution associated with the theoretical probabilities.

e) If a person is chosen at random and asked for her favorite digit, what is the experimental probability that the digit will be 5 or greater? the theoretical probability?

f) If 1 000 000 people were asked for their favorite digit, would the resulting distribution be better modelled by the experimental or theoretical distribution? Why?

6. There are 8 black and 12 white marbles in a bag. A marble is randomly selected, its color observed, and then returned to the bag. This is repeated six times.
   a) Establish the theoretical probability distribution which gives the probability of selecting a black marble x of the six times.
   b) Make a graph of the probability distribution.

7. Choose a paragraph from a book and count the number of letters in each of the first 100 words.
   a) Make a frequency and cumulative relative frequency diagram of the resulting distribution.
   b) Find the median and interquartile range of the distribution.
   c) Make a box and whisker plot of the distribution.
   d) Find the mean and standard deviation of the distribution.
   e) What is the probability that the number of letters in a word chosen at random from the paragraphs will be 5 or greater? 10 or greater? 15 or greater?

8. Find the area of the shaded regions under the standard normal curves.

   a)
   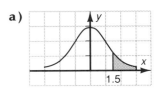

   b)
   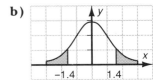

   c)
   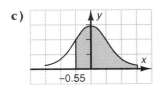

9. In the normal curves below, convert each x-coordinate to its standard score and then find the areas of the shaded regions.

   a)
   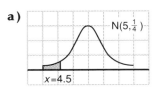

   b)
   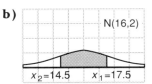

   c)
   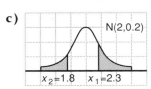

10. A normally distributed population has a mean of 25 and a standard deviation of 2.5.
    a) What percent of the population has a score of 28 or greater?
    b) What is the percentile rank of the measure 21?
    c) What is the least measure to be in the 80th percentile?
    d) What is the probability that a measure randomly chosen from the population is between 23 and 27?
    e) Find a range of values centred on the mean that encompasses 60% of the population.

11. The distance of an arrow from the centre of the target is normally distributed for a particular archer. The mean distance is 6 cm with a standard deviation of 2 cm.
    a) What percent of the archer's shots will land more than 9 cm from the centre? less than 5 cm?
    b) What percent of the archer's shots will land on the target's centre?

12. Car seats are designed to be comfortable for an adult person of average height plus or minus two standard deviations. What percent of the population is likely to be uncomfortable in these cars?

13. A single die is rolled. You win if 6 dots show on the up face.
The game is played 180 times.
a) Establish a binomial random variable to model the situation.
b) Specify a normal distribution N(M,s) which can be used to approximate the probability distribution of the random variable.
Use N(M,s) to approximate the probability that you will win as follows.
c) 25 times or less
d) more than 40 times
e) 35 times or more, but less than 40
f) exactly 40 times

14. a) Using the standard normal distribution N(0,1), find a value a such that the area under the curve from $-a$ to a is approximately 0.5000.
b) Interpret $-a$ and a in terms of percentiles.
c) Find the interquartile range of a normally distributed population with a mean of 100 and standard deviation of 8.

15. The number of defective microprocessor chips per 1000 chips is known to be normally distributed. There is an average of 350 defective chips with a standard deviation of 50 in every batch of 1000.
a) Find the probability that more than half the chips in a batch are defective.
b) Find the probability that a batch has more than 700 working chips.
c) A batch is rejected if it has less than 575 working chips. How many of 800 batches will have to be rejected?

16. The time required by a bureaucracy to complete a particular form is normally distributed. The mean time required is 6 minutes with a 40 second standard deviation.
What is the probability that a form will be completely processed in less than
a) 5 minutes?
b) 8 minutes?
c) between 7 and 8 minutes?

17. The number of times daily a catalog of a library is accessed is normally distributed, with a mean of 150 requests for information and a standard deviation of 20. The library is open 300 days a year. On how many days in a year would the following occur?
a) more than 180 requests for information
b) between 125 and 135 requests
c) less than 100 requests

18. For a particular type of casino game, the probability of winning any one game is $\frac{7}{15}$.
If the game is played 56 times, what is the probability of 'coming out ahead', that is, winning more than half the games?

19. A salesman is able to make a sale to one out of every three people to whom he makes a presentation. If he makes presentations to 54 people in one week, then what is the probability that he will make 25 sales or more?

20. A baseball player has a batting average of 0.300. That is, every time he comes to bat he has a 30% chance of making a hit. In a particular series of games, the player comes to bat 21 times and makes 10 hits. Based on his 0.300 average, what is the probability of the player having 10 or more hits in 21 times at bat?

1. The information shown below was gathered from a survey of people entering a sports store.
   50% played tennis.
   60% jogged.
   50% played hockey.
   30% played tennis and jogged.
   20% jogged and played hockey.
   30% played tennis and hockey.
   10% did all three.
   a) What percent of those surveyed participated in exactly two of the activities?
   b) What percent were not involved in any of the three activities?

2. A menu lists four appetisers, six entrees and five desserts. How many different complete meals can be ordered?

3. In how many ways can ten different gifts be distributed between two children? Among three children? (Include the case where one child receives all of the gifts.)

4. Six points lie in a plane, in 'general position', that is, no three points lie in the same straight line.
   a) How many different line segments can be drawn having these points as end points?
   b) How many different triangles can be drawn with these points as vertices?

5. Ten 1-hour operations have to be scheduled. In how many ways can the schedule shown below be completed?

Operating Rm 1	Operating Rm 2
9:00—10:00	9:00—10:00
10:30—11:30	10:30—11:30
12:00—13:00	12:00—13:00
13:30—14:30	13:30—14:30
15:00—16:00	15:00—16:00

6. Four coins are drawn at random from a bag containing ten quarters, eight nickels and six dimes. How many different sets of coins can be drawn from the bag?

7. Students are asked to solve the quadratic equation $ax^2 + bx + c = 0$ where the coefficients, a, b and c can be any value 1, 2, 3, 4, or 5, no two the same. How many different quadratic equations would the students have to solve?

8. A student sees $P(5,5) = 5 \times 4 \times 3 \times 2 \times 1$ and thinks. "The last factor, 1, in $5 \times 4 \times 3 \times 2 \times 1$ means that the fifth position can be filled in *one* way. If the fifth position can be filled in only one way, how can there be five different objects filling that position?" How would you answer this student's question?

9. Two dice are rolled. Find the probability of each of the following events.
   a) The sum on the up faces is five.
   b) The sum on the up faces is nine.
   c) The sum on the up faces is not five.
   d) The sum on the up faces is five or the sum is nine.
   e) A five appears on at least one die.
   f) A five appears on at least one die and the sum of the up faces is eight.

10. A bag contains four white balls, three green balls, and three red balls. You take out three balls at the same time.
    a) What is the probability that the three will be green?
    b) What is the probability that none of the three will be green?

11. Two cards are selected at random one after the other, without replacement, from a deck of playing cards. Find the probability of each of the following events.
    a) Both cards are red.

b) The first card is red and the second card is black.

c) One card is red and the other card is an ace.

d) The second card is red given that the first card is an ace.

12. A bag contains two white balls, three green balls, and four red balls. You take out two balls at the same time.
    a) What is the probability that the two will be red?
    b) What is the probability that the two will be white?
    c) What is the probability that one will be red and the other will be green?

13. You play a game of rolling two dice. You lose the game if you roll an 11 before you roll a 7. You continue to roll until either 11 or 7 appears. What is the probability that you will lose the game?

14. Three cards are drawn at random from a deck of playing cards, without replacement. What is the probability that all three cards will be aces?

15. The probability of snow in the next three days is 40% on Monday, 60% on Tuesday and 30% on Wednesday.
    a) What is the probability that it will snow on each of the three days?
    b) What is the probability that there will be no snow on any of the three days?

16. Your track coach has six stopwatches, three of which are accurate, one is slow and two are equally fast. Your coach makes a random selection of two watches to time the first place finisher of your race. Find the probability of each of the following.
    a) Both watches are accurate.
    b) At least one watch is accurate.
    c) Both watches show the same time.
    d) You win the race.

17. How long does it take your calculator/computer to multiply two 7×7 matrices? two 10×10 matrices? How long do you think your calculator/computer would take to multiply two 100×100 matrices? What are the maximum dimensions of the matrices that your calculator/computer can multiply?

18. The following chart shows the number of items manufactured in an electronics factory during each week in February.

	Radios	Calculators	Watches
Week 1	195	300	550
Week 2	210	320	500
Week 3	250	290	480
Week 4	200	310	470

The selling price of each item is given below:
Radios $25 Calculators $20 Watches $15
Use matrix multiplication to calculate the value of goods produced each week.

19. Encode the following messages using the encoding matrix $\begin{bmatrix} 3 & -2 \\ -4 & 3 \end{bmatrix}$
    a) ROCK AND ROLL
    b) COUNTRY AND WESTERN
    c) BACH AND HANDEL

20. Choose a 2×2 encoding matrix, E, and determine the corresponding decoding matrix, D. Encode a message using E and give it to a friend, together with matrix D. See if your friend can decode your message. Then, your friend should use matrix D to encode a reply to you. See if you can use E to decode the reply.

21. Decode the following messages using the decoding matrix $D = \begin{bmatrix} 5 & 3 \\ 3 & 2 \end{bmatrix}$
    a) $-32 \quad -65 \quad -17 \quad -10 \quad 19 \quad 57$
    $\quad\;\; 110 \quad 30 \quad 22 \quad -25$
    b) $-5 \quad -33 \quad -37 \quad -17 \quad -20 \quad 15$
    $\quad\;\; 58 \quad 66 \quad 30 \quad 40$

22. The diagram below shows the communication links between various space stations. Use matrices to determine which stations can communicate with each other using at most one intermediate station.

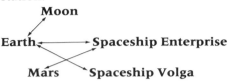

23. Given the following matrices

$$A = \begin{bmatrix} 10 & -2 \\ 0 & 5 \end{bmatrix} \qquad B = \begin{bmatrix} 2 & 1 & 3 \\ -4 & 0 & 5 \end{bmatrix}$$

$$C = \begin{bmatrix} 0 \\ 1 \\ 5 \end{bmatrix} \qquad D = \begin{bmatrix} 4 & -2 & 1 \\ 0 & -3 & 2 \end{bmatrix}$$

evaluate the following, where possible.

a) $B + D$ g) B^2
b) $B - D$ h) BC
c) $A + B$ i) CB
d) $4A$ j) AB
e) $2B - 5D$ k) BD
f) A^2

24. Determine the values of a, b, c, d, such that
$$\begin{bmatrix} 2 & 4 \\ -1 & 3 \end{bmatrix}\begin{bmatrix} a & b \\ b & d \end{bmatrix} = \begin{bmatrix} 4 & 18 \\ 3 & 1 \end{bmatrix}$$

25. Determine the values of $a, b, c, d, e, f, g, h, i$ such that
$$\begin{bmatrix} a & b & c \\ d & e & f \\ g & h & i \end{bmatrix}\begin{bmatrix} 1 & 2 & 0 \\ -3 & 4 & -2 \\ 5 & 1 & 0 \end{bmatrix} = \begin{bmatrix} 14 & -1 & 4 \\ 14 & 10 & 0 \\ -2 & -16 & 6 \end{bmatrix}$$

26. The height, h, in metres of a javelin at a horizontal distance, x metres, from the point where it was thrown is given by the equation $h = \dfrac{100x - x^2}{250}$

a) Determine the domain for x.
b) Is this a continuous or a discrete function?

27. If a communication matrix is symmetric, what does this imply for the corresponding network?

28. A manufacturer of metal alloys is making an alloy of lead, zinc and tin with the following composition.

Metal	% in alloy
lead	60%
zinc	20%
tin	20%

Five raw material sources containing the various metals and impurities are available. The percentage compositions of each metal and the impurities are given below.

Source of raw material / Metal	1	2	3	4	5
lead	40	10	20	0	50
zinc	10	30	10	20	20
tin	20	10	20	10	10
Impurities	30	50	50	70	20
Cost of Processing 1 tonne	$27	$21	$15	$18	$30

Determine how much of each source should be used in order to produce 1 tonne of alloy at minimum cost.

29. Patel believes that best indication of whether it will rain tomorrow is whether it rained today. She believes that if it rained today, there is an 80% chance that it will rain tomorrow. If it has not rained today, there is only a 30% chance that it will rain tomorrow.

a) Use this data to set up a transition matrix, T.
b) If it has rained today, what is the probability that it will rain in three days time?

30. Choose any square matrix A, and show that $A^3 = A^2(A) = A(A^2)$.

31. A supermarket in Montreal imports frozen juices and fresh fruit from a certain company in Florida. The supermarket can rent two types of trucks to transport these commodities. Truck type A has 100 m^3 of refrigerated space and 40 m^3 of non-refrigerated space. Truck type B has 60 m^3 of refrigerated space and 80 m^3 of non-refrigerated space. The trucking company charges $2000 for each truck of type A per trip and $1600 for each truck of type B per trip. The total volumes of juice and fruit to be transported each month are 1600 m^3 and 1200 m^3 respectively. The juice must be refrigerated; the fruit does not need refrigeration. How many trucks of each type should be rented so that the cost of transportation is minimized? Formulate this problem as a linear programming problem.

32. In a laboratory experiment there are three different types of bacteria in each sample that is weighed. It is impossible to separate the different types of bacteria, but it is possible to count the number of each type of bacteria in each sample.
The following results were obtained.

Sample Number	Bacteria A # in sample in 1000's	Bacteria B # in sample in 1000's	Bacteria C # in sample in 1000's	Total Weight (units)
1	150	200	300	35
2	500	300	200	51
3	750	500	500	74

Form a set of equations to model this situation.

33. Expand the following using the binomial theorem.
a) $(a + x)^6$
b) $(m - k)^4$
c) $(a + 3b)^3$
d) $(3a + 2y)^8$
e) $(3 - 2x)^5$
f) $(m + k)^3$
g) $(8 - 3a)^6$
h) $(2 - 2a)^5$
i) $(4k - 1)^7$
j) $(k^2 + 4)^4$

34. Determine the ranks of the coefficient and augmented matrices for each of the following systems. State whether the system is consistent-independent, consistent-dependent or inconsistent.
a) $\begin{aligned} 2x - 3y + z &= 1 \\ y + z &= 2 \\ z &= 0 \end{aligned}$
b) $\begin{aligned} 3x - 4y + z &= 2 \\ 2y + z &= 1 \\ 0z &= 5 \end{aligned}$
c) $\begin{aligned} x + y + z + t &= 0 \\ y - z - t &= 5 \\ z + 3t &= 11 \end{aligned}$
d) $\begin{aligned} x - y + 2z + 4t &= 9 \\ 2y - 4z + t &= 7 \\ z + t &= 1 \\ 0t &= 4 \end{aligned}$

35. Find the first three terms of the expansion of each of the following. Do not simplify.
a) $(a + x)^{123}$
b) $(2 + 3c)^{15}$

36. Expand.
a) $\left(x + \dfrac{4}{x}\right)^3$
b) $\left(x - \dfrac{1}{x}\right)^5$

37. Write the general term of each of the following. Leave your answer in terms of $C(n,k)$.
a) $(a + x)^8$
b) $(5 + t)^{17}$

38. Write the seventh term of $(p + q)^{14}$.

39. Evaluate the fifth term of $(0.2 + 0.8)^6$, correct to 4 decimal places.

40. For each of the following, find the general term, and, if possible, the term containing x^5.
a) $\left(x^2 + \dfrac{2}{x}\right)^4$
b) $\left(x + \dfrac{1}{x}\right)^7$

41. Find the indicated term in the expansion of each of the following.
a) $(m + 6)^{34}$; tenth term
b) $\left(2x + \dfrac{3}{b}\right)^{40}$; thirtieth term

42. Find the middle term of $(3 + 4b)^{13}$.

43. For the expansion of $\left(x + \dfrac{1}{x}\right)^{10}$ find the term that does not contain an x.

44. Prove that $C(n + 1, k) = C(n, k - 1) + C(n, k)$.

45. Prove that the sum of the binomial coefficients in row $n = t$ of Pascal's triangle is 2^t.

46. Find the 9th term and the sum of 9 terms of each of the following arithmetic or geometric series.
  a) $14 + 21 + 28 + \ldots$
  b) $35 - 5 - 45 - \ldots$
  c) $1.19 + 1.21 + 1.23 + \ldots$
  d) $-8 + 1 - 0.125 + \ldots$
  e) $1.2 + 0.12 + 0.012 + \ldots$
  f) $14 + 28 + 56 + \ldots$

47. For each geometric series in question 46 that converges find the S_∞.

48. For each of the following arithemetic or geometric series find the general term then write n terms of the series in compact form using sigma notation.
  a) $7 + 21 + 63 + \ldots$ **c)** $4 + 12 + 20 + \ldots$
  b) $2 + \dfrac{6}{5} + \dfrac{18}{25} + \ldots$ **d)** $25 + 2 - 21 - \ldots$

49. How many terms are there in each of the following arithmetic or geometric series?
  a) $29 + 34 + \ldots + 349$
  b) $4 - 12 + 36 - \ldots - 8748$

50. Find the first term and the 5th term for the arithmetic series having third term equal to 28 and seventh term equal to 8.

51. Determine a and r for the geometric series of real numbers having 5th term equal to 20 and 9th term equal to 1620.

52. Find the sum of 10 terms for each of the following arithmetic-geometric series. Find the sum in **a)** correct to 7 significant figures.
  a) $0.5 + 0.5 + 0.375 + \ldots$
  b) $3m^2 + 18m^4 + 81m^6 + \ldots$

53. Use the fact that
$$\frac{4}{(4n - 2)(4n + 2)} = \frac{1}{4n - 2} - \frac{1}{4n + 2}$$
to find the sum of n terms of the series
$$\frac{1}{2(6)} + \frac{1}{6(10)} + \frac{1}{10(14)} + \ldots + \frac{1}{(4n - 2)(4n + 2)}$$

54. The music scale on a piano has 12 notes from A to G, including black keys. This scale is repeated several times on the keyboard. The A below middle C on the piano has a frequency of 220 vibrations per second (vps) while the A above middle C has a frequency of 440 vps. The frequencies of each of the 11 notes between successive A's form a geometric sequence with the two A's.
  a) Find the common ratio of this musical scale sequence.
  b) Calculate, correct to 1 decimal place, the frequency of each note between A-220 vps and A-440 vps.
  c) What note on the piano has a frequency of 1175 vps?

55. Express $C(23, 12)$ in terms of summations $C(18, k)$ and $C(5, m)$.

56. Prove the following statements using mathematical induction, where $n \in N$.
  a) $6 + 11 + 16 + \ldots + (5n + 1) = \dfrac{n(5n + 7)}{2}$
  b) $\displaystyle\sum_{j=1}^{n} \dfrac{1}{j(j + 2)} = \dfrac{3n^2 + 5n}{4(n + 1)(n + 2)}$

57. Two cubic dice are rolled and the number of dots on the up face of each die is noted. Let V be the random variable which maps each roll to the larger number of dots showing on one up face. For example, the roll represented by $(5, 3)$ maps to 5.
  a) List the probability distribution for V.
  b) Use the distribution from a) to calculate $P(V > 4)$ and $P(2 \leqslant V \leqslant 4)$.

58. If X is random variable and k is a constant, then prove that
  a) $E(X + k) = E(X) + k$ and
  b) $E(kX) = kE(X)$.

59. A coin is weighted so that there is a $\frac{3}{4}$ chance on any flip that the coin will land heads. The coin is flipped three times and the number of heads occurring is noted. Z is the random variable mapping each possible experiment of three flips to the number of heads occurring in the three flips.

a) Calculate and list the probability for each simple event. For example, the outcome HTH corresponds to the simple event {HTH}. The probability that this event occurs is $\frac{3}{4} \times \frac{1}{4} \times \frac{3}{4} = \frac{9}{64}$.

b) Calculate $P(Z = k)$ by adding the probabilities of each simple event where exactly k heads occur.

c) List the probability distribution for Z.

d) Calculate $E(Z)$.

60. a) Use the definition of expected value to show by example that
$E(Z + Y) = E(X) + E(Y)$
for any two random variables X and Y defined in the same sample space.

b) Let T be the random variable which maps each roll of a pair of cubic dice to the total number of dots showing on the up faces. Use the results from a) to show that $E(T) = 7$. (Hint: Let X map each roll to the number of dots showing on one die and Y map each roll to the number of dots on the other die.)

61. In a group of 12 students, eight students are expert skiiers. Five students are randomly selected from the group. Find the probability of each of the following.

a) None of the five chosen can ski well.

b) All of the five chosen can ski well.

c) At least one of the students chosen cannot ski well.

62. A roulette wheel has 38 compartments, of which 18 are red. For ten games in a row, a person bet that the ball would land red. Find the probability that this person won more often than lost.

63. U is a random variable with a uniform probability distribution. The range of U is $\{-10, -5, 0, 5, 20\}$.

a) Find $P(U = 5)$.

b) Find the probability that U has a non-negative value for any trial of the experiment.

c) Find $E(U)$.

64. Forty-five objects are of type A and thirty objects are of type B. n objects are randomly selected without replacement. H is the hypergeometric random variable which maps each possible n-tuple to the number of objects of type A in the selection.

a) What is the largest value of n for which it would be appropriate to use a binomial distribution to approximate $P(H = x)$, $x \leqslant n$?

b) If $n = 6$, calculate $P(H = 3)$.

c) Use a binomial distribution to approximate $P(H = 3)$ when $n = 6$. Compare this approximation to your result in b).

65. An urn contains 10 white marbles, 10 blue marbles, 10 green, 10 red and 10 yellow marbles. A marble is chosen at random, its color noted, and then returned to the urn. The random variable X is defined as

color	white	blue	green	red	yellow
X (color)	1	2	3	4	5

a) What type of random variable is X?

b) List the probability distribution of X.

c) Find the expected value of X.

d) Find $P(3 \leqslant X < 5)$.

66. A restaurant knew that 15% of the parties making reservations would not show. One evening there were thirty reservations.

a) Find the probability that everyone showed up for their reservations.

b) Find the probability that at least four of the parties who made reservations did not show.

67. A public television station phones people soliciting donations. 6% of the phone calls result in a donation. Twenty people are telephoned. Find the probability of each of the following.
  a) None of the people telephoned made donations.
  b) More than two of the people telephoned made donations.

68. A game is played. The random variable T maps each game to the amount of money won or lost by player A. Following is the probability distribution of T.

x	−20	−10	0	10	20	30
$P(T = x)$	0.15	0.25	0.10	0.15	0.10	0.25

  a) Find $E(T)$.
  b) Interpret $E(T)$ as the amount of money won or lost by player A over a large number of games.
  c) If 300 games were played, in how many of the games would you expect player A to lose money?

69. In a group of fifteen vacationers, five played tennis well and ten did not. Six people were randomly selected from the fifteen. Find the probability of each of the following.
  a) All six chosen were good tennis players.
  b) Exactly two of the six were good players.
  c) At least two of the six chosen were good players.

70. Variance of a distribution is the square of the standard deviation for the distribution. Using the calculation in the text for standard deviation, variance is "the mean of the squares of the deviation scores". Show that an equivalent calculation of variance is "the mean of the squares of the data minus the square of the mean of the data". That is, show

$$\frac{1}{N} \sum (x_i - \overline{x})^2 = \frac{1}{N} \sum x_i^2 - \left(\frac{1}{N} \sum x_i\right)^2$$

71. A pair of dice is rolled. You win on a roll if doubles is rolled or the total number of dots showing on the up faces is 7 or 11. The dice are rolled five times. X is the random variable which maps each possible five rolls to the number of wins in the five rolls. Use the expansion of $(q + p)^5$ to list the probability distribution of X.

72. Eighty words were chosen at random from an essay. The number of syllables in each word was counted. The following frequency table resulted.

syllables	1	2	3	4	5
frequency	32	20	16	8	4

  a) Find the mean, mode and median of this distribution.
  b) Find the mean deviation of this distribution.
  c) Find the interquartile range of the distribution.

73. Choose a paragraph at random from each of three textbooks for different subjects.
  a) Count the number of syllables in the first 80 words in each paragraph and make a frequency distribution table for each text.
  b) Calculate the mean and median of each distribution.
  c) Calculate the mean deviation of each distribution.
  d) Compare the 'average word lengths'.

74. A group of 20 people underwent a fitness program. A control group did not follow any organized program. At the end of the program, both groups did a three minute step test, had one minute of rest and then had their heart rates recorded in beats/minute. Following are the results.
Control group: 86, 95, 72, 68, 106, 78, 118, 80, 102, 93, 75, 84, 96, 112, 105, 81, 70, 96, 103, 73
Fitness group: 68, 75, 90, 60, 105, 87, 70, 90, 100, 80, 71, 76, 92, 88, 102, 96, 68, 75, 80, 85

a) Find the mean and standard deviation for each group.

b) Make a box and whisker plot for each group.

c) Which group shows the greatest variability?

d) Which analysis of the data, the one in a) or b), was the easiest to perform? the most informative?

75. Each of the following populations are normally distributed with a mean of M and a standard deviation of s. Use tables (page 344) to find the percent of the populations which have measures in the specified ranges of values.

a) $M = 0$, $s = 1$. Measures are greater than 1.5 or less than -1.5.

b) $M = 10$, $s = 2$. Measures are less than 8.5.

c) $M = 1.5$, $s = 0.4$. Measures are between 1 and 2.

d) $M = 50$, $s = 6$. Measures are between 47 and 59.

e) $M = 23$, $s = 2.5$. Measures are less than 20 or greater than 25.

76. The weights of wheels of cheese are normally distributed with a mean of 26.8 kg and a standard deviation of 1.2 kg. A dozen gross of wheels are shipped. (1 gross = 144 wheels).

a) How many of the wheels weigh more than 28 kg?

b) How many wheels weigh less than 25 kg?

c) A wheel is selected at random from the shipment. What is the probability that the wheel weighs more than 29.8 kg or less than 23.8 kg?

d) Specify a range of weights centered on the mean such that the probability of a randomly selected wheel not having a weight in that range is less than 5%.

77. At a ski resort that waiting time to use a particular chairlift is normally distributed. The mean waiting time is 15 minutes with a standard deviation of 4 minutes. Without using tables of values, complete the following statements.

a) 68% of the wait times will be between _____ and _____ minutes.

b) The probability of waiting more than _____ minutes in the lift line is less than 0.5%.

c) The probability that any wait time will be more then seven minutes is _____.

78. A population has the normal distribution $N(M,s)$. 99% of the measures in the population lie between 20 and 42.

a) Find a possible pair of values for M and s.

b) Specify a range of values such that approximated 68% of the population has measures in that range.

c) Find the percentile rank of the measure 32.

79. A binomial distribution is based on 2100 trials and a probability of success of 30% on each trial.

a) Find the appropriate values of M and s for a normal distribution $N(M,s)$ which can be used to approximate the probability values in the binomial distribution.

b) Use the $N(M,s)$ from a) to approximate the probability of more than 640 successes occurring in the 2100 trials.

c) Use the $N(M,s)$ from a) to approximate the probability that there will be less than 662 successes, but at least 620 successes in the 2100 trials.

80. Use a normal distribution to approximate the probability that when a pair of dice is rolled 180 times, doubles will occur at least 20% of the time.

Generally, answer is not provided where this is implied in the question.
Answers which will vary are also not provided.
Some answers have been left in unsimplified form, as a hint.

Chapter One
Combinatories

1.1 Exercises, page 9

1. $U = \{1, 2, 3, \ldots 18, 19, 20\}$
   $n(U) = 20$
   $A = \{1, 3, 5, 7, 9, 11, 13, 15, 17, 19\}, n(A) = 10$
   $B = \{2, 4, 6, 8, 10, 12, 14, 16, 18, 20\}, n(B) = 10$
   $C = \{10, 11, 12, 13, 14, 15, 16, 17, 18, 19, 20\}, n(C) = 11$

2. a)

   b)

   c)

   d)

3. a) the even numbers to 20, inclusive
   b) the first twenty natural numbers
   c) all odd 2-digit numbers, to 19
   d) the even 1-digit numbers
   e) all odd numbers to 19, together with even 2-digit numbers to 20
   f) the even 1-digit numbers

4. a) $A' = \{2, 4, 6, \ldots, 20\}$,
      $n(A') = 10$
   b) $A \cup B = \{1, 2, 3, \ldots, 20\}$,
      $n(A \cup B) = 20$
   c) $A \cap C = \{11, 13, 15, 17, 19\}$,
      $n(A \cap C) = 5$
   d) $(A \cup C)' = \{2, 4, 6, 8\}$,
      $n((A \cup C)') = 4$
   e) $A \cup C = \{1, 3, 5, 7, 9, 10, 11, 12, \ldots, 20\}, n(A \cup C) = 16$
   f) $A' \cap C' = \{2, 4, 6, 8\}$,
      $n(A' \cap C') = 4$

5. A and B

6. Answers will vary.

7. a) 11
   b) 7
   c) 3
   d) 15
   e) 4
   f) 8
   g) 12
   h) 7
   i) 15

8. Answers will vary.

9. a) 13
   b) 14
   c) 22
   d) 8
   e) 12
   f) 9
   g) 21
   h) 28

10. a) 16
    b) 16
    c) 13
    d) 0
    e) 3
    f) 5
    g) 28
    h) 19
    i) 22
    j) 12
    k) 28
    l) 0

11. 122

12. 50; 4

13. Answers will vary.

1.2 Exercises, pages 14-16
No answer provided for question 18.

1. Answers will vary.
2. 676
3. 17 576
4. 17 576 000
5. The counting principle would count ham and olives as different from olives and ham, thus 'double-counting'.
6. 15
7. 9 000 000
8. 208 860
9. a) 17 576 000
   b) 100 000
10. 810
11. a) 90
    b) 7290
    c) 6570
    d) 41 040
12. 2, 4, 8, 16, 32, 1024, 2^n
13. 18
14. a) 216
    b) 120
    c) 96
15. a) 64
    b) 24
    c) 40
16. 175
17. 900, 270 000
19. 2400 pairs of shoes; value will vary.
20. 30
21. 64, yes
22. 6
23. 3 628 799
24. Answers will vary.
25. 120
26. 40 320
27. a) 256
    b) 24
    c) 232

28. a) 625
    b) 120
    c) 505
29. a) 5
    b) $b - a + 1$
30. a) 46
    b) $(b - a + 1)c + (c - a + 1)b$
31. a) 416
    b) $d[(b - a + 1)c + (c - a + 1)b] +$
       $(d - a + 1)bc$

1.3 Exercises, page 20

1. Answers will vary.
2. Answers will vary.
3. $\{+-, +\times, -\times, -+, \times+, \times-\}$
   $\{+-\times, +\times-, -+\times, -\times+, \times+-, \times-+\}$
4.

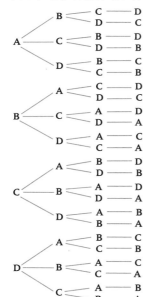

5. a) 2
   b) 6
   c) 12
   d) 380
   e) 9900
   f) $n(n - 1)$
   g) 6
   h) 24
   i) 60
   j) 24 360
   k) 120
   l) undefined
6. $P(20,20)$

7. $P(4,3)$
8. $P(10,2), P(100,1), P(5,4), P(7,3)$
9. a) $n = 6, r = 6$
   b) $n = 8, r = 3$
   c) $n = 510, r = 4$
   d) $n = a, r = 3$
   e) $n = 9, r = 7$
   f) not defined, no possible
      values
10. 60
11. a) 5040
    b) 6
    c) 720
    d) 2160, 2880
    e) The sum of the answers in
       part d) equals the answer in
       part a)
12. 399 168 seconds
13. a) 40 320
    b) 336
14. a) 120
    b) 2520
15. a) 120
    b) 24
    c) 48
    d) 72
    e) 12
    f) 36

1.4 Exercises, page 23
*No answers provided for questions 2, 3, 4,
7, 17, 18, 19.*

1. a) 120
   b) 10
   c) 380
   d) 1
5. a) n
   b) $a(a - 1)$
   c) $a - 1$
   d) $(a + 1)a$
6. a) 7!
   b) $\dfrac{7!}{2!}$
   c) $m!$
   d) $\dfrac{a!}{(a - b)!}$
8. 2
9. 69!
10. $5! = 5 \cdot 4!$
    but $4! = 4 \cdot 3!$
    $\therefore 5! = 5 \cdot 4 \cdot 3! \ldots$
11. 1

12. $\dfrac{n!}{(n - n)!} = \dfrac{n!}{0!}$
    but $0! = 1$
    $\therefore P(n,n) = n!$
13. a) 2.43×10^{18}
    b) 5.19×10^8
    c) 1.304×10^{39}
    d) 1.31×10^{12}
    e) 3.95×10^{21}
    f) 3.930×10^{20}
14. 39 916 800
15. $n > 3$ or $n \geqslant 4$
16. 26!

In Search of, page 26
The last 9 should be 0.

1.5 Exercises, page 29

1. Answers will vary.
2. E, F, C, D, A, B
3. A 60 B 120 C 20
   D 30 E 5 F 10
4. CALCULATE, 45360;
   ARRANGE, 1260;
   LETTERS, 1260;
   UNDERLINED, 453 600
5. AARDVARK
6. 10
7. a)

Outcomes	0H	1H	2H	3H	4H	5H	6H
Number	1	6	15	20	15	6	1

   b) 3H
8. 420
9. 3 527 160
10. 4200
11. Answers will vary.
12. a) $\dfrac{12!}{2!4!6!} = 13\ 860$
    b) $\dfrac{6!}{2!3!} = 60$
13. $\dfrac{11!}{6!5!} = 462$
14. 300

1.6 Exercises, pages 35-36

No answers provided for questions 19, 21.

1. Answers will vary.
2. important for a) b) g)
3. a) $P(10,3)$; 6 times
   b) $P(n,r)$; $r!$ times
4. Answers will vary.
5. a) 56
   b) 252
   c) not defined
   d) n
   e) $\dfrac{n(n-1)}{2}$
   f) n
6. $C(7,2)$
7. a) 1
   b) 1000
   c) 1000
   d) 1
8. largest $n = 3$; smallest $n = 0, 6$
9. largest $n = 3,4$; smallest $n = 0, 7$
10. a) 120
    b) 720
    c) 10
    d) 10
    e) 6.35×10^{11}
    f) 20
    g) 120
    h) 56
    i) 45
    j) 126, 126
11. Answers will vary.
12. Answers will vary.
13. a) 1326
    b) 66
    c) 780
    d) 546
14. a) 35
    b) True for $n \geqslant 3$
    c) 47
15. 56
16. a) $C(8,4) + C(8,3) = 126$
    b) $C(n,4) + C(n,3)$
17. a) 252
    b) 252 252
18. Answers will vary.
20. a) 21
    b) 315
22. 1.17×10^{10}

In Search of, page 37

No answers provided.

1.7 Exercises, page 40

No answer provided for question 13.

1. $\{\ \}, \{A\}, \{B\}, \{C\}, \{A,B\}, \{A,C\},$
   $\{B,C\}, \{A,B,C\}$
2. a) 32
   b) 16
   c) 7
3. a) 1
   b) 2
   c) 3
   d) 6
   e) 9
   f) 10
4. a) 32
   b) 2^{26}
   c) 64
   d) 192
5. 63
6. 63
7. a) 120
   b) 1023 days
8. 32
9. Answers will vary.
10. 944
11. 1.27 seconds
12. a) $\{2\}, \{3\}, \{5\}, \{2,3\}, \{2,5\}, \{3,5\},$
    $\{2,3,5\}$
    b) 2, 3, 5, 6, 10, 15, 30
    c) They are all factors.
    d) 1260, 36
    e) $2 \times 2 \times 5 \times 5 \times 3$, 17

Inventory, page 42

1. F
2. T
3. T
4. F
5. T
6. F
7. T
8. T
9. T
10. T
11. T
12. F
13. F
14. T
15. T
16. T
17. T
18. F
19. F
20. T

Review Exercises, pages 43-45

No answers provided for questions 33, 34, 35, 36.

1. a) $\{B, C, D, F, G, H, J\}$
   b) $\{F, G, J\}$
   c) $\{A, E, I\}$
   d) $\{A, B, C, D, E, H, I\}$
   e) $\{(A,A), (A,E), (A,I), (E,A),$
      $(E,E), (E,I), (I,A), (I,E), (I,I)\}$
   f) 100
   g) 2^{10}
   h) 0
   i) 10
2. 47
3. 4
4. a)

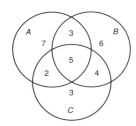

   b) 70
   c) A, 7; B, 6; C, 3
   d) 30
5. Answers will vary.
6. 2^{10}
7. 4^{10}
8. 144
9. a) 256
   b) 24
   c) 81
10. 1000
11. 88 572
12. 3^8

13. a) 6
    b) 120
    c) 60
    d) 1 663 200
    e) 5
    f) 35
14. a) permutations of a objects in
       groups of b
    b) number of d subsets of
       c objects
15. a) $P(9,2)$ is 2! times larger than
       $C(9,2)$.
    b) $P(a,b)$ is b! times larger than
       $C(a,b)$.
16. a) 120
    b) 20
    c) 1
    d) 120
    e) $8! = 40\ 320$
    f) 66
    g) 1
    h) 1
    i) 1
    j) n
    k) n
    l) 6
17. a) 120
    b) 3125
    c) 48
    d) 48
18. a) 255
    b) 56
    c) 56
19. a) 1140
    b) 171
    c) 969
20. a) 380
    b) 6840
    c) 1140
21. B
22. a) 3 628 800
    b) 28 800
23. a) Answers will vary.
    b) Answers will vary.
24. a) $2\ 598\ 960 = C(52,5)$
    b) $792 = C(12,5)$
    c) $658\ 008 = C(40,5)$
    d) $65\ 780 = C(26,5)$
    e) $1287 = C(13,5)$
25. a) 32
    b) 64
    c) 12
    d) 192

26. 63
27. 70
28. a) 48
    b) 49
29. a) 42 504
    b) 494 236 512
    c) 1.25×10^{14}
30. 945
31. 120 120
32. They are mutually exclusive.
37. 15

Chapter Two
Probability

2.1 Exercises, page 50

1. a) unlikely
   b) certain
   c) impossible
   d) half the time
   e) certain
   f) impossible
   g) unlikely
   h) likely
   i) Answers will vary.
   j) likely

2. a) likely
   b) unlikely
   c) certain
   d) impossible

3. Answers will vary.

4. 60%

5. a) $\dfrac{7}{60} \doteq 11.7\%$
   b) 20%
   c) 0%
   d) 100%

6. Answers will vary.

7. Answers will vary.

2.2 Exercises, pages 55–56

1. a) $S = \{1, 2, 3, 4, 5, 6\}$
   b) $E = \{5\}$
   c) $F = \{5,6\}$
   d) $G = \{1, 2, 3, 4\}$
   e) $n(S) = 6, n(E) = 1, n(F) = 2,$
      $n(G) = 4$

2. a)

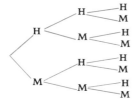

   $S = \{$HHH, HHM, HMH,
   HMM, MHH, MHM,
   MMH, MMM$\}$

   b) $E_1 = \{$M,M,M$\}$
   c) $E_2 = \{$HHM,HMH,MHH$\}$
   d) $E_3 = \{$HHH,HHM,HMH,MHH$\}$
   e) $n(S) = 8, n(E_1) = 1, n(E_2) = 3,$
      $n(E_3) = 4$

3. a)

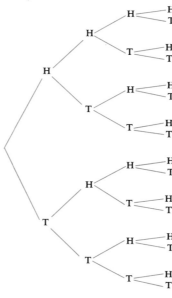

   $S = \{$HHHH, HHHT, HHTH,
   HHTT, HTHH, HTHT,
   HTTH, HTTT, THHH,
   THHT, THTH, THTT,
   TTTH, TTHH, TTHT,
   TTTT$\}$

   b) $E_1 = \{$TTTH, TTHT, THTT,
   HTTT$\}$
   c) $E_2 = \{$HHTT, HTHT, THHT,
   TTHH, HTTH, THTH$\}$
   d) $E_3 = \{$TTTH, TTHT, THTT,
   HTTT, TTTT$\}$
   e) $n(S) = 16, n(E_1) = 4,$
      $n(E_2) = 6, n(E_3) = 5$

4. a)

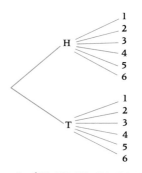

   $S = \{$H1, H2, H3, H4, H5, H6,
   T1, T2, T3, T4, T5, T6$\}$
   b) $E = \{$H2, H4, H6$\}$
   c) $n(S) = 12, n(E) = 3$

5. a)

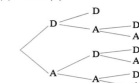

   $S = \{$DD, DAD, DAA, ADD,
   ADA, AAD, AAA$\}$
   b) $E = \{$DAA, ADA, AAD$\}$
   c) $F = \{$DAA, ADA, AAD$\}$

6. a) $S = \{(1,1), (1,2), (1,3), (1,4),$
   $(1,5), (1,6),$
   $(2,1), (2,2), (2,3), (2,4),$
   $(2,5), (2,6),$
   $(3,1), (3,2), (3,3), (3,4),$
   $(3,5), (3,6),$
   $(4,1), (4,2), (4,3), (4,4),$
   $(4,5), (4,6),$
   $(5,1), (5,2), (5,3), (5,4),$
   $(5,5), (5,6),$
   $(6,1), (6,2), (6,3), (6,4),$
   $(6,5), (6,6)\}$
   b) $E = \{(1,2), (2,1)\}$
   c) $F = \{(1,1), (1,2), (1,3), (1,4),$
   $(1,5), (1,6),$
   $(2,1), (2,2), (2,3), (2,4),$
   $(2,5), (2,6),$
   $(3,1), (3,2), (3,3), (3,4),$
   $(3,5), (3,6),$
   $(4,1), (4,2), (4,3), (5,1),$
   $(5,2), (5,3),$
   $(6,1), (6,2), (6,3)\}$
   d) $n(S) = 36, n(E) = 2, n(F) = 27$

7. a) $E = \{$AH, KH, QH, JH, 10H,
9H, 8H, 7H, 6H, 5H, 4H,
3H, 2H, AD, KD, QD, JD,
10D, 9D, 8D, 7D, 6D, 5D,
4D, 3D, 2D$\}$
b) $F = \{$KH, QH, JH, KD, QD, JD$\}$
c) $G = \{$3C, 5C, 7C, 9C$\}$

8. a)
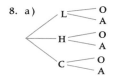
$S = \{$LO, LA, HO, HA, CO, CA$\}$
b) $E = \{$LA, HA, CA$\}$

9. a) $S = \{$ $R_1, R_2, W_1, W_2, W_3\}$
b) $E = \{R_1, R_2\}$
c) $S_2 = \{R_1R_2, R_1W_1, R_1W_2, R_1W_3$
R_2R_1, R_2W_1 etc.$\}$
d) $E_2 = \{W_1W_2, W_1W_3$ etc.$\}$

10. $S = \{$even, odd$\}$

11. a) Answers will vary. Each
outcome consists of three parts.
b) For example, (H, 6, Q)
(H, 1, 2) etc.
c) 156

12. a) $S = \{$(H,1,1), (T,1,1),
(H,1,2), (T,1,2),
(H,1,3), (T,1,3),…,
(H,6,6), (T,6,6)$\}$
b) 72

13. a) $S = \{$(1,2), (1,3), (1,4), (1,5),
(2,1) (2,3), (2,4), (2,5),
(3,1), (3,2) (3,4), (3,5),
(4,1), (4,2), (4,3) (4,5),
(5,1), (5,2), (5,3), (5,4)$\}$
b) $E = \{$(2,4), (4,2)$\}$
c) $F = \{$(1,4), (4,1)$\}$
d) $G = \{$ $\}$
e) $n(S) = 20, n(E) = 2, n(F) = 2,$
$n(G) = 0$

14. a) $S = \{$(1,a), (1,b), (1,c), (2,a),
(2,b), (2,c), (3,a), (3,b),
(3c), (4,a), (4,b), (4c)$\}$
b) $E = \{$(1,a), (1,b), (1,c), (3,a),
(3,b), (3,c)$\}$
c) $F = \{$(1,a), (2,a), (3,a), (4,a)$\}$
d) $G = \{$(1,a), (3,a)$\}$

15. a)
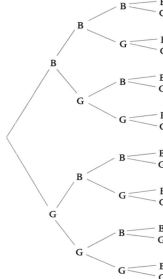
$S = \{$BBBB, BBBG, BBGB,
BBGG, BGBB, BGBG,
BGGB, BGGG, GBBB,
GBBG, GBGB, GBGG,
GGBB, GGBG, GGGB,
GGGG$\}$
b) 6

16. a) (T_1,T_2,T_3), (T_1,T_2,T_4),
(T_1,T_2,U) (T_1,T_3,T_4),
(T_1,T_3,T_2), (T_1,T_3,U), etc.
Answers will vary.
b) 60

2.3 Exercises, pages 63–64
*No answer provided for questions
16b, 17.*

1. a) $\dfrac{1}{2}$
b) $\dfrac{1}{6}$
c) $\dfrac{1}{2}$
d) $\dfrac{1}{100}$
e) $\dfrac{1}{20}$
f) $\dfrac{1}{5}$
g) $\dfrac{1}{8}$
h) $\dfrac{1}{5}$

2. a) $\dfrac{1}{6}$
b) $\dfrac{1}{3}$
c) $\dfrac{2}{3}$

3. $1 : 2$

4. a) $\dfrac{1}{6}$
b) $\dfrac{1}{12}$
c) $\dfrac{11}{36}$
d) $\dfrac{1}{4}$
e) $\dfrac{1}{3}$

5. a) $1 : 5$
d) $1 : 3$

6. a) $\dfrac{8}{13}$
b) $\dfrac{5}{13}$
c) $8 : 5$

7. a) $\dfrac{1}{8}$
b) $\dfrac{3}{8}$

8. a) $0.000\ 000\ 000\dot{3}$
b) $0.000\ 000\ 020\dot{3}$
c) $0.999\ 999\ 646$

9. a) $\dfrac{1}{4}$

b) $\dfrac{3}{4}$

10. $\dfrac{1}{2}$

11. a) $\dfrac{2}{5}$

  b) $3:2$

12. $\dfrac{3}{10}$

13. 95%

14. $\dfrac{9}{14}$

15. $\dfrac{3}{50}$ or 6%

16. a) $\dfrac{2}{5}$

18. a) 0.87

  b) 0.13

2.4 Exercises, pages 68–69

1. a) $\dfrac{3}{10}$

  b) $\dfrac{1}{30}$

  c) $\dfrac{5}{6}$

2. a) $\dfrac{1}{40}$

  b) $\dfrac{7}{30}$

3. a) $\dfrac{7}{12}$

  b) $\dfrac{7}{18}$

4. a) $\dfrac{4}{7}$

  b) $\dfrac{2}{7}$

5. $\dfrac{42}{105} = 0.4$

6. $\dfrac{1}{11}$

7. $0.09\dot{7}$

8. a) 0.102

  b) 0.014

  c) 0.363

  d) 0.153

9. a) 4.95×10^{-4}

  b) 9.23×10^{-6}

  c) 1.44×10^{-3}

  d) 2.4×10^{-4}

  e) 3.94×10^{-3}

10. a) $\dfrac{1}{3}$

  b) $\dfrac{1}{2}$

11. a) $\dfrac{1}{4}$

  b) $\dfrac{1}{12}$

12. $\dfrac{5}{12}$

13. 0.3874

14. $\dfrac{8}{15}$

15. $\dfrac{3}{5}$

16. $\dfrac{1}{6}$

17. 0.1538

18. a) 2.0×10^{-6}

  b) 1.2×10^{-5}

  c) 1.12×10^{-4}

19. $0.4\dot{2}$

2.5 Exercises, pages 73-74

1. 3.0×10^{-13}

2. 1.8×10^{-7}

3. $\dfrac{2}{11}$

4. 0.8924

5. a) $\dfrac{9}{64}$

  b) $\dfrac{39}{64}$

  c) $\dfrac{17}{32}$

6. a) $\dfrac{1}{32}$

  b) $\dfrac{1}{2}$

7. $\dfrac{1}{36}$

8. a) $\dfrac{1}{16}$

  b) $\dfrac{9}{2704}$

9. 0.56

10. a) $\dfrac{1}{4}$

  b) $\dfrac{1}{12}$

  c) $\dfrac{1}{4}$

11. a) 0.72

  b) 0.18

  c) 0.02

  d) 0.98

12. a) 0.12

  b) 0.32

  c) 0.08

13. 0.9996

14. 1×10^{-12}

15. $\dfrac{1}{125}$

16. $\dfrac{1}{64}$

17. a) 0.195

  b) 0.805

18. $\dfrac{49}{120}$

In Search of, page 77

1. a)

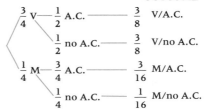

  b) $\dfrac{9}{16}$

2. 18%

3. a) $\dfrac{1}{20}$

  b) $\dfrac{1}{4}$

2.6 Exercises, pages 82–83
No answer provided for 14.

1. a) $\dfrac{1}{2}$

  b) $\dfrac{2}{5}$

2. a) $\dfrac{1}{3}$

  b) $\dfrac{1}{5}$

  c) $\dfrac{2}{11}$

3. 0.62

4. $\frac{1}{3}$

5. $\frac{2}{5}$

6. a) 0

 b) $\frac{1}{3}$

 c) 1

7. a) $\frac{4}{17}$

 b) $\frac{1}{17}$

 c) $\frac{25}{51}$

8. a) $\frac{5}{12}$

 b) $\frac{1}{12}$

 c) $\frac{3}{4}$

 d) $\frac{1}{4}$

 e) $\frac{1}{2}$

9. a) $\frac{1}{10}$

 b) $\frac{3}{10}$

10. $\frac{1}{6}, \frac{5}{36}, \frac{25}{216}$

11. a) $\frac{1}{33}$

 b) $\frac{2}{11}$

12. $\frac{5}{7}$

13. a) $\frac{185}{250}$

 b) $\frac{115}{300}$

15. a) $\frac{11}{4165}$

 b) $\frac{11}{245}$

 c) 0

16. approximately 0.25

17. a) no; $P(A) \neq P(A$ given $B)$
 b) $P(G) = P(G$ given $H)$
 c) no;
 $P(E) \neq P(E$ given $F)$ and
 $P(F) \neq P(F$ given $E)$

In Search of, page 85
Answers not provided.

Inventory, page 89

1. 1, 0

2. 1, 0

3. 6

4. 36

5. 2

6. 8

7. 52

8. 6

9. 0.7

10. 0.4

11. 0.06

12. 0.4

13. 3 : 7

14. 0.4, 0.2

Review Exercises, pages 90–91

1. a) $\frac{1}{6}$

 b) $\frac{1}{6}$

 c) $\frac{5}{6}$

 d) 0

 e) 1

 f) $\frac{1}{3}$

 g) 0

2. a) $\frac{1}{12}$

 b) $\frac{1}{6}$

 c) $\frac{5}{6}$

 d) $\frac{1}{4}$

 e) $\frac{11}{36}$

 f) $\frac{1}{18}$

 g) $\frac{1}{3}$

3. a) $\frac{1}{2}$

 b) $\frac{1}{26}$

 c) $\frac{7}{13}$

4. a) $\frac{4}{11}$

 b) $\frac{3}{11}$

5. a) 0.2036
 b) 0.2466

6. a) 4%
 b) 54%
 c) 58%
 d) 42%

7. a) 1 : 35
 b) 1 : 17

8. a) $\frac{1}{8}$

 b) $\frac{3}{8}$

 c) $\frac{3}{4}$

9. a) $\frac{1}{36}$

 b) $\frac{1}{12}$

10. $\frac{18}{77}$

11. a) $\frac{3}{7}$

 b) $\frac{1}{14}$

12. $\frac{1}{20}$

13. $\frac{1}{9}$

14. $\frac{1}{6}$

15. 0.57

16. 0.43

17. $\frac{5}{16}$

18. a) $\frac{5}{64}$

 b) $\frac{43}{64}$

19. $\frac{1}{81}$

20. $\frac{1}{30}$

21. a) $\frac{5}{16}$

    b) $\frac{15}{32}$

    c) $\frac{3}{16}$

Chapter Three
Matrices

3.1 Exercises, pages 96–97

1.

Matrix	Number of rows	Number of columns	Dimension	Number of elements
A	3	3	3×3	9
B	7	5	7×5	35
C	4	1	4×1	4
D	1	5	1×5	5

2. a) A
   b) D
   c) C

3. a) a_{21}, a_{22}, a_{23}
   b) c_{21}
   c) d_{15}
   d) $b_{31}, b_{32}, b_{33}, b_{34}, b_{35}$

4. a) Dimension changes to 3×4.
   b) Row 2 becomes 7 4 0.636 62 57
      Row 7 becomes 1 9 0.100 51 74
   c) dimension 3×1 $\begin{bmatrix} 3.95 \\ 5.95 \\ 8.95 \end{bmatrix}$
   d) dimension 4×5 (three rows added)

5. a) cost of three models of cars constructed in Plant 2
   b) Toronto has 37 runs scored.
   c) runs scored against
   d) the price of twill pants
   e) The second show of *Fantasia* is at 3:30.
   f) the cost of building a Bug at the three plants

6. $18 \times 1, 9 \times 2, 6 \times 3, 3 \times 6, 2 \times 9, 1 \times 18$

7. a) mn
   b) m rows, n columns
   c) $(m - 1) \times n$
   d) $(m - 1)(n - 1)$

8. $a = 3, b = -4, c = 2, x = 5, y = 7, z = 8$

9. They are equal

10. $m \in N, n = 1$

11. $m = 1, n \in N$

12. $m, n \in N, m = n$

13. Answers will vary.

14. A, C, and F Note: E is not square.

15. a) 6×5
    b) Chicago's statistics
    c) fraction of games won
    d) Chicago's fraction of games won
    e) row 4, column 5
    f) $\begin{bmatrix} 8 & 2 & 0.800 & 46 & 32 \\ 7 & 3 & 0.700 & 37 & 31 \\ 4 & 4 & 0.800 & 30 & 29 \\ 3 & 5 & 0.375 & 32 & 26 \\ 3 & 5 & 0.375 & 33 & 36 \\ 2 & 8 & 0.200 & 30 & 54 \end{bmatrix}$

3.2 Exercises, pages 103–104
No answers provided for questions 10, 14c).

1. a) $\begin{bmatrix} 5 & 12 & 15 \\ 19 & 24 & 16 \end{bmatrix}$

   b) $\begin{bmatrix} 19 & 18 & 5 \\ 3 & 16 & 12 \end{bmatrix}$

   c) not possible

   d) $\begin{bmatrix} 8 & 16 \\ 12 & 32 \\ 24 & 28 \end{bmatrix}$

   e) $\begin{bmatrix} 71 & 60 & 5 \\ -7 & 40 & 32 \end{bmatrix}$

   f) $\begin{bmatrix} 3 & 21 & 35 \\ 46 & 52 & 34 \end{bmatrix}$

2. a) $\begin{bmatrix} 6 & 12 \\ -9 & 21 \end{bmatrix}$

   b) $\begin{bmatrix} 10 & 22 \\ 0 & -6 \end{bmatrix}$

   c) $\begin{bmatrix} -4 & -10 \\ -9 & 27 \end{bmatrix}$

   d) $\begin{bmatrix} 100 \\ 245 \\ -60 \end{bmatrix}$

   e) $\begin{bmatrix} \frac{15}{2} \\ -10 \\ 17 \end{bmatrix}$

   f) $\begin{bmatrix} \frac{215}{2} \\ 235 \\ -43 \end{bmatrix}$

   g) not possible

3. a) $\begin{bmatrix} -2 & 6 \\ -2 & -1 \end{bmatrix}$

   b) $\begin{bmatrix} -4 & 12 & 20 \\ 32 & 0 & -8 \end{bmatrix}$

   c) not possible

   d) $\begin{bmatrix} -6 & 29 \\ -5 & 0 \end{bmatrix}$

4. a) $[3 \quad 4 \quad 5]$

   b) $\begin{bmatrix} 10 \\ 1 \\ 11 \end{bmatrix}$

   c) $[0.6 \quad 0.8 \quad 1]$

   d) $\begin{bmatrix} 0.1 \\ 0.01 \\ 0.11 \end{bmatrix}$

5. $\begin{bmatrix} 380 & 450 & 550 \\ 270 & 325 & 385 \\ 100 & 52 & 70 \end{bmatrix}$

6. $\begin{bmatrix} 220 & 275 & 330 \\ 165 & 193 & 220 \\ 44 & 22 & 33 \end{bmatrix}$

7. $\begin{bmatrix} 3600 & 4000 & 3800 \\ 7880 & 7120 & 8000 \\ 9600 & 9200 & 8800 \end{bmatrix}$

8. a) $\begin{bmatrix} 1 & 1 & 0 & 0 & 21 & 20 \\ 1 & 1 & 0 & 0 & 20 & 11 \\ 1 & 0 & 1 & 0 & 11 & 20 \\ 1 & 0 & 1 & 0 & 20 & 21 \end{bmatrix}$

   b) $\begin{bmatrix} 1 & 0 & 1 & 0 & 12 & 19 \\ 1 & 0 & 0 & 1 & 32 & 32 \\ 1 & 0 & 0 & 1 & 32 & 32 \\ 1 & 1 & 0 & 0 & 19 & 12 \end{bmatrix}$

   c) $\begin{bmatrix} 2 & 1 & 1 & 0 & 33 & 39 \\ 2 & 1 & 0 & 1 & 52 & 43 \\ 2 & 0 & 1 & 1 & 43 & 52 \\ 2 & 1 & 1 & 0 & 39 & 33 \end{bmatrix}$

9. $a = 3, b = 5, c = -3, d = -25,$
   $f = 2, p = 22$

11. a) $\begin{bmatrix} 7 & 12 & 5 \\ 6 & 8 & 10 \\ 11 & 4 & 9 \end{bmatrix}$
   $\begin{bmatrix} 6 & 11 & 4 \\ 5 & 7 & 9 \\ 10 & 3 & 8 \end{bmatrix}$
   $\begin{bmatrix} 11 & 16 & 9 \\ 10 & 12 & 14 \\ 15 & 8 & 13 \end{bmatrix}$

   b) The sum of each row, column, or diagonal is the same.

   c) Answers will vary.

   d) The sum of the rows, columns, or diagonals is 0.

   e) Answers will vary.

12. $a = 5, b = 1, c = -3$

13. $\begin{bmatrix} -13 & -13 \\ 2 & 0 \end{bmatrix}$

14. a) $\begin{bmatrix} -a & -b & -c \\ -d & -e & -f \end{bmatrix}$

   b) B

3.3 Exercises, pages 110–111
No answer provided for question 20.

1. $a = 3, b = 7, c = 4$

2. a) $(2 \times 2)(2 \times 3) = 2 \times 3$
   $\begin{bmatrix} 36 & 70 & 92 \\ 24 & 47 & 62 \end{bmatrix}$

   b) $(2 \times 3)(3 \times 1) = 2 \times 1$
   $\begin{bmatrix} 35 \\ -2 \end{bmatrix}$

   c) not possible

   d) $(2 \times 2)(2 \times 2) = 2 \times 2$
   $\begin{bmatrix} 224 & 190 \\ 152 & 129 \end{bmatrix}$

3. a) $TS = \begin{bmatrix} 5 & -66 \\ 22 & -28 \end{bmatrix}$
   $ST = \begin{bmatrix} -28 & -44 \\ 33 & 5 \end{bmatrix}$

   b) no

4. a) $KI = \begin{bmatrix} 2 & 5 \\ 3 & 4 \end{bmatrix} IK = \begin{bmatrix} 2 & 5 \\ 3 & 4 \end{bmatrix}$

   b) same

   c) $ZI = IZ = Z$

5. a) $IA = \begin{bmatrix} 3 & 6 & 2 \\ 4 & 1 & 0 \\ -6 & 2 & 5 \end{bmatrix} = AI$

   b) same

   c) $QI = IQ = Q$

6. a) $\begin{bmatrix} 1 & 0 & 0 & 0 \\ 0 & 1 & 0 & 0 \\ 0 & 0 & 1 & 0 \\ 0 & 0 & 0 & 1 \end{bmatrix}$

   b) Answers will vary.

7. $m = n$ or if $A_{m \times n}$, then $B_{n \times m}$

8. $m = n$

9. $S^2 = \begin{bmatrix} 9 & 25 \\ 5 & 14 \end{bmatrix} S^3 = \begin{bmatrix} 43 & 120 \\ 24 & 67 \end{bmatrix}$
   $S^4 = \begin{bmatrix} 206 & 575 \\ 115 & 321 \end{bmatrix}$

10. $\begin{bmatrix} 116 \\ 108 \\ 85 \\ 77 \end{bmatrix}$

11. $\begin{bmatrix} \$5004.50 \\ \$4936.20 \\ \$4862.40 \\ \$5072.50 \end{bmatrix}$

12. $\begin{bmatrix} \$14\,938.75 \\ \$14\,385.75 \\ \$14\,477.75 \\ \$14\,976.75 \end{bmatrix}$

13. $\begin{bmatrix} \$287\ 500 \\ \$564\ 000 \\ \$695\ 000 \end{bmatrix}$

The cost of producing 60 cars of each type:
20 at Plant 1,
30 at Plant 2,
10 at Plant 3

14. a) false
    b) false
    c) false

15. Answers will vary.

16. $C = \begin{bmatrix} 20 & 4 \\ -32 & -3 \end{bmatrix}$

17. $\begin{bmatrix} 8 & 5 \\ 12 & 16 \end{bmatrix}$

18. a) $TP = \begin{bmatrix} 58\ 610 \\ 48\ 390 \end{bmatrix}$
    b) the number of people who will take transit
       the number of people who will drive

19. a) inverses
    b) not inverses

In Search of, pages 112–113

1. dimensions of matrix A
2. dimensions of matrix B
3. element a_{ij}
4. element b_{ij}
5. 350–410

3.4 Exercises, page 117
No answers provided for questions 3b), 5.

1. a) $\begin{bmatrix} -2 & 0 & -5 & 2 & 2 & 0 & 12 & -19 & 20 \\ 12 & 9 & 29 & 3 & 14 & 5 & -23 & 58 & -40 \end{bmatrix}$

   b) $\begin{bmatrix} 52 & 63 & 123 & 53 & 130 & 35 & 31 & 102 & 40 \\ 30 & 36 & 71 & 30 & 74 & 20 & 16 & 61 & 20 \end{bmatrix}$

   c) $\begin{bmatrix} -18 & -18 & 43 & -12 & -34 & -10 & 10 & -59 & 20 \\ 62 & 63 & 148 & 43 & 120 & 35 & -29 & 197 & -60 \end{bmatrix}$

2. a) HELP
   b) SKI FOR FUN
   c) SCHOOL IS OUT

3. a) $E_1^{-1} = \begin{bmatrix} 3 & 1 \\ 2 & 1 \end{bmatrix}$ $E_2^{-1} = \begin{bmatrix} 3 & -5 \\ -1 & 2 \end{bmatrix}$

   $E_3^{-1} = \begin{bmatrix} 10 & 3 \\ 3 & 1 \end{bmatrix}$

4. a) 3
   b) $\begin{bmatrix} 37 & 15 & 22 \\ 137 & 126 & 105 \\ -136 & -106 & -96 \end{bmatrix}$
   c) $DE = I$

6. a) 2
   b) $\begin{bmatrix} 45 & 68 \\ 32 & 55 \\ 45 & 68 \\ 6 & 11 \\ 7 & 11 \end{bmatrix}$
   c) $\begin{bmatrix} 2 & -3 \\ -1 & 2 \end{bmatrix}$
   d) $\begin{bmatrix} 22 & 1 \\ 9 & 14 \\ 22 & 1 \\ 1 & 4 \\ 3 & 1 \end{bmatrix}$
   e) no

7. a) $\begin{bmatrix} \dfrac{d}{ad-bc} & \dfrac{-b}{ad-bc} \\ \dfrac{-c}{ad-bc} & \dfrac{a}{ad-bc} \end{bmatrix}$
   b) $ad - bc \neq 0$

8. a) $\begin{bmatrix} -1 & \dfrac{1}{2} \\ \dfrac{3}{5} & \dfrac{-1}{5} \end{bmatrix}$
   b) $\begin{bmatrix} 1 & 2 \\ \dfrac{1}{2} & \dfrac{3}{2} \end{bmatrix}$
   c) not possible (no inverse)
   d) $\begin{bmatrix} 5 & 7 \\ 2 & 3 \end{bmatrix}$

In Search of, page 118–119

No answer provided for question 2.

1. $\begin{bmatrix} 3 & 1 & 2 \\ 0 & 1 & -2 \\ 2 & 1 & 1 \end{bmatrix}$

3. $\begin{bmatrix} 2 & 5 \\ 1 & 3 \end{bmatrix} x = 19, y = 11$

4. $x = 9, y = -10, z = 15$

3.5 Exercises, pages 126–127

1. a) $\begin{array}{c} P \\ A \\ M \\ S \end{array} \begin{bmatrix} 0 & 1 & 1 & 0 \\ 0 & 0 & 0 & 1 \\ 0 & 0 & 0 & 0 \\ 1 & 0 & 0 & 0 \end{bmatrix}$

   b) $\begin{array}{c} T \\ R \\ M \\ P \end{array} \begin{bmatrix} 0 & 0 & 0 & 0 \\ 1 & 0 & 0 & 0 \\ 1 & 0 & 0 & 1 \\ 1 & 1 & 0 & 0 \end{bmatrix}$

   c) $\begin{array}{c} T \\ V \\ H \\ M \end{array} \begin{bmatrix} 0 & 1 & 1 & 0 \\ 1 & 0 & 0 & 1 \\ 1 & 0 & 0 & 1 \\ 0 & 1 & 1 & 0 \end{bmatrix}$

   d) $\begin{array}{c} X \\ Y \\ Z \end{array} \begin{bmatrix} 0 & 1 & 1 \\ 1 & 0 & 1 \\ 1 & 1 & 0 \end{bmatrix}$

2. a)

   b)

   c)

   d)

   e)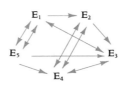

   f)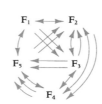

3. a) no ability to communicate outward

   b) total isolation

4. a) $\begin{bmatrix} 1 & 1 & 1 \\ 1 & 1 & 0 \\ 0 & 1 & 2 \end{bmatrix}$

   b) $\begin{bmatrix} 1 & 2 & 2 \\ 0 & 1 & 2 \\ 2 & 2 & 1 \end{bmatrix}$

   c) $\begin{bmatrix} 5 & 1 & 2 \\ 1 & 5 & 2 \\ 2 & 2 & 2 \end{bmatrix}$

   d) $\begin{bmatrix} 4 & 12 & 6 \\ 12 & 4 & 6 \\ 6 & 6 & 4 \end{bmatrix}$

5. a) and c) indicate the number of two-stage paths.

   b) and d) indicate the number of three-stage paths

6. RED ROSE: two relay points
   VENICE QUEEN: two relay points
   SAUDI PRINCESS: three relay points
   ARMAGEDDON } Cannot communicate
   LAST SUNSET } with other ships

7. Not Montreal ↔ Winnipeg nor New York ↔ Winnipeg

8. a) $\begin{bmatrix} 0 & 1 & 1 & 0 & 0 & 0 \\ 0 & 0 & 0 & 1 & 1 & 0 \\ 0 & 0 & 0 & 0 & 1 & 0 \\ 0 & 0 & 0 & 0 & 0 & 0 \\ 0 & 0 & 0 & 0 & 0 & 1 \\ 0 & 0 & 0 & 0 & 0 & 0 \end{bmatrix}$

   b) $\begin{bmatrix} 0 & 0 & 0 & 1 & 2 & 0 \\ 0 & 0 & 0 & 0 & 0 & 1 \\ 0 & 0 & 0 & 0 & 0 & 1 \\ 0 & 0 & 0 & 0 & 0 & 0 \\ 0 & 0 & 0 & 0 & 0 & 0 \\ 0 & 0 & 0 & 0 & 0 & 0 \end{bmatrix}$

   indirect communication links through one intermediate point

9. $\begin{bmatrix} 0 & 0 & 0 & 0 & 0 & 0 & 0 \\ 1 & 1 & 0 & 1 & 0 & 1 & 0 \\ 0 & 0 & 1 & 1 & 1 & 0 & 0 \\ 0 & 0 & 0 & 0 & 0 & 0 & 1 \\ 0 & 0 & 0 & 0 & 0 & 1 & 0 \\ 0 & 0 & 0 & 0 & 1 & 0 & 0 \\ 0 & 0 & 0 & 1 & 0 & 0 & 0 \end{bmatrix}$

   affected species: humans, grass, cows, flies, birds, frogs

10. a)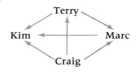

    b) $\begin{bmatrix} 0 & 2 & 0 & 1 \\ 0 & 0 & 0 & 0 \\ 1 & 3 & 0 & 2 \\ 0 & 1 & 0 & 0 \end{bmatrix} \begin{array}{l} = 3 \\ = 0 \\ = 6 \\ = 1 \end{array}$

    1st Craig
    2nd Terry
    3rd Marc
    4th Kim

11. $\begin{bmatrix} 0 & 1 & 2 & 1 & 0 \\ 0 & 0 & 1 & 1 & 0 \\ 1 & 1 & 0 & 1 & 0 \\ 1 & 2 & 2 & 0 & 0 \\ 2 & 3 & 3 & 2 & 0 \end{bmatrix}$

    1st Hawks
    2nd Dodgers
    3rd Lions
    4th Cheetahs
    5th Braves

3.6 Exercises, page 132

1. a) $\begin{bmatrix} 0.7 & 0.1 \\ 0.3 & 0.9 \end{bmatrix}$

   b) $\begin{bmatrix} 619 \\ 471 \end{bmatrix}$

   There will be 619 math students next year.

2. a) $\begin{bmatrix} 0.85 & 0.05 \\ 0.15 & 0.95 \end{bmatrix}$

   b) 34.6%

   c) 32.7%

3. $\frac{2}{3}$ chance unacceptable

4. a) Conservatives   24 258
       Liberals   23 987
       NDP   16 215

   b) People will vote the way they say they will.

   c) Answers will vary.

   d) 35.4%

5. 57%

6. 67% small

7. all white collar

Inventory, page 134

1. -1

2. $i = 2, j = 3$

3. A

4. C

5. 1×3

6. $\begin{bmatrix} 10 & 20 & 30 \\ 0 & 15 & 35 \\ -5 & 25 & 40 \end{bmatrix}$

7. not possible

8. 3×1

9. no

10. [17]

11. TEST TIME

12. a) I

    b) inverses

13. $\begin{bmatrix} 0 & 0 & 0 & 1 \\ 1 & 0 & 0 & 0 \\ 0 & 1 & 0 & 0 \\ 0 & 0 & 1 & 0 \end{bmatrix}$

14. no

15. 1

Review Exercises, pages 135–137

1.

Matrix	Number of rows	Number of columns	Dimension	Number of elements
A	3	3	3×3	9
B	1	7	1×7	7
C	3	1	3×1	3

2. a) a_{12}, a_{22}, a_{32}

   b) a_{21}, a_{22}, a_{23}

   c) c_{31}

   d) b_{17}

3. a) Greg's weight: 75 kg

   b) There is no such element.

   c) cost of blueberry muffins: $1.50

   d) Sue's statistics: 15 a, 162 cm, 48 kg

   e) student's ages: 15 a, 18 a, 16 a

   f) student's heights: 162 cm, 185 cm, 150 cm

4. a) dimension 5×3

   b) dimension 1×14

   c) $c_{11} = \$2.50, c_{21} = \$3.00, c_{31} = \$3.50$

5. a) $\begin{bmatrix} 20 & -5 \\ 20 & -15 \end{bmatrix}$

   b) not possible

   c) $\begin{bmatrix} -13 & 5 & 27 \\ -13 & -10 & -2 \end{bmatrix}$

   d) not possible

   e) $\begin{bmatrix} -9 & 20 \\ -8 & -1 \end{bmatrix}$

   f) $\begin{bmatrix} 16 & 15 \\ 22 & 19 \end{bmatrix}$

6. $b = c, a = e, d = f$

7. $14 000, $17 800, $14 700

8. a) 44 115 85 105 109 40 15
      45 33 38 41 15

   b) 52 161 120 171 19 62 45
      64

   c) 160 34 40 19 135 87 70
      64 133 57 60 12 15 7 51
      34 27 23 49 19

9. $\begin{bmatrix} 2 & -5 \\ -1 & 3 \end{bmatrix}$

10. a) PATIENCE

    b) CODES ARE FUN

    c) PRACTICE MAKES PERFECT

11. a)

	F	MM	003	B	X	L	H
F	0	0	0	0	0	0	0
MM	1	0	0	1	0	0	0
003	0	1	0	0	0	0	0
B	0	0	0	0	0	1	1
X	0	0	0	1	0	0	0
L	0	0	0	0	0	0	1
H	0	0	1	0	1	0	0

b)

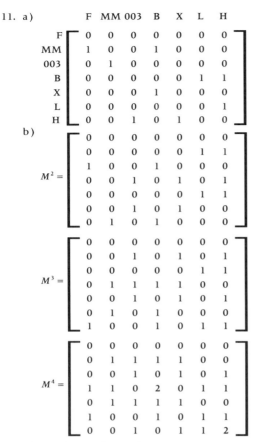

$$M^2 = \begin{bmatrix} 0 & 0 & 0 & 0 & 0 & 0 & 0 \\ 0 & 0 & 0 & 0 & 0 & 1 & 1 \\ 1 & 0 & 0 & 1 & 0 & 0 & 0 \\ 0 & 0 & 1 & 0 & 1 & 0 & 1 \\ 0 & 0 & 0 & 0 & 0 & 1 & 1 \\ 0 & 0 & 1 & 0 & 1 & 0 & 0 \\ 0 & 1 & 0 & 1 & 0 & 0 & 0 \end{bmatrix}$$

$$M^3 = \begin{bmatrix} 0 & 0 & 0 & 0 & 0 & 0 & 0 \\ 0 & 0 & 1 & 0 & 1 & 0 & 1 \\ 0 & 0 & 0 & 0 & 0 & 1 & 1 \\ 0 & 1 & 1 & 1 & 1 & 0 & 0 \\ 0 & 0 & 1 & 0 & 1 & 0 & 1 \\ 0 & 1 & 0 & 1 & 0 & 0 & 0 \\ 1 & 0 & 0 & 1 & 0 & 1 & 1 \end{bmatrix}$$

$$M^4 = \begin{bmatrix} 0 & 0 & 0 & 0 & 0 & 0 & 0 \\ 0 & 1 & 1 & 1 & 1 & 0 & 0 \\ 0 & 0 & 1 & 0 & 1 & 0 & 1 \\ 1 & 1 & 0 & 2 & 0 & 1 & 1 \\ 0 & 1 & 1 & 1 & 1 & 0 & 0 \\ 1 & 0 & 0 & 1 & 0 & 1 & 1 \\ 0 & 0 & 1 & 0 & 1 & 1 & 2 \end{bmatrix}$$

c) one intermediate point between possible communications

d) yes

e) Answers will vary.

f) two intermediate points between possible communications

12. no

13. a) 67% left turns
   b) 67

14. 3% 6-12 Store,
   80% Corner Variety,
   17% Quik-Serve

15. a) $\begin{bmatrix} 0 & 0 & 1 & 1 & 0 \\ 1 & 0 & 0 & 0 & 0 \\ 0 & 1 & 0 & 0 & 0 \\ 0 & 0 & 1 & 0 & 1 \\ 0 & 0 & 0 & 0 & 0 \end{bmatrix}$

b)
$$D^2 = \begin{bmatrix} 0 & 1 & 1 & 0 & 1 \\ 0 & 0 & 1 & 1 & 0 \\ 1 & 0 & 0 & 0 & 0 \\ 0 & 1 & 0 & 0 & 0 \\ 0 & 0 & 0 & 0 & 0 \end{bmatrix}$$

$$D^3 = \begin{bmatrix} 1 & 1 & 0 & 0 & 0 \\ 0 & 1 & 1 & 0 & 1 \\ 0 & 0 & 1 & 1 & 0 \\ 1 & 0 & 0 & 0 & 0 \\ 0 & 0 & 0 & 0 & 0 \end{bmatrix}$$

$$D^4 = \begin{bmatrix} 1 & 0 & 1 & 1 & 0 \\ 1 & 1 & 0 & 0 & 0 \\ 0 & 1 & 1 & 0 & 1 \\ 0 & 0 & 1 & 1 & 0 \\ 0 & 0 & 0 & 0 & 0 \end{bmatrix}$$

$$D^5 = \begin{bmatrix} 0 & 1 & 2 & 1 & 1 \\ 1 & 0 & 1 & 1 & 0 \\ 1 & 1 & 0 & 0 & 0 \\ 0 & 1 & 1 & 0 & 1 \\ 0 & 0 & 0 & 0 & 0 \end{bmatrix}$$

c) Anna $\frac{355}{60}$, Bessi $\frac{246}{60}$,
   Chris $\frac{199}{60}$, Dion $\frac{236}{60}$,
   Elizaveta 0

d) Anna

16. 7 51 31 18 95 57 3 64 42 27 56 24
   −18 31 31 5 10 5

17. NOT CLEAR

18. a) no
   b) $\begin{bmatrix} 0.65 & 0.2 & 0.2 \\ 0.3 & 0.7 & 0.1 \\ 0.05 & 0.1 & 0.7 \end{bmatrix} \begin{bmatrix} 13 \\ 9 \\ 4 \end{bmatrix}$
   c) City: 10.17 million,
   Suburbs: 11.17 million
   Country: 4.66 million

19. [28　26　16]
   required: 28 kg Mocha,
   26 kg Jamaican,
   16 kg Columbian.

**Chapter Four
Solving Systems of
Equations and Inequalities**

4.1 Exercises, page 143

1. a) $d = 60t$
   b) $p = 2x$
   c) $m = 2.5v$
   d) $t = 500 + 50x$

2. a)

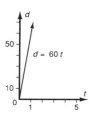

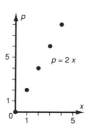

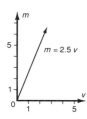

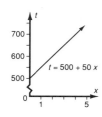

b) continuous, discrete,
   continuous, continuous
c) $\{t \,|\, t \geqslant 0, t \in R\}$,
   $\{x \,|\, x \geqslant 0, x \in I\}$
   $\{v \,|\, v \geqslant 0, v \in R\}$,
   $\{x \,|\, x \geqslant 0, x \in R\}$

3. a) $\$c = 200 + 200k$,
   $\{k \,|\, 70k + 1 \leqslant x \leqslant 70k + 70,$
   $k \in W\}$

   b)

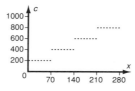

   c) step
   d) discrete

4. a) $c = 5x, \{x \,|\, x \leqslant 40, x \in N\}$
   $c = 200 + 3.5(x - 40)$,
   $\{x \,|\, x > 40, x \in N\}$
   b)

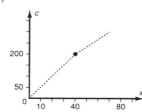

   c) $D = \{x \,|\, x > 0, x \in W\}$

5. a) $c = 35 + 0.25x$
   b) $c = 35d + 100$
   c) $c = 35d + 0.25x$
   d) $c = 35 + 35k$,
   $\{k \,|\, 24k < h \leqslant 24k + 24,$
   $k \in W\}$
   e)

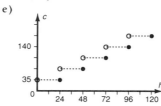

   f) $c = 35 + 35k + 15h$,
   $\{k \,|\, 24k < h \leqslant 24k + 24,$
   $0 < h \leqslant 120, k \in I, h \in R\}$

g)

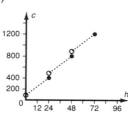

h) piece-wise linear;
   step function

6. a)

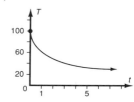

   b) $D = \{t \,|\, t \geqslant 0, t \in R\}$
   c) continuous

7. $6s + 2t = 45.5, 5s + 3t = 49.25$

4.2 Exercises, pages 150–151
*No answers provided for questions 8c,
11b.*

1. a) $(3, -2)$
   b) $\left(\dfrac{29}{34}, \dfrac{47}{17}\right)$
   c) $(4, -3, 2)$
   d) $(0, -1, 7)$

2. 8.75 m^2

3. 12 L 12% acid, 40 L water

4. (mechanics, apprentices, pump
   attendants) = $(6, 2, 4)$

5. (ties, socks) = $(\$8.50, \$4.75)$

6. (chocolate bars, cans pop) = $(3, 4)$

7. $(1, -1, -1)$

8. a) $x = \dfrac{de - bf}{ad - bc}, y = \dfrac{af - ce}{ad - bc}$
   b) no

```
9.  110  REM INPUT EQUATIONS
    120  DIM M(3,4)
    130  PRINT "TYPE IN THE COEF-
    FICIENTS OF THE EQUATIONS"
    140  PRINT "AX+BY+CZ=D"
    150  FOR I = 1 TO 3
    160  FOR J=1 TO 4
    170  INPUT M(I,J)
    180  NEXT J
    190  NEXT I
    200  GOSUB 590
    210  FOR T=1 TO 100
    220  PRINT "WOULD YOU LIKE TO
    MULTIPLY AN EQUATION BY A CON-
    STANT?"
    230  INPUT AN$
    240  IF AN$="Y" THEN GOSUB 350
    250  PRINT "WOULD YOU LIKE TO
    SUBTRACT TWO EQUATIONS?"
    260  INPUT A$
    270  IF A$="Y" THEN GOSUB 440
    280  PRINT "ARE YOU READY TO
    SOLVE THE EQUATIONS?"
    290  INPUT B$
    300  IF B$="Y" THEN GOSUB 530
    310  IF B$="Y" THEN LET T=101
    320  NEXT T
    330  STOP
    340  :
    350  REM MULTIPLY AN EQUATION
    BY A CONSTANT
    360  PRINT "WHICH EQUATION BY
    WHAT CONSTANT?"
    370  INPUT P,D
    380  FOR J=1 TO 4
    390  LET M(P,J)=M(P,J)*D
    400  NEXT J
    410  GOSUB 590
    420  RETURN
    430  REM SUBTRACT TWO EQUA-
    TIONS
    440  PRINT "WHICH EQUATIONS
    WOULD YOU LIKE TO SUBTRACT?"
    450  INPUT A,B
    460  PRINT "WHICH EQUATION
    WOULD YOU LIKE THIS DIFFERENCE
    TO REPLACE?
    470  INPUT C
    480  FOR J=1 TO 4
    490  LET M(C,J)=M(A,J)-M(B,J)
    500  NEXT J
    510  GOSUB 590
    520  RETURN
    530  REM SOLVING THE SYSTEM
    540  Z=M(3,4)/M(3,3)
    550  Y=(M(2,4)-M(2,3)*Z)/
    M(2,2)
    560  X=(M(1,4)-M(1,3)*Z-
    M(1,2)*Y)/M(1,1)
    570  PRINT "(X,Y,Z)=("X,Y,Z")"
    580  RETURN
```

```
    590  REM DISPLAY MATRIX
    600  FOR I=1 TO 3
    610  FOR J=1 TO 4
    620  PRINT M(I,J)" ";
    630  NEXT J
    640  PRINT
    650  NEXT I
    660  RETURN
    670  END
```

10. (0,1028,0.1458,02797)

```
11. a) 110  REM INPUT EQUATIONS
       120  DIM M(3,4)
       130  PRINT "TYPE IN THE
       VALUES OF A,B,C,D FOR EACH
       EQUATION AX+BY+CZ=D"
       140  FOR I=1 TO 3
       150  FOR J=1 TO 4
       160  INPUT M(I,J)
       170  NEXT J
       180  NEXT I
       190  :
       200  REM PUT ZERO IN M(3,1)
       210  LET D=M(3,1)
       220  LET E=M(2,1)
       230  FOR J=1 TO 4
       240  LET M(3,J)=M(3,J)*E
       250  LET M(2,J)=M(2,J)*D
       260  NEXT J
       270  FOR J=1 TO 4
       280  M(3,J)=M(3,J)-M(2,J)
       290  NEXT J
       300  REM PUT ZERO IN M(2,1)
       310  LET B=M(1,1)
       320  LET C=M(2,1)
       330  FOR J=1 TO 4
       340  LET M(1,J)=M(1,J)*C
       350  LET M(2,J)=M(2,J)*B
       360  NEXT J
       370  FOR J=1 TO 4
       380  M(2,J)=M(1,J)-M(2,J)
       390  NEXT J
       400  :
       410  REM PUT ZERO IN M(3,2)
       420  LET A=M(3,2)
       430  LET C=M(2,2)
       440  FOR J=1 TO 4
       450  LET M(2,J)=M(2,J)*A
       460  LET M(3,J)=M(3,J)*C
       470  NEXT J
       480  FOR J=1 TO 4
       490  LET
       M(3,J)=M(3,J)-M(2,J)
       500  NEXT J
       510  Z=M(3,4)/M(3,3)
       520  Y=(M(2,4)-M(2,3)*Z)/
       M(2,2)
       530  X=(M(1,4)-M(1,3)*Z-
       M(1,2)*Y)/M(1,1)
       540  PRINT
       "(X,Y,Z)=(",X,Y,Z")"
       550  END
```

11. c) (3,0,1)

12. $a = -2, b = 20, c = -38$

13. a) (2,1,0,−3)
    b) (1,0,−2,4)

14. a) (0,0)
    b) (0,0,0)
    c) (0,0,0,0)

15. Yes. Setting all the variables equal to zero will always satisfy homogeneous equations.

In Search of, page 152

1. a) (3,2)
   b) (2,3)
   c) (−2,5)

2. Answers will vary.

4.3 Exercises, pages 156

1. a) $\begin{bmatrix} 3 & -4 & | & 17 \\ 2 & -3 & | & 12 \end{bmatrix}$

   b) $\begin{bmatrix} 1 & 3 & 4 & | & 3 \\ 4 & 1 & 4 & | & 21 \\ 2 & -2 & -3 & | & 8 \end{bmatrix}$

   c) $\begin{bmatrix} 1 & 2 & -2 & 4 & | & 5 \\ 1 & -2 & 2 & -2 & | & -5 \\ 2 & -3 & 1 & -1 & | & -10 \\ 3 & 4 & -1 & -1 & | & 6 \end{bmatrix}$

2. a) $8x - 5y = -9$
      $2x + 3y = 10$
   b) $x - 5y + 3z = 26$
      $x + 8y + 2z = 6$
      $2x + 6y + z = 1$
   c) $x - 2y + z + w = 3$
      $2x + y - z + 3w = 12$
      $x + y + z + w = 6$
      $x - y + z - 5w = -20$

3. a) no
   b) yes
   c) yes
   d) yes
   e) yes
   f) yes

4. a) (0,0)
   b) (0,0,0)
   c) (0,0,0,0)

5. a) (3,−2)
   b) (4,−3,2)
   c) (−1,3,2,1)
   d) $\left(\dfrac{29}{34}, \dfrac{47}{17}\right)$
   e) (0,−1,7)
   f) (0,1,1,4)

6.
```
110   REM INPUT MATRIX
120   DIM M (3,4)
130   PRINT "TYPE IN THE COEF-
FICIENTS OF THE MATRIX"
140   FOR I=1 TO 3
150   FOR J=1 TO 4
160   INPUT M(I,J)
170   NEXT J
180   NEXT I
190   GOSUB 510
200   FOR T=1 TO 100
210   PRINT "WOULD YOU LIKE TO
MULTIPLY A ROW BY A REAL NUM-
BER ?"
220   INPUT AN$
230   IF AN$="Y" THEN GOSUB 330
240   PRINT "WOULD YOU LIKE TO
REPLACE ROW F BY ROW F PLUS K
TIMES ROW G?"
250   INPUT A$
260   IF A$="Y" THEN GOSUB 410
270   PRINT "WOULD YOU LIKE TO
STOP YET?"
280   INPUT B$
290   IF B$="Y" THEN T=101
300   NEXT T
310   STOP
320   :
330   REM MULTIPLY A ROW BY A
CONSTANT
340   PRINT "WHICH ROW, BY WHAT
CONSTANT"
350   INPUT P,D
360   FOR J=1 TO 4
370   LET M(P,J)=M(P,J)*D
380   NEXT J
390   GOSUB 510
400   RETURN
410   PRINT "WHICH ROW SHOULD
BE REPLACED?"
420   INPUT S
430   PRINT "BY ROW "S" ADDED
TO K TIMES ROW L, PLEASE INPUT
K AND L"
440   INPUT K, L
450   FOR J=1 TO 4
460   M(S,J)=M(S,J)+K*M(L,J)
470   NEXT J
480   GOSUB 510
490   RETURN
500   :
510   REM DISPLAY MATRIX
520   FOR I=1 TO 3
530   FOR J=1 TO 4
540   PRINT M(I,J)" ";
550   NEXT J
560   PRINT
570   NEXT I
580   RETURN
590   END
```

7. Test matrix in 2b) only.

8.
```
110   REM INPUT MATRIX
120   DIM M(3,4)
130   PRINT "TYPE IN THE COEF-
FICIENTS OF THE MATRIX"
140   FOR I=1 TO 3
150   FOR J=1 TO 4
160   INPUT M(I,J)
170   NEXT J
180   NEXT I
190   GOSUB 600
200   :
210   REM PUT ZERO IN M(3,1)
220   LET D=M(3,1)
230   LET E=M(2,1)
240   FOR J=1 TO 4
250   LET M(3,J)=M(3,J)*E
260   LET M(2,J)=M(2,J)*D
270   NEXT J
280   GOSUB 600
290   FOR J=1 TO 4
300   M(3,J)=M(3,J)-M(2,J)
310   NEXT J
320   GOSUB 600
330   REM PUT ZERO IN M(2,1)
340   LET B=M(1,1)
350   LET C=M(2,1)
360   FOR J=1 TO 4
370   LET M(1,J)=M(1,J)*C
380   LET M(2,J)=M(2,J)*B
390   NEXT J
400   GOSUB 600
410   FOR J=1 TO 4
420   M(2,J)=M(1,J)-M(2,J)
430   NEXT J
440   GOSUB 600
450   :
460   REM PUT ZERO IN M(3,2)
470   LET A=M(3,2)
480   LET C=M(2,2)
490   FOR J=1 TO 4
500   LET M(2,J)=M(2,J)*A
510   LET M(3,J)=M(3,J)*C
520   NEXT J
530   GOSUB 600
540   FOR J=1 TO 4
550   LETM(3,J)=M(3,J)-M(2,J)
560   NEXT J
570   GOSUB 600
580   STOP
590   :
600   REM DISPLAY MATRIX
610   FOR I=1 TO 3
620   FOR J=1 TO 4
630   PRINT M(I,J)" ";
640   NEXT J
650   PRINT
660   NEXT I
670   PRINT
680   RETURN
690   END
```

9.
```
110  REM INPUT MATRIX
120  DIM M(3,4)
130  PRINT "TYPE IN THE COEF-
FICIENTS OF THE MATRIX"
140  FOR I=1 TO 3
150  FOR J =1 TO 4
160  INPUT M(I,J)
170  NEXT J
180  NEXT I
190  GOSUB 620
200  REM CHOOSE OPERATION
210  FOR K=1 TO 100
220  PRINT "WOULD YOU LIKE TO
MULTIPLY A ROW BY A CONSTANT?"
230  INPUT A1$
240  IF A1$="Y" THEN GOSUB 410
250  PRINT "WOULD YOU LIKE TO
REPLACE ONE ROW BY THE SUM OF
THAT ROW AND A MULTIPLE OF
ANOTHER?"
260  INPUT A2$
270  IF A2$="Y" THEN GOSUB 500
280  PRINT "WOULD YOU LIKE TO
STOP YET?"
290  INPUT A$
300  IF A$="Y" THEN K=101
310  NEXT K
320  :
330  REM SOLVE EQUATIONS
340  Z=M(3,4)/M(3,3)
350  PRINT "Z="Z
360  Y=(M(2,4)-M(2,3)*Z)/M(2,2)

370  PRINT "Y="Y
380  X=(M(1,4)-M(1,3)*Z-
M(1,2)*Y)/M(1,1)
390  PRINT "X="X
400  STOP
410  REM MULTIPLY A ROW BY A
CONSTANT
420  PRINT "WHICH ROW?"
430  INPUT C
440  INPUT "BY WHAT CON-
STANT?"; D
450  FOR J=1 TO 4
460  LET M(C,J)=M(C,J)*D
470  NEXT J
480  GOSUB 620
490  RETURN
500  REM REPLACE A ROW
510  PRINT "WHICH ROW SHOULD
BE REPLACED?"
520  INPUT U
530  PRINT "BY THE SUM OF ROW
WHAT?"
540  INPUT V
550  PRINT "AND WHAT TIMES
WHICH ROW?"
560  INPUT W,X
570  FOR J=1 TO 4
580  LET
M(U,J)=M(V,J)+W*M(X,J)
```

```
590  NEXT J
600  GOSUB 620
610  RETURN
620  REM DISPLAY MATRIX
630  FOR I=1 TO 3
640  FOR J=1 TO 4
650  PRINT M(I,J)" ";
660  NEXT J
670  PRINT
680  NEXT I
690  RETURN
700  END
```

4.4 Exercises, page 165

1. a) 1
   b) none
   c) infinite
   d) none
   e) infinite
   f) 1
   g) infinite
   h) none
   i) 1

2. a) $(8,0)$
   f) $(5,0,0)$
   i) $(-9,3,1,1)$

3. c) $(8,y)$
   e) $\left(\dfrac{-5z}{2},0,z\right)$
   g) $\left(\dfrac{24-29w}{4},\dfrac{8-w}{4},0,w\right)$

4. a)

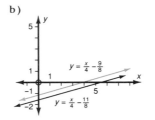

$y=-\dfrac{x}{5}+\dfrac{8}{5}$
$(8,0)$
$y=0$

b)

$y=\dfrac{x}{4}-\dfrac{9}{8}$
$y=\dfrac{x}{4}-\dfrac{11}{8}$

c)

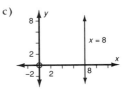

$x=8$

5. a) 1
   b) infinite
   c) none
   d) infinite
   e) none
   f) 1
   g) none
   h) none

6. a) $(2,1)$
   f) $(-1,-2,-1)$
   i) $(2.18, 3.49, -1.04, -1.54)$

7. b) $\left(\dfrac{5y-7}{3}, y\right)$
   d) $\left(\dfrac{-z+44}{14}, \dfrac{9z-4}{14}, z\right)$

8. a)

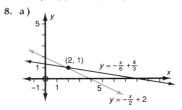

$(2,1)$
$y=-\dfrac{x}{6}+\dfrac{4}{3}$
$y=-\dfrac{x}{2}+2$

b)

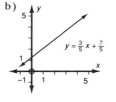

$y=\dfrac{3}{5}x+\dfrac{7}{5}$

c)

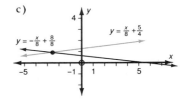

$y=-\dfrac{x}{8}+\dfrac{8}{8}$
$y=\dfrac{x}{8}+\dfrac{5}{4}$

9.
```
110  REM INPUT MATRIX
120  DIM M(3,4)
130  PRINT "TYPE IN THE VALUES
OF A,B,C,D FOR EACH EQUATION
AX+BY+CZ=D"
140  FOR I=1 TO 3
150  FOR J=1 TO 4
160  INPUT M(I,J)
170  NEXT J
180  NEXT I
190  IF M(3,1)=0 THEN GOTO 380
200  IF M(2,1) > < 0 THEN GOTO
280
210  FOR J=1 TO 4
220  LET M=(3,J)
230  LET M(3,J)=M(2,J)
240  LET M(2,J)=M
250  NEXT J
260  GOTO 380
270  :
280  REM PUT ZERO IN M(3,1)
290  LET D=M(3,1)
300  LET E=M(2,1)
310  FOR J=1 TO 4
320  LET M(3,J)=M(3,J)*E
330  LET M(2,J)=M(2,J)*D
340  NEXT J
350  FOR J=1 TO 4
360  M(3,J)=M(3,J)-M(2,J)
370  NEXT J
380  REM PUT ZERO IN M(2,1)
390  IF M(2,1)=0 THEN GOTO 560
400  LET B=M(1,1)
410  IF B=0 THEN GOTO 500
420  LET C=M(2,1)
430  FOR J=1 TO 4
440  LET M(1,J)=M(1,J)*C
450  LET M(2,J)=M(2,J)*B
460  NEXT J
470  FOR J=1 TO 4
480  M(2,J)=M(1,J)-M(2,J)
490  NEXT J
500  FOR J=1 TO 4
510  LET M=M(2,J)
520  LET M(2,J)=M(1,J)
530  LET M(1,J)=M
540  NEXT J
550  :
560  REM PUT ZERO IN M(3,2)
570  IF M(3,2)=0 THEN GOTO 740
580  IF M(2,2)=0 THEN GOTO 650
590  LET A=M(3,2)
600  LET C=M(2,2)
610  FOR J=1 TO 4
620  LET M(2,J)=M(2,J)*A
630  LET M(3,J)=M(3,J)*C
640  NEXT J
650  FOR J=2 TO 4
660  LET M=M(2,J)
670  LET M(2,J)=M(3,J)
680  LET M(3,J)=M
690  NEXT J
700  IF M(3,2)=0 THEN GOTO 740
710  FOR J=1 TO 4
720  LET M(3,J)=M(3,J)-M(2,J)
730  NEXT J
740  IF M(3,3)=0 AND M(3,4)=0
THEN GOSUB 840
750  IF M(3,3)=0 AND M(3,4) <
> 0 THEN GOSUB 860
760  IF M(3,3) < > 0 THEN
GOSUB 780
770  STOP
780  REM SOLVING THE SYSTEM
790  Z=M(3,4)/M(3,3)
800  Y=(M(2,4)-M(2,3)*Z)/
M(2,2)
810  X=(M(1,4)-M(1,3)*Z-
M(1,2)*Y)/M(1,1)
820  PRINT "(X,Y,Z)="X,Y,Z")"
830  RETURN
840  PRINT "THERE ARE AN INFI-
NITE NUMBER OF SOLUTIONS"
850  RETURN
860  PRINT "THERE ARE NO SOLU-
TIONS"
870  RETURN
880  END
```

4.5 Exercises, page 168

1. a) $(7,-1)$
   b) $(3,1)$
   c) none
   d) $(3y,y)$
   e) none
   f) $(3,1)$
   g) none
   h) $(3y,y)$
   i) $(3,1)$
   j) none
   k) none
   l) none

2. Your graphs will be straight lines, intersecting at one, none, or all points, as given in **1**.

3. 110 REM INPUT EQUATIONS
120 PRINT "HOW MANY EQUATIONS ARE THERE?"
130 INPUT K
140 IF K < 3 THEN GOSUB 290
150 DIM M(K,4)
160 IF K < 3 THEN GOTO 240
170 PRINT "TYPE IN THE COEFFICIENTS OF EACH EQUATION."
180 FOR I=1 TO K
190 FOR J=1 TO 4
200 INPUT M(I,J)
210 NEXT J
220 NEXT I
230 :
240 IF K>=3 THEN GOSUB 330
250 IF K=3 THEN PRINT "(X,Y,Z)=("X","Y","Z")"
260 IF K=4 THEN GOSUB 690
270 STOP
280 :
290 REM LESS THAN 3 EQUATIONS
300 PRINT "THERE ARE AN INFINITE NUMBER OF SOLUTIONS"
310 RETURN
320 :
330 REM SOLVE 3 EQUATIONS
340 REM PUT ZERO IN M(3,1)
350 LET D=M(3,1)
360 LET E=M(2,1)
370 FOR J=1 TO 4
380 LET M(3,J)=M(3,J)*E
390 LET M(2,J)=M(2,J)*D
400 NEXT J
410 FOR J=1 TO 4
420 M(3,J)=M(3,J)-M(2,J)
430 NEXT J
440 REM PUT ZERO IN M(2,1)
450 LET B=M(1,1)
460 LET C=M(2,1)
470 FOR J=1 TO 4
480 M(1,J)=M(1,J)*C
490 LET M(2,J)=M(2,J)*B
500 NEXT J
510 FOR J=1 TO 4
520 M(2,J)=M(1,J)-M(2,J)
530 NEXT J
540 :
550 REM PUT ZERO IN M(3,2)
560 LET A=M(3,2)
570 LET C=M(2,2)
580 FOR J=1 TO 4
590 LET M(2,J)=M(2,J)*A
600 LET M(3,J)=M(3,J)*C
610 NEXT J
620 FOR J=1 TO 4
630 LET M(3,J)=M(3,J)-M(2,J)
640 NEXT J
650 Z=M(3,4)/M(3,3)
660 Y=(M(2,4)-M(2,3)*Z)/M(2,2)

670 X=(M(1,4)-M(1,3)*Z-M(1,2)*Y)/M(1,1)
680 RETURN
690 REM 4 EQUATIONS
700 IF X*M(4,1)+Y*M(4,2)+Z*M(4,3)=M(4,4) THEN PRINT "(X,Y,Z)=)"X","Y","Z")"
710 IF X*M(4,1)+Y*M(4,2)+Z*M(4,3) > < M(4,4) THEN PRINT "THERE ARE NO SOLUTIONS"
720 RETURN
730 END

Note: This program will solve for up to four variables.

4. a) $(1,4,0)$
   b) no solution

5. a) $\left(-\dfrac{11}{3}t, 2 - \dfrac{10}{3}t, t\right)$

   b) $\left(\dfrac{s+5}{5}, \dfrac{7s}{5}, s, 0\right)$

   c) $(4 - 3t, t)$

   d) $(5 - 3s - t, s, t)$

   e) $\left(\dfrac{3r + s - t}{2}, r, s, t\right)$

   f) $\left(\dfrac{-5s + 9t + 7}{7}, \dfrac{s + 8t}{7}, s, t\right)$

6. 110 PRINT "HOW MANY EQUATIONS ARE THERE?"
120 INPUT M
130 DIM M(M,3)
140 REM INPUT COEFFICIENTS
150 PRINT "INPUT THE COEFFICIENTS OF THE EQUATIONS"
160 PRINT "AX+BY=C"
170 FOR I=1 TO M
180 FOR J=1 TO 3
190 INPUT M(I,J)
200 NEXT J
210 NEXT I
220 IF M=1 THEN GOSUB 2470
230 IF M > 1 THEN GOSUB 260
240 STOP
250 :
260 REM ELIMINATE X FROM EQUATION 1
270 LET A=M(1,1)
280 LET B=M(2,1)
290 FOR J=1 TO 3
300 LET M(1,J)=M(1,J)*B
310 LET M(2,J)=M(2,J)*A
320 LET M(2,J)=M(1,J)-M(2,J)
330 NEXT J
340 IF M(2,2) > < 0 THEN GOSUB 400
350 IF M(2,3)=0 AND M(2,2)=0 THEN GOSUB 2470

360 IF M(2,2)=0 AND M(2,3) > < 0 THEN GOSUB 2520
370 RETURN
380 :
390 REM SOLVE SYSTEM
400 LET Y=M(2,3)/M(2,2)
410 LET X=(M(1,3)-M(1,2)*Y)/M(1,1)
415 IF M=2 THEN GOSUB 1440
420 IF M=3 THEN GOSUB 560
430 IF M=4 THEN GOSUB 590
435 RETURN
560 IF M(3,1)*X+M(3,2)*Y=M(3,3) THEN GOSUB 1440
570 IF M(3,1)*X+M(3,2)*Y > < M(3,3) THEN GOSUB 2520
580 RETURN
590 IF M(3,1)*X+M(3,2)*Y > < M(3,3) OR M(4,1)*X+M(4,2)*Y > < M(4,3) THEN GOSUB 2520
600 IF M(3,1)*X+M(3,2)*Y=M(3,3) AND M(4,1)*X+M(4,2)*Y=M(4,3) THEN GOSUB 1440
610 RETURN
620 END
1440 PRINT "(X,Y)=("X","Y")"
1450 RETURN
1460 :
2470 REM INFINITE SOLUTIONS
2480 PRINT "THERE ARE AN INFINITE NUMBER OF SOLUTIONS"
2490 PRINT "(X,("M(1,3)"-"M(1,1)"X)/"M(1,2)")"
2500 RETURN
2520 :
2530 PRINT "THERE ARE NO SOLUTIONS"
2540 RETURN
2550 END

7. 110 REM INPUT EQUATIONS
120 PRINT "HOW MANY EQUATIONS ARE THERE?"
130 INPUT K
140 IF K < 3 THEN GOSUB 290
150 DIM M(K,4)
160 IF K < 3 THEN GOTO 240
170 PRINT "TYPE IN THE COEFFICIENTS OF EACH EQUATION."
180 FOR I=1 TO K
190 FOR J=1 TO 4
200 INPUT M(I,J)
210 NEXT J
220 NEXT I
230 :
240 IF K >=3 THEN GOSUB 330
250 IF K=3 THEN PRINT "(X,Y,Z)=("X","Y","Z")"

```
260 IF K=4 THEN GOSUB 690
270 STOP
280 :
290 REM LESS THAN 3 EQUATIONS
300 PRINT "THERE ARE AN INFI-
NITE NUMBER OF SOLUTIONS"
310 RETURN
320 :
330 REM SOLVE 3 EQUATIONS
340 REM PUT ZERO IN M(3,1)
350 LET D=M(3,1)
360 LET E=M(2,1)
370 FOR J=1 TO 4
380 LET M(3,J)=M(3,J)*E
390 LET M(2,J)=M(2,J)*D
400 NEXT J
410 FOR J=1 TO 4
420 (3,J)=M(3,J)-M(2,J)
430 NEXT J
440 REM PUT ZERO IN M(2,1)
450 LET B=M(1,1)
460 LET C=M(2,1)
470 FOR J=1 TO 4
480 LET M(1,J)=M(1,J)*C
490 LET M(2,J)=M(2,J)*B
500 NEXT J
510 FOR J=1 TO 4
520 M(2,J)=M(1,J)-M(2,J)
530 NEXT J
540 :
550 REM PUT ZERO IN M(3,2)
560 LET A=M(3,2)
570 LET C=M(2,2)
580 FOR J=1 TO 4
590 LET M(2,J)=M(2,J)*A
600 LET M(3,J)=M(3,J)*C
610 NEXT J
620 FOR J=1 TO 4
630 LET M(3,J)=M(3,J)-M(2,J)
640 NEXT J
650 Z=M(3,4)/M(3,3)
660 Y=(M(2,4)-M(2,3)*Z)/
M(2,2)
670 X=(M(1,4)-M(1,3)*Z-
M(1,2)*Y)/M(1,1)
680 RETURN
690 REM 4 EQUATIONS
700 IF
X*M(4,1)+Y*M(4,2)+Z*M(4,3)=M(4,4)
THEN PRINT
"(X,Y,Z)=)"X","Y","Z")"
710 IF
X*M(4,1)+Y*M(4,2)+Z*M(4,3) >
< M(4,4) THEN PRINT "THERE ARE
NO SOLUTIONS"
720 RETURN
730 END
```

8. a) $(0,0)$
   b) $(-2t, t, t)$
   c) $(0,0)$
   d) $(0,0,0)$

9.

a)
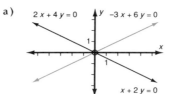

c)
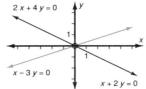

4.6 Exercises, page 174

1. a)
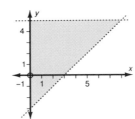

b)
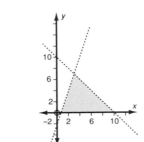

c)
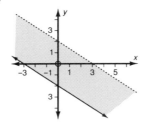

2. a) $(8,5), (0,5), (0,-3)$
   b) $(10,0), \left(\frac{2}{3},0\right), (3,7)$
   c) no vertices

3. a) $t \leqslant 5$
   b) $a + y \leqslant 90$
   c) $x \geqslant 0, y \geqslant 0, z \geqslant 0$
   d) $s - 10 \leqslant p$
   e) $m - d \leqslant 50$

4. b)
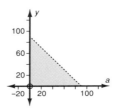

d)
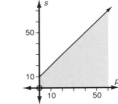

e)
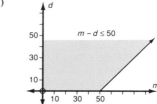

5. a) a; part A. b; part B
   $0 \leqslant a \leqslant 6, 0 \leqslant b \leqslant 4$
   b) $a \geqslant 3$ and $b \geqslant 2$; $4a + 6b \geqslant 36$
   c)
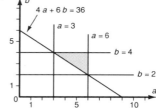

6. a) C: 100 g packet of Camp-Grub
   P: 100 g packet of Pack-
   Rations
   n: number of packets
   $C + P = n$, C, P, $n \in W$
   b) $80C + 20P \geqslant 3000$
   $160C + 150P \geqslant 15\,000$
   $8C + 32P \geqslant 700$
   $25C + 30P \geqslant 3500$
   $C + P \leqslant 150$

   c)

   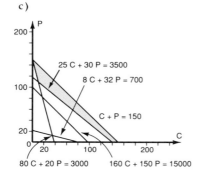

   d) $\left(10\frac{1}{2}, 108\right)$, (0,150), (150,0),
   (140,0)

7. a) $x + y \leqslant 5$, $-x + y \geqslant 0$, $x \geqslant 0$
   b) $s \geqslant 2$, $p \geqslant 2s - 4$, $p < s + 3$

4.7 Exercises, page 177

1. b) *B* Beaver, *M* Moose
   $B, M \in W$
   $150B + 60M \leqslant 30\,000$
   $50B + 40M \leqslant 13\,000$
   $10B + 20M \leqslant 5\,000$
   Objective function
   $400B + 300M$

2. *x* volume of crude oil (in L) to
   Refinery 1
   y volume of crude oil (in L) to
   Refinery 2
   $x, y \in W$
   $x \geqslant 0$, $y \geqslant 0$
   $0.5x + 0.3y \geqslant 59\,000$
   $0.3(x + y) \geqslant 42\,000$
   $0.2x + 0.4y \geqslant 40\,000$
   Objective function $x + y$

3. *P* hours Pat works, *F* hours Frank
   works
   $P, F \in W$
   $600P + 1000F \geqslant 6000$
   $400P + 400F \geqslant 32\,000$
   Objective function $15P + 20F$

4. X_A, X_B, X_C cartons shipped from X
   to each of A, B, C respectively
   Y_A, Y_B, Y_C cartons shipped from Y
   to each of A, B, C respectively
   X_A, X_B, X_C, Y_A, Y_B, $Y_C \in W$
   $X_A + X_B + X_C = 12$
   $Y_A + Y_B + Y_C = 12$
   $X_A + Y_A = X_B + Y_B = X_C + Y_C = 8$
   Objective function
   $2X_A + 2X_B + 3X_C + 4Y_A + 3Y_B + 4Y_C$

5. *B* Beginner skis, *R* Racing skis
   $B, R \in W$
   $30B + 60R \leqslant 480$
   $60B + 30R \leqslant 480$
   $48B + 48R \leqslant 480$
   Objective function $40B + 30R$

4.8 Exercises, page 183

1. a)

   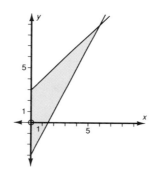

   b)

   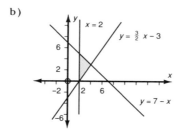

c)

2. 15
3. 18
4. 0
5. $480\,000; 12 of each
6. 140 Beavers, 150 Moose
7. Pat   5 hours, Frank   3 hours
8. 8 cartons from X to store A;
   4 cartons from X in any
   combination to store B or C;
   from Y 12 cartons to store B or C
   so that each store would have
   8 cartons

	A	B	C
X	8	x	$4 - x$
Y	0	$8 - x$	$4 + x$

9. 6 beginner skis and 4 racing skis
10. a) 140 000 L
    b) Answers will vary.
11. 4320 large, 0 small

4.9 Exercises, page 187

1. (0,12,0)
2. maximum profit $2 932 600
3. 7 cabin A
4. 625 large pizzas only

Inventory, page 189

1. c)
2. b)
3. a)
4. $10, x, 20, -10, 20$
5. $10n - 10$
6. $\frac{1}{2}x + 10$
7. $2, 2, z, 2$
8. $\begin{bmatrix} 2 & 3 & -4 & | & 7 \\ 1 & -2 & 1 & | & 11 \\ 3 & 1 & 2 & | & 8 \end{bmatrix}$
9. B, C
10. $2, 3$
11. $t \geqslant 0$
12. $t + c \geqslant 50$
13.

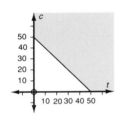

14. 0
15. $\begin{aligned} 2x + 5y - 3z - 2t + u &= 5 \\ 3x - 2y + 4z + 3t + v &= 2 \\ x - 4y - 5z + 6t + w &= 7 \\ -4x + 7y + 6z - 4t + M &= 0 \end{aligned}$
16.

$$\begin{bmatrix} x & y & z & t & u & v & w & M & \\ 2 & 5 & -3 & -2 & 1 & 0 & 0 & 0 & | & 5 \\ 3 & -2 & 4 & 3 & 0 & 1 & 0 & 0 & | & 2 \\ 1 & -4 & -5 & 6 & 0 & 0 & 1 & 0 & | & 7 \\ -4 & 7 & 6 & -4 & 0 & 0 & 0 & 1 & | & 0 \end{bmatrix}$$

17. $x = y = z = t = 0, u = 5, v = 2,$
$w = 7, M = 0$

Review Exercises, pages 191–193

1. a)

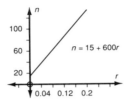

b) linear, discrete
2. a) $n = 3t - \frac{3}{2}$
b)

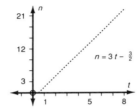

c) discrete
d) $D = \{t \mid 0 \leqslant t \leqslant 8, t \in R\}$
$R = \{n \mid 0, \leqslant n \leqslant 22, n \in I\}$
3. $\begin{cases} c = 1, x \leqslant 1 \\ c = 1 + 0.5\left(\frac{x-1}{2}\right), x > 1 \end{cases}$
4. a) $\$c = 5.5 + (n - 1)$
b)

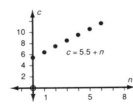

c) discrete
d) $\{n \mid 1 \leqslant n \leqslant 5, n \in N\}$

5. a) $(2,2)$
b) $\left(\frac{1}{2}, -2\right)$
c) $(3,1,2)$
d) $(-1,1,-5)$
e) $(-1,1,-2,3)$

6. a) $\begin{bmatrix} 2 & 1 & | & 6 \\ 1 & -1 & | & 0 \end{bmatrix}$

b) $\begin{bmatrix} 4 & -7 & | & 16 \\ 6 & 4 & | & -5 \end{bmatrix}$

c) $\begin{bmatrix} 3 & -2 & 5 & | & -1 \\ 2 & 5 & -4 & | & -9 \\ 4 & 3 & -2 & | & -13 \end{bmatrix}$

d) $\begin{bmatrix} 5 & -4 & -6 & | & 21 \\ -2 & 3 & 4 & | & -15 \\ 3 & -7 & -5 & | & 15 \end{bmatrix}$

e) $\begin{bmatrix} 4 & 1 & 2 & -3 & | & -16 \\ -3 & 3 & -1 & 4 & | & 20 \\ 5 & 4 & 3 & -1 & | & -10 \\ -1 & 2 & 5 & 1 & | & -4 \end{bmatrix}$

7. a) $(2,2)$

b) $\left(\dfrac{1}{2}, -2\right)$

c) $(3,1,2)$

d) $(-1,1,-5)$

e) $(-1,1,-2,3)$

8. a) 2, 3
b) none

9. a) 2, 3; none
b) 3, 3; 1
c) 3, 2; infinite
d) 3, 1; infinite

10. c) 2
b) 3

11. a) none
b) $(1 + 3z, 2 - z, z)$
c) $(y + 2t + 3, y, -t - 1, t)$
d) $\left(\dfrac{8}{5}, \dfrac{6}{5}\right)$
e) none
f) $\left(\dfrac{7}{4} - \dfrac{7t}{8}, \dfrac{z}{2} - \dfrac{5t}{16} - \dfrac{3}{8}, z, t\right)$

12. 60 km/h

13. $(28,42,56)$

14. $I_1 = 0.208$
$I_2 = 0.196$
$I_3 = 0.350$

15. a) $x = y = 0$
b) no solution
c) $x = y = z = 0$

16. a) $0 \leqslant C \leqslant 75\,000$,
$0 \leqslant P \leqslant 75\,000$,
$C > P, C + P \leqslant 100\,000$

b)

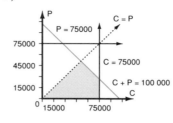

17. a)

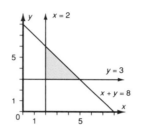

b)

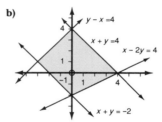

18. 18

19. 20

20. 50 sets from Manston ro Radio World and Cut-Price. From the Picton warehouse 20 sets to Cut-Price and 40 to TV City.

21. 25 tests, 11 medicals, 4 consultations

22. a) $a + b + c = 38.4$
$4a + 2b + c = 21.6$
$9a + 3b + c = 9.6$

b) $\begin{bmatrix} 1 & 1 & 1 & | & 38.4 \\ 4 & 2 & 1 & | & 21.6 \\ 9 & 3 & 1 & | & 9.6 \end{bmatrix}$

c) $\begin{bmatrix} 1 & 1 & 1 & | & 38.4 \\ 0 & 2 & 3 & | & 132.0 \\ 0 & 0 & 1 & | & 60.0 \end{bmatrix}$

d) $a = 2.4$
$b = -24$
$c = 60$

e) 5 min

23. a) x 3-mark questions,
y 12-mark questions

b) $x + y \leqslant 20, x + 3y \leqslant 30$,
$x \leqslant 18, y \leqslant 7$

c) $3x + 12y = M$

d) 17 12-mark questions
13 5-mark questions

Chapter Five
The Binomial Theorem

5.2 Exercises, page 199

1. a) 13
   b) 31
   c) 40

2. $a^{30}, 30a^{29}x, x^{30}$

3. a) 13
   b) 8
   c) 11
   d) 3

4. a) b) c) $a^7 + 7a^6x + 21a^5x^2 +$
   $35a^4x^3 + 35a^3x^4 + 21a^2x^5 +$
   $7ax^6 + x^7$

5. a) $a^8 + 8a^7x + 28a^6x^2 + \ldots$
   $+ 8ax^7 + x^8$
   b) $a^9 + 9a^8x + 36a^7x^2 + \ldots$
   $+ 9ax^8 + x^9$
   c) $a^{10} + 10a^9x + 45a^8x^2 + \ldots$
   $+ 10ax^9 + x^{10}$
   d) $a^{11} + 11a^{10}x + 55a^9x^2 + \ldots$
   $+ 11ax^{10} + x^{11}$
   e) $a^{12} + 12a^{11}x + 66a^{10}x^2 + \ldots$
   $+ 12ax^{11} + x^{12}$

6.
```
                    1
                 1    1
              1    2    1
           1    3    3    1
        1    4    6    4    1
      1    5   10   10    5    1
    1    6   15   20   15    6    1
  1    7   21   35   35   21    7    1
1    8   28   56   70   56   28    8    1
1  9  36  84  126  126  84  36   9   1
1 10 45 120 210 252 210 120 45  10  1
1 11 55 165 330 462 462 330 165 55 11 1
1 12 66 220 495 792 924 792 495 220 66 12 1
```

7. a) b) c) $m^5 + 5m^4k + 10m^3k^2$
   $+ 10m^2k^3 + 5mk^4 + k^5$

8. a) $a^5 + 5a^4k + 10a^3k^2 + 10a^2k^3 +$
   $5ak^4 + k^5$
   b) $y^4 + 4y^3t + 6y^2t^2 + 4yt^3 + t^4$
   c) $w^8 + 8w^7b + 28w^6b^2 + 56w^5b^3$
   $+ 70w^4b^4 + 56w^3b^5 + 28w^2b^6 +$
   $8wb^7 + b^8$
   d) $H^6 + 6H^5T + 15H^4T^2 + 20H^3T^3$
   $+ 15H^2T^4 + 6HT^5 + T^6$

9. a) $a^3 + 3a^2x + 3ax^2 + x^3$
   b) $8 + 12x + 6x^2 + x^3$

10. a) $a^4 + 4a^3x + 6a^2x^2$
    $+ 4ax^3 + x^4$
    b) $a^4 + 12a^3 + 54a^2$
    $+ 108a + 81$

11. a) $a^5 + 5a^4x + 10a^3x^2$
    $+ 10a^2x^3 + 5ax^4 + x^5$
    b) $32k^5 + 320k^4 + 1280k^3$
    $+ 2560k^2 + 2560k + 1024$

12. a) $a^7 + 7a^6x + 21a^5x^2 + 35a^4x^3 +$
    $35a^3x^4 + 21a^2x^5 + 7ax^6 + x^7$
    b) $a^7 - 7a^6b + 21a^5b^2 - 35a^4b^3 +$
    $35a^3b^4 - 21a^2b^5 + 7ab^6 - b^7$
    c) $2187 - 5103x + 5103x^2$
    $- 2835x^3 + 945x^4 - 189x^5$
    $+ 21x^6 - x^7$

13. a) $a^{100} + 100a^{99}x + 4950a^{98}x^2 +$
    $161\,700a^{97}x^3 \ldots$
    b) $\ldots 5050, 101, 1$
    c) $\ldots 161\,700a^3x^{97} + 4950a^2x^{98} +$
    $100ax^{99} + x^{100}$

14. a) $1, 90, 4005, 129\,495 \ldots$
    b) $\ldots 129\,495, 4005, 90, 1$
    c) $\ldots 129\,495a^3x^{87} + 4005a^2x^{88} +$
    $90ax^{89} + x^{90}$

15. a) $H^5 + 5H^4T + 10H^3T^2 + 10H^2T^3$
    $+ 5HT^4 + T^5$

    b)
```
H  H  H  H  H
H  H  H  H  T
H  H  H  T  H
H  H  T  H  H
H  T  H  H  H
T  H  H  H  H
H  H  H  T  T
H  H  T  T  H
H  T  T  H  H
T  T  H  H  H
H  H  T  H  T
H  T  H  H  T
T  H  H  H  T
H  T  H  T  H
T  H  H  T  H
T  H  T  H  H
T  T  T  H  H
T  T  H  H  T
T  H  H  T  T
H  H  T  T  T
T  T  H  T  H
T  H  T  T  H
H  T  T  T  H
T  H  T  H  T
H  T  T  H  T
H  T  H  T  T
T  T  T  H  T
T  T  T  T  H  T
T  T  H  T  T
T  H  T  T  T
H  T  T  T  T
T  T  T  T  T
```

5.3 Exercises, page 204

No answer provided for questions 9, 11, 12.

1. a) 21
   b) 10
   c) 56
   d) 125 970

2. a) $a^6 + 6a^5x + 15a^4x^2 + 20a^3x^3 + 15a^2x^4 + 6ax^5 + x^6$
   b) $a^b + 6a^5x + 15a^4x^2 + 20a^3x^3 + 15a^2x^4 + 6ax^5 + x^6$

3. a) $a^7 + 7a^6x + 21a^5x^2 + 35a^4x^3 + 35a^3x^4 + 21a^2x^5 + 7ax^6 + x^7$
   b) $b^5 - 5b^4c + 10b^3c^2 - 10b^2c^3 + 5bc^4 - c^5$
   c) $m^5 + 5m^4z + 10m^3z^2 + 10m^2z^3 + 5mz^4 + z^5$
   d) $32 + 80x + 80x^2 + 40x^3 + 10x^4 + x^5$
   e) $a^8 + 8a^7 + 28a^6 + 56a^5 + 70a^4 + 56a^3 + 28a^2 + 8a + 1$
   f) $81 - 108b + 54b^2 - 12b^3 + b^4$

4. a) $a^4 + 8a^3b + 24a^2b^2 + 32ab^3 + 16b^4$
   b) $81a^4 + 432a^3b + 864a^2b^2 + 768ab^3 + 256b^4$
   c) $27 - 54m + 36m^2 - 8m^3$
   d) $64a^3 - 240a^2 + 300a - 125$
   e) $32x^5 + 240x^4a + 720x^3a^2 + 1080x^2a^3 + 810xa^4 + 243a^5$
   f) $1 - 5m^2 + 10m^4 - 10m^6 + 5m^8 - m^{10}$
   g) $729 + 1458x + 1215x^2 + 540x^3 + 135x^4 + 18x^5 + x^6$
   h) $H^7 + 7H^6T + 21H^5T^2 + 35H^4T^3 + 35H^3T^4 + 21H^2T^5 + 7HT^6 + T^7$

5. a) $32 - 240x + 720x^2 - 1080x^3 + 810x^4 - 243x^5$
   b) $1 + 5x^2 + 10x^4 + 10x^6 + 5x^8 + x^{10}$
   c) $8k^3 + 48k^2b + 96kb^2 + 64b^3$
   d) $r^4 - 8r^3s + 24r^2s^2 - 32rs^3 + 16s^4$
   e) $125 - 150k + 60k^2 - 8k^3$
   f) $m^{10} - 5m^8 + 10m^6 - 10m^4 + 5m^2 - 1$

6. a) $\frac{1}{8} + \frac{3}{4}x + \frac{3}{2}x^2 + x^3$
   b) $0.0001 + 0.002x + 0.015x^2 + 0.05x^3 + 0.0625x^4$
   c) $\frac{27}{125} + \frac{27}{100}x + \frac{9}{80}x^2 + \frac{1}{64}x^3$
   d) $40.8 + 311.2x + 948.3x^2 + 1445.1x^3 + 1101.0x^4 + 335.5x^5$

7. a) $C(50,0)H^{50} + C(50,1)H^{49}T + C(50,2)H^{48}T^2$
   b) $C(30,0)a^{30} + C(30,1)a^{29}(-b) + C(30,2)a^{28}(-b)^2$
   c) $C(8,0)(2k)^8 + C(8,1)(2k)^7(4b)^1 + C(8,2)(2k)^6(4b)^2$
   d) $C(4,0)r^4 + C(4,1)r^3(-2s)^1 + C(4,2)r^2(-2s)^2$
   e) $C(50,0)(1)^{50} + C(50,1)(1)^{49}x + C(50,2)(1)^{48}x^2$
   f) $C(90,0)b^{90} + C(90,1)b^{89}(-3) + C(90,2)b^{88}(-3)^2$

8. a) $\ldots C(50,48)H^2T^{48} + C(50,49)HT^{49} + C(50,50)T^{50}$
   b) $\ldots C(30,28)a^2(-b)^{28} + C(30,29)a(-b)^{29} + C(30,30)(-b)^{30}$
   c) $\ldots C(8,6)(2k)^2(4b)^6 + C(8,7)(2k)(4b)^7 + C(8,8)(4b)^8$

10. a) $\frac{1}{8} + \frac{3}{8} + \frac{3}{8} + \frac{1}{8}$
    b) $\frac{1}{16} + \frac{4}{16} + \frac{6}{16} + \frac{4}{16} + \frac{1}{16}$
    c) $\frac{1}{64} + \frac{9}{64} + \frac{27}{64} + \frac{27}{64}$
    d) $0.001 + 0.027 + 0.243 + 0.729$

13. a) $x^4 + 8x^2 + 24 + \frac{32}{x^2} + \frac{16}{x^4}$
    b) $x^3 - 3x + \frac{3}{x} - \frac{1}{x^3}$
    c) $x^5 - 10x^2 + \frac{40}{x} - \frac{80}{x^4} + \frac{80}{x^7} - \frac{32}{x^{10}}$

14. a) $C(20,6)a^{14}x^6$
    b) $C(50,29)a^{21}x^{29}$

15. a) $12a^3x$
    b) $108ax^3$

16. 6

17. $b = 1.5, n = 5$

18. a) $1 + 3x + 3x^2 + x^3$
    b) $1 + 6m + 9m^2 - 4m^3 - 9m^4 + 6m^5 - m^6$

In Search of, page 205

a) 5.196
b) 5.013
c) 4.003

5.4 Exercises, page 210

No answers provided for questions 12, 13, 15, 17.

1. a) $C(5,k)p^{5-k}q^k$
   b) $10p^3q^2$
   c) $10p^2q^3$
   d) $10p^2q^3$

2. a) $C(12,k)a^{12-k}b^k$
   b) $792a^5b^7$
   c) $792a^7b^5$
   d) $924a^6b^6$

3. a) $C(20,k)m^{20-k}t^k$
   b) $15\,504m^{15}t^5$
   c) $77\,520m^{13}t^7$
   d) $77\,520m^7t^{13}$

4. a) $5HT^4$
   b) $38\,760m^{14}t^6$
   c) $55\,427\,328y^7a^5$

5. a) $C(5,k)(0.9^{5-k})(0.1^k)$
   b) $0.008\,10$
   c) $0.328\,05$

6. a) $C(8,k)(0.4^{8-k})(0.6^k)$
   b) $0.209\,02$
   c) $0.278\,69$

7. a) $p^5 + 5p^4q + 10p^3q^2$
   b) $0.964\,51$

8. a) $C(9,k)x^{9-k}\left(\frac{1}{x}\right)^k$; $36x^5$
   b) $C(5,k)(x^2)^{5-k}\left(\frac{3}{x^2}\right)^k$
   c) $C(5,k)(x^2)^{5-k}\left(\frac{1}{x}\right)^k$

9. 0.1201

10. 0.2160

11. 0.2936

14. 5985

16. 495

5.5 Exercises, page 213

No answers provided for questions 5-12.

1. a)
```
                         1
                       1   1
                     1   2   1
                   1   3   3   1
                 1   4   6   4   1
               1   5  10  10   5   1
             1   6  15  20  15   6   1
           1   7  21  35  35  21   7   1
         1   8  28  56  70  56  28   8   1
       1   9  36  84 126 126  84  36   9   1
     1  10  45 120 210 252 210 120  45  10   1
   1  11  55 165 330 462 462 330 165  55  11   1
```

b)
```
                                C(0,0)
                            C(1,0)   C(1,1)
                        C(2,0)   C(2,1)   C(2,2)
                    C(3,0)   C(3,1)   C(3,2)   C(3,3)
                C(4,0)   C(4,1)   C(4,2)   C(4,3)   C(4,4)
            C(5,0)   C(5,1)   C(5,2)   C(5,3)   C(5,4)   C(5,5)
        C(6,0)   C(6,1)   C(6,2)   C(6,3)   C(6,4)   C(6,5)   C(6,6)
      C(7,0)   C(7,1)   C(7,2)   C(7,3)   C(7,4)   C(7,5)   C(7,6)   C(7,7)
    C(8,0)   C(8,1)   C(8,2)   C(8,3)   C(8,4)   C(8,5)   C(8,6)   C(8,7)   C(8,8)
  C(9,0)   C(9,1)   C(9,2)   C(9,3)   C(9,4)   C(9,5)   C(9,6)   C(9,7)   C(9,8)   C(9,9)
C(10,0) C(10,1) C(10,2) C(10,3) C(10,4) C(10,5) C(10,6) C(10,7) C(10,8) C(10,9) C(10,10)
C(11,0) C(11,1) C(11,2) C(11,3) C(11,4) C(11,5) C(11,6) C(11,7) C(11,8) C(11,9) C(11,10) C(11,11)
```

2. a) 56
   b) 462
   c) 35
   d) 126

3. a) $C(10,5) = C(9,4) + C(9,5)$
   b) $C(32,8) = C(31,7) + C(31,8)$
   c) $C(35,15)$

4. a) $C(46,33)$
   b) $m + t = 12$

In Search of, pages 214–215

Pattern 2

No answer provided for a), d)

   b) $11; k - 1$
   c) $C(n - 1,2)$

Pattern 3

No answer provided for b) e) f).

   a) 89, 144, 223, 377, 600
   c) $1, -1, 1, -1$
      $(-1)^{n-1}$
   d) 6, 15, 40, 104, 273,...
      $t_k \times t_{k+1}, k > 2$

Inventory, page 216

1. a) 16
   b) 10
   c) 9
   d) 455
   e) 5005
   f) $6435a^8x^7$

2. a) 1 9 36 84 126 126
      84 36 9 1
   b) 10; 8th, 9th, 10th, 11th

3. a) $C(7,k)a^{7-k}x^k$
   b) $(m + b)^{12}$

4. 1, 6

Review Exercises, page 217

No answers provided for questions 12, 13, 15, 18.

1. a) refer to answer for question 6
   Exercise 5.2

$$1$$
$$1 \quad 1$$
$$1 \quad 2 \quad 1$$
$$\vdots$$

| 1 | 13 | 78 | 286 | 715 | 1287 | 1716 | 1716 | 1287 | 715 | 286 | 78 | 13 | 1 |

| 1 | 14 | 81 | 364 | 1001 | 2002 | 3003 | 3432 | 3003 | 2002 | 1001 | 364 | 81 | 14 | 1 |

b) $C(15,0)\ C(15,1)\ C(15,2)\dots$
   $C(15,13),\ C(15,14)\ C(15,15)$

2. a) $a^5 + 5a^4x + 10a^3x^2 + 10a^2x^3 + 5ax^4 + x^5$

   b) $a^5 - 5a^4c + 10a^3c^2 - 10a^2c^3 + 5ac^4 - c^5$

   c) $m^6 + 6m^5b + 15m^4b^2 + 20m^3b^3 + 15m^2b^4 + 6mb^5 + b^6$

   d) $81 + 108x + 54x^2 + 12x^3 + x^4$

   e) $a^7 + 14a^6 + 84a^5 + 280a^4 + 560a^3 + 672a^2 + 448a + 128$

   f) $64 - 48b + 12b^2 - b^3$

3. a) $a^3 + 6a^2b + 12ab^2 + 8b^3$

   b) $81a^4 + 216a^3b + 216a^2b^2 + 96b^3 + 16b^4$

   c) $128 - 896a + 2688a^2 - 4480a^3 + 4480a^4 - 2688a^5 + 896a^6 - 128a^7$

   d) $16t^4 - 224t^3 + 1176t^2 - 2744t + 2401$

   e) $32x^5 + 240x^4a + 720x^3a^2 + 1080x^2a^3 + 810xa^4 + 243a^5$

   f) $1 - 4b^2 + 6b^4 - 4b^6 + b^8$

4. a) $64 - 576x + 2160x^2 - 4320x^3 + 4860x^4 - 2916x^5 + 729x^6$

   b) $1 + 5x^2 + 10x^4 + 10x^6 + 5x^8 + x^{10}$

   c) $8t^3 + 48t^2b + 96tb^2 + 64b^3$

   d) $r^4 - 8r^3s + 24r^2s^2 - 32rs^3 + 16r^4$

   e) $12s - 150s + 60s^2 - 8s^3$

   f) $m^{10} - 5m^8 + 10m^6 - 10m^4 + 5m^6 - 1$

5. a) $a^{200} + C(200,1)a^{199}x + C(200,2)a^{198}x^2$

   b) $w^{40} + C(40,1)w^{39}(-2) + C(40,2)w^{38}(-2)^2$

   c) $2^5 + C(5,1)2^4(4b) + C(5,2)2^3(4b)^2$

   d) $s^{30} + C(30,1)s^{29}(-2r) + C(30,2)s^{28}(-2r)^2$

e) $1^{50} + C(50,1)1^{49}(x^2) + C(50,2)1^{48}(x^2)^2$

f) $f^{95} + C(95,1)f^{94}(-3) + C(95,2)f^{93}(-3)^2$

6. a) $\dfrac{1}{16} + \dfrac{1}{4} + \dfrac{3}{8} + \dfrac{1}{4} + \dfrac{1}{16}$

   b) $\dfrac{1}{27} + \dfrac{2}{9} + \dfrac{4}{9} + \dfrac{8}{27}$

   c) $0.09 + 0.42 + 0.49$

7. a) $x^3 + 6x + \dfrac{12}{x} + \dfrac{8}{x^3}$

   b) $x^4 - 4x^2 + 6 - \dfrac{4}{x^2} + \dfrac{1}{x^4}$

   c) $x^{10} + 15x^6 + 90x^2 + \dfrac{270}{x^2} + \dfrac{405}{x^6} + \dfrac{243}{x^{10}}$

8. a) $C(7,k)a^{7-k}x^k$

   b) $C(24,k)2^{24-k}m^k$

   c) $C(50,k)H^{50-k}T^k$

9. a) $C(11,k)p^{11-k}q^k$

   b) $55p^9q^2$

   c) $462p^5q^6$

   d) $462p^5q^6$

10. a) $C(7,k)x^{7-k}\left(\dfrac{1}{x}\right)^k; 21x^3$

    b) $C(3,k)(x^2)^{3-k}\left(\dfrac{2}{x}\right)^k; 6x^3$

    c) $C(9,k)(x^2)^{9-k}\left(\dfrac{1}{x^3}\right)^k; 84x^3$

11. a) $220m^3(5^9)$

    b) $C(72,29)(2x)^{43}\left(\dfrac{3}{b}\right)^{29}$

    c) 70

    d) 20

14. 0.0806

16. a) $1 - 4x + 6x^2 - 4x^3 + x^4$

    b) $1 + 6x + 12x^2 + 8x^3$

    c) -6

17. $2C(n,o) + 2C(n,2)x^2 + 2C(n,4)x^4$

19. 14

20. $n = 2r$

Chapter Six
Finite and Infinite Series

Activities, page 219

No answers provided for questions 1, 2, 5, 6, 7.

3.

t(s)	0	1	2	3
A d(m)	0	10	20	30
t d(m)	100	101	102	103
t(s)	4	5	6	
A d(m)	40	50	60	
t d(m)	104	105	106	
t(s)	7	8	9	
A d(m)	70	80	90	
t d(m)	107	108	109	
t(s)	10	11	12	
A d(m)	100	110	120	
t d(m)	110	111	112	

4. approximately 11.1 s

6.1 Exercises, page 223

No answers provided for questions 11, 12, 13.

1. a) 6
   b) 28
   c) 6
   d) 4, 23
   e) $8 + 13 + 18 + 23 + 28 + 33$

2. a) 6, 10, 14, 18
   b) 6, 12, 24, 48
   c) $\dfrac{1}{7}, \dfrac{1}{9}, \dfrac{1}{11}, \dfrac{1}{13}$

3. a) $\displaystyle\sum_{k=1}^{4} 2 + 4k$
   b) $\displaystyle\sum_{n=1}^{4} 3 \times 2^n$
   c) $\displaystyle\sum_{a=1}^{4} \dfrac{1}{2a + 5}$

4. b)

5. a) $6; 24; 3n \times 2$
   b) $2; 65; n^3 + 1$
   c) $\dfrac{1}{2}; \dfrac{1}{11}; \dfrac{1}{3n - 1}$

6. a) $1 + 2 + 3 + 4$
   b) $8 + 16 + 32 + 64 + 128$
   c) $1 + 4 + 9 + 16 + 25$
   d) $3 + 6 + 9 + 12 + 15 + 18$
   e) $5 + 7 + 9 + 11 + 13$
   f) $-5 + 5 - 5 + 5$

7. a) $\displaystyle\sum_{k=1}^{5} k$
   b) $\displaystyle\sum_{k=1}^{5} k^3$
   c) $\displaystyle\sum_{k=4}^{8} k^2$
   d) $\displaystyle\sum_{k=1}^{5} c^k$
   e) $\displaystyle\sum_{k=4}^{7} 2(3^k)$
   f) $\displaystyle\sum_{k=1}^{6} t_k$

8. a) $3 + 6 + 9 + 12$
   b) $3 + 6 + 9 + 12$
   c) $3 + 6 + 9 + 12$
   Same number of terms, same sums.

9. a) $3 + 6 + 9 + 12$
   b) $6 + 9 + 12 + 15$
   Same number of terms; different sums.

10. a) $\displaystyle\sum_{k=1}^{n} \dfrac{1}{k}$
    b) $\displaystyle\sum_{k=1}^{n} 5k - 3$
    c) $\displaystyle\sum_{k=1}^{n} (-1)^k \times 2$
    d) $\displaystyle\sum_{i=1}^{n} ik^{i-1}$

6.2 Exercises, page 230

1. a) arithmetic; $d = 3$; 12, 15
   b) arithmetic; $d = 4$; 13, 17
   c) geometric; $r = \dfrac{1}{3}$; 1, $\dfrac{1}{3}$
   d) arithmetic; $d = 3$; $k + 12$, $k + 15$
   e) geometric; $r = 2c$; $16c^5$, $32c^6$
   f) arithmetic; $d = -3$; -5, -8
   g) geometric; $r = 2$; 1, 2
   h) geometric; $r = 0.1$; 0.0013, 0.00013

2. a) 896; 3584
   b) 32 805; 295 245
   c) 1.5×10^{-7}; 1.5×10^{-9}
   d) 0.0625; 0.015 625
   e) -5; -17
   f) 9.9; 9.3

3. a) $t_n = 4n - 1$; $\displaystyle\sum_{i=1}^{n} 4i - 1$
   b) $t_n = 8\left(\dfrac{1}{3}\right)^{n-1}$; $\displaystyle\sum_{i=1}^{n} 8\left(\dfrac{1}{3}\right)^{i-1}$
   c) $t_n = 5(3)^{n-1}$; $\displaystyle\sum_{i=1}^{n} 5(3)^{i-1}$
   d) $t_n = -13n + 38$; $\displaystyle\sum_{i=1}^{n} -13i + 38$

4. a) 36
   b) 12

5. a) $a = -7; d = 4$
   b) $a = 50; d = -8$

6. a) $a = 4; r = 3$ or $a = -4; r = -3$
   b) $a = -312\ 500; r = -0.2$

7. a) 81.45%
   b) 24

8. $\dfrac{5}{4}$

9. a) 5
   b) 320
   c) 20 480
   d) 2.199×10^{13}

10. 650; 1250

11. $655

6.3 Exercises, page 234

1. a) 335
   b) 1232

2. a) 460
   b) -720
   c) 1520
   d) 455

3. a) 1000
   b) 3069
   c) 3184
   d) 34.2

4. a) 175
   b) 1090
   c) -9300

5. 11 or 1

6. $0.42 per record

7. $\dfrac{1}{2}(n^2 + n)$

8. a) 122.5 m
   b) 19 s

9. 336

10. a) 117
    b) 3.13

11. a) $2780
    b) $125 250

6.4 Exercises, page 237
No answer provided for 6a).

1. a) 5 465
   b) 1.593 75
2. a) 3580.5
   b) 13.5
   c) 19 662
   d) 0.033 333
   e) 51.2
   f) 0.3333
3. a) 3066
   b) 64
4. a) 2044
   b) 1.5
5. 0.0769
6. b) 1261.62
7. a) $\dfrac{1}{2}, \dfrac{3}{4}, \dfrac{7}{8}, \dfrac{15}{16}$
   b) no
   c) no
8. 2 097 150
9. b)
10. $7(2^{36})$
11. $56 + 24\sqrt{2}$

6.5 Exercises page 243
No answers provided for 5, 10a, 11.

1. a) converges; $S_\infty = \dfrac{15}{4}$
   b) converges; $S_\infty = \dfrac{64}{7}$
   c) does not converge
   d) converges; $S_\infty = 10$
   e) does not converge
   f) converges; $S_\infty = \dfrac{35}{4}$
2. a) $0.67 + 0.0067 + 0.000067 + \ldots$;
      $\dfrac{67}{99}$
   b) $0.5431 + 0.0000\,5431 +$
      $0.0000\,0000\,5431 + \ldots$;
      $\dfrac{5431}{999}$
   c) $0.1243 + 0.000043 +$
      $0.00000043 + \ldots$;
      $\dfrac{1231}{9900}$

d) $2.365 + .000365 +$
   $0.000\,000\,365 + \ldots$;
   $\dfrac{2363}{999}$
e) $0.001 + 0.000\,001 +$
   $0.000\,000\,001 + \ldots$;
   $\dfrac{1}{999}$
f) $0.9 + 0.09 + 0.009 + 0.0009 + \ldots$;
   $\dfrac{1}{1}$
3. $111.\dot{1}$ or $111\dfrac{1}{9}$
4. 37.1 m
6. 0.6
7. 800 cm
8. 23.12 units
9. $1 000 000
10. b) $ar < 0$

6.6 Exercises, page 250
No answers provided for questions 4a, 5a, 7, 8, 10, 11, 14.

1. $\dfrac{4n\,5^{n+1} - 5^{n+1} + 5}{16}$ or
   $\dfrac{(4n - 1)(5^{n+1}) + 5}{16}$
2. a) $\dfrac{7n\,8^{n+1} - 8^{n+1} + 8}{49}$ or
      $\dfrac{(7n - 1)8^{n+1} + 8}{49}$
   b) $\dfrac{2n\,3^{n+1} - 3^{n+1} + 3}{4}$ or
      $\dfrac{(2n - 1)3^{n+1} + 3}{4}$
   c) $\dfrac{(-20n - 25)5^{-n-1} + 5}{16}$
   d) $\dfrac{(-0.8n - 1)(0.2)^{n+1} + 0.2}{0.64}$
3. 3.7450
4. b) $\dfrac{5}{16}$
   c) 3.75
5. b) $\dfrac{3n}{3n + 1}$
6. $\dfrac{n}{2n + 1}$

9. a) $x^5 - (x - 1)^5$
   b) $\dfrac{n(n + 1)(6n^3 + 9n^2 + n - 1)}{30}$
12. a) $\displaystyle\sum_{j=0}^{6} C(15,j)C(10,6 - j)$
   b) $C(30,k) = \displaystyle\sum_{j=0}^{k} C(18,j)C(12,k - j)$
   c) $C(17,3) = \displaystyle\sum_{j=0}^{3} C(12,j)C(5,3 - j)$
13. $S_n = \dfrac{45(3^n) - 33}{2} - (5n - 3)3^{n+1}$

6.7 Exercises, page 256
No answers provided for questions 1, 3–10.

2. a) $6k + 6$
   b) $2k + 3$
   c) $3k + 1$
   d) $2k + 2$

Inventory, page 258

1. $t_8 = a + 7d; S_8 = 4[2a + 7d]$
2. $t_6 = ar^5; S_{13} = \dfrac{a(r^{13} - 1)}{r - 1}$
3. $3; 5; t_{14}$
4. $6; 4; 6 \times 4^{13}$
5. $\dfrac{a}{1 - r}; |r| < 1$
6. 30
7. $0.2; -0.2$
8. $nx^n; \dfrac{nx^{n+1}}{x - 1} - \dfrac{x(x^n - 1)}{(x - 1)^2}$
9. $t_{100} - t_1$
10. a) $\displaystyle\sum_{j=0}^{k} C(n,j)C(t,k - j) = C(n + t,k)$
    b) $\displaystyle\sum_{j=0}^{8} C(7,j)C(9,8 - j) = C(16,8)$
    c) $\displaystyle\sum_{j=0}^{9} C(5,j)C(38,9 - j) = C(43,9)$
    d) $\displaystyle\sum_{j=0}^{14} C(12,j)C(8,14 - j) = C(20,14)$

Review Exercises, pages 259–261
No answers provided for questions 25, 26, 27, 38.

1. a) $1 + 4 + 9 + 16$
   b) $1 + 16 + 81 + 256 + 625$
   c) $15 + 75 + 375 + 1875 + 9375$
   d) $1 + \dfrac{1}{2} + \dfrac{1}{3} + \dfrac{1}{4} + \dfrac{1}{5} + \dfrac{1}{6}$
   e) $8 + 11 + 14 + 17$
   f) $-5 + 5 - 5 + 5$

2. a) $\displaystyle\sum_{i=1}^{6} i$
   b) $\displaystyle\sum_{i=1}^{4} i^3$
   c) $\displaystyle\sum_{i=1}^{5} (i + 2)^2$
   d) $\displaystyle\sum_{i=1}^{4} y^i$
   e) $\displaystyle\sum_{i=4}^{7} 5(3^i)$
   f) $\displaystyle\sum_{i=3}^{7} t_i$

3. a) geometric; 3; 54, 162
   b) arithmetic; -4; $-3, -7$
   c) geometric; $\dfrac{1}{7}; \dfrac{4}{49}, \dfrac{4}{343}$
   d) arithmetic; -3; $m - 12$, $m - 15$
   e) geometric; $2a$; $24a^5, 48a^6$
   f) arithmetic; -4; $-4, -8$
   g) arithmetic; $-\dfrac{2}{8}; \dfrac{1}{8}, -\dfrac{1}{8}$
   h) geometric; 0.1; 0.0024; 0.000 24

4. a) 98; 168
   b) $\dfrac{5}{27}$; 0.000 76
   c) 0.000 0019; 0.000 000 000 019
   d) $-0.093\ 75$; 0.002 93
   e) 11; -19
   f) 11.6; 9.6

5. $a = \dfrac{8}{2 \pm \sqrt{3}}$ $r = \pm\dfrac{\sqrt{3}}{2}$

6. a) $4n; \displaystyle\sum_{k=1}^{n} 4k$
   b) $\dfrac{7}{5^{n-1}}; \displaystyle\sum_{k=1}^{n} \dfrac{7}{5^{k-1}}$
   c) $4 \times 3^{n-1}; \displaystyle\sum_{k=1}^{n} 4 \times 3^{k-1}$
   d) $28 - 13n; \displaystyle\sum_{k=1}^{n} 28 - 13k$

7. a) 66
   b) 7

8. a) -1; 4
   b) 93; -7

9. a) $\dfrac{4}{9}$; ± 3
   b) $-327\ 680$; $-\dfrac{1}{4}$

10. a) $-294, -138, 18$
    b) 2, 6, 18

11. a) 360
    b) -1116
    c) -120
    d) 2576

12. a) 602
    b) 6771

13. a) 450
    b) -9405

14. a) -1534.5
    b) 80.963

15. a) 726
    b) 32

16. a) 7161
    b) 0.05

17. 3

18. a) yes; 9.33
    b) no
    c) no
    d) yes; 162

19. a) $0.51 + 0.0051 + 0.000\ 51 + \dots$; $\dfrac{51}{99}$
    b) $0.631 + 0.000\ 631 + 0.000\ 000\ 631 + \dots$; $\dfrac{631}{999}$
    c) $5.34 + 0.0017 + 0.000\ 017 + \dots$; $\dfrac{52\ 883}{9900}$

20. $-\dfrac{1}{3}$

21. a) $\dfrac{5^{n+1}[4n - 1] + 5}{16}$
    b) $\dfrac{2^{n+1}c^{n+2}(n(2c - 1) - 1) + 2c^2}{(2c - 1)^2}$
    c) $\dfrac{\left(-\dfrac{2}{3}n - 1\right)\left(\dfrac{1}{3}\right)^{n+1} + \dfrac{1}{3}}{\left(-\dfrac{2}{3}\right)^2}$
    d) $\dfrac{(0.3n - 1)(1.3)^{n+1} + 1.3}{(0.3)^2}$

22. 0.312 50

23. a) 0.312 50
    b) $|c| < \dfrac{1}{2}, c \neq 0$

24. $\dfrac{3n - 4}{2(3n + 2)}$

28. $S_{10} = \dfrac{20}{9} - \dfrac{19}{3(4^9)} - \dfrac{2}{9(4^8)}$
    $\doteq 2.\dot{2}$

29. a) 409.705 cm
    b) 1800 cm²

30. 1.13 mm

31. a) $-2728, -1767, -806$
    b) 19.375, 38.75, 77.5

32. 37.1 m

33. c) $\left(\dfrac{n - 1}{2}\right)(3n - 2)$

34. about 90 turns per second

35. a) 45 mm
    b) 50 mm

36. $1350

37. a) $2400 + 2480 + 2560 + 2640 + 2720 + 2800 + 2880 + 2960 + 3040$
    b) $24\ 480

Chapter Seven
Applications of Probability

7.1 Exercises, pages 269-270

1. a) {2, 3, 4,..., 9, 10, 11}
   b) 10
   c) $\frac{1}{13}, \frac{3}{13}, \frac{5}{13}$

2. a) {4, 5, 6,..., 21, 22}
   b) 12
   c) 1326
   d) 6
   e) $\frac{6}{1326}, \frac{22}{1326}, \frac{6}{1326}$

3. a) {3, 4, 5,..., 17, 18}
   b) 10
   c) (5,4,3) (5,3,4) (4,5,3) (4,3,5)
      (3,4,5) (3,5,4) (6,5,1) (6,1,5)
      (1,5,6) (1,6,5) (5,1,6) (5,6,1)
      (6,4,2) (6,2,4) (4,6,2) (4,2,6)
      (2,4,6) (2,6,4) (6,3,3) (3,6,3)
      (3,3,6) (5,5,2) (5,2,5) (2,5,5)
      (4,4,4)
   d) 216
   e) $\frac{25}{216}$

4. a) 64
   b) {0, 1, 2, 3}
   c) $\frac{9}{64}$

5. a) Let $s \in S$, $Z(s) = n$ where n is
      the length of the string of 0's
      and 1's. i.e. $Z(0001) = 4$.
   b) infinite
   c) {1, 2, 3, 4,...}

6. Example X(Wolf) = age in years
   Y(Wolf) = 1 if age > 5
              0 otherwise

7. b) 0.4; 0.6

8. a) (H,1) (H,2) (H,3) (H,4) (H,5)
      (H,6)
      (T,1) (T,2) (T,3) (T,4) (T,5)
      (T,6)
   b) $\left. \begin{array}{l} X(\text{H},a) = -a \\ X(\text{T},a) = a \end{array} \right\}$ for $a = 1,2,\ldots,6$
   c) $\left. \begin{array}{l} Y(\text{H},a) = 0 \\ Y(\text{T},a) = 1 \end{array} \right\}$ for $a = 1, 2,\ldots,6$

9. a) Range (X) = {0, 1, 2, 3}
      X(HTH) = 2, etc.
   b) Range (Y) = {0,1}
      $X(5,5) = 1$
      $X(5,2) = 0$, etc.

c) Range (Z) = {age of students}
   Z(student) = age of student
d) Range (W) = {0, 1,..., 10}
   W(10 people) = number of
   color-blind in group
e) Range (U) = {0, 1,..., 144}
   U(case lot) = number defective in case lot.

10. a) S = {red, black}; X(red) = 1;
       X(black) = 0
    b) S is set of $C(10,3) = 120$
       selections of 3 marbles from 10.
       $Y(S)$ = number of red marbles
       $Z(S)$ = number of black
                marbles
    c) S has $10^3 = 1000$ equally
       likely outcomes.
    d) S has $C(10,6) = 210$ outcomes
    e) S has $10^6 = 1\,000\,000$
       outcomes

11. a) {−5, −4, −3, −2, −1, 0, 1, 2, 3,
       4, 5}
    b) {0, 1, 2, 3, 4, 5}
    c) −3; 3; 4, 3

7.2 Exercises, page 275

1. a) {0,1,2}
   b) $P(X = 0) = 0.30$;
      $P(X = 1) = 0.60$;
      $P(X = 2) = 0.10$

k	f(k)
c) 0	0.30
1	0.60
2	0.10

2. a) 0.10

k	f(x)
b) 0	0.10
1	0.20
2	0.20
3	0.10
4	0.30
5	0.10

   c) $P(Y = 3) = 0.60$
      $P(Y = 3) = 0.40$

3. a) 2.2
   b) 803

4. 0.80; 2.6; 4.4723

5. a) 0.40
   b) 0.25
   c) 2.2
   d) Over many weeks the average
      number of cars sold per week
      will be approx. 2.2.

6. a)

n	1	2	3	4	5	6
$W(n)$	−1	4	−9	16	−25	36

   b)

−1	$\frac{1}{6}$
4	$\frac{1}{6}$
−9	$\frac{1}{6}$
16	$\frac{1}{6}$
−25	$\frac{1}{6}$
36	$\frac{1}{6}$

   c) $E(W) = 3.5$
   d) Average winnings per game
      after many games can be
      expected to be $3.50
   e) yes

7.3 Exercises, page 281
No Answers provided for 13, 14.

1. a) {2, 3, 4, 5, 6, 7, 8, 9, 10}
   b) $\frac{4}{36} = \frac{1}{9}$

c) 2	$\frac{1}{9}$
3	$\frac{1}{9}$
4	$\frac{1}{9}$
5	$\frac{1}{9}$
6	$\frac{1}{9}$
7	$\frac{1}{9}$
8	$\frac{1}{9}$
9	$\frac{1}{9}$
10	$\frac{1}{9}$

   d) $E(X) = 6$

2. a) $\frac{1}{7}$
   b) $\frac{4}{7}$
   c) $\frac{2}{7}$
   d) $\frac{50}{7}$

3. a) 5 green; 5 white; 5 red;
      5 yellow

   b) $\frac{1}{4}$; $\frac{3}{4}$

4. $\frac{n}{k}$ balls of each color.

5. a) $\frac{1}{2}$

   b) $\frac{1}{3}$

   c) $\frac{1}{6}$

   d) $\frac{1}{3}$

6. a) $\{0, 1, 2, 3, 4, 5, 6, 7, 8, 9\}$

   b) 0   0.1
      1   0.1
      2   0.1
      3   0.1
      4   0.1
      5   0.1
      6   0.1
      7   0.1
      8   0.1
      9   0.1

   c) 4.5

   d) For a uniform distribution
      $E(X)$ = average.

7. a) $\frac{1}{1000}$

   b) $\frac{1}{100}$

8. a) $\frac{1}{10\,000}$

   b) 0.35

9. Example $X(a) = X(b) = X(c) =$
   $X(d) = X(e) = 1$
   $X(f) = X(g) = X(h) = X(i)$
   $= X(j) = 2$

10. a) $\frac{30}{365}$; $\frac{6}{365}$

    b) Answers will vary.

11. a) $\frac{1}{5}$

    b) $\frac{1}{10}$

    c) $\frac{12}{30} = \frac{2}{5}$

    d) $\frac{12}{30} = \frac{2}{5}$

12. a) $P((X \times Y) = 4) = \frac{1}{6}$ but,

       $P((X \times Y) = 3) = \frac{1}{2}$

    b) $P((X \times Y) = k) = \frac{1}{12}$,
       $k \in \{7,14,21,28,35,42,$
       $11,22,33,44,55,66\}$

    c) No. $P((Z + Y) = 8) = \frac{1}{12}$ but

       $P((Z + y) = 12) = \frac{1}{6}$

    d) T (heads) = 7
       T (tails) = 13

15. a) $n_1 = n_2 = n_3 = n_4 = n_5 = 520$
    b) 0.8
    c) $08 : 15$
    d) Answers will vary.

7.4 Exercises, page 287
No answer provided for question 3.

1. (n, p, q)
   a) $(50, 0.4, 0.6)$
   b) $(12, 0.82, 0.18)$
   c) $(200, 0.035, 0.965)$
   d) $(10, 0.2, 0.8)$
   e) $\left(100, \frac{1}{12}, \frac{11}{12}\right)$
   f) $(20, 0.5, 0.5)$
   g) $(80, 0.38, 0.62)$

2. a) Each trial has more than two
      possible outcomes.
   b) Each card dealt affects the
      probability of a spade being
      dealt next.
   c) Each trial is not independent
      of the others.
   d) Number of trials is not fixed.
   e) Probability of success for
      each trial is different.

7.5 Exercises, pages 296–297
No answers provided for 8b, 12c.

1. a) 0.3125
   b) 2.861×10^{-5}
   c) 0.13 824
   d) 5.3255×10^{-5}

2. a) $x = 3$ $n = 4$ $p = 0.5$
   b) $x = 5$ $n = 10$ $p = 0.25$
   c) $x = 6$ $n = 6$ $p = \frac{2}{3}$
   d) $x = 4$ $n = 20$ $p = 0.20$
   e) $x = 6$ $n = 6$ $p = 0.90$
   f) $x = 3$ $n = 4$ $p = 0.0001$
   g) $x = 5$ $n = 50$ $p = 0.02$

3. a) 0.25
   b) 0.0584
   c) 0.087 79
   d) 0.2182
   e) 0.5314
   f) 3.9996×10^{-12}
   g) 0.002 7315

4. a) 0.2062
   b) 0.5583
   c) 0.999 9954
   d) 0.5583

5. x $b(x; 7, 0.2)$
   0   0.2097
   1   0.3670
   2   0.2753
   3   0.1147
   4   0.0287
   5   0.0043
   6   0.0004
   7   0.000 001

6. a) 0.156 25
   b) 0.3125
   c) 0.625

7. a) 0.4783
   b) 0.9743
   c) 0.000 0063
   d) 0.0257

8. a) 1.3804×10^{-8}

9. a) 0.5404
   b) 0.4596

10. a) 0.5438
    b) 0.2181

11. a) $\{0, 1, 2, \ldots, 6\}$

b)

k	$P(B = k)$
0	0.1176
1	0.3026
2	0.3241
3	0.1852
4	0.0595
5	0.0102
6	0.000 73

c) 2

12. a) $E(B) = 1.8$

b)

x	$b(x; 6, 0.30)$
0	0.1176
1	0.3026
2	0.3241
3	0.1852
4	0.0595
5	0.0102
6	0.000 73

13. a) 7

b) 0.6861

In Search of, page 298

1. a) 0.063 06
   b) 0.1606
2. a) 0.063 06
   b) 0.1606

7.6 Exercises, page 302

No answer provided for question 3.

	success, failure;	range
1. a)	4, 8;	$R = \{0, 1, 2, 3, 4\}$
b)	13, 39;	$R = \{0, 1, 2, \ldots, 13\}$
c)	4, 8;	$R = \{0, 1, 2, 3, 4\}$
d)	5, 95;	$R = \{0, 1, 2, 3, 4, 5\}$
e)	8, 136;	$R = \{0, 1, 2, \ldots, 8\}$
f)	4, 7;	$R = \{0, 1, 2, 3, 4\}$
g)	42, 8;	$R = \{2, 3, 4, \ldots, 10\}$

2. a) selection with replacement
   b) objects of three types, rather than two types
   c) number of selections not fixed
   d) selection with replacement
   e) size of random selection not specified

7.7 Exercises, pages 307–308

No answer provided for question 15.

1. a) $\{0, 1, 2, 3, 4, 5\}$
   b) 0.003 61
   c) 0.9422
2. a) 0.1414
   b) 0.0707
   c) 0
3. a) 0.012 79
   b) 1.5748×10^{-12}
   c) 9.1819×10^{-8}
4. a) 0.039 93
   b) 1.8469×10^{-5}
   c) 2162
5. 0.1475
6. a) 0.0909
   b) 0.0909
   c) same
7. a) 0.1432
   b) 8.3818×10^{-8}
8. a) 0.4968
   b) 0.005 92
9. 0.3193
10. a) 0.004 46
    b) 0.7518
11. a) $a = 35, b = 20, n = 5$;

$$\frac{n}{a + b} = \frac{5}{55} < 0.1$$

b) 0.3636 if a success is defined as selecting a man; 0.6363 for selecting a woman.
    c) 0.006 36; 0.7434
12. a) $\dfrac{C(1200,5) \times C(1800,15)}{C(3000,20)}$

b) $p = 0.4$
    c) 0.0746
13. a) 0.012 94
    b) 0.015 63
    c) hypergeometric; binomial
    d) yes, $\dfrac{3}{52} < 0.1$
    e) no, $\dfrac{8}{52} > 0.1$
    f) a) 1.7102×10^{-6}
       b) 1.5259×10^{-5}
14. 0.212 12

Inventory, page 310

1. a) random variable
   b) $\{1, 2, 3, 4, 5, 6, 8, 9, 10, 12, 14, 15, 16, 18, 20, 24, 25, 30, 36\}$
2. a) 4   b) $\dfrac{1}{4}$ c) uniform
3. $\dfrac{2}{3}$
4. a) hypergeometric
   b) $\{0, 1, 2, 3\}$
5. hypergeometric
6. binomial
7. hypergeometric
8. uniform
9. $5\left(\dfrac{1}{26}\right)$
10. $C(5,3)(0.2)^3(0.8)^2$
11. $\dfrac{C(3,3) \times C(12,2)}{C(15,5)}$

Review Exercises, pages 311–313
No answers provided for 1g, 19e.

1. a) 28
   b) Range(X) = {3, 4, 5, 6, 7, 8, 9, 10, 11, 12, 13, 14, 15}
   Range(Y) = {2, 3, 4, 5, 6, 7, 8, 10, 12, 14, 15, 16, 18, 20, 21, 24, 28, 30, 32, 35, 40, 42, 48, 56}
   c) $\frac{1}{28}, \frac{1}{14}, \frac{3}{28}$
   d) $\frac{3}{7}, \frac{1}{7}$
   e)

k	$P(X = K)$
3	$\frac{1}{28}$
4	$\frac{1}{28}$
5	$\frac{2}{28}$
6	$\frac{2}{28}$
7	$\frac{3}{28}$
8	$\frac{3}{28}$
9	$\frac{4}{28}$
10	$\frac{3}{28}$
11	$\frac{3}{28}$
12	$\frac{2}{28}$
13	$\frac{2}{28}$
14	$\frac{1}{28}$
15	$\frac{1}{28}$

   f) $\frac{252}{28} = 9$

2. a) X maps each group to number of blue-eyed people.
   Range (X) = {0, 1, 2,..., 15}
   b) Range (W) = {0,1,2}
   c) $G(a,b) = (a \times b) - (a + b)$
   $a = 1, 2,..., 6; b = 1, 2,..., 6$
   Range (G) = {−1, 0, 1, 2, 3, 4, 5, 7, 8, 9, 11, 14, 15, 19, 24}

3. 0.1642

4. a) uniform
   b) $\frac{1}{30}, \frac{17}{30}, \frac{3}{10}$
   c) 15.5, 41.5
   d) $U(x) = \begin{cases} 1 & 1 \leq x \leq 10 \\ 2 & 11 \leq x \leq 20 \\ 3 & 21 \leq x \leq 30 \end{cases}$
   e) $U(x) \begin{cases} 1 & x = 1 \\ 2 & x = 2 \\ 3 & \text{otherwise} \end{cases}$

5. a) 0.001
   b) 0.09
   c) 13.5 (13 or 14);
   (0.168)(15) = 2.52 (2 or 3)

6. a) $\frac{1}{3}$
   b) $31\frac{2}{3}$
   c) Range ($\sqrt{X}$) = {1, 2, 3,..., 9};
   $P(\sqrt{X} = k) = \frac{1}{9}$
   $\sqrt{E(X)} = \sqrt{31\frac{2}{3}} \neq E(\sqrt{X}) = 5$

7. a) 0.95
   b)

k	$P(V = K)$
0	0.05
1	0.20
2	0.40
3	0.25
4	0.10

   c) $E(V) = 2.15$.
   Average number of licenses per family about 2.15.

8. a) 0.278 69
   b) 0.016 649
   c) 0.128 51
   d) $3.316\ 95 \times 10^{-10}$

9. 0.4914

10. a) 14.2%
    b) 26.4%

11. a) 0.246 09
    b) 2 blocks away
    c) a) 0.136 56
    b) 2 blocks away

12. a) 36%
    b) 24.8%
    c) 7

13. a) hypergeometric; {0, 1, 2, 3, 4, 5}
    b) 0.003 612
    c) 0.3065
    d) 7.1445×10^{-5}

14. a) 0.3526
    b) $\frac{n}{a + b} = \frac{4}{50} < 0.1; 0.3456$

15. a) 0.3277
    b) 4

16. a) 57.67
    b) 25.63, 129.75
    c) 0.017 34, 1 048 576

17. a) 0.024 34
    b) 0.118 27
    c) 1.5931×10^{-10}

18. a) 0.3528
    b) 5.0878×10^{-3}

19. a)

x	$P(B = x)$
1	0.1395
2	0.2283
3	0.2387
4	0.1790
5	0.1025
6	0.0466

    b) 3
    c) $E(B) = 3$
    d) 3

Chapter Eight
Statistics

8.1 Exercises, pages 319–320

1. a)

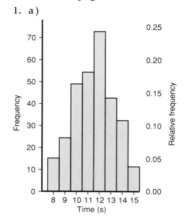

  b) 56%
  c) 29%

2. a)

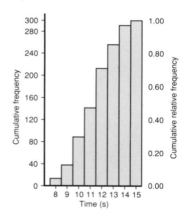

  b) 85%
  c) 125
  d) 95%

3. a)

Hours TV/evening	f.
0	20
1	8
2	16
3	20
4	12
5	4

  b) 35%; 28
  c) 45%
  d) 800

4. a)

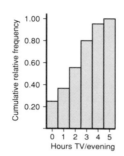

  b) 2
  c) 20%

5. 1

6. a)

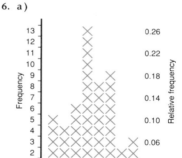

  b) $20; 26%
  c) 10%; 20%; 42%; 28%

  d)
Amount spent	f.
$10	9
$20	19
$30	17
$40	5

7. a)

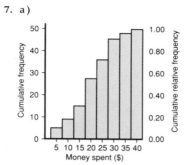

  b) $15; $30; 72%

8. a) 0.18
   b) 0.28
   c) 0.542

9. a) 40%
   b) 60%
   c) Sum is 100%.
   d) Frequency for 4, 5, 6 and 7 h is zero.
   e) 12 h; 2 h

10. a) 3; 9
    b)

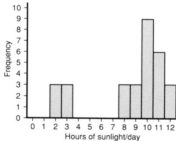

    c) 3
    d) 10
    e) greatest 'jump' from previous c.f.

8.2 Exercises, pages 326–327

1. a) $34 000
   b) $40 000; $24 000
   c) $46 000
   d) 40th

2. a) $16 000
   b) 50%

3.

20 24   34   40   50

4. a) East 0.517, 0.0926
      West 0.484, 0.0507
   b) East
   c) East
   d) East 7.167
      West 5
      They are similar.

5. East   Cleveland
   West   Kansas City

6. a) mean East, std. dev West
   b) East 0.530, 0.0530
      West 0.423, 0.1078
   c) West

7. a) 20
   b) 19
   c) 13

8. a) 10.36
   b) 10
   c) 10

9. a) 20, 5.143, 5.916
   b) 50%
   c) 50%

10. a) 9, 1.745, 2.223
    b) 64%
    c) 64%

11. maximums (50% are more than
    one mean/standard deviation
    from mean, whereas only 36% of
    the minimum temperatures are.)

12. a) 11, −9
    b) 4.64, −4.36
    c) −1, −7
    d) −0.36, −0.36

13. a) 9.643
    b) same
    c) no

14. a)

Score	f.A	f.B
1	0	0
2	1	0
3	4	4
4	5	6
5	8	8
6	1	0

   b) A 4.2; B 4.2
   c) A 4, 5; B 5, 5
   d) B
   c) A 1.03; B 0.7857

In Search of, page 328
No answers provided.

8.3 Exercises, page 334

1.

Dots	Probability
2	0.02
3	0.07
4	0.09
5	0.11
6	0.15
7	0.18
8	0.12
9	0.10
10	0.07
11	0.05
12	0.04

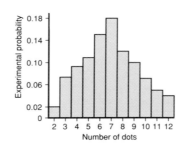

2. a) 0.10
   b) 0.18
   c) 0.16
   d) 0.56

3. 150

4. a)

Dots	Probability
2	0.028
3	0.056
4	0.083
5	0.111
6	0.139
7	0.167
8	0.139
9	0.111
10	0.083
11	0.056
12	0.028

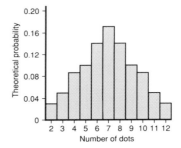

   b)

Dots	Frequency
2	1
3	2
4	3
5	4
6	5
7	6
8	5
9	4
10	3
11	2
12	1

   c) 7; 2.415
   d)

Dots	Frequency
2	50
3	100
4	150
5	200
6	250
7	300
8	250
9	200
10	150
11	100
12	50

   e) 7; 2.415
   f) equal

5.

Dots	Probability
2	0.028
3	0.056
4	0.083
5	0.111
6	0.139
7	0.167
8	0.139
9	0.111
10	0.083
11	0.056
12	0.028

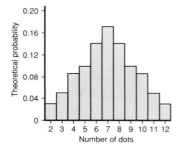

6. a) 0.111
   b) 0.167
   c) 0.167
   d) 0.5553

7. 139

8. a) 0.16
   b) 0.16
   c) 240

9. a) 0.20
   b) 20% probability that randomly selected grain will be 23 cm or less in height

10. a)

Height (m)	Frequency
20	30
21	30
22	120
23	120
24	300
25	330
26	240
27	150
28	90
29	60
30	30

   b) 25.02; 2.0735
   c) 12%; 88%

11. 1. Each rectangle has width 1, and height equal to the probability of the outcome relating to that rectangle. Probabilities sum to 1.

8.4 Exercises, pages 340–341
No answers provided for questions 8, 9.

1. a) 34%
   b) 1%
   c) 47.5%
   d) 81.5%
   e) 52.5%

2. a) −1
   b) 1.5
   c) −0.5
   d) −2
   e) 0.67
   f) −1.67

3. a) 54
   b) 12
   c) 60
   d) 33

4. a) 68%
   b) 2.5%
   c) 0.5%
   d) 81.5%
   e) 13.5%

5. a) 160, 25
   b) 80 a to 280 a
   c) 97.5%

6. a) 84th; 97.5th; 99.5th
   b) 85 to 115
   c) 84

7. a) 19
   b) 219
   c) 125 g, 275 g

10. a)

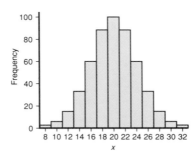

   b) 20; 3
   c) 17 to 23; 14 to 26; 12.5 to 27.5

11. a)

Dots	Probability
2	0.028
3	0.056
4	0.083
5	0.111
6	0.139
7	0.167
8	0.139
9	0.111
10	0.083
11	0.056
12	0.028

   b) 7; 2.415
   c) yes

12. yes, mean 5, std dev. 1.58

8.5 Exercises, pages 349–350

1. a) 0.1587
   b) 0.5328
   c) 0.8944
   d) 0.5156
   e) 0.3954
   f) 0.2718

2. a) 1.5
   b) 0.65
   c) −1.9
   d) 1.2

3. a) 2.5
   b) −1.5
   c) 0.25
   d) −0.85
   e) −0.7
   f) 2.15

4. a) 0.8664
   b) 0.8185
   c) 0.1770
   d) 0.0531
   e) 0.8621
   f) 0.3033

5. a) $a' = -0.5; b' = 0.5$
   b) $a' = -3.0; b' = 3.0$

6. a) 0.2266
   b) 0.1056
   c) 0.8664
   d) 0.0802
   e) 0.6678
   f) 0.2426

7. 0.2742

8. 0.9938

9. 0.0228

10. 145

11. 0.9938

12. 53

13. a) 84.13th
    b) 2.28th
    c) 40.13th
    d) 77.34th

14. a) 50
    b) 57.68
    c) 64
    d) 45

15. a) 86th (86.43)
    b) 1st   (00.82)

16. a) 0.4%
    b) 4.8%

17. a) 0.82th
    b) 1 000 000

In Search of, pages 351–352
No answers provided.

8.6 Exercises, page 357

1. a) $M = 14.4; s = 2.4$
   b) $b' \doteq 1.71$
   c) $a' \doteq -1.63$
   d) $a' \doteq -0.79, b' \doteq 0.46$
   e) $a' \doteq -1.21, b' \doteq 0.88$
   f) $a' \doteq 0.04, b' \doteq 0.46$

2. a) $M = 50; s = 5$
   b) 72.86%
   c) 2.87%
   d) 1.79%

3. b) 0.9564
   c) 0.9484
   d) 0.4624
   c) 0.6975
   f) 0.1612

4. a) $M = 12.5; s = 2.5$
   b) 2.28%
   c) 11.5%
   d) 77%

5. a) $b(1; 100,0.02) +$
      $b(2; 100,0.02) +$
      $\ldots + b(100; 100, 0.02)$
   b) $N(20,4)$
   c) 0.0088

6. a) $b(1; 27,0.25) + b(2; 27,0.25) +$
      $\ldots + b(27; 27,0.25)$
   b) $N(6.75,2.25)$
   c) 15.87%
   d) 11.12%
   e) 10.65%

7. a) 0.0001
   b) more than 1000 times
      less likely

Inventory, page 360

1. 5
2. 4
3. 85th
4. 0.30
5. 3.55
6. 2.45
7. 0.20
8. 0.$\dot{3}$
9. 2.83
10. 6%
11. 5, 15
12. 0.4332
13. −2
14. 14.4, 2.4
15. 15.5, 18.5

Review Exercises, pages 361–363

1. a)

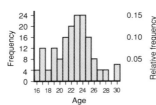

   b)

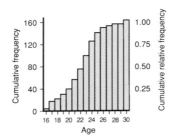

   c) 23, 21, 24
   d) 5%; 85%
   e) 90th
   f) 20 − 24
   g)

2. a) $100 000; $93 333
   b) $90 000; $80 000 − $110 000
   c) 1.95; 2.36
   d) 75%

3. 0.0168

4. a)

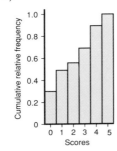

   b) 2; 2.2
   c) 1.8; 1.83
   d) 46.6%

5. a)
Digit	Probability
0	0
1	0.125
2	0.05
3	0.025
4	0.10
5	0.125
6	0.20
7	0.30
8	0.05
9	0.025

   b) mean   5.25
      standard deviation 2.2

   c)
Digit	Frequency
0	4
1	4
2	4
3	4
4	4
5	4
6	4
7	4
8	4
9	4

   d) mean   4
      standard deviation   0
   e) 70%; 50%
   f) experimental

6. a)

Black	Probability
0	0.047
1	0.187
2	0.311
3	0.276
4	0.138
5	0.037
6	0.004

b)

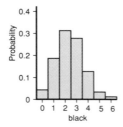

7. Answers will vary.

8. 0.0668; 0.1616; 0.7088

9. a) −2; 0.0228
   b) −0.75, 0.75; 0.5468
   c) −1, 1.5; 0.7745

10. a) 11.51%
    b) 5.48th
    c) 27.1
    d) 57.62%
    e) 22.9 − 27.1

11. a) 6.68%; 30.85%
    b) 0.13%

12. 5%

13. a) $b(1; 180, 0.167) +$
       $b(2; 180, 0.167) +$
       $\ldots+ b(180; 180, 0.167)$
    b) $N(30,5)$
    c) 18.41%
    d) 1.79%
    e) 15.54%
    f) 1.08%

14. a) $a \doteq 0.68$
    b) $-a$ 25th, a 75th
    c) 94.56 to 105.44

15. a) 0.0013
    b) 0.1587
    c) 53

16. a) 0.0668
    b) 0.9987
    c) 0.0655

17. a) 20
    b) 36
    c) 2

18. 35.7%

19. 3.1%

20. 0.0643

Problem Supplement, pages 364–371

1. a) 50%
   b) 10%

2. 120

3. 2^{10} or 1024
   3^{10} or 59 049

4. a) 15 or $C(6,2)$
   b) 20 or $C(6,3)$

5. 10!

6. 15

7. 60

8. One of five objects can fill the position. Which of the five depends on how the other four positions are to be filled.

9. a) $\frac{1}{9}$
   b) $\frac{1}{9}$
   c) $\frac{8}{9}$
   d) $\frac{2}{9}$
   e) $\frac{11}{36}$
   f) $\frac{1}{18}$

10. a) $\frac{1}{120}$
    b) $\frac{7}{24}$

11. a) $\frac{25}{109}$
    b) $\frac{13}{51}$
    c) $\frac{1}{26}$
    d) $\frac{1}{2}$

12. a) $\frac{1}{6}$
    b) $\frac{1}{36}$
    c) $\frac{1}{3}$

13. $\frac{1}{4}$

14. $\frac{1}{5525}$

15. a) 7.2%
    b) 16.8%

16. a) $\frac{1}{5}$
    b) $\frac{4}{5}$
    c) $\frac{4}{15}$
    d) Answers will vary.

17. Answers will vary.

18. Week 1 19 125
    Week 2 19 150
    Week 3 19 250
    Week 4 18 250

19. a) 46 9 −21 9 −21 42
       −60 −6 33 −8 32 −56
    b) 1 −1 53 4 20 44
       31 −25 42 0 9 −69
       1 −20 −57 −46 38 −56
    c) −10 1 −19 16 −7 18 12
       16 −1 30 −20 11 −20
       −16

20. Answers will vary.

21. a) KEEP TRYING
    b) TIME TO QUIT

22. Earth with Moon, Enterprise, Volga, Mars.
    Moon with Enterprise, Volga, Earth.
    Enterprise with Volga, Mars, Earth, Moon.
    Volga with Earth, Enterprise, Moon.
    Mars with Earth, Enterprise.

23. a) $\begin{bmatrix} 6 & -1 & 4 \\ -4 & -3 & 7 \end{bmatrix}$
    b) $\begin{bmatrix} -2 & 3 & 2 \\ -4 & 3 & 3 \end{bmatrix}$
    d) $\begin{bmatrix} 40 & -8 \\ 0 & 20 \end{bmatrix}$
    e) $\begin{bmatrix} -16 & 12 & 1 \\ -8 & 15 & 0 \end{bmatrix}$
    f) $\begin{bmatrix} 100 & -30 \\ 0 & 25 \end{bmatrix}$
    h) $\begin{bmatrix} 16 \\ 25 \end{bmatrix}$
    i) $\begin{bmatrix} 28 & 10 & 20 \\ -20 & 0 & 25 \end{bmatrix}$

24. $a = 0, b = 5, c = 1, d = 2$

25. $a = 3, b = -2, c = 1,$
    $d = 4, e = 0, f = 2,$
    $g = -1, h = -3, i = -2$

26. a) $0 \leqslant x \leqslant 100$
    b) continuous

27. Each link is two-way. (Answers will vary.)

28. Two tonnes of source 5 should be used

29. a)
$$T = \begin{bmatrix} 0.80 & 0.30 \\ 0.20 & 0.70 \end{bmatrix} \begin{matrix} \text{Rain tomorrow} \\ \text{No rain tomorrow} \end{matrix}$$
    with columns: Rain today, No rain today
    b) 65%

31. Let A be the number of Type A trucks used.
    Let B be the number of Type B trucks used.
    $A \geqslant 0, B \geqslant 0$
    $100A + 60B \geqslant 1600$
    $40A + 80B \geqslant 1200$
    Minimize $\$2000A + \$1600B$

    (10 Type A trucks and 10 Type B trucks should be used. The total transportation cost would be $\$36\ 000$.)

32. $150A + 200B + 300C = 35$
    $500A + 300B + 200C = 51$
    $750A + 500B + 500C = 75$

33. a) $a^6 + 6a^5x + 15a^4x^2 + 20a^3x^3 + 15a^2x^4 + 6ax^5 + x^6$
    b) $m^4 - 4m^3k + 6m^2k^2 - 4mk^3 + k^4$
    c) $a^3 + 9a^2b + 27ab^2 + 27b^3$
    d) $(3a)^8 + 8(3a)^7(2y) + 28(3a)^6(2y)^2 + 6(3a)^5(2y)^3 + 70(3a)^4(2y)^4 + 56(3a)^3(2y)^5 + 28(3a)^2(2y)^6 + 8(3a)(2y)^7 + (2y)^8$
    e) $243 - 162x + 108x^2 - 72x^3 + 48x^4 - 32x^5$
    f) $m^3 + 3m^2k + 3mk^2 + k^3$
    g) $(8)^6 - 6(8)^5(3a) + 15(8)^4(3a)^2 - 70(8)^3(3a)^3 + 15(8)^2(3a)^4 - 6(8)(3a)^5 + (3a)^6$
    h) $32 - 160a + 320a^2 - 320a^3 + 160a^4 + 32a^5$
    i) $(4k)^7 - 7(4k)^6 + 21(4k)^5 - 35(4k)^4 + 35(4k)^3 - 21(4k)^2 + 7(4k) - 1$
    j) $k^8 + 16k^6 + 96k^4 + 256k^2 + 256$

34. a) rank 3, 3;
   consistent-independent
   b) rank 2, 3; inconsistent
   c) rank 4, 4;
   consistent-dependent
   d) rank 3, 4; inconsistent

35. a) $a^{123} + 123a^{122}x$
   $+ \dfrac{(123)(122)}{2}a^{121}x^2$
   b) $2^{15} + 15(2^{14})(3c)$
   $+ \dfrac{(15)(14)}{2}(2^{13})(3c)^2$

36. a) $x^3 + 12x + \dfrac{48}{x} + \dfrac{64}{x^3}$
   b) $x^5 - 5x^3 + 10x - \dfrac{10}{x} + \dfrac{5}{x^3} - \dfrac{1}{x^5}$

37. a) $C(8,k)a^{8-k}x^k$
   b) $C(17,k)5^{17-k}t^k$

38. $C(14,6)p^8q^6$

39. 0.245 76

40. a) $C(4,k)(x^2)^{4-k}\left(\dfrac{2}{x}\right)^k$; $8x^5$
   b) $C(7,k)x^{7-k}\left(\dfrac{1}{x}\right)^k$; $7x^5$

41. a) $C(34,9)m^{25}(6)^9$
   b) $C(40,29)(2x)^{11}\left(\dfrac{3}{6}\right)^{29}$

42. $C(13,6)(3)^7(4b)^6$ and
   $C(13,7)(3)^6(4b)^7$

43. $C(10,5)$ or 252

46. a) 70; 378
   b) -285; -1125
   c) 1.35; 11.43
   d) -4.77×10^{-7}; $7.\dot{1}$
   e) 1.2×10^{-8}; $1.\dot{3}$
   f) 3584; 7154

47. d) $S_\infty = -7.\dot{1}$
   e) $S_\infty = 1.\dot{3}$

48. a) $7(3^{n-1})$
   $\displaystyle\sum_{k=1}^{n} 7(3^{k-1})$
   b) $2\left(\dfrac{3}{5}\right)^{n-1}$
   $\displaystyle\sum_{k=1}^{n} 2\left(\dfrac{3}{5}\right)^{k-1}$
   c) $8n - 4$
   $\displaystyle\sum_{k=1}^{n} 8k - 4$
   d) $48 - 23n$
   $\displaystyle\sum_{k=1}^{n} 48 - 23k$

49. a) 65
   b) 8

50. $t_1 = 38, t_5 = 18$

51. a) $a = \dfrac{20}{81}, r = \pm 3$

52. a) 1.988 281
   b) $\dfrac{177\ 147\ m^{22}}{3m^2 - 1}$
   $- \dfrac{3m^2(59\ 049\ m^{20} - 1)}{(3m^2 - 1)^2}$

53. $\dfrac{n}{8n + 4}$

54. a) $r = 1.0595$

   b)
A	220vps
A#	233.1
B	246.9
C	261.6
C#	277.2
D	293.7
D#	311.1
E	329.6
F	349.2
F#	370.0
G	392.0
G#	415.3
A	

   c) The second C above
   middle C. 29 notes
   above A.

55. $C(23,12) = \displaystyle\sum_{j=0}^{12} C(18,j)\, C(5,12 - j)$

57. a) $P(V = 1) = \dfrac{1}{36}$
   $P(V = 2) = \dfrac{3}{36}$
   $P(V = 3) = \dfrac{5}{36}$
   $P(V = 4) = \dfrac{7}{36}$
   $P(V = 5) = \dfrac{9}{36}$
   $P(V = 6) = \dfrac{11}{36}$
   b) $P(V > 4) = \dfrac{20}{36}$
   $P(2 \leqslant V \leqslant 4) = \dfrac{15}{36}$

58. X has range
   $\{x_1, x_2, \ldots x_n\}$
   a) $E(X + k) = \displaystyle\sum_{j=1}^{n} (x_j + k)f(x_j)$
   $= \displaystyle\sum_{j=1}^{n} (x_j)f(x_j) + k \sum_{j=1}^{n} f(x_j)$
   $= E(X) + k$, since $\displaystyle\sum_{j=1}^{n} f(x_j) = 1$
   b) $E(kX) = \displaystyle\sum_{j=1}^{n} (kx_j)\, f(x_j)$
   $= k \displaystyle\sum_{j=1}^{n} (x_j)\, f(x_j)$
   $= kE(x)$

59. a) $P(HHH) = \dfrac{27}{64}$
   $P(HHT) = P(HTH) =$
   $P(THH) = \dfrac{9}{64}$
   $P(HTT) = P(HTH) =$
   $P(THT) = \dfrac{3}{64}$
   $P(TTT) = \dfrac{1}{64}$
   b) c) $P(Z = 0) = \dfrac{1}{64}$
   $P(Z = 1) = \dfrac{9}{64}$
   $P(Z = 2) = \dfrac{27}{64}$
   $P(Z = 3) = \dfrac{27}{64}$
   d) $E(Z) = \dfrac{144}{64} = 2.25$

60. b) Range $(X) = \{1, 2, 3, 4, 5, 6\}$
Range $(Y) = \{1, 2, 3, 4, 5, 6\}$
Range $(X + Y) = \{2, 3, \ldots, 12\}$
$E(X) = 3.5$
$E(Y) = 3.5$

k	$P(T = k)$
2	$\frac{1}{36}$
3	$\frac{2}{36}$
4	$\frac{3}{36}$
5	$\frac{4}{36}$
6	$\frac{5}{36}$
7	$\frac{6}{36}$
8	$\frac{5}{36}$
9	$\frac{4}{36}$
10	$\frac{3}{36}$
11	$\frac{2}{36}$
12	$\frac{1}{36}$

$E(T) = \dfrac{252}{36} = 7$

61. a) 0
b) 0.0707
c) 0.9293

62. $P(X > 5) = 0.3141$

63. a) 0.2
b) 0.6
c) 2

64. a) 7
b) $P(H = 3) = 0.2861$
c) $P(H = 3) = 0.2765$

65. a) uniform
b) $P(X = 1) = P(X = 2) = P(X = 3)$
$= P(X = 4) = P(X = 5) = 0.2$
c) 3
d) 0.4

66. a) $P(X = 30) = 0.0076$
b) $P(X \leqslant 26) = 0.6783$

67. a) 0.2901
b) 0.1150

68. a) $E(T) = 5.5$
b) Average of winnings per game over many games is $5.50
c) 100

69. a) 0
b) 0.4196
c) 0.7133

70. $\Sigma(x_i - \overline{x})^2$
$= \Sigma(x_i^2 - 2x_i\overline{x} + \overline{x}^2)$
$= \Sigma x_i^2 - 2\overline{x}\,\Sigma x_i + N\overline{x}^2$
$= \Sigma x_i^2 - 2\left(\dfrac{1}{N}\,\Sigma x_i\right)(\Sigma x_i)$
$\qquad + N(\dfrac{1}{N}\,\Sigma x_i)^2$
$= \Sigma x_i^2 - \dfrac{1}{N}(\Sigma x_i)^2$

So,

$\dfrac{1}{N}\,\Sigma(x_i - \overline{x})^2 = \dfrac{1}{N}\,\Sigma x_i^2 - \dfrac{1}{N^2}(\Sigma x_i)^2$
$\qquad\qquad = \dfrac{1}{N}\,\Sigma x_i^2 - \left(\dfrac{1}{N}\Sigma x_1\right)^2$

71.
k	$P(X = k)$
0	0.085
1	0.271
2	0.345
3	0.220
4	0.070
5	0.009

72. a) 2.4, 1, 2
b) 1.07
c) 2

73. Answers will vary.

74. a) control 89.65, 14.60
fitness 83.20, 11.78

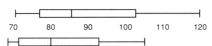

c) control
d) Answers will vary.

75. a) 0.1336
b) 0.2266
c) 0.7888
d) 0.6247
e) 0.3270

76. a) 274
b) 115
c) 0.0124
d) 24.45 kg – 29.15 kg

77. a) 11, 19
b) 25 min
c) 0.975

78. a) $M = 35, s = 2.8$
b) 32.2 – 37.8
c) 36th

79. a) $M = 630, s = 21$
b) 0.3085
c) 0.6247

80. 0.1357

This abbreviated glossary provides definitions for mathematical terms as they are used in this text. Consult a mathematics dictionary for more complete or alternative definitions.

Addition of matrices. Two matrices of the same dimension are added by summing corresponding elements. The resulting matrix has the same dimension as the original matrices.

Arithmetic series. The indicated sum of the terms of an arithmetic sequence of numbers. See **Common difference**.

Arithmetic-geometric series. A series in which each term consists of the product of one term from an arithmetic series and the corresponding term from a geometric series.

Augmented matrix. A coefficient matrix with an additional column consisting of the equations' constant terms.

Bernoulli experiment (or Binomial experiment). An experiment consisting of repeated trials with the following four characteristics.
1. Each trial has exactly two outcomes, "success" and "failure."
2. Each trial is independent of any other trial of the experiment.
3. The number of trials is specified.
4. The probability of "success" and of "failure" in each trial remains the same for each trial.

Binomial distribution. The probability distribution, $\sum_{k=0}^{n} P(X = k)$, associated with a binomial random variable X on a binomial experiment with n trials.

Binomial expansion.
$$(a + x)^n = \sum_{k=0}^{n} \frac{n(n - 1)\ldots(n - k + 1)}{k!} a^{n-k} x^k \text{ or}$$
$$(a + x)^n = \sum_{k=0}^{n} C(n, k)a^{n-k} x^k$$

Binomial random variable. The random variable S which maps each possible outcome of a binomial experiment to the number of successes occurring in that outcome.

Binomial theorem. See **Binomial expansion**.

Cardinal number. If A is any set, then $n(A)$ represents the number of elements in a set A. $n(A)$ is called the cardinal number or cardinality of set A.

Cartesian product. If A lists the ways in which one task can be performed and B lists the ways a second task can be performed, then $A \times B$ lists all ways in which the first task followed by the second task can be performed.

Coefficient matrix. A matrix comprised of the coefficients of a system of linear equations.

Column matrix. A matrix with dimension $k \times 1$.

Common difference. The constant difference between successive terms of an arithmetic series.

Common ratio. The constant ratio between successive terms of a geometric series.

Communication matrix. See **Network matrix**.

Commutative matrices. Two square matrices A and B for which $AB = BA$.

Complement. If A is a subset of a universe U, then A' is the complement of A, that is, the subset of elements in U that are not in subset A.

Consistent. Systems of equations that have at least one solution are said to be consistent.

Continuous probability distribution. A distribution with an uncountable number of measures which form an unbroken spectrum.

Converge. An infinite series is said to converge if there exists a finite value for the series sum S_∞.

Corresponding elements. Two matrices A and B, of the same dimension, have corresponding elements a_{ij} and b_{ij}.

Cumulative frequency. The sum of the frequency of a measure and the preceding frequencies in an ordered set of measures.

Cumulative relative frequency. The sum of the relative frequency of a measure and the preceding relative frequencies in an ordered set of measures.

Data set. A collection of measurements of an observed characteristic of a population or process.

Dependent. Consistent systems of equations that have an infinite number of solutions.

Descriptive statistics. Techniques for organizing, summarizing and analysing data.

Deviation. The difference between a number in a data set and the mean of that distribution.

Dimension (of a matrix). The number of rows m and columns n of a matrix, written $m \times n$.

Discrete distribution. A distribution in which the measures are separable and do not form a continuous spectrum.

Discrete function. A function whose graph consists only of separable points.

Disjoint. Two sets which have no elements in common are called disjoint.

Diverge. An infinite series is said to diverge if there does not exist a finite value for the series' sum S_∞.

Dominance matrix. A matrix, whose elements are either 0 or 1, in which a 1 indicates a dominance of that row over that column.

Dot product. The dot product is defined by

$$[a \ b \ c] \bullet \begin{bmatrix} u \\ v \\ w \end{bmatrix} = au + bv + cw,$$ and, therefore, always results in a scalar.

Element. Each number in an array is an element of the matrix.

Elementary row operations.
1. Two rows of a matrix can be interchanged.
2. Any row of matrix can be multiplied by a non-zero real number.
3. Any row of a matrix may be replaced by the sum of that row and a multiple of any other row.

Equal matrices. Two matrices A and B are equal if they have the same dimensions, $m \times n$, and if $a_{ij} = b_{ij}$ for all i,j, such that $1 \leqslant i \leqslant m$, $1 \leqslant j \leqslant n$, $i,j \in$ N.

Equally likely. Two events are equally likely if their probabilities of occurrence are the same.

Equivalent systems. Systems of equations that have the same solution sets are equivalent.

Event. Any subset of a sample space is an event, E, for that sample space.

Expansion of $(a + x)^n$. See **Binomial expansion**.

Expected value. The mean value of a random variable.

Experiment. Any operation or process of doing or observing something under certain conditions, resulting in some final outcome.

Experimental probability. The probability of an event occurring is determined by dividing the "successful" outcomes of an experiment by the number of trials.

Experimental probability distribution. A probability distribution based only on experimental evidence or results.

Factorial notation. $n! = n(n-1)(n-2)\ldots(2)(1)$

Finite series. A series with n terms, where n is a non-negative integer.

Finite set. A set containing n elements, where n is a non-negative integer.

Frequency distribution diagram (or Histogram). A graph of frequencies of items of data divided into categories. The frequencies are represented by bars of height proportional to the frequency.

Frequency distribution table. A table indicating how many times each measurement occurs in a data set.

Fundamental counting principle. This rule states that if task A can be conducted in s ways and task B can be conducted in t ways, then task A followed by task B can be conducted in st different ways.

General term (of $(a + x)^n$). The general term is $C(n,k)a^{n-k}x^k$ and is the $(k + 1)$ st term, that is t_{k+1}.

Generalized fundamental counting principle. This rule states that if n tasks $A_1, A_2, A_3, \ldots, A_n$ can be conducted in $a_1, a_2, a_3, \ldots, a_n$ ways respectively, then the n tasks can be conducted, in order, in $a_1 a_2 a_3 \ldots a_n$ different ways.

Geometric series. The indicated sum of the terms of a geometric sequence of numbers. See **Common ratio**.

Homogenous equation. An equation in which each term is of the same degree in the variables. The constant term is zero.

Hypergeometric distribution. The function that maps each $x \in$ range (H) to $P(H = x)$ where H is a hypergeometric random variable.

Hypergeometric model. An experiment similar to a Bernoulli experiment except that the probability of "success" or "failure" changes for each trial. Such models are typefied by sampling without replacement in a population divided into two categories of objects.

Hypergeometric random variable. The hypergeometric random variable H maps each possible selection of n objects, from a set of objects divided into type A and type B, to the number of objects of type A in the n-tuple.

Identity matrix. A square matrix with ones on the main diagonal and zeros everywhere else.

Inconsistent. Systems of equations that have no solution are said to be inconsistent.

Independent. Consistent systems of equations that have a unique solution.

Independent events. Two events are independent if the occurrence of one does not affect the probability of the occurrence of the other.

Index of summation. The dummy variable used to write a compact form of a series in sigma notation.

Induction. A method of proving a law or theorem by showing that it holds in the first case, and showing that, if it holds for all the cases preceding a given one, then it also holds for this case.

Infinite series. A series whose number of terms is not equal to n, for any non-negative integer n.

Inverse matrices. Two $m \times m$ matrices whose product is the $m \times m$ identity matrix.

Linear function. A function with defining equation of degree one and whose graph is either a straight line, or consists of points in a straight line.

Linear Programming. The mathematical theory of the minimization or maximization of a linear function subject to linear constraints.

Lower limit (or Initial value). The smaller value for substitution in a summation given in sigma notation.

Lower quartile. The lower quartile of a distribution is the measure such that 25% of the measures in the distribution are less than or equal to that measure.

Markov process. A Markov process satisfies the three following conditions.
1. There are a fixed number of states.
2. At each stage, every element in the process must be in one of these states.
3. The probability of transferring from one state to another depends on the two states only, and not on preceding transitions.

Matrix. A rectangular array of numbers that can be used to record information.

Mean. The arithmetic average of all the numbers in the data set.

Mean deviation. The mean of the absolute values of the deviation of each number in the data set.

Median. A measure in a distribution such that 50% of the measures are less than or equal to that measure.

Mutually exclusive (events). Two or more events containing no common outcomes.

Network matrix A. $a_{ij} = 1$, $i \neq j$, if there is a connection between point i and point j. $a_{ij} = 0$, if $i = j$ or if there is no connection between point i and point j.

Non-linear function. A function with defining equation of degree not equal to one, and whose graph is not a straight line.

Normal distribution. A continuous distribution having a bell-shaped distribution curve. The normal distribution also is the limit of a sequence of binomial distributions where the number of trials is increasing.

Order (of a matrix). See **Dimension**.

Orthogonal vector. Two vectors are orthogonal if their dot product equals zero.

Outcomes. The possible results of an experiment are outcomes.

Parameter. An arbitrary constant or variable.

Pascal's triangle. A triangular array of numbers composed of the coefficients in the expansion of $(a + x)^n$ for $n = 0,1,2,3....$ The 'triangle' extends down indefinitely, the coefficients in the expansion of $(a + x)^n$ being in the $(n + 1)$st row.

Percentile. One of the set of division points which divide a set of data into one hundred equal parts.

Piece-wise linear function. A function, defined throughout some interval, which can be separated into a finite number of linear pieces.

Poisson distribution. A probability distribution function which can approximate the binomial distribution where the value of n is large and the value of p is small.

Power set. The set of all subsets of F is known as the power set of F and is denoted $\mathcal{P}(F)$.

Probability distribution. If X is a random variable, then the probability distribution of X is the function f which maps each value k in the range of X to the probability $P(X = k)$. That is, for each k in the range of X, $f(k) = P(X = k)$.

Probability distribution graph. The relative frequency diagram for a data set can be used as a probability distribution graph.

r-arrangements (of n different objects). The possible arrangements of n objects, taken r at a time.

Random variable. Let S be a (discrete) sample space for an experiment. Let X be a function mapping each outcome in S to a real number, then X is a random variable on S.

Range. The difference between the greatest and least measures in a data set.

Rank (of a matrix). The number of non-zero rows in the row-reduced form of the matrix.

Relative frequency. The number of items in a given category, divided by the total number of items in the data set.

Row matrix. A matrix with dimensions $1 \times k$.

Row-reduced echelon form. A matrix after elementary row operations have been performed such that
1. any zero row occurs last and
2. the first non-zero element in a row occurs anywhere to the right of the first non-zero element in the row above.

Sample. A finite subset of a population.

Sample space. The set of all possible outcomes for an experiment.

Scalar. A number having magnitude but not direction (as opposed to a vector).

Scalar multiplication of matrices. Multiplying each element of a matrix by the same real number (or scalar).

Sequence. A set of terms forming the range of a function whose domain is a set of consecutive natural numbers starting with 1.

Simple event. An event that consists of only one outcome.

Simplex method. A matrix technique for linear programming.

Slack variable. A variable which 'takes up the slack' between left- and right-hand sides of an inequality.

Square matrix. A matrix in which the number of rows equals the number of columns (i.e. dimension $k \times k$).

Standard deviation. The square root of the mean of the squares of the deviation of each measure in a distribution.

Standard normal distributions. A normal distribution with a mean of 0 and a standard deviation of 1.

Standard score. The number of standard deviations a measure is from the mean of the distribution.

Statistical inference. The mathematical basis for using surveys.

Statistics. Numbers which are used to describe characteristics of data sets and their distributions.

Step function. A function which is defined throughout some interval I and is constant on each one of a finite set of non-intersecting intervals whose union is I.

Subset. If every element in set B is found in set A, then set B is said to be a subset of set A, written $B \subset A$.

Tchebychev inequality. For any collection of numbers with mean M and standard deviation s, let k be a number greater than s. Then the fraction of the numbers in the collection which are between $M - k$ and $M + k$ is *at least* $1 - \dfrac{s^2}{k^2}$.

Theoretical probability distribution. A probability distribution based on mathematical theory rather than direct observation.

Transition matrix. A matrix, T, which allows the calculation of probabilities of future events.

Trial. Each repetition of an experiment is called a trial.

Uniform distribution. A probability distribution in which the distribution function is a constant function.

Uniform probability model. A model for which the associated probability distribution is uniform.

Universal set (or Universe). The complete set containing all the elements concerned is referred to as the universal set.

Upper limit (or Final value). The larger value for substitution in a summation given in sigma notation.

Upper quartile. The upper quartile of a distribution is a measure such that 75% of the measures in the distribution are less than or equal to that measure.

Vector. A column or row matrix.

INDEX

$(a + x)^n$, 201
Addition of matrices, 100, 101
"and" property of conditional probability, 80
Arithmetic series, 226, 227, 232, 257
Arithmetic-geometric series, 245, 246, 257
At least one, probability of, 65
Augmented matrix, 153

Bernoulli experiment, 284
Binomial distribution, 290
Binomial expansion, 202
Binomial experiment, 284
Binomial random variable, 290
Binomial theorem, 200, 256
Birthday problem, 84

$C(n,r)$, 31
Cardinal number (or Cardinality), 4
Cartesian product of two sets, 11
Certain, probability is, 49
Coding, 114
Coefficient matrix, 153
Coefficients of $(a + x)^t$, 216
Column matrix, 96
Column, 94
Combinatorics, 3
Common difference, 226, 257
Common ratio, 226
Communication matrix, 123
Commutative matrix, 111
Complement, 5, 58
Complement property, 58, 88
Conditional events, 88
Conditional probability, 78
Consistent systems, 157
Continuous probability distribution, 335
Converge, 240
Corresponding elements, 95
Cumulative frequency, 317
Cumulative relative frequency, 317

Data set, 316
Decoding matrix, 114
Dependent systems, 159
Descriptive statistics, 316
Deviation, 322

Dimension of a matrix, 94
Discrete distribution, 335
Discrete function, 142
Disjoint (of a set), 6
Diverge, 240
Dominance matrix, 124
Dot product, 152
Dummy variable, 222

Element, 94
Elementary row operations, 153
Elimination, 146
Encoding matrix, 114
Equal matrices, 95
Equally likely, 57, 88
Equivalent systems, 153
Event, 51, 88
Expansion of $(a + x)^n$ for $n \in R$, 205
Expected value, 272
Experiment, 264
Experimental probability, 48
Experimental probability distribution, 331

Factorial notation, 21
"Failure", 284
Feasible region, 173
Final value, 221
Finite series, 226
Finite set, 4
Frequency distribution diagram, 316
Frequency distribution table, 316
Fundamental counting principle, 10, 11

General term of a series, 220
General term of $(a + x)^n$, 208
Generalized fundamental counting principle, 12
Geometric series, 226, 227, 236, 241, 247

Harmonic series, 244
Histogram, 316
Homogeneous equations, 149
Hypergeometric distribution, 249, 303
Hypergeometric model, 299
Hypergeometric probability distribution, 303
Hypergeometric random variable, 300

Identity matrix, 109, 116
Impossible, probability is, 49
Inconsistent systems, 158
Independent systems, 159
Independent events, 70, 81, 88
Index of summation, 221
Induction, proof by, 253
Inductive property, 252
Inequalities, 169
Infinite geometric series, 238
Infinite series, 220
Initial value, 221
Intersection of two sets, 6
Inverse matrices, 111, 116

Limit of the partial sum, 239
Linear function, 140
Linear programming, 175
Lower limit, 221
Lower quartile, 321

Markov process, 130
Mathematical induction, 252, 257
Matrix, 94
Matrix, not symmetric, 123
Mean, 322
Mean deviation, 323
Mean value, 272
Measures of central tendency, 324
Measures of dispersion, 324
Median, 321
Multiplication of matrices, 105
Mutually exclusive events, 59, 81

$n(E)$, 51
$n(S)$, 51
n-arrangement of n objects with some alike, 28
Natural numbers, sum of, 248
Network matrix, 120
Network, 120
Non-linear continuous function, 142
Non-uniform probability, 75
Normal distribution, 335

Objective function, 175
Odds in favor, 62
"or" property, 58, 88
Order of a matrix, 94
Orthogonal vectors, 152
Other infinite series, 244
Other series, 245, 257
Outcome, 51, 88

$P(E)$, 57
$P(n,r)$, 18
Parameter, 159
Partial fractions, 248
Pascal, Blaise, 196
Pascal's triangle, 196, 214
Patterns in Pascal's triangle, 214
Percentile, 321
Piece-wise linear function, 141
Pivot, 185
Poisson distribution, 298
Power rating, 125
Power set, 38
Principle of mathematical induction, 252
Probability and combinatorics, 65
Probability distribution, 272, 330
Probability distribution graph, 330
Probability distribution of an experiment, 272
Probability of an event, 57, 88
Product matrix, 108
Properties of probability, 88

r-arrangement of n different objects, 18
r-subset of n objects, 31
Random variable, 264
Range, 322
Range property, 58, 88
Rank of a matrix, 162
Relative frequency, 48, 316
Row matrix, 96
Row-reduced echelon form, 154
Row, 94

S_∞, 239, 241
Sample, 342
Sample space, 51, 88
Scalar, 101
Scalar multiplication of matrices, 101
Sequence, 220, 257
Series, 220
Series converges, 240
Sigma notation, 221
Simple event, 51, 88
Simplex technique (or simplex method), 184
Slack variables, 184
Square matrix, 96
Standard deviation, 323
Standard normal distribution, 337
Standard score, 339
Statistical inference, 342
Statistics, 321
Step function, 141
Subset, 4

Subtraction of matrices, 101
"Success", 284
Sum of a geometric series, 235
Sum of an arithmetic series, 231
Sum of an infinite series, 239, 257
Sum of the natural numbers, 248
Systems of equations, 146

Tally count, 316
Tchebychev inequality, 328
Term number, 220, 257
Term value, 220, 257
Test point, 169
Theoretical probability distribution, 332
Transition matrix, 128
Trial, 51, 88, 264, 284
Two-stage dominance, 125

Uniform distribution, 276
Uniform probability model, 57, 58, 88
Union, 6
Union, number of elements in, 7
Universal set (or Universe), 4
Upper limit, 221
Upper quartile, 321

Vector, 152

Zeno's paradox, 218, 238